Ruth P. Allen

# CHRISTIAN SCIENCE HYMNAL

WITH SEVEN HYMNS WRITTEN BY

THE REVEREND MARY BAKER EDDY

*Discoverer and Founder of Christian Science*

THE CHRISTIAN SCIENCE PUBLISHING SOCIETY

BOSTON • MASSACHUSETTS • U • S • A

Revised and Enlarged



[Printed in U. S. A.]

# PREFACE

MARY BAKER EDDY, the Discoverer and Founder of Christian Science, was an appreciator of music. She knew that it could have a religious character. For ages psalms and hymns have been used by Christian people to express their hopes and aspirations. This greatly enlarged Christian Science Hymnal offers a wide selection of tunes and words which will enable many to express in song that harmony of aspiration and realization which makes music in the heart. The beloved Leader of our movement has said in the Christian Science textbook, "Science and Health with Key to the Scriptures" (p. 304), "Harmony in man is as beautiful as in music, and discord is unnatural, unreal."

## *Arrangement of Hymns*

With the exception of the Communion Doxology, No. 1, the hymns are arranged alphabetically according to their first lines, slight deviations being due to the desirability of printing two-page tunes on facing pages.

In many instances a hymn has two or more settings, separately numbered, and marked with the sign † after the hymn number. With one exception, No. 271, familiar or simpler tunes appear first.

## *Our Leader's Hymns*

Two of our Leader's poems, "Love" and "Satisfied," have been added to the five already in the 1910 edition of the Hymnal. As Mrs. Eddy's hymns are sung oftener than others, more alternative tunes are provided.

## *Types of Hymns*

In order that every congregation, large or small, may find suitable musical material, there is wide variety in types of tunes herein.

The range of the average voice has been given careful and sympathetic attention; while evidence has been sought that the tunes have been successfully sung by congregations. These considerations, together with that of musical excellence, have governed the final selection of tune and key.

Some are very ancient hymns, others embody well-established standards, while still others find new modes of expression. Certain hymns have been inserted because of association with the early history of our movement. The hymns, "I need Thee every hour," "I'm a pilgrim and I'm a stranger," and "Eternity" were originally included in the Hymnal in accordance with Mrs. Eddy's wish. Many tunes of unusual interest and beauty from England and Continental Europe have also been included.

There are occasional slight changes in the poems to make word accent conform to music accent. Where such adaptation was impracticable, alternative tunes with better accentuation have been added. Other changes have been made in order to bring the thought of the poem into harmony with the teachings of Christian Science; but, as far as possible, original forms have been preserved. An asterisk after the author's name indicates slight changes. For some hymns already familiar, stanzas from the originals have been added; and, in some cases, stanzas have been replaced by others from the same poem.

## *Notation*

The quarter note or crotchet, generally used in the hymnody of many countries, is the unit of notation in this Hymnal. The half note or minim has been used for most of the chorales. The time values of each will of course vary with the character of hymn or tune, and, to a certain extent, with the size of the congregation. Metronome marks are not provided with each hymn; but some general indications as to tempo are presented in a special index.

## *Holds or Pauses*

Bars and holds which merely serve to mark line ends of hymns have been generally omitted, except when stanzas are printed outside the music. Commas above the music staff indicate the necessity of a slight break between phrases. In small details of notation (such, for instance, as adjusting note values in partial first and last measures) uniformity has not been sought, since usage varies with different composers.

## *Supplement and Indexes*

In a few cases the familiar arrangement of a tune has been placed in the Supplement, and a new arrangement in the body of the book. This has been noted at the bottom of the music page. The Supplement, which is serially numbered, though not alphabetically arranged, includes also hymns and tunes which are more or less locally or nationally rather than internationally serviceable. All hymns and tunes are of course alphabetically listed in their respective indexes.

## *Acknowledgments*

Grateful acknowledgment is due to the many contributors to the Hymnal and to authors and composers who have permitted such revision as would promote the unity and serviceableness of the collection. The Christian Science Publishing Society has given permission for the use of poems already published in the Christian Science periodicals; copyright permissions from others are acknowledged on the respective pages. The Publishers will welcome any report of omission of proper copyright acknowledgment and will gladly make correction in subsequent editions.

The love and truth expressed through the hymns in the Christian Science Hymnal have helped and comforted many, and will continue to do so in increased measure. Woven throughout the structure of this Hymnal, with its songs of praise and gratitude to God, is the thought contained in the "Daily Prayer" of Christian Scientists, "May Thy Word enrich the affections of all mankind" (Church Manual, by Mary Baker Eddy, p. 41).

THE CHRISTIAN SCIENCE BOARD OF DIRECTORS.

# CHRISTIAN SCIENCE HYMNAL

## 1

**OLD HUNDREDTH** L. M.
Genevan Psalter, 1551

Communion Doxology
Tate and Brady

Be Thou, O God, ex - alt - ed high; And

as Thy glo - ry fills the sky, So let it be on

earth dis - played, Till Thou art here and now o - beyed.

# 2

**MISSIONARY HYMN** 7. 6. 7. 6. D.

LOWELL MASON | Author Unknown

1. A glo - rious day is dawn - ing, And
2. The ad - vo - cates of er - ror Fore -
3. The watch - word has been spo - ken, The
o'er the wak - ing earth . . The her - alds of the
see the glo - rious morn, . . And hear in shrink - ing
light has bro - ken forth, . . Far shines the bless - ed
morn - ing Are spring - ing in - to birth.
ter - ror, The watch - word of re - form:
to - ken Up - on the star - tled earth.

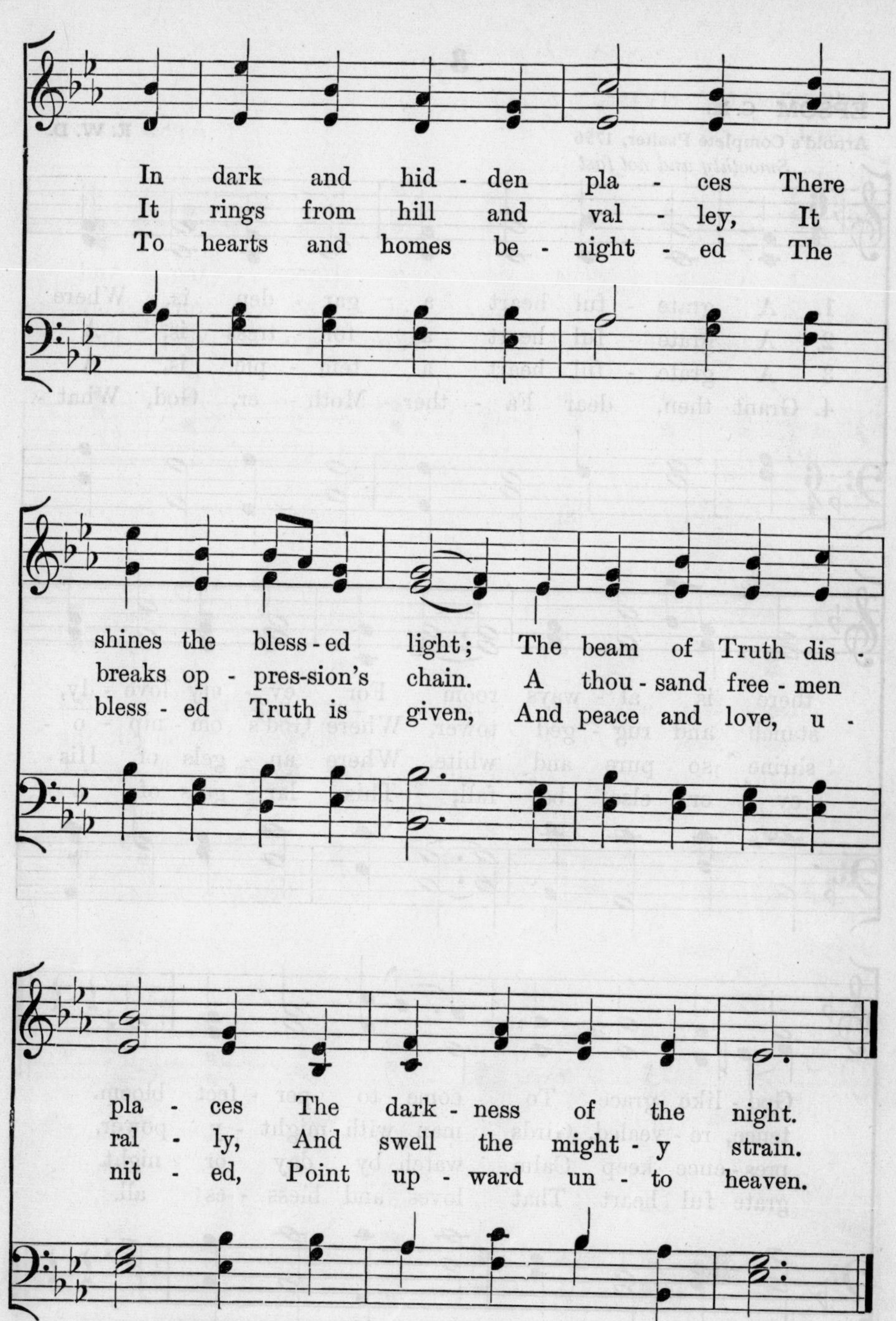
In dark and hid - den pla - ces There
It rings from hill and val - ley, It
To hearts and homes be - night - ed The
shines the bless - ed light; The beam of Truth dis -
breaks op - pres-sion's chain. A thou - sand free - men
bless - ed Truth is given, And peace and love, u -
pla - ces The dark - ness of the night.
ral - ly, And swell the might - y strain.
nit - ed, Point up - ward un - to heaven.

3

EPSOM C. M.
Arnold's Complete Psalter, 1756
E. W. D.
Smoothly and not fast
1. A grate - ful heart a gar - den is, Where
2. A grate - ful heart a for - tress is, A
3. A grate - ful heart a tem - ple is, A
4. Grant then, dear Fa - ther - Moth - er, God, What -
there is al - ways room For ev - ery love - ly,
stanch and rug - ged tower, Where God's om - nip - o -
shrine so pure and white, Where an - gels of His
ev - er else be - fall, This lar - gess of a
God - like grace To come to per - fect bloom.
tence, re - vealed, Girds man with might - y power.
pres - ence keep Calm watch by day or night.
grate - ful heart That loves and bless - es all.

## PATER NOSTER C. M

PERCY C. BUCK — ABIEL ABBOT LIVERMORE*

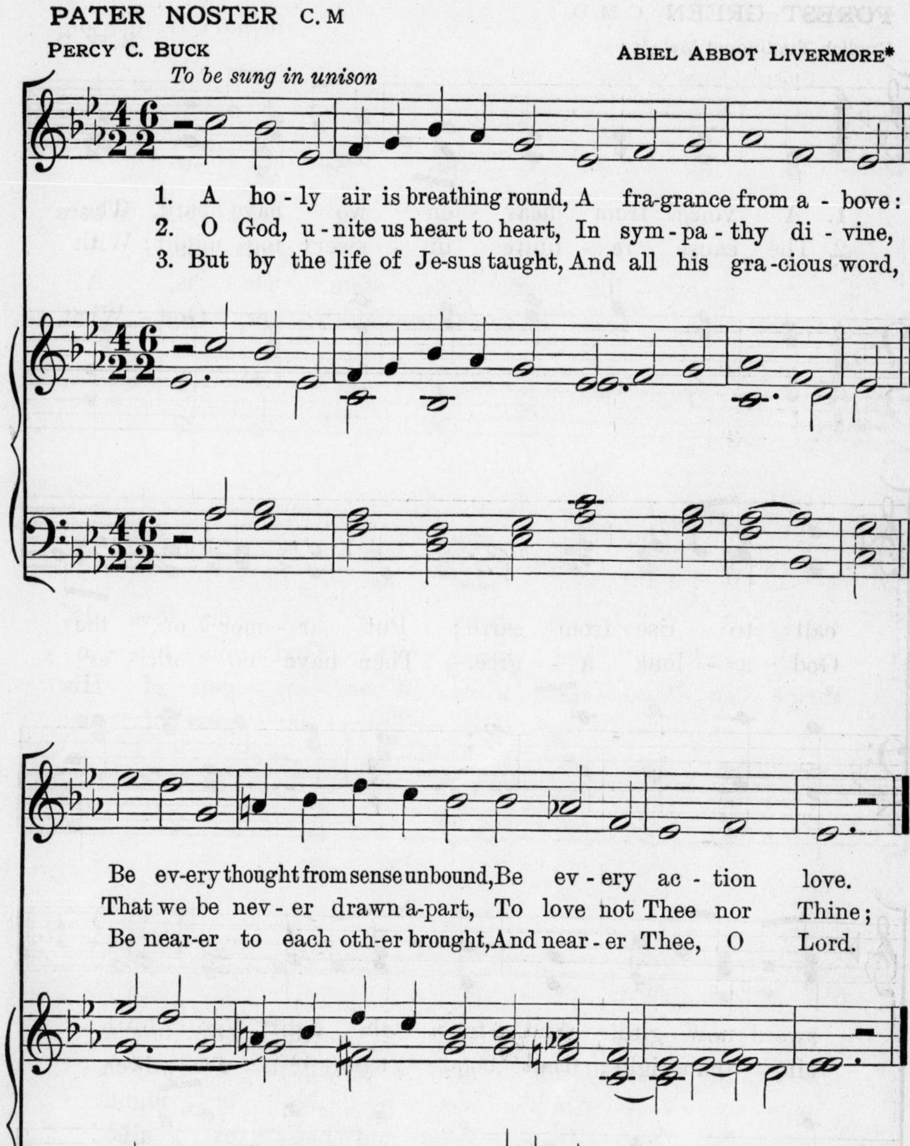
To be sung in unison
46
22
1. A ho - ly air is breathing round, A fra-grance from a - bove:
2. O God, u - nite us heart to heart, In sym - pa - thy di - vine,
3. But by the life of Je-sus taught, And all his gra-cious word,
Be ev-ery thought from sense unbound, Be ev - ery ac - tion love.
That we be nev - er drawn a-part, To love not Thee nor Thine;
Be near-er to each oth-er brought, And near - er Thee, O Lord.

Music by permission of PERCY C. BUCK

# 5

FOREST GREEN C. M. D.
English Traditional Melody
IRVING C TOMLINSON
1. A voice from heav - en we have heard, The
2. The cause re - quires un - swerv - ing might: With
call to rise from earth; Put ar - mor on, the
God a - lone a - gree. Then have no oth - er
sword now gird, And for the fight go forth.
aim than right; End bond - age, O be free.

The foe in am - bush claims our prize, Then
De - part from sin, a - wake to love: Your

heed high heav - en's call. O - bey the voice of
mis - sion is to heal. Then all of Truth you

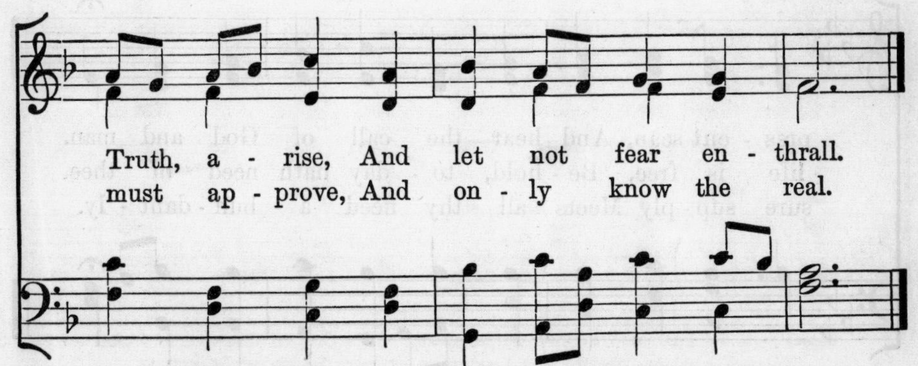
Truth, a - rise, And let not fear en - thrall.
must ap - prove, And on - ly know the real.

# 6

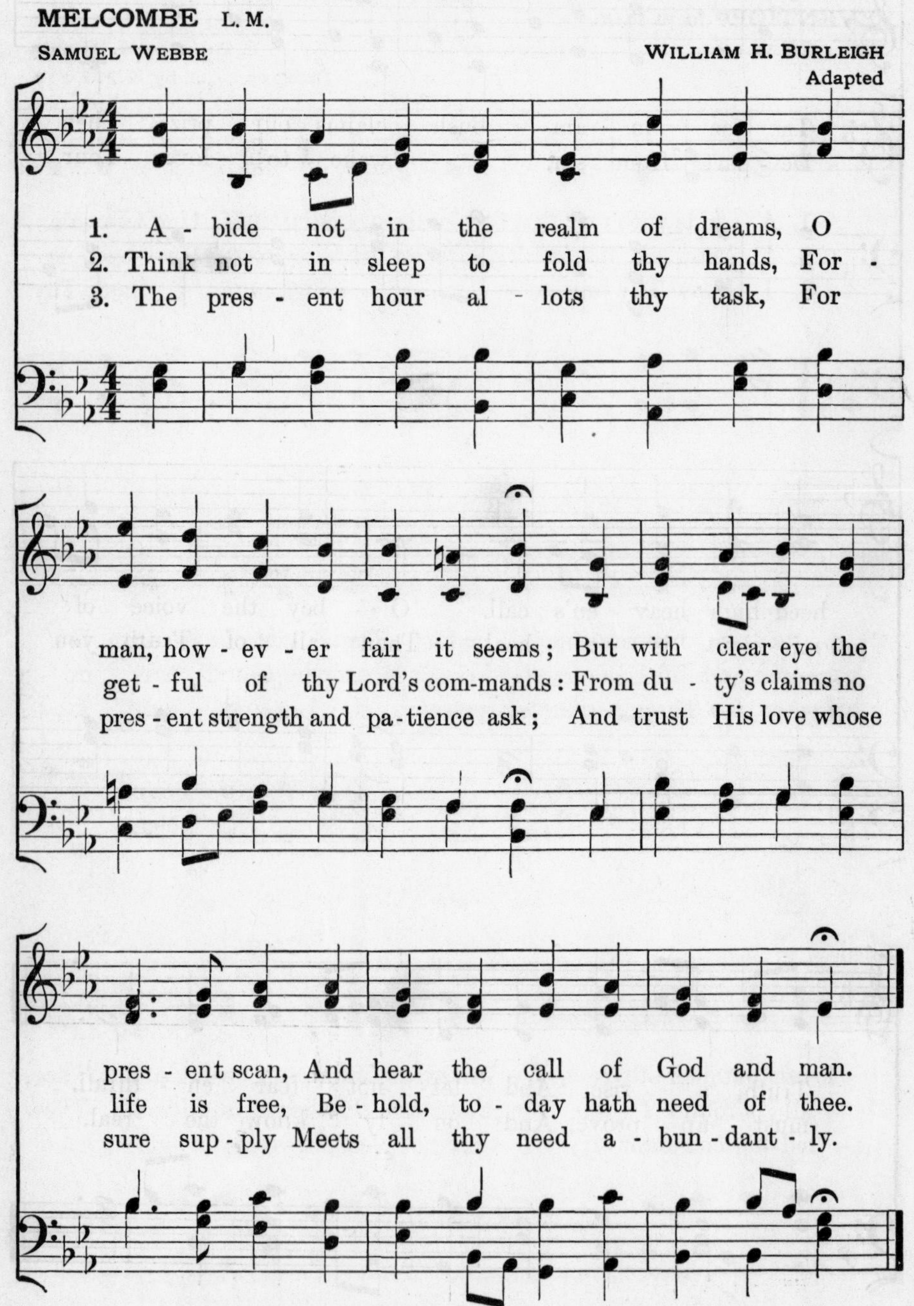
MELCOMBE L. M.
SAMUEL WEBBE
WILLIAM H. BURLEIGH
Adapted
1. A - bide not in the realm of dreams, O
2. Think not in sleep to fold thy hands, For -
3. The pres - ent hour al - lots thy task, For
man, how - ev - er fair it seems; But with clear eye the
get - ful of thy Lord's com-mands: From du - ty's claims no
pres - ent strength and pa - tience ask; And trust His love whose
pres - ent scan, And hear the call of God and man.
life is free, Be - hold, to - day hath need of thee.
sure sup - ply Meets all thy need a - bun - dant - ly.

# 7

**EVENTIDE** 10. 10. 10. 10.

WILLIAM H. MONK | BERTHA H. WOODS
Based on hymn by H. F. LYTE

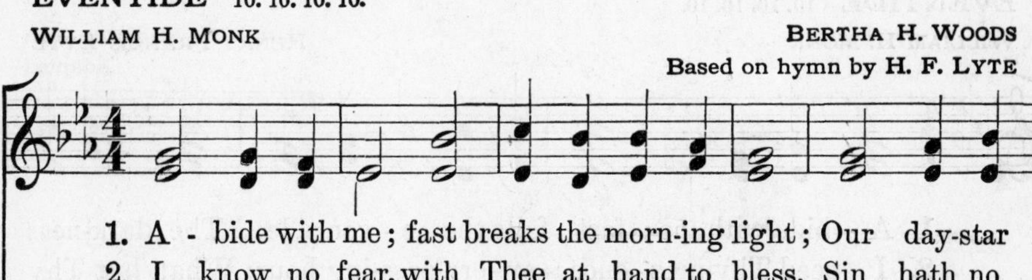

1. A - bide with me; fast breaks the morn-ing light; Our day-star
2. I know no fear, with Thee at hand to bless, Sin hath no
3. I know Thy pres-ence ev - ery pass-ing hour, I know Thy

ris - es, ban-ish-ing all night; Thou art our strength, O
power and life no wretch-ed-ness; Health, hope and love in
peace, for Thou a - lone art power; O Love di - vine, a -

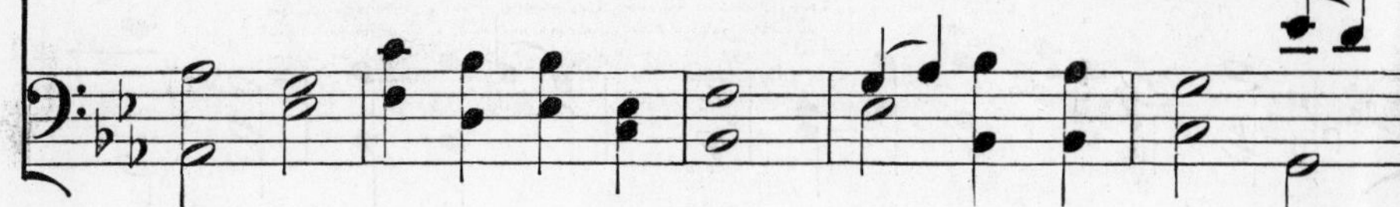

Truth that mak-eth free, We would un-fail-ing - ly a - bide in Thee.
all a-round I see For those who trust-ing-ly a - bide in Thee.
bid-ing con-stant - ly, I need not plead, Thou dost a-bide with me.

## 8

**EVENTIDE** 10. 10. 10. 10.

WILLIAM H. MONK — HENRY FRANCIS LYTE

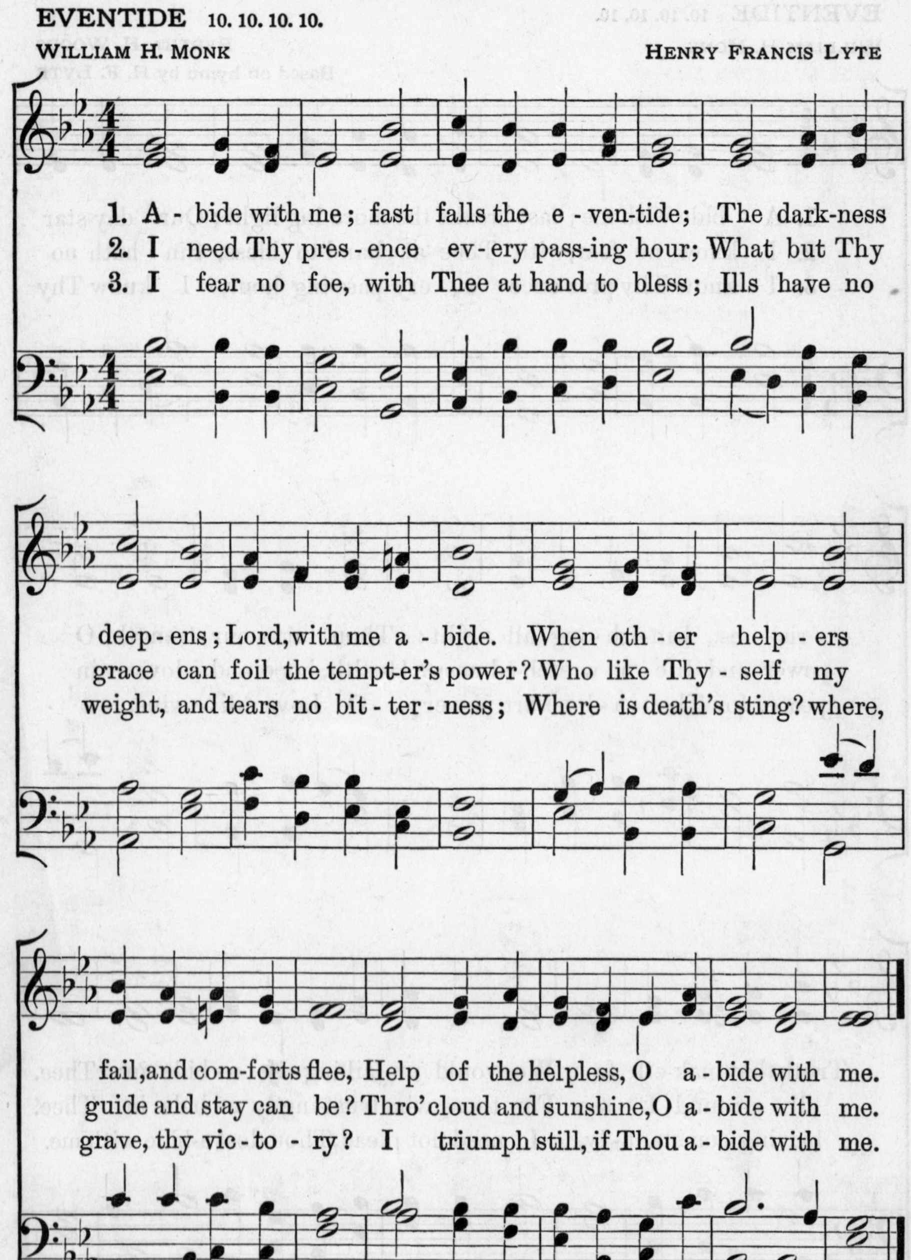

1. A - bide with me; fast falls the e - ven-tide; The dark-ness
2. I need Thy pres - ence ev - ery pass-ing hour; What but Thy
3. I fear no foe, with Thee at hand to bless; Ills have no
deep - ens; Lord, with me a - bide. When oth - er help - ers
grace can foil the tempt-er's power? Who like Thy - self my
weight, and tears no bit - ter - ness; Where is death's sting? where,
fail, and com-forts flee, Help of the helpless, O a - bide with me.
guide and stay can be? Thro' cloud and sunshine, O a - bide with me.
grave, thy vic - to - ry? I triumph still, if Thou a - bide with me.

**CAROL** 86. 86. 6.

Arranged from DAVID G. CORNER
by H. WALFORD DAVIES

V. H.

*To be sung in unison*

1. All glo - ry be to God most high,
And on the earth be peace, . .
The an - gels sang, in days of yore,
The song that ne'er shall cease, . .
Till all the world knows peace.

2. God's an - gels ev - er come and go,
All winged with light and love ; . .
They bring us bless - ings from on high,
They lift our thoughts a - bove, . .
They whis - per God is Love.

3. O long - ing hearts that wait on God
Through all the world so wide ; . .
He knows the an - gels that you need,
And sends them to your side, . .
To com - fort, guard and guide.

4. O wake and hear the an - gel-song
That bids all dis - cord cease, . .
From pain and sor - row, doubt and fear,
It brings us sweet re - lease ; . .
And so our hearts find peace.

Music by permission of H. WALFORD DAVIES

10

EIN' FESTE BURG 87. 87. 66. 667.

MARTIN LUTHER FREDERIC W. ROOT

1. All power is given un - to our Lord, On
2. Re - joice, ye peo - ple, praise His name, His
3. O then give thanks to God on high, Who
Him we place re - li - ance; With truth from out His
care doth e'er sur - round . . us. His love to er - ror's
life to all is giv - ing; The hosts of death be -
sa - cred word We bid our foes de - fi - ance.
thral - dom came, And from its chains un - bound . . us.
fore Him fly, In Him we all are liv - - ing.

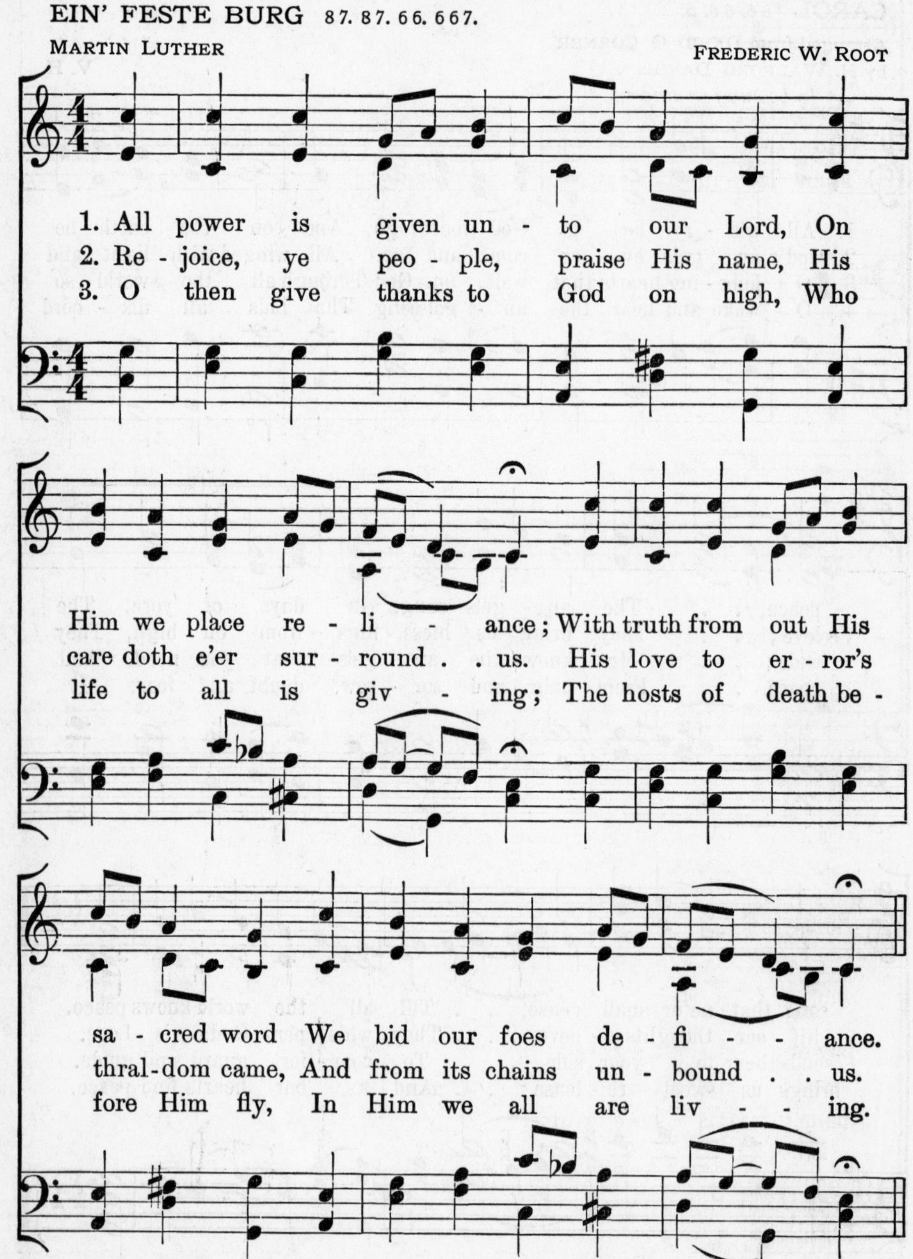

*Another version of this music will be found in the* SUPPLEMENT, No. 411

With Him we shall pre - vail, What - ev - er may as - sail;
Our Lord is God a - lone, No oth - er power we own;
Then let us know no fear, Our King is ev - er near;
He is our shield and tower, Al - might - y is His
No oth - er voice we heed, No oth - er help we
Our stay and for - tress strong, Our strength, our hope, our
power; His king - dom is for - ev - - er.
need; His king - dom is for - ev - - er.
song; His king - dom is for - ev - - er.

SALZBURG 7.7.7.7.D.
Jakob Hintze
Harmonized by J. S. Bach

M. S. C.

1. An - gels at the Sav - iour's birth
2. Star of be - ing, still thy light
Woke with mu - sic all the earth, Shep-herds in the
Shines be - fore us in the night, By those ra - diant
east - ern sky Saw a pale star pass - ing by,
beams we find Christ, the Truth, for all man - kind,

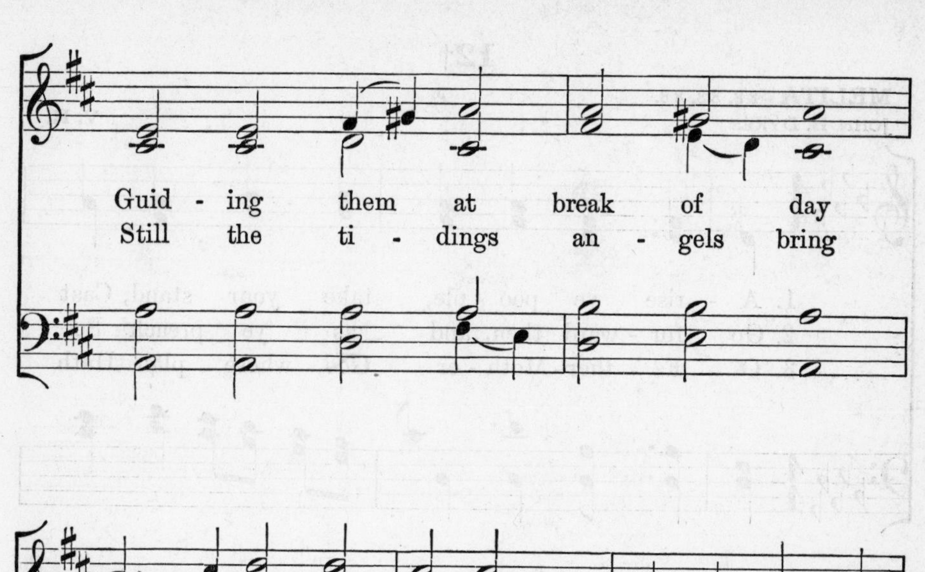
Guid - ing them at break of day
Still the ti - dings an - gels bring

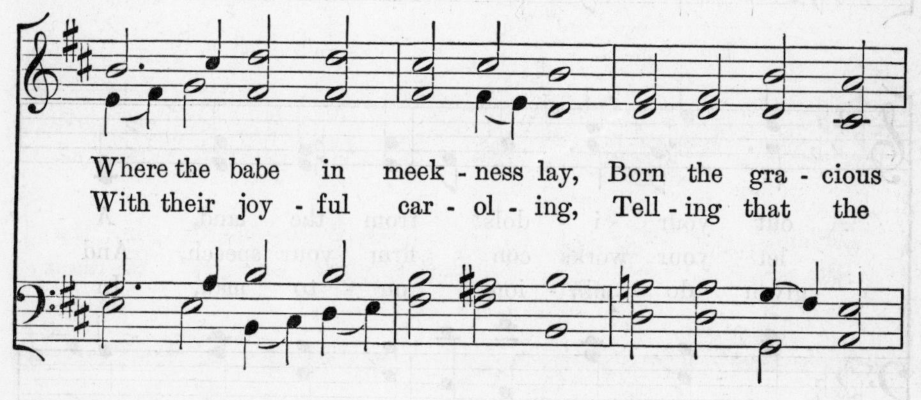
Where the babe in meek - ness lay, Born the gra - cious
With their joy - ful car - ol - ing, Tell - ing that the

news to tell, God with us, Im - man - u - el.
dawn has come, God and man for - e'er at one.

# 12†

MELITA 88. 88. 88.
JOHN B. DYKES
V. H.
1. A - rise ye peo - ple, take your stand, Cast
2. Go for - ward then, and as ye preach So
3. O Fa - ther - Moth - er God, whose plan Hath
out your i - dols from the land, A -
let your works con - firm your speech, And
given do - min - ion un - to man, In
bove all doc - trine, form or creed Is
prove to all with fol - lowing sign The
Thine own im - age we may see Man

found the Truth that meets your need. Christ's
Word of God is power di - vine. In
pure and up - right, whole and free. And

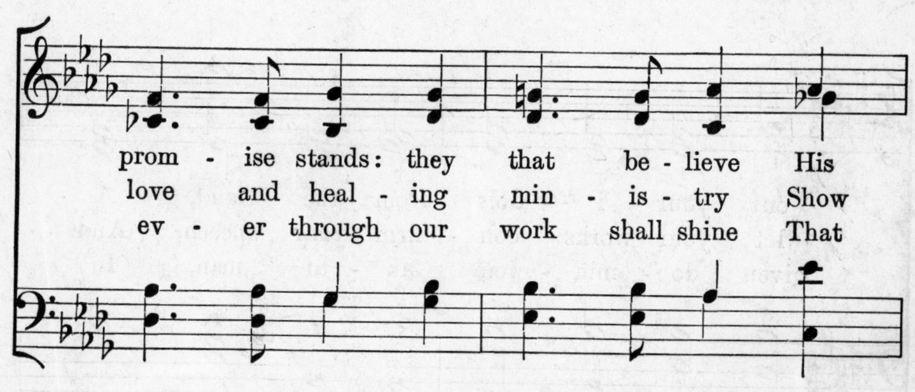
prom - ise stands: they that be - lieve His
love and heal - ing min - is - try Show
ev - er through our work shall shine That

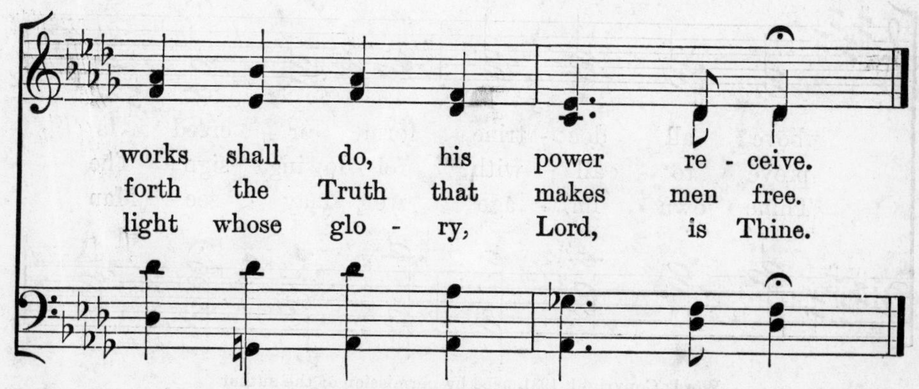
works shall do, his power re - ceive.
forth the Truth that makes men free.
light whose glo - ry, Lord, is Thine.

# 13†

ERMUNTRE DICH 88. 88. 88.
JOHANN SCHOP
V. H.
Not slow
1. A - rise ye peo - ple, take your stand, Cast
2. Go for - ward then, and as ye preach So
3. O Fa - ther - Moth - er God, whose plan Hath
out your i - dols from the land, A -
let your works con - firm your speech, And
given do - min - ion un - to man, In
bove all doc - trine, form or creed Is
prove to all with fol - lowing sign The
Thine own im - age we may see Man

found the Truth that meets your need. Christ's
Word of God is power di - vine. In
pure and up - right, whole and free. And
prom - ise stands: they that be - lieve His
love and heal - ing min - is - try Show
ev - er through our work shall shine That
works shall do, his power re - ceive.
forth the Truth that makes men free.
light whose glo - ry, Lord, is Thine.

## 14

**POTSDAM** S. M.

Arranged from
JOHANN SEBASTIAN BACH

MARY I. MESECHRE

Not too slow
1. A - rise, a - rise and shine, On
2. Sing praise, O wak - ing heart, For
3. No more shall sin and wrong Ob -
4. A - rise, a - rise and shine, Up -
thee hath dawned the day; God is thy sun, and
all thy God hath wrought; For Truth's clear light on
scure the light di - vine, For God hath giv - en
lift thee from the sod, And let thy liv - ing
Christ thy light, Be thou a stead - fast ray.
thee hath shone, And pu - ri - fied thy thought.
thee His Son, And lo, all things are thine.
light show forth Man's u - ni - ty with God.

**FULFILLMENT** 7. 6. 8. 6.

Den store Mester kommer
C. CHRISTIAN HOFFMAN

Based on the Danish of
BERNHARD S. INGEMANN

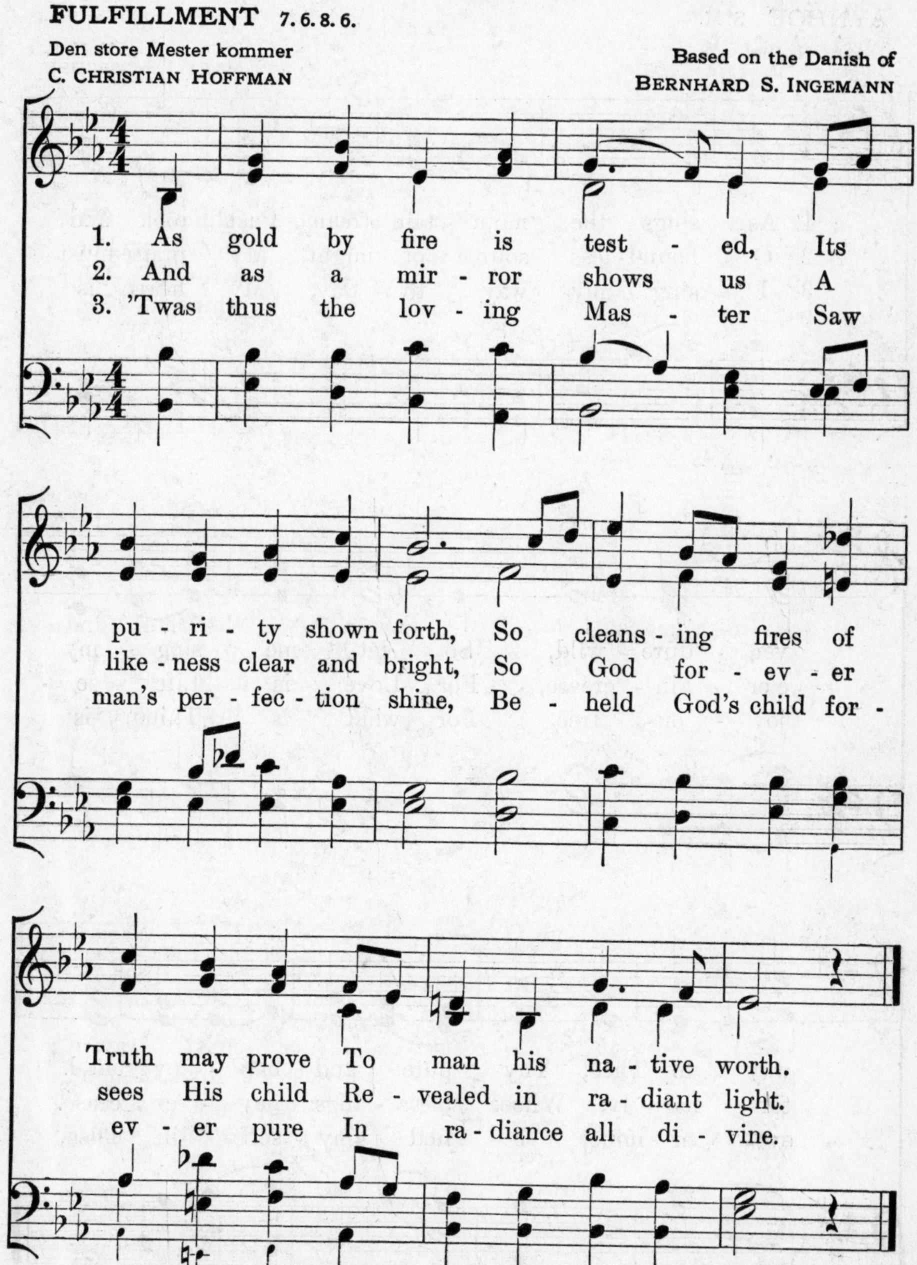

1. As gold by fire is test - ed, Its
2. And as a mir - ror shows us A
3. 'Twas thus the lov - ing Mas - ter Saw
pu - ri - ty shown forth, So cleans - ing fires of
like - ness clear and bright, So God for - ev - er
man's per - fec - tion shine, Be - held God's child for -
Truth may prove To man his na - tive worth.
sees His child Re - vealed in ra - diant light.
ev - er pure In ra - diance all di - vine.

# 16

**AYNHOE** S. M.

JAMES NARES — V. K. S.

1. As sings the moun - tain stream, Past rock and ver - dure wild, So let me sing my way to Thee, Thy pure and hap - py child.
2. O bound - less source of might, My praise must e'er in - crease, For Love is Life e - ter - nal - ly, Whose bless - ings nev - er cease.
3. I sing my way to - day, My heart is joy - ous, free, For what is Thine is ev - er mine, I find my - self in Thee.

## WALSALL C. M.

Attributed to HENRY PURCELL — EDMUND BEALE SARGANT *

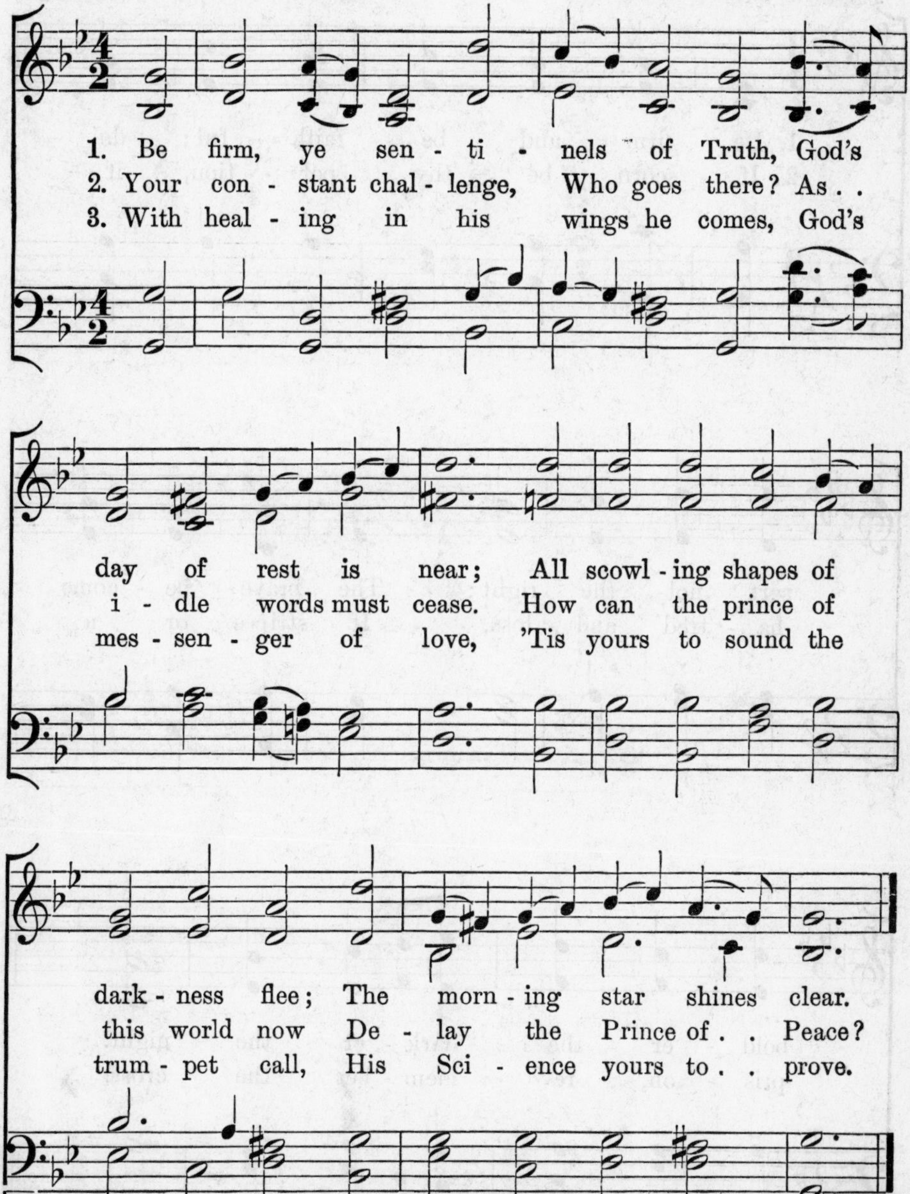

1. Be firm, ye sen - ti - nels of Truth, God's
2. Your con - stant chal - lenge, Who goes there? As . .
3. With heal - ing in his wings he comes, God's

day of rest is near; All scowl - ing shapes of
i - dle words must cease. How can the prince of
mes - sen - ger of love, 'Tis yours to sound the

dark - ness flee; The morn - ing star shines clear.
this world now De - lay the Prince of . . Peace?
trum - pet call, His Sci - ence yours to . . prove.

Words by permission of the author

# 18

**LYONS** 11. 11. 11. 11.

J. Michael Haydn | Anonymous

1. Be firm and be faith - ful; de -
2. If scorn be thy por - tion, if

sert not the right; The brave be - come
ha - tred and loss, If stripes or a

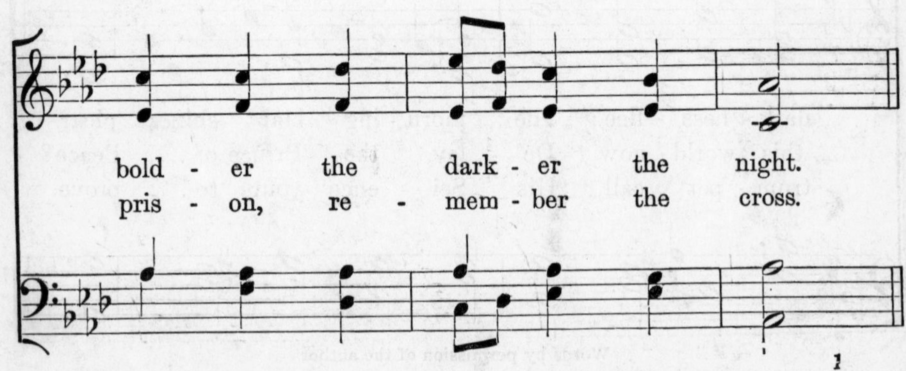
bold - er the dark - er the night.
pris - on, re - mem - ber the cross.

Then up and be do - ing, though
God watch - es a - bove thee, and

cow - ards may fail; Thy du - ty pur -
He will re - quite; For - sake those that

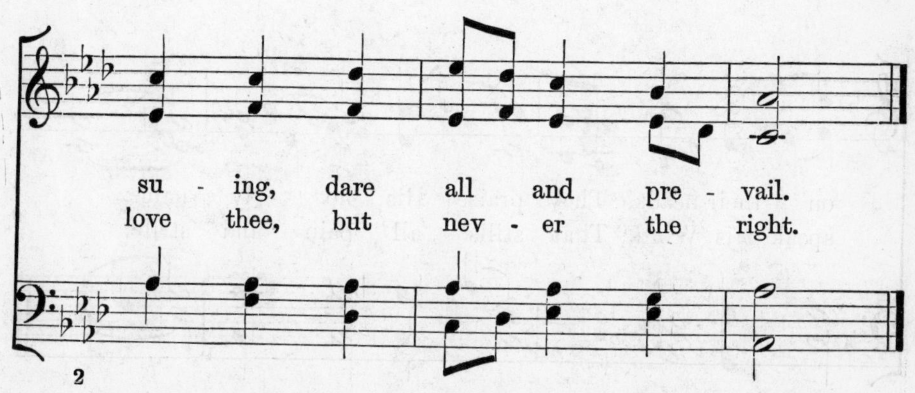
su - ing, dare all and pre - vail.
love thee, but nev - er the right.

# 19

**PURITY** 8. 8. 8. 6. D.

Den store, hvite flokk
Norwegian Folk Melody

Based on the Danish of
HANS A. BRORSON

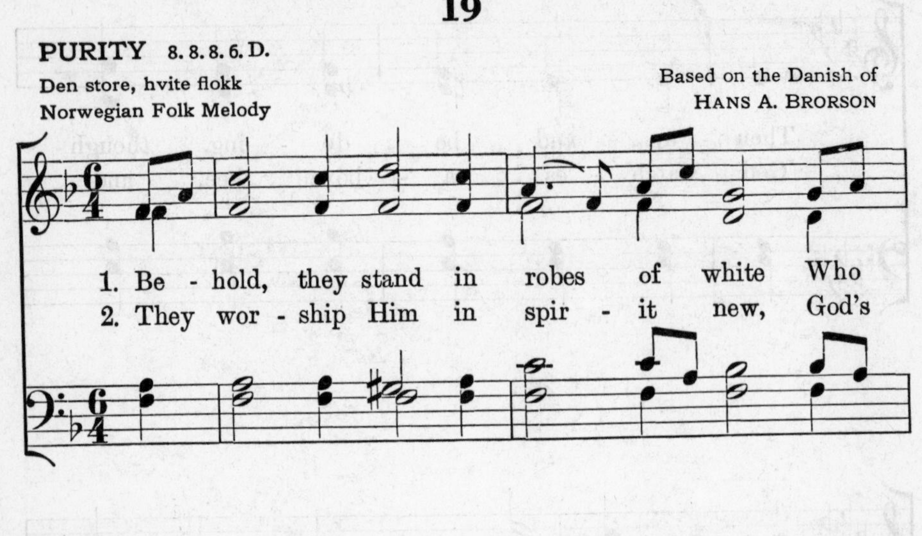
1. Be - hold, they stand in robes of white Who
2. They wor - ship Him in spir - it new, God's

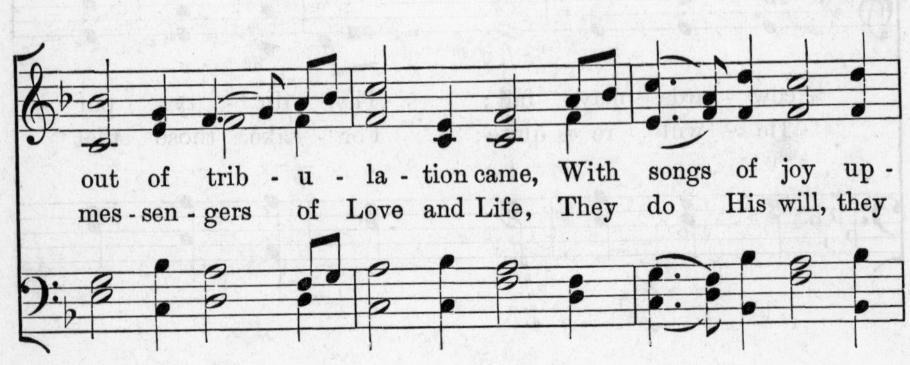
out of trib - u - la - tion came, With songs of joy up -
mes - sen - gers of Love and Life, They do His will, they

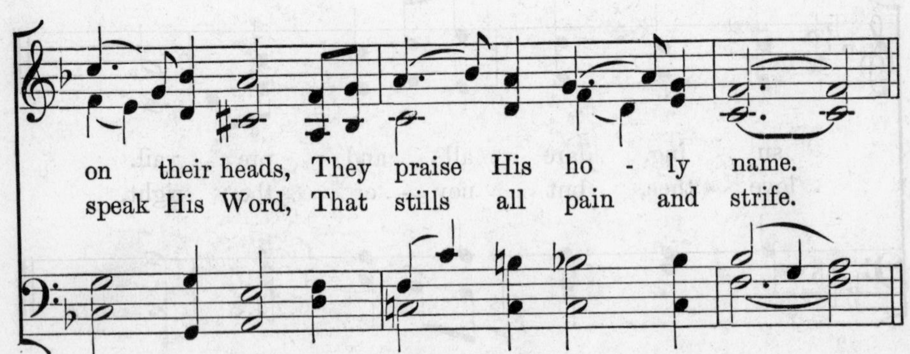
on their heads, They praise His ho - ly name.
speak His Word, That stills all pain and strife.

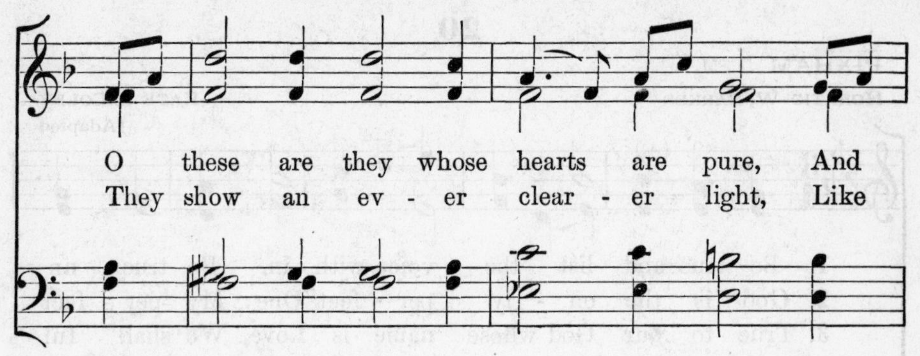
O these are they whose hearts are pure, And
They show an ev - er clear - er light, Like

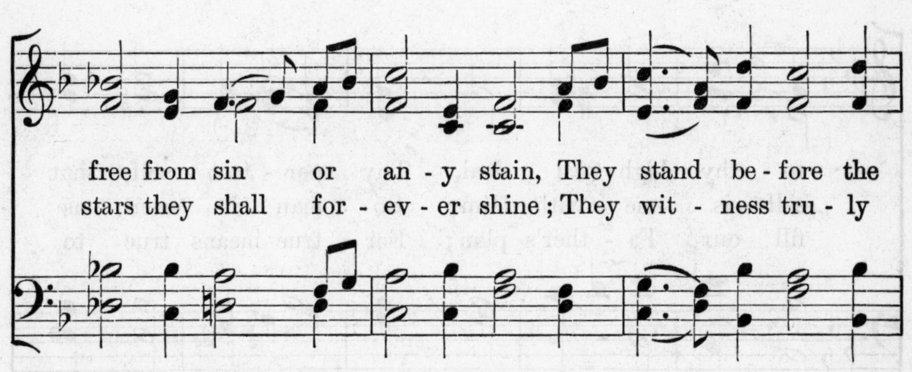
free from sin or an - y stain, They stand be - fore the
stars they shall for - ev - er shine; They wit - ness tru - ly

throne of light, Their joy shall nev - er wane.
to His Word, And God saith, These are Mine.

PIXHAM L. M.

HORATIO W. PARKER

KATE L. COLBY
Adapted

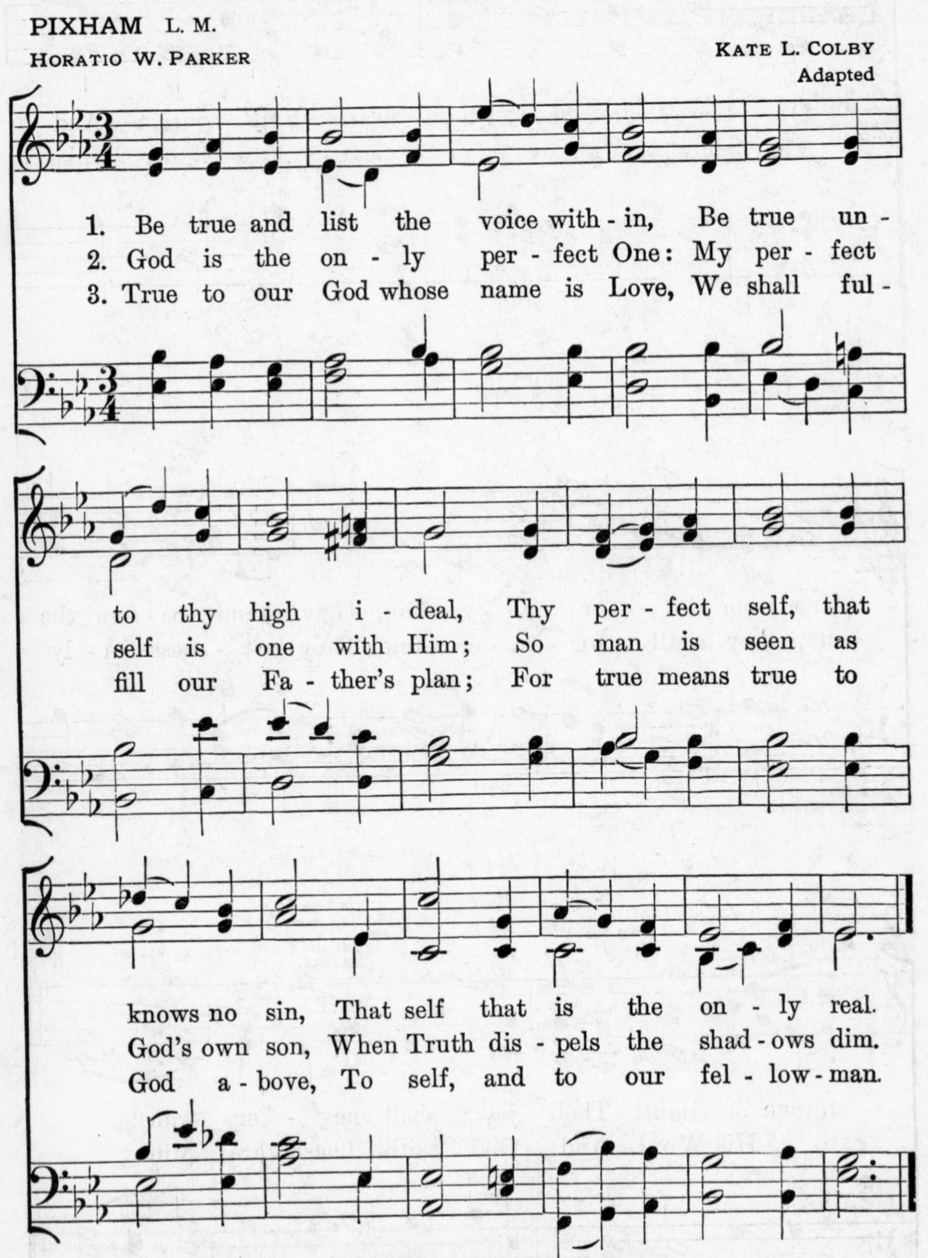
1. Be true and list the voice with - in, Be true un - to thy high i - deal, Thy per - fect self, that knows no sin, That self that is the on - ly real.
2. God is the on - ly per - fect One: My per - fect self is one with Him; So man is seen as God's own son, When Truth dis - pels the shad - ows dim.
3. True to our God whose name is Love, We shall ful - fill our Fa - ther's plan; For true means true to God a - bove, To self, and to our fel - low - man.

Music by permission of Mrs. H. W. PARKER

*These words have another setting in the* SUPPLEMENT, No. 416

# 21†

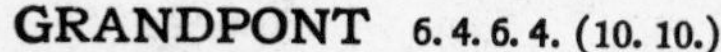

**GRANDPONT** 6. 4. 6. 4. (10. 10.)

JOHN STAINER — HORATIUS BONAR

1. Be - lov - ed, let us love: for
2. Be - lov - ed, let us love: for
3. Be - lov - ed, let us love: for
4. Be - lov - ed, let us love: for

Love is God; . . In God a - lone hath
they who love, . . They on - ly, are His
love is light, . . And he who lov - eth
on - ly thus . . Shall we be - hold that

love its . . . true . . a - bode.
sons, born . . from . . a - bove.
not dwell - eth . . in . . night.
God who . . lov - eth . . us.

Music by permission of NOVELLO & Co. Ltd.

# 22†

**DENNIS** 6. 4. 6. 4. (10. 10.)

G. THALBEN-BALL — HORATIUS BONAR

1. Be - lov - ed, let us love: for
2. Be - lov - ed, let us love: for
3. Be - lov - ed, let us love: for
4. Be - lov - ed, let us love: for
Love is . . God; In God a - lone hath
they who . love, They on - ly, are His
love is . . light, And he who lov - eth
on - ly . . thus Shall we be - hold that
love . . its true a - bode.
sons, . . born from a - bove.
not . . dwell - eth in night.
God . . who lov - eth us.

Music by permission of G. THALBEN-BALL

SERENITY 8. 4. 8. 4.
Arranged from
WILLIAM V. WALLACE

CHRISTMAS MORN
MARY BAKER EDDY

1. Blest Christ - mas morn, though murk - y clouds Pur - sue thy way, Thy light was born where storm en - shrouds Nor dawn nor . . day!
2. Dear Christ, for - ev - er here and near, No cra - dle song, No na - tal hour and moth - er's tear, To thee be - long.
3. Thou God - i - de - a, Life - en - crowned, The Beth - lehem babe— Be - loved, re - plete, by flesh em - bound—Was but thy . . shade!
4. Thou gen - tle beam of liv - ing Love, And death - less Life! Truth in - fi - nite,— so far a - bove All mor - tal . . strife,
5. Or cru - el creed, or earth - born taint: Fill us to - day With all thou art— be thou our saint, Our stay, al - way.

## CHRISTMAS MORN 8. 4. 8. 4.

ALBERT F. CONANT

CHRISTMAS MORN
MARY BAKER EDDY

1. Blest Christ - mas morn, though murk - y clouds Pur -
2. Dear Christ, for - ev - er here and near, No
3. Thou God - i - de - a, Life - en - crowned, The
4. Thou gen - tle beam of liv - ing Love, And
5. Or cru - el creed, or earth - born taint: Fill
sue . . thy . . way, Thy light was born where
cra - dle . . song, No na - tal hour and
Beth - lehem babe— Be - loved, re - plete, by
death - less. . Life! Truth in - fi - nite,— so
us . . to - day With all thou art— be
storm en - shrouds Nor dawn nor . . day!
moth - er's tear, To thee be - long.
flesh em - bound— Was but thy . . shade!
far a - bove All mor - tal . . strife,
thou our saint, Our stay, al - way.

KINGTON 8. 4. 8. 4.
F. LLEWELLYN EDWARDS

CHRISTMAS MORN
MARY BAKER EDDY

1. Blest Christ - mas morn, though murk - y clouds Pur -
2. Dear Christ, for - ev - er here and near, No
3. Thou God - i - de - a, Life - en - crowned, The
4. Thou gen - tle beam of liv - ing Love, And
5. Or cru - el creed, or earth - born taint: Fill
sue . . . thy way, Thy light was born where
cra - dle song, No na - tal hour and
Beth - - lehem babe— Be - loved, re - plete, by
death - - less Life! Truth in - fi - nite,— so
us . . . to - day With all thou art— be
storm en - shrouds Nor dawn . . nor day!
moth - er's tear, To thee . . be - long.
flesh em - bound— Was but . . thy shade!
far a - bove All mor - tal strife,
thou our saint, Our stay, . . al - way.

# 26†

DRANSFIELD 8. 4. 8. 4.
G. THALBEN-BALL
CHRISTMAS MORN
MARY BAKER EDDY
1. Blest Christmas morn, though murky clouds Pursue thy way, Thy light was born where storm enshrouds Nor dawn nor day!
2. Dear Christ, forever here and near, No cradle song, No natal hour and mother's tear, To thee belong.
3. Thou God-idea, Life-encrowned, The Bethlehem babe— Beloved, replete, by flesh embound— Was but thy shade!
4. Thou gentle beam of living Love, And deathless Life! Truth infinite,—so far above All mortal strife,
5. Or cruel creed, or earth-born taint: Fill us today With all thou art— be thou our saint, Our stay, alway.

INFINITAS 8.4.8.4.
PERCY WHITLOCK
CHRISTMAS MORN
MARY BAKER EDDY
1. Blest Christ - mas morn, though murk - y clouds
2. Dear Christ, for - ev - er here and near,
3. Thou God - i - de - a, Life - en - crowned,
4. Thou gen - tle beam of liv - ing Love,
5. Or cru - el creed, or earth - born taint:
Pur - sue . . thy way, Thy light was born where
No cra - dle song, No na - tal hour and
The Beth - lehem babe— Be - loved, re - plete, by
And death - less Life! Truth in - fi - nite,— so
Fill us . . to - day With all thou art— be
storm en - shrouds Nor dawn nor . . day!
moth - er's tear, To thee be - long.
flesh em - bound— Was but thy . . shade!
far a - bove All mor - tal . . strife,
thou our saint, Our stay, al - way.

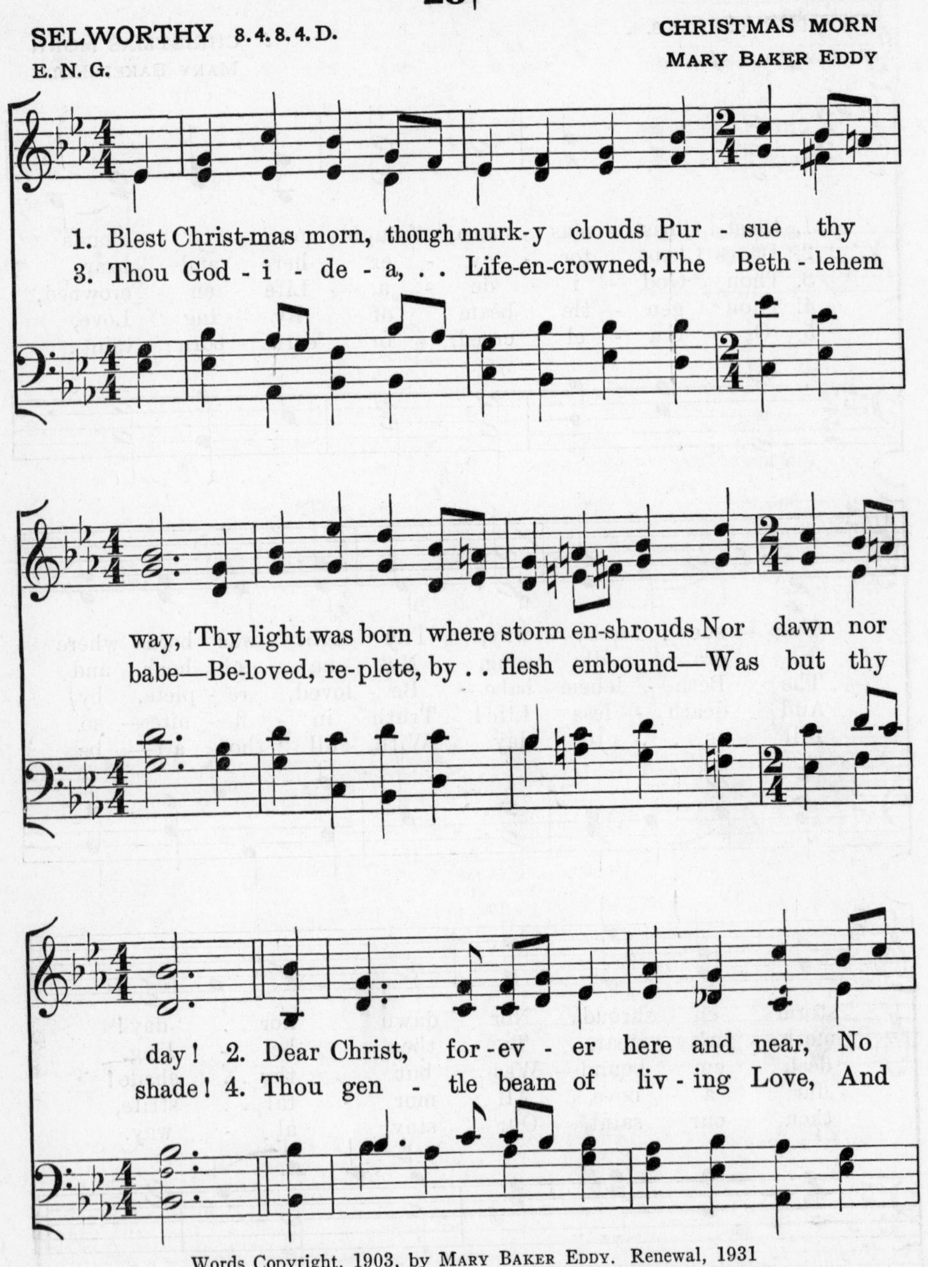
SELWORTHY 8. 4. 8. 4. D.
E. N. G.
CHRISTMAS MORN
MARY BAKER EDDY
1. Blest Christ-mas morn, though murk-y clouds Pur - sue thy
3. Thou God - i - de - a, . . Life-en-crowned, The Beth - lehem
way, Thy light was born where storm en-shrouds Nor dawn nor
babe—Be-loved, re-plete, by . . flesh embound—Was but thy
day! 2. Dear Christ, for - ev - er here and near, No
shade! 4. Thou gen - tle beam of liv - ing Love, And

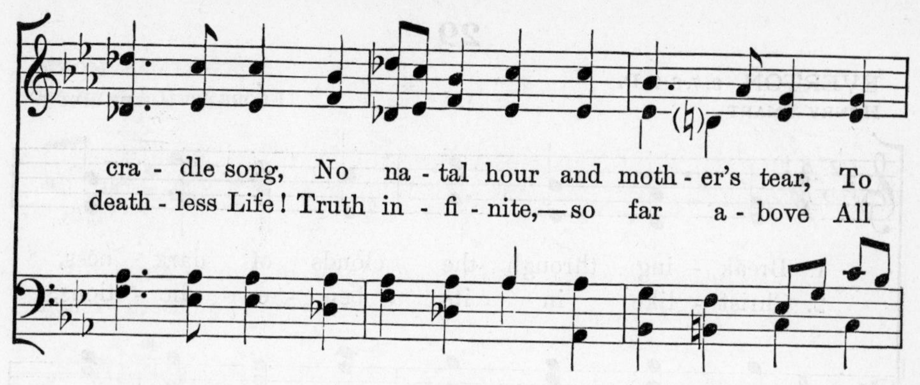
cra - dle song, No na - tal hour and moth - er's tear, To
death - less Life! Truth in - fi - nite,—so far a - bove All

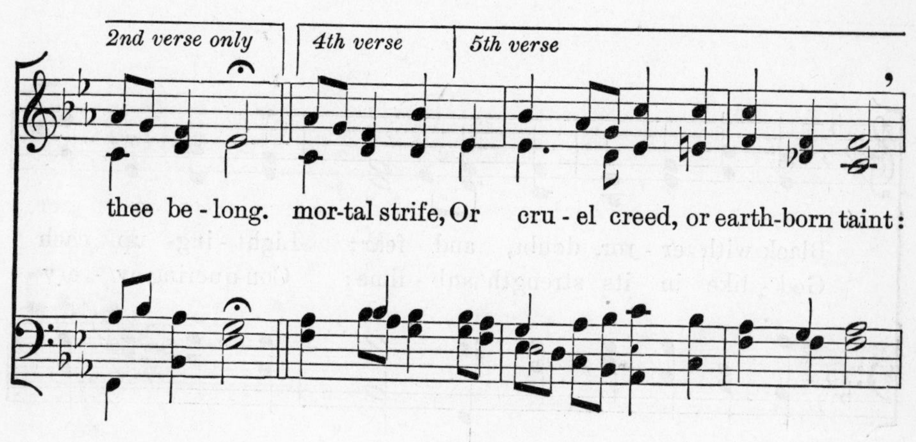
2nd verse only
4th verse
5th verse
thee be - long. mor-tal strife, Or cru - el creed, or earth-born taint:

Fill us to-day With all thou art— be thou our saint, Our stay, al - way.

EVERTON 8.7.8.7.D.
HENRY SMART

FLORENCE L. HEYWOOD

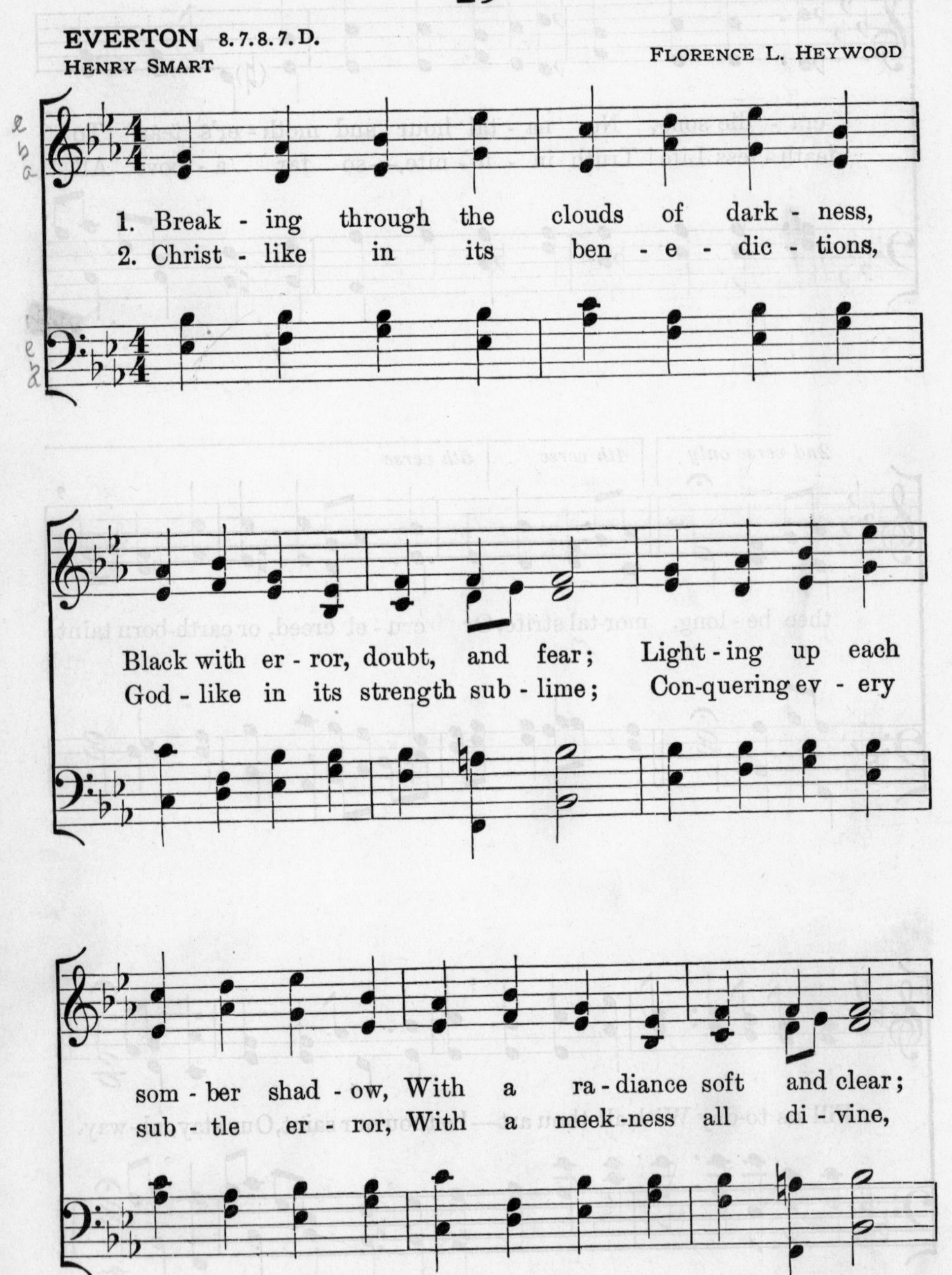
1. Break - ing through the clouds of dark - ness,
2. Christ - like in its ben - e - dic - tions,
Black with er - ror, doubt, and fear; Light - ing up each
God - like in its strength sub - lime; Con-quering ev - ery
som - ber shad - ow, With a ra - diance soft and clear;
sub - tle er - ror, With a meek - ness all di - vine,

Fill - ing ev - ery heart with glad - ness,
It has gone a - cross the o - cean,
That its ho - ly pow - er feels, Comes the Chris - tian
It is known in ev - ery land, And our sis - ters
Sci - ence gos - pel, Sin it kills and grief it heals.
and our broth - ers Are u - nit - ed in one band.

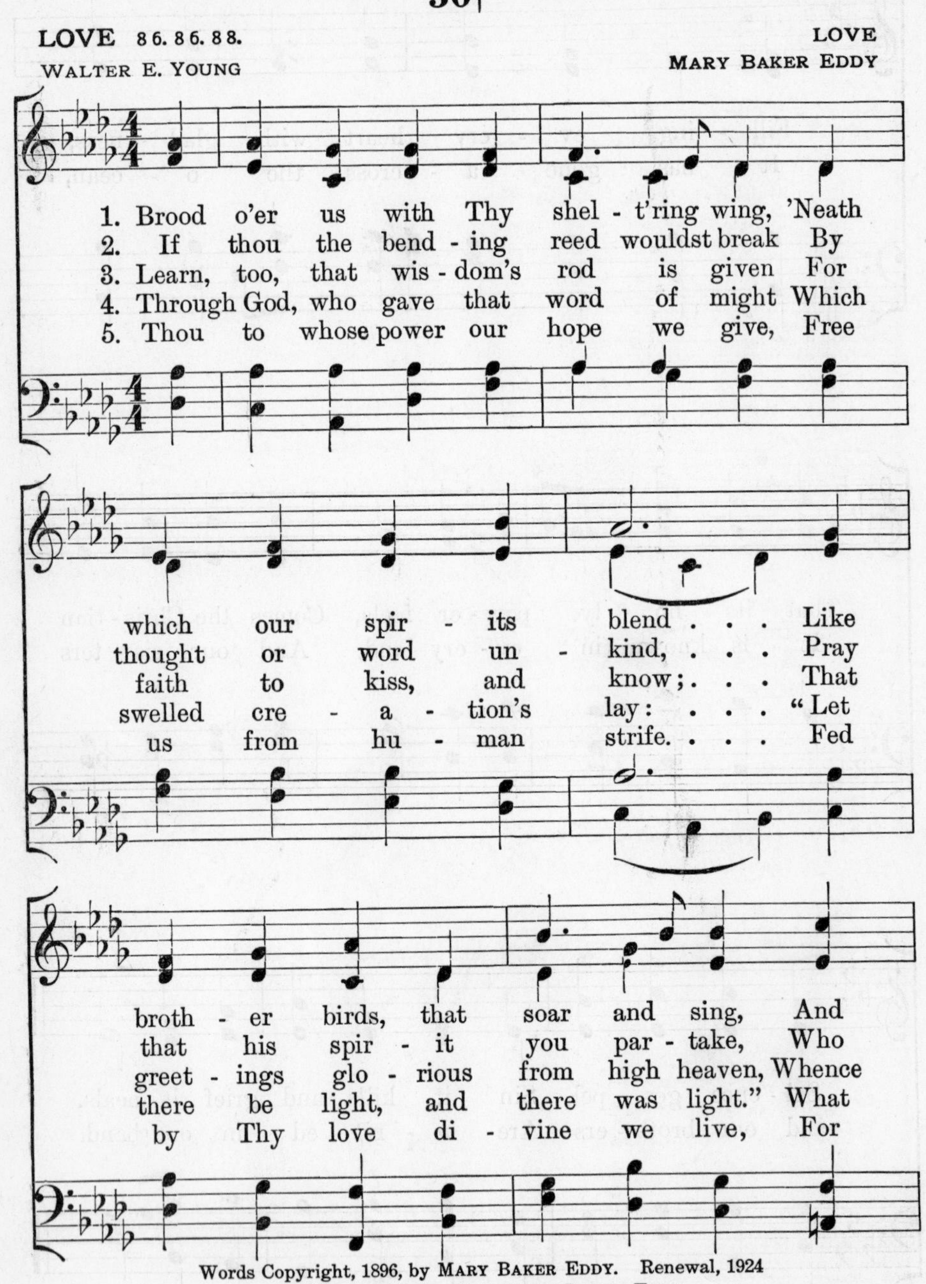

LOVE 86. 86. 88.
LOVE
WALTER E. YOUNG
MARY BAKER EDDY
1. Brood o'er us with Thy shel - t'ring wing, 'Neath
2. If thou the bend - ing reed wouldst break By
3. Learn, too, that wis - dom's rod is given For
4. Through God, who gave that word of might Which
5. Thou to whose power our hope we give, Free
which our spir - its blend . . . Like
thought or word un - kind, . . . Pray
faith to kiss, and know; . . . That
swelled cre - a - tion's lay: . . . "Let
us from hu - man strife. . . . Fed
broth - er birds, that soar and sing, And
that his spir - it you par - take, Who
greet - ings glo - rious from high heaven, Whence
there be light, and there was light." What
by Thy love di - vine we live, For

on the same branch bend. The
loved and healed man - kind: Seek
joys su - per - nal flow, Come
chased the clouds a - way? 'Twas
Love a - lone is Life; And
ar - row that doth wound the dove Darts
ho - ly thoughts and heaven - ly strain, That
from that Love, di - vine - ly near, Which
Love whose fin - ger traced a - loud A
life most sweet, as heart to heart Speaks
not from those who watch and . . love.
make men one in love . . re - main.
chas - tens pride and earth - born . . fear,
bow of prom - ise on . . . the . . cloud.
kind - ly when we meet . . and . . part.

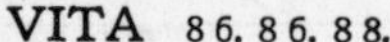

**VITA** 86. 86. 88. **LOVE**

EATON FANING MARY BAKER EDDY

*To be sung in unison*

1. Brood o'er us with Thy shel-t'ring wing, 'Neath which our spir - its
2. If thou the bend-ing reed wouldst break By thought or word un -
3. Learn, too, that wis-dom's rod is given For faith to kiss, and
4. Through God, who gave that word of might Which swelled cre-a-tion's
5. Thou to whose power our hope we give, Free us from hu - man

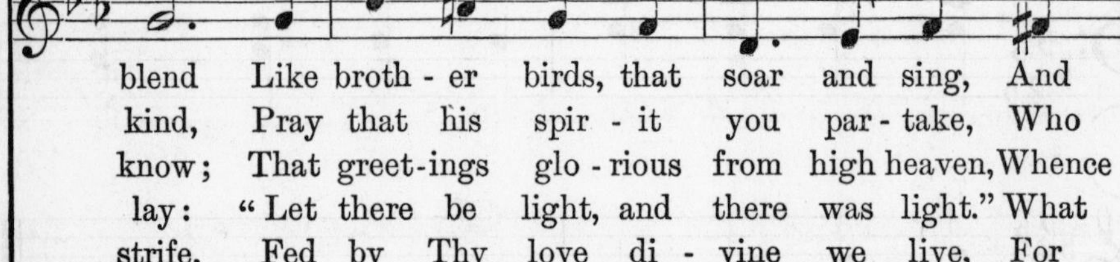

blend Like broth - er birds, that soar and sing, And
kind, Pray that his spir - it you par - take, Who
know; That greet-ings glo - rious from high heaven, Whence
lay: "Let there be light, and there was light." What
strife. Fed by Thy love di - vine we live, For

on the same branch bend. The ar - row that doth
loved and healed man - kind: Seek ho - ly thoughts and
joys su - per - nal flow, Come from that Love, di -
chased the clouds a - way? 'Twas Love whose fin - ger
Love a - lone is Life; And life most sweet, as

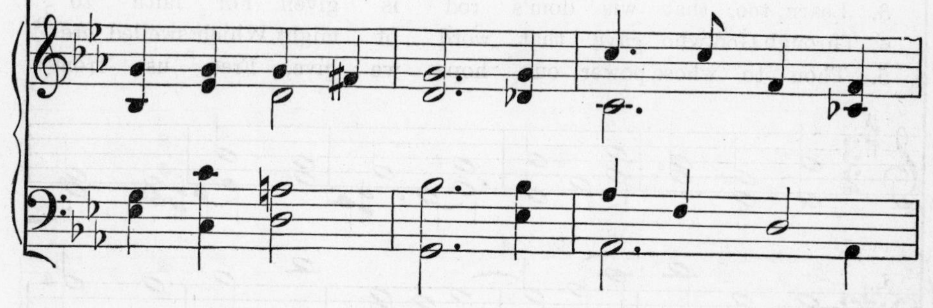

wound the dove Darts not from those who watch and love.
heaven-ly strain, That make men one in love re - main.
vine - ly near, Which chas - tens pride and earth-born fear,
traced a - loud A bow of prom - ise on the cloud.
heart to heart Speaks kind - ly when we meet and part.

# 32†

**GOTTLOB** 86. 86. 88. | **LOVE**

JOHANN SEBASTIAN BACH | MARY BAKER EDDY

Slightly altered

*To be sung in unison*

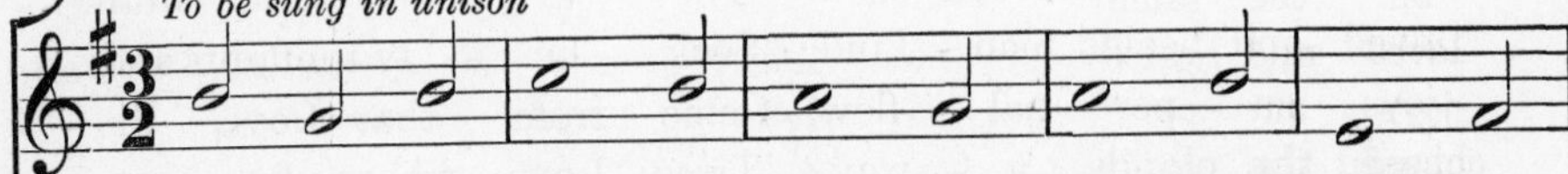

1. Brood o'er us with Thy shel - t'ring wing, 'Neath which our
2. If thou the bend - ing reed wouldst break By thought or
3. Learn, too, that wis - dom's rod is given For faith to
4. Through God, who gave that word of might Which swelled cre -
5. Thou to whose power our hope we give, Free us from

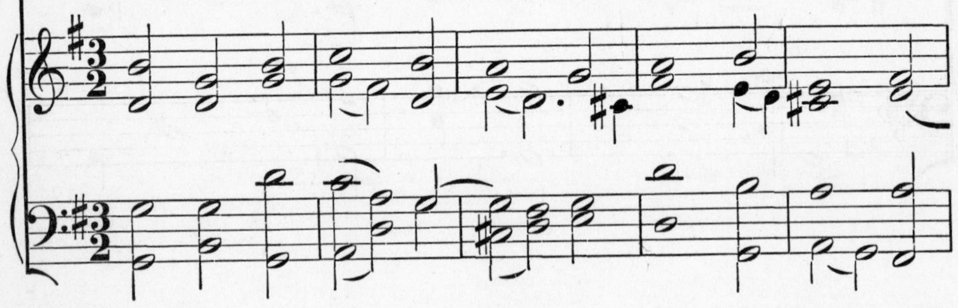

spir - its blend Like broth - er birds, that soar and sing, And
word un - kind, Pray that his spir - it you par - take, Who
kiss, and know; That greet-ings glo - rious from high heaven, Whence
a - tion's lay: "Let there be light, and there was light." What
hu - man strife. Fed by Thy love di - vine we live, For

on the same branch bend. The ar - row that doth
loved and healed man - kind: Seek ho - ly thoughts and
joys su - per - nal flow, Come from that Love, di -
chased the clouds a - way? 'Twas Love whose fin - ger
Love a - lone is Life; And life most sweet, as
wound the dove Darts not from those who watch and love.
heaven - ly strain, That make men one in love re - main.
vine - ly near, Which chas - tens pride and earth - born fear,
traced a - loud A bow of prom - ise on the cloud.
heart to heart Speaks kind - ly when we meet and part.

# 33

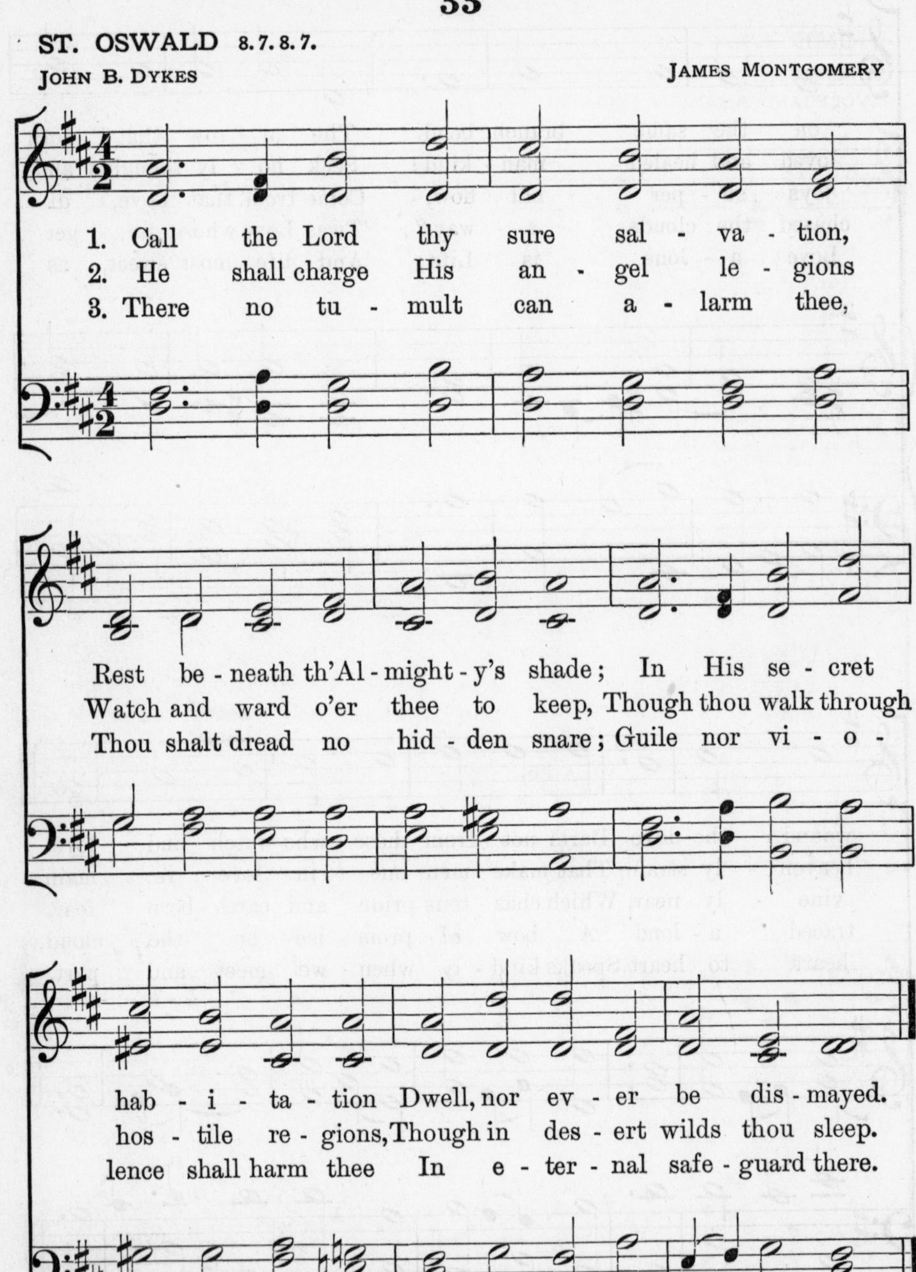
ST. OSWALD 8.7.8.7.
JOHN B. DYKES
JAMES MONTGOMERY
1. Call the Lord thy sure sal - va - tion,
2. He shall charge His an - gel le - gions
3. There no tu - mult can a - larm thee,
Rest be - neath th'Al - might - y's shade; In His se - cret
Watch and ward o'er thee to keep, Though thou walk through
Thou shalt dread no hid - den snare; Guile nor vi - o -
hab - i - ta - tion Dwell, nor ev - er be dis - mayed.
hos - tile re - gions, Though in des - ert wilds thou sleep.
lence shall harm thee In e - ter - nal safe - guard there.

HOME L. M.

Arranged from
WOLFGANG AMADEUS MOZART M. S. C.

1. Christ comes a - gain with ho - ly power, To lift our blind - ed eyes to see; The sick are healed, the sin - ner blest, As on that eve in Gal - i - lee.
2. Once more the lone - ly heart is fed. Who dwells with Love hath per - fect ease, Faith, hope, and joy are with us all; Great are com - pan - ions such as these.
3. The weak and thirst - y are re - freshed, A - gain each emp - ty cup is filled; The ten - der Christ is here to bless, And all the storms of earth are stilled.
4. In Truth there is no pain or death Nor an - y shades of com - ing night; The prom - ise of our God still stands: At e - ven - tide it shall be light.

# 35

**DIX** 77. 77. 77.

Arranged from "TREUER HEILAND"
CONRAD KOCHER — CHARLES WESLEY

1. Christ, whose glo-ry fills the skies, Christ, the true, the per-fect Light,
2. Dark and cheer-less is the morn Un-com-pan-ioned, Lord, by thee;
3. Vis-it then this soul of mine, Pierce the gloom of sin and grief;

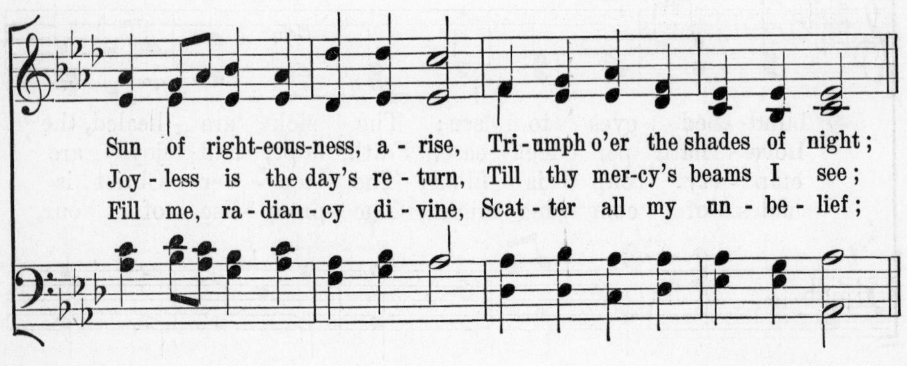
Sun of right-eous-ness, a-rise, Tri-umph o'er the shades of night;
Joy-less is the day's re-turn, Till thy mer-cy's beams I see;
Fill me, ra-dian-cy di-vine, Scat-ter all my un-be-lief;

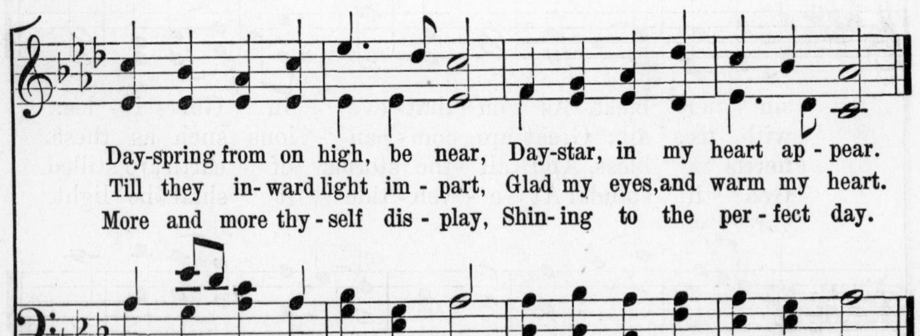
Day-spring from on high, be near, Day-star, in my heart ap-pear.
Till they in-ward light im-part, Glad my eyes, and warm my heart.
More and more thy-self dis-play, Shin-ing to the per-fect day.

# 36

**FALMOUTH** C. M.

WALTER E. YOUNG

HORATIUS BONAR
Adapted

1. Church of the ev - er - liv - ing God, The
2. Thy words, a - mid the words of earth, How
3. A - mid the rest - less eyes of earth How
4. Un - tir - ing praise we lift on high, Un -
Fa - ther's gra - cious choice; A - mid the voi - ces
noise - less and how pure; A - mid the hurry - ing
stead - fast is thine eye, Fixed on the si - lent
fal - tering songs we sing, Un - end - ing fes - ti -
of this earth How might - y is thy voice.
crowds of time Thy step how calm and sure.
love - li - ness That fills the morn - ing sky.
val we keep In pres - ence of the King.

## 37†

**ST. AGNES** C.M.

JOHN B. DYKES

SAMUEL JOHNSON*

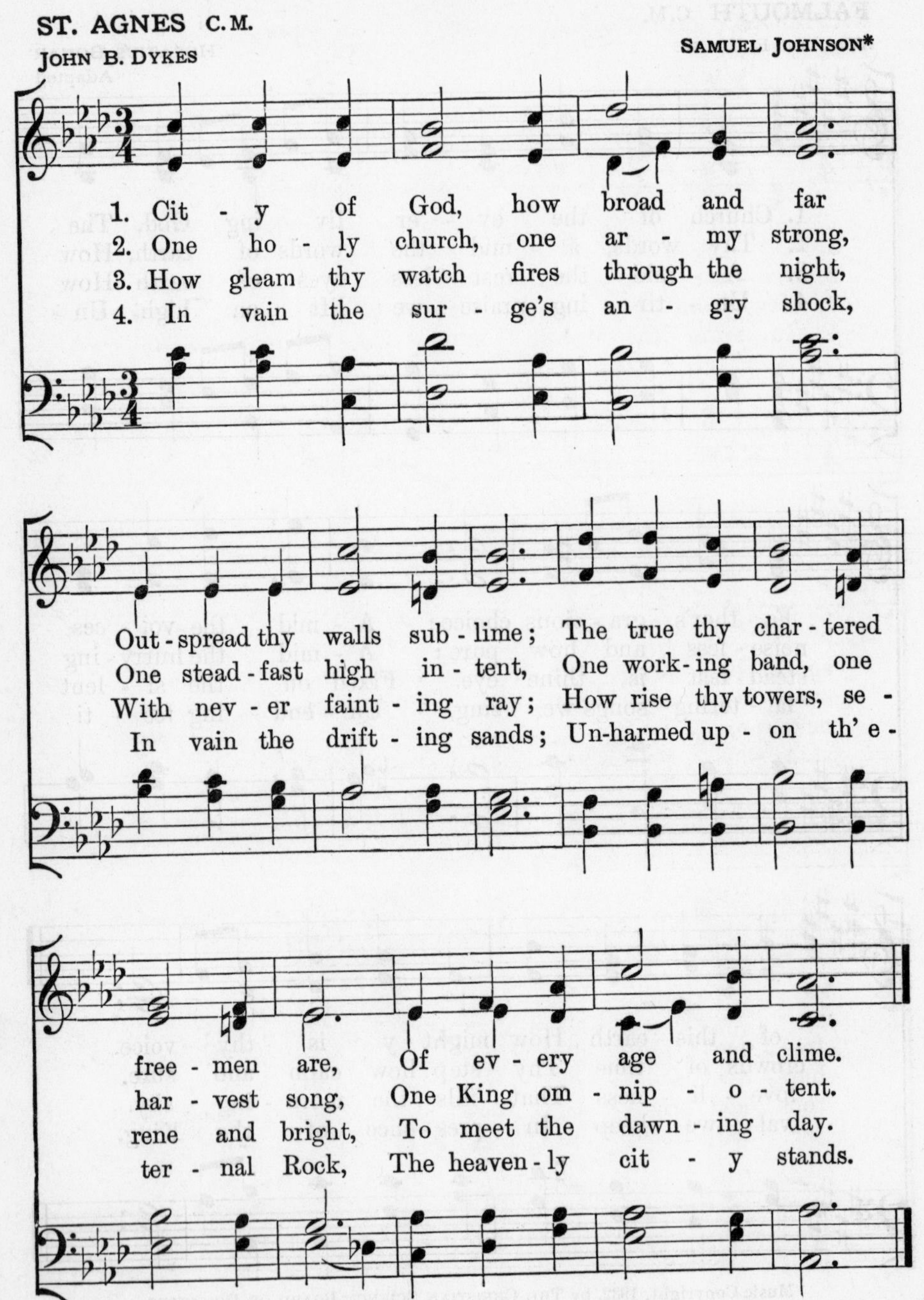
1. Cit - y of God, how broad and far
2. One ho - ly church, one ar - my strong,
3. How gleam thy watch fires through the night,
4. In vain the sur - ge's an - gry shock,
Out-spread thy walls sub - lime; The true thy char - tered
One stead - fast high in - tent, One work - ing band, one
With nev - er faint - ing ray; How rise thy towers, se -
In vain the drift - ing sands; Un-harmed up - on th' e -
free - men are, Of ev - ery age and clime.
har - vest song, One King om - nip - o - tent.
rene and bright, To meet the dawn - ing day.
ter - nal Rock, The heaven - ly cit - y stands.

## 38†

**RICHMOND (CHESTERFIELD) C. M.**

THOMAS HAWEIS
Arranged by S. WEBBE, Jr.

SAMUEL JOHNSON*

1. City of God, how broad and far Outspread thy walls sublime; The true thy chartered freemen are, Of every age and clime.
2. One holy church, one army strong, One steadfast high intent, One working band, one harvest song, One King omnipotent.
3. How gleam thy watch fires through the night, With never fainting ray; How rise thy towers, serene and bright, To meet the dawning day.
4. In vain the surge's angry shock, In vain the drifting sands; Unharmed upon th' eternal Rock, The heavenly city stands.

**FRAINSBY** L. M.

GEORGE DYSON

SIMON BROWNE
Adapted

1. Come, gra - cious Spir - it, heaven - ly Love, With light and
2. The light of Truth to us dis - play, That we may
3. Lead us, O Christ, thou liv - ing Way, Nor let us
com - fort from a - bove; Be Thou our guard - ian, Thou our
know and choose Thy way; Plant ho - ly joy in ev - ery
from thy pre - cepts stray; Lead us to God, our heaven-ly
guide, O'er ev - ery thought and step pre - side.
heart, That we from Thee may ne'er de - part.
rest, That we may be for - ev - er blest.

Music by permission of GEORGE DYSON

## CONSOLATOR 11. 10. 11. 10.

SAMUEL WEBBE

THOMAS MOORE
and
THOMAS HASTINGS
Adapted

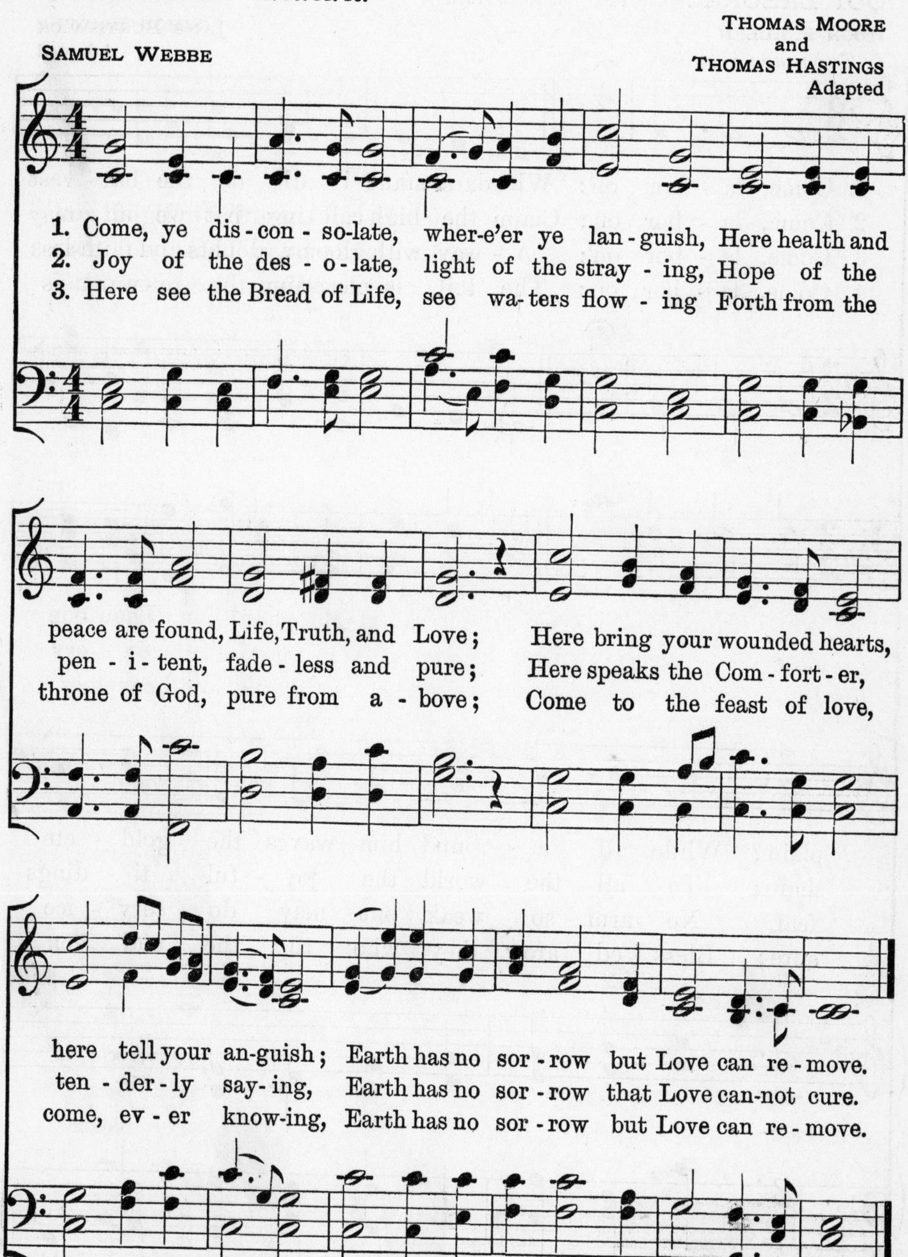
1. Come, ye dis - con - so-late, wher-e'er ye lan - guish, Here health and
2. Joy of the des - o - late, light of the stray - ing, Hope of the
3. Here see the Bread of Life, see wa-ters flow - ing Forth from the
peace are found, Life, Truth, and Love; Here bring your wounded hearts,
pen - i - tent, fade - less and pure; Here speaks the Com - fort - er,
throne of God, pure from a - bove; Come to the feast of love,
here tell your an-guish; Earth has no sor - row but Love can re - move.
ten - der - ly say- ing, Earth has no sor - row that Love can-not cure.
come, ev - er know-ing, Earth has no sor - row but Love can re - move.

# 41

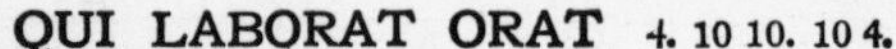

## QUI LABORAT ORAT 4. 10 10. 10 4.

HUGH P. ALLEN — JANE BORTHWICK, Adapted

*To be sung in unison*

1. Come, la - bor on: Who dares stand i - dle on the har - vest
2. Come, la - bor on: Claim the high call - ing that we all may
3. Come, la - bor on: A - way with gloomy doubts and faith-less
4. Come, la - bor on: The toil is pleas-ant, the re - ward is

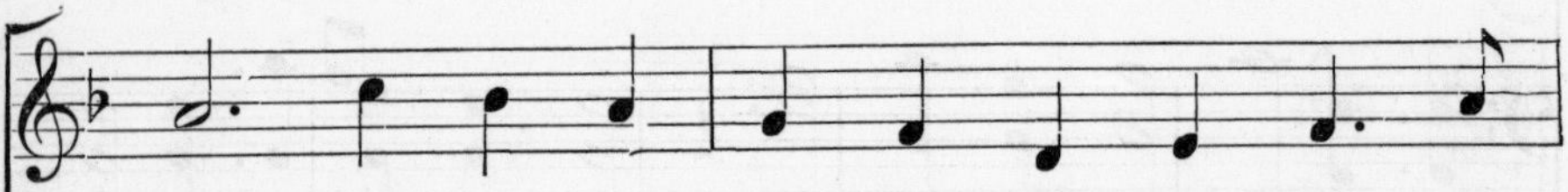

plain? While all a - round him waves the gold - en
share; To all the world the joy - ful ti - dings
fear. No arm so weak but may do serv - ice
sure; Bless - ed are they who to the end en -

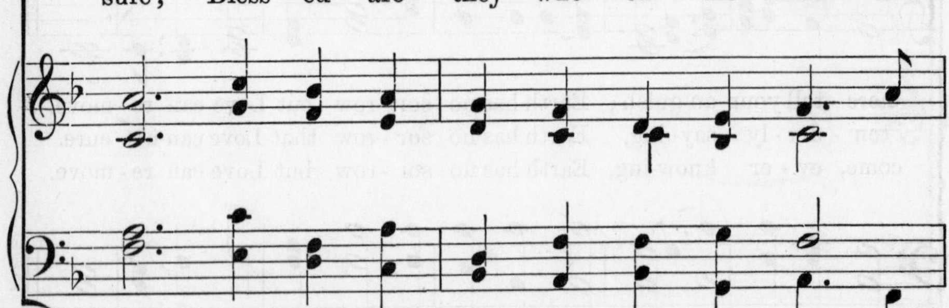

Music by permission of HUGH P. ALLEN

grain, And to each serv - ant does the Mas - ter
bear; Re - deem the time: its hours too swift - ly
here; By means the sim - plest can our God ful -
dure; How full their joy, how sweet their rest shall

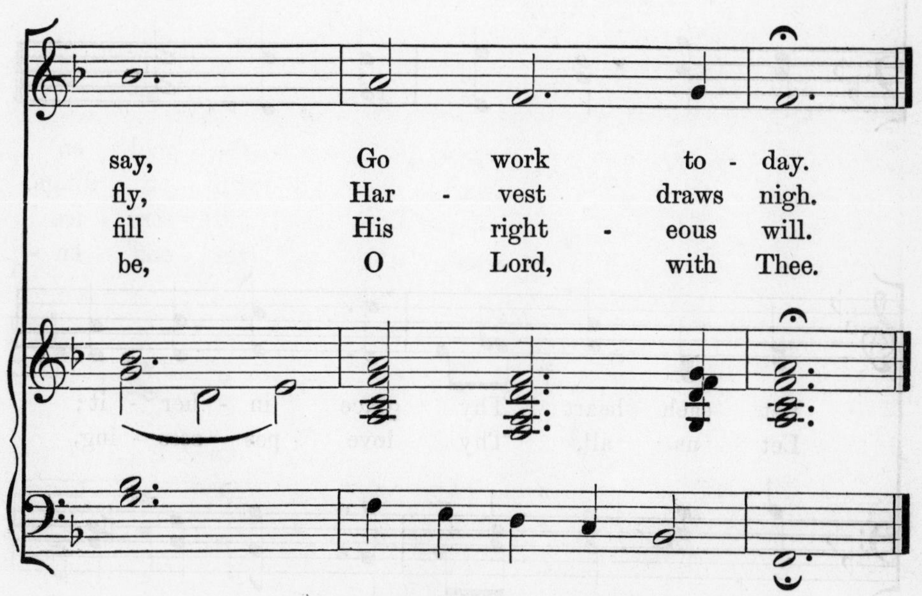
say, Go work to - day.
fly, Har - vest draws nigh.
fill His right - eous will.
be, O Lord, with Thee.

REGENT SQUARE 87. 87. 87.

HENRY SMART JONATHAN EVANS*

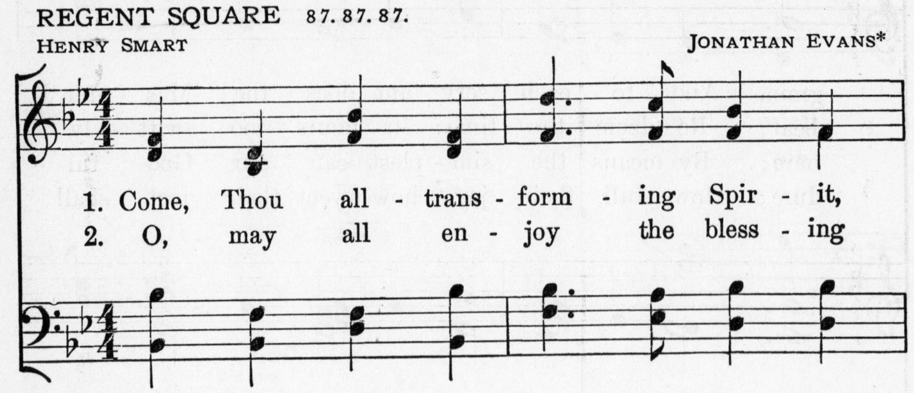
1. Come, Thou all - trans - form - ing Spir - it,
2. O, may all en - joy the bless - ing

Bless the sow - er and the seed;
Which Thy ho - ly word doth give;

Let each heart Thy grace in - her - it;
Let us all, Thy love pos - sess - ing,

Raise the weak, the hun - gry feed;
Joy - ful - ly Thy truth re - ceive;

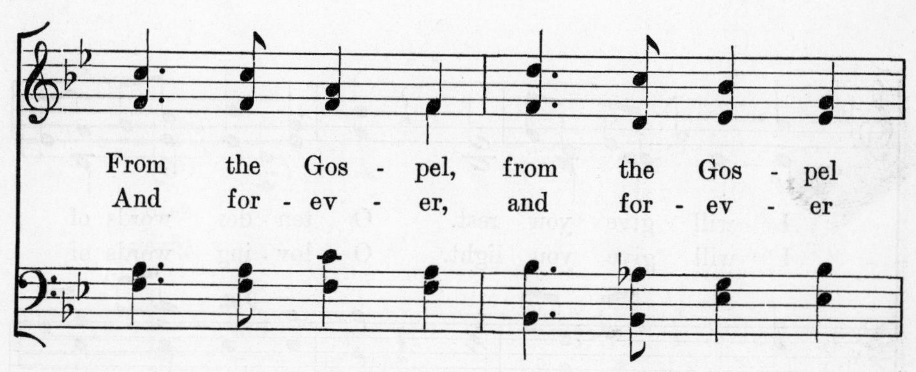
From the Gos - pel, from the Gos - pel
And for - ev - er, and for - ev - er

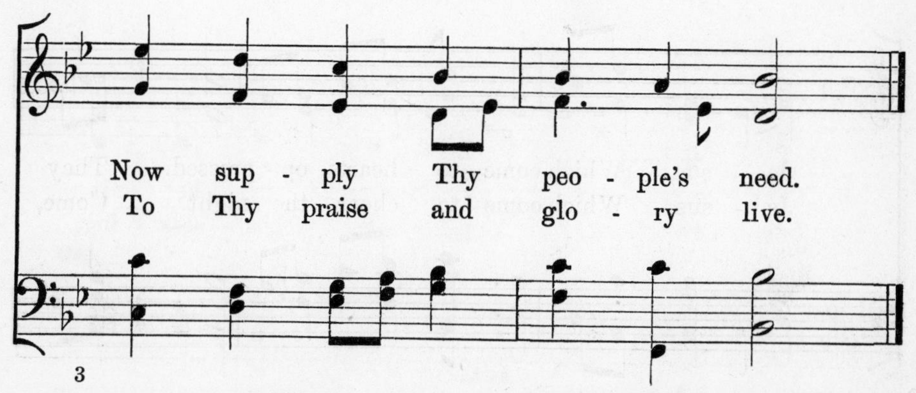
Now sup - ply Thy peo - ple's need.
To Thy praise and glo - ry live.

43

ABENDLIED 7. 6. 7. 6. D.
FRANZ SCHUBERT
WILLIAM CHATTERTON DIX
Adapted
1. Come un - to me, ye wea - ry, And I will give you rest. O ten - der words of Je - sus, Which come to hearts op - pressed. They
2. Come un - to me, ye wan - derers, And I will give you light. O lov - ing words of Je - sus, Which come to cheer the night. Come,

tell of ben - e - dic - tion, Of
all ye heav - y lad - en, And

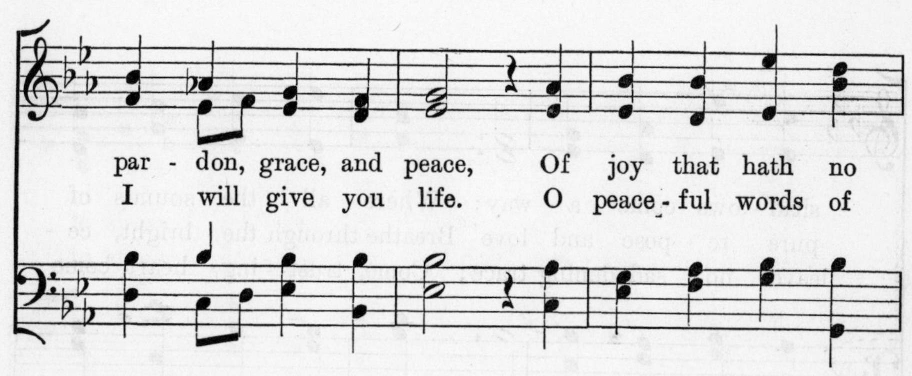
par - don, grace, and peace, Of joy that hath no
I will give you life. O peace - ful words of

end - ing, Of love which can - not cease.
Je - sus, Which come to end all strife.

**FRANCONIA** S.M.

König's Choralbuch
Arranged by W. H. HAVERGAL

FELICIA D. HEMANS
Adapted

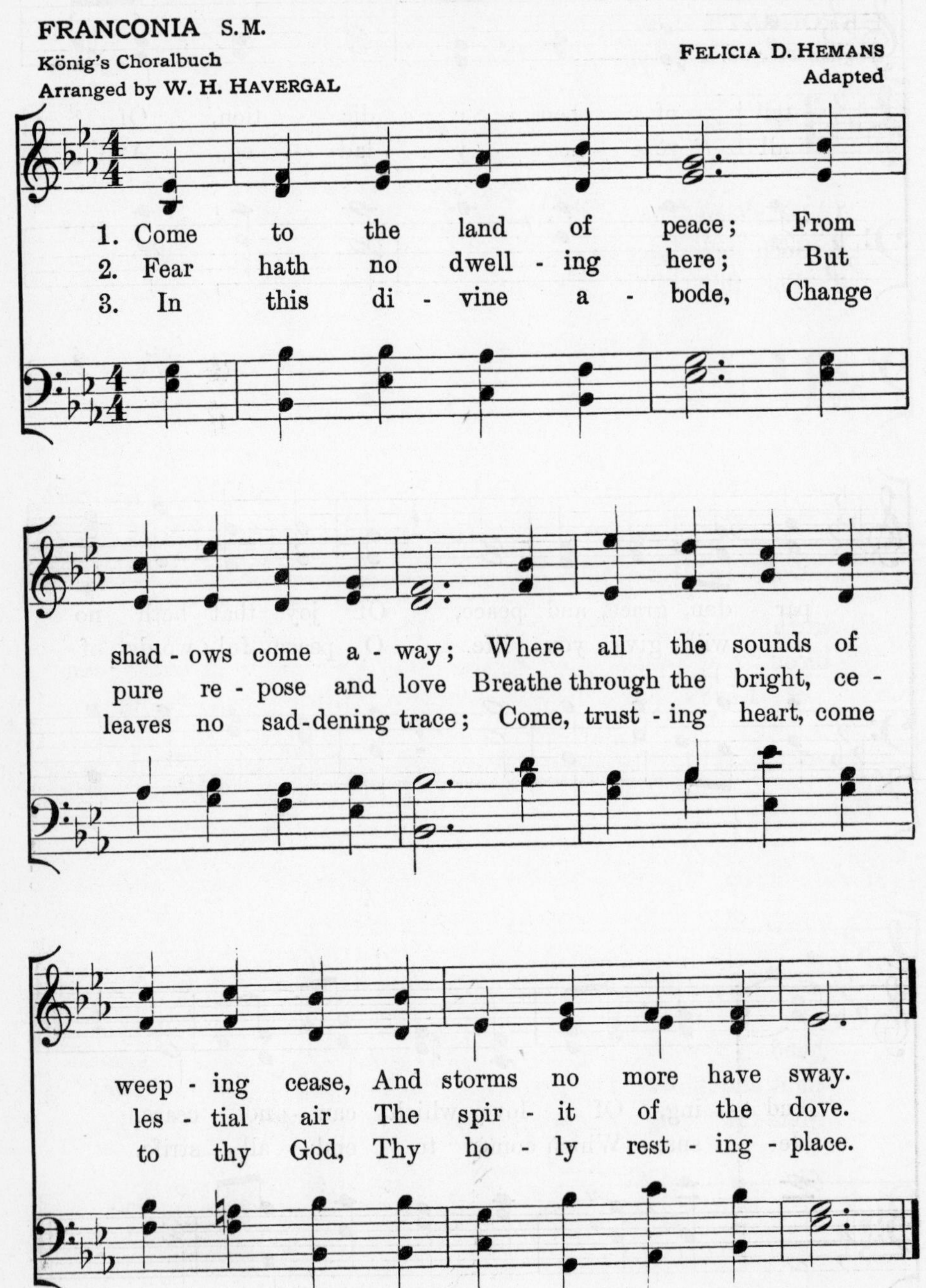
1. Come to the land of peace; From shad-ows come a-way; Where all the sounds of weep-ing cease, And storms no more have sway.
2. Fear hath no dwell-ing here; But pure re-pose and love Breathe through the bright, ce-les-tial air The spir-it of the dove.
3. In this di-vine a-bode, Change leaves no sad-dening trace; Come, trust-ing heart, come to thy God, Thy ho-ly rest-ing-place.

**HERONGATE** L. M.

English Traditional Melody

J. P. S.

1. Dear God, how glo - rious is Thy name Through all the
2. Such ten - der beau - ty, Lord, from Thee Is shed a -
3. For this Thy gift un - speak - a - ble, The beau - ty
earth and sea and sky. The won - drous heavens, Thy
broad o'er all the earth; In bird, in sun - beam,
of Love's ho - li - ness, We lift our hearts in
hand - i - work, The moon and stars hast Thou or - dained.
light and flower Thy grace and good - ness may be seen.
grate-ful song And would be al - ways prais-ing Thee.

Music from the ENGLISH HYMNAL: By permission of the OXFORD UNIVERSITY PRESS

**MANNA** 7.7.7.7.

Arranged from
Louis M. Gottschalk

Josiah Conder*

1. Day by day the man - na fell: O, to
2. Day by day the prom - ise reads, Dai - ly
3. Lord, my times are in Thy hand: All my
4. Thou my dai - ly task shalt give; Day by
learn this les - son well. Still by con - stant
strength for dai - ly needs: Cast fore - bod - ing
san - guine hopes have planned, To Thy wis - dom
day to Thee I live; So shall add - ed
mer - cy fed, Give me, Lord, my dai - ly bread.
fears a - way; Take the man - na of to - day.
I re - sign, And would mold my will to Thine.
years ful - fill Not my own, my Fa - ther's will.

**NOTTINGHAM** 7.7.7.7.

Attributed to
WOLFGANG AMADEUS MOZART
Arranged

JOSIAH CONDER*

1. Day by day the man - na fell: O, to
2. Day by day the prom - ise reads, Dai - ly
3. Lord, my times are in Thy hand: All my
4. Thou my dai - ly task shalt give; Day by

learn this les - son well. Still by con - stant
strength for dai - ly needs: Cast fore - bod - ing
san - guine hopes have planned, To Thy wis - dom
day to Thee I live; So shall add - ed

mer - cy fed, Give me, Lord, my dai - ly bread.
fears a - way; Take the man - na of to - day.
I re - sign, And would mold my will to Thine.
years ful - fill Not my own, my Fa - ther's will.

SAFFRON WALDEN 8.8.8.6.

ARTHUR H. BROWN

EDMUND BEALE SARGANT

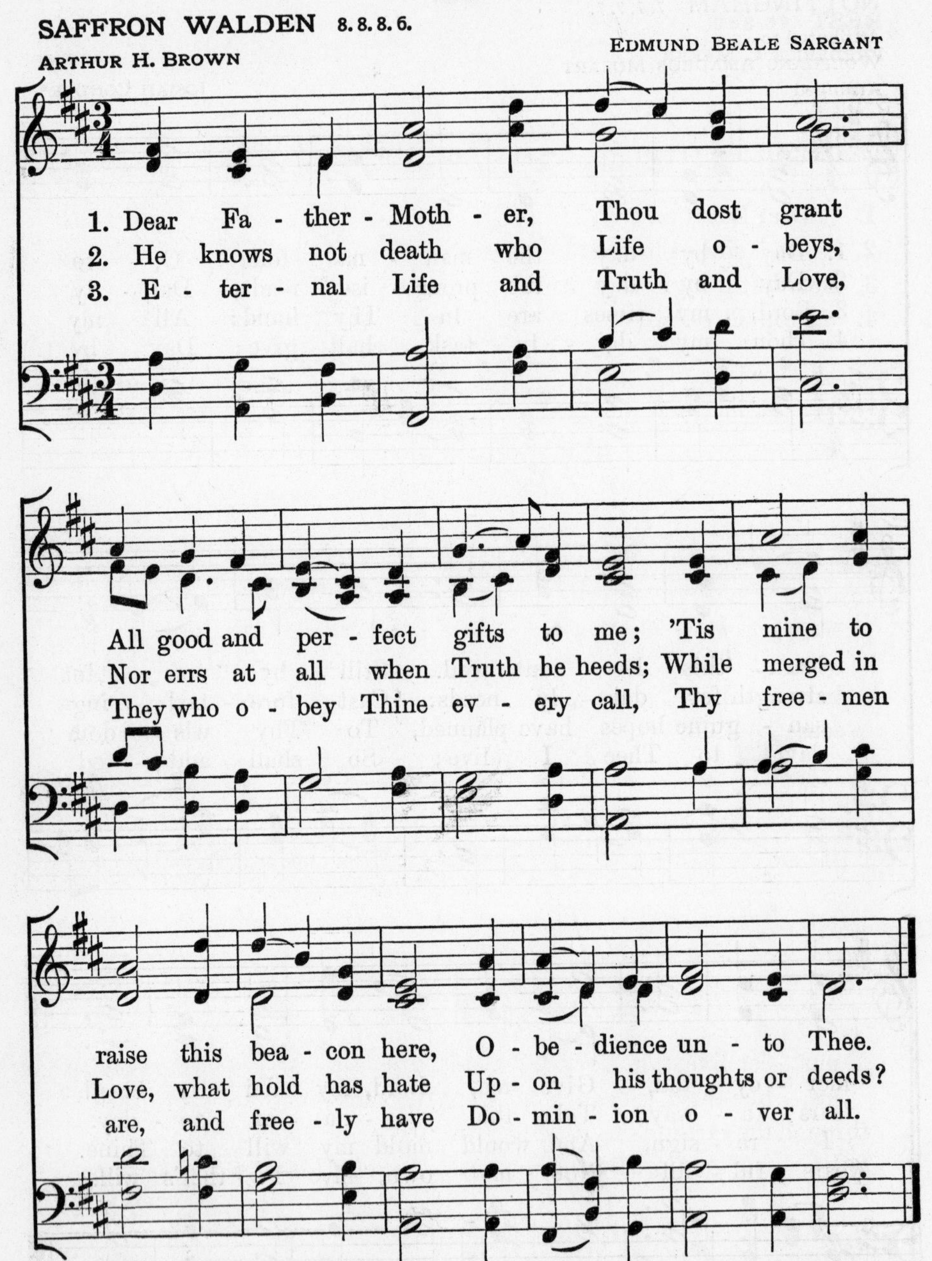
1. Dear Fa - ther - Moth - er, Thou dost grant
2. He knows not death who Life o - beys,
3. E - ter - nal Life and Truth and Love,
All good and per - fect gifts to me; 'Tis mine to
Nor errs at all when Truth he heeds; While merged in
They who o - bey Thine ev - ery call, Thy free - men
raise this bea - con here, O - be - dience un - to Thee.
Love, what hold has hate Up - on his thoughts or deeds?
are, and free - ly have Do - min - ion o - ver all.

Music from the REVISED CHURCH HYMNARY: By permission of the OXFORD UNIVERSITY PRESS
Words by permission of the author

# 49†

**REST** 86. 886.

FREDERICK C. MAKER — JOHN GREENLEAF WHITTIER*

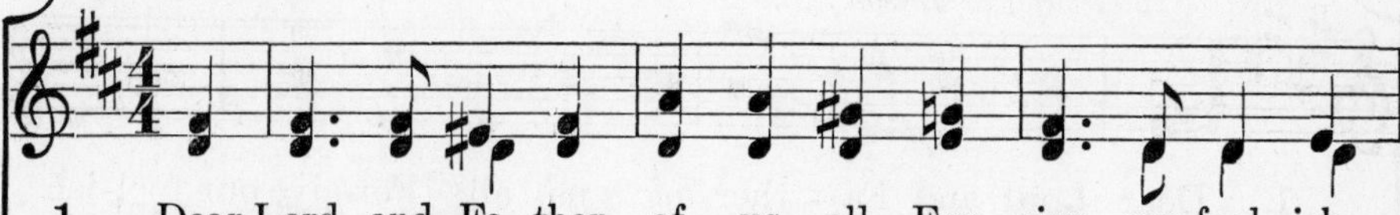

1. Dear Lord and Fa - ther of us all, For - give our fool - ish
2. In sim - ple trust like theirs who heard, Be - side the Syr - ian
3. Breathe through the puls - es of de - sire Thy cool - ness and Thy
4. Drop Thy still dews of qui - et - ness, Till all our striv - ings

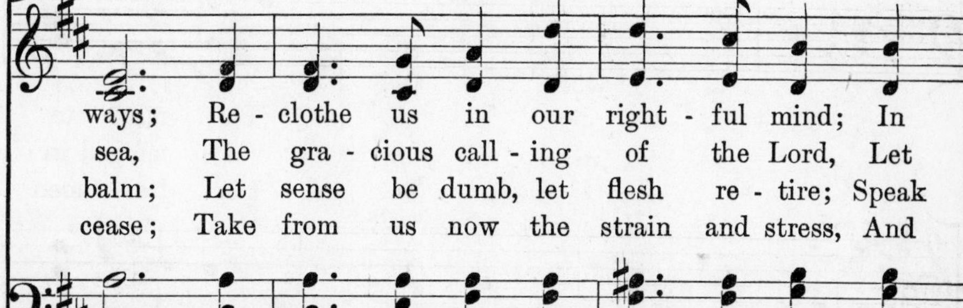

ways; Re - clothe us in our right - ful mind; In
sea, The gra - cious call - ing of the Lord, Let
balm; Let sense be dumb, let flesh re - tire; Speak
cease; Take from us now the strain and stress, And

pur - er lives Thy serv - ice find, In deep - er reverence, praise.
us, like them, without a word Rise up and fol low thee.
through the earthquake, wind and fire, O still small voice of calm.
let our or - dered lives con - fess The beau - ty of Thy peace.

# 50†

**REPTON** 86. 886.

C. HUBERT H. PARRY — JOHN GREENLEAF WHITTIER*

*To be sung in unison*

1. Dear Lord and Fa - ther of us all, For-give our fool-ish
2. In sim - ple trust like theirs who heard, Be-side the Syr-ian
3. Breathe through the puls - es of de - sire Thy cool-ness and Thy
4. Drop Thy still dews of qui - et - ness, Till all our strivings

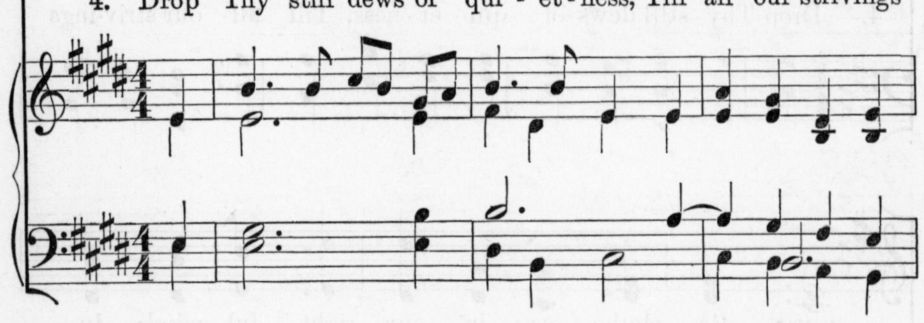

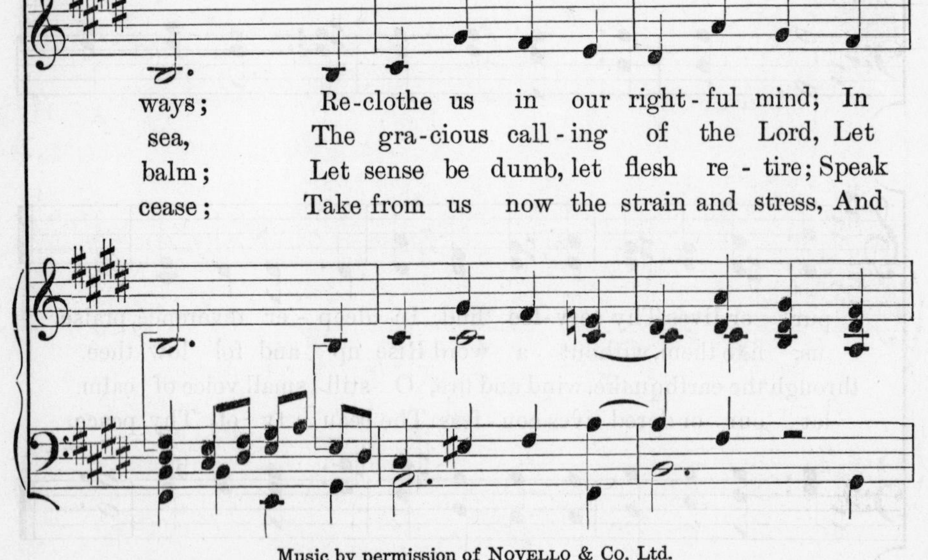

ways; Re-clothe us in our right - ful mind; In
sea, The gra-cious call - ing of the Lord, Let
balm; Let sense be dumb, let flesh re - tire; Speak
cease; Take from us now the strain and stress, And

Music by permission of NOVELLO & Co. Ltd.

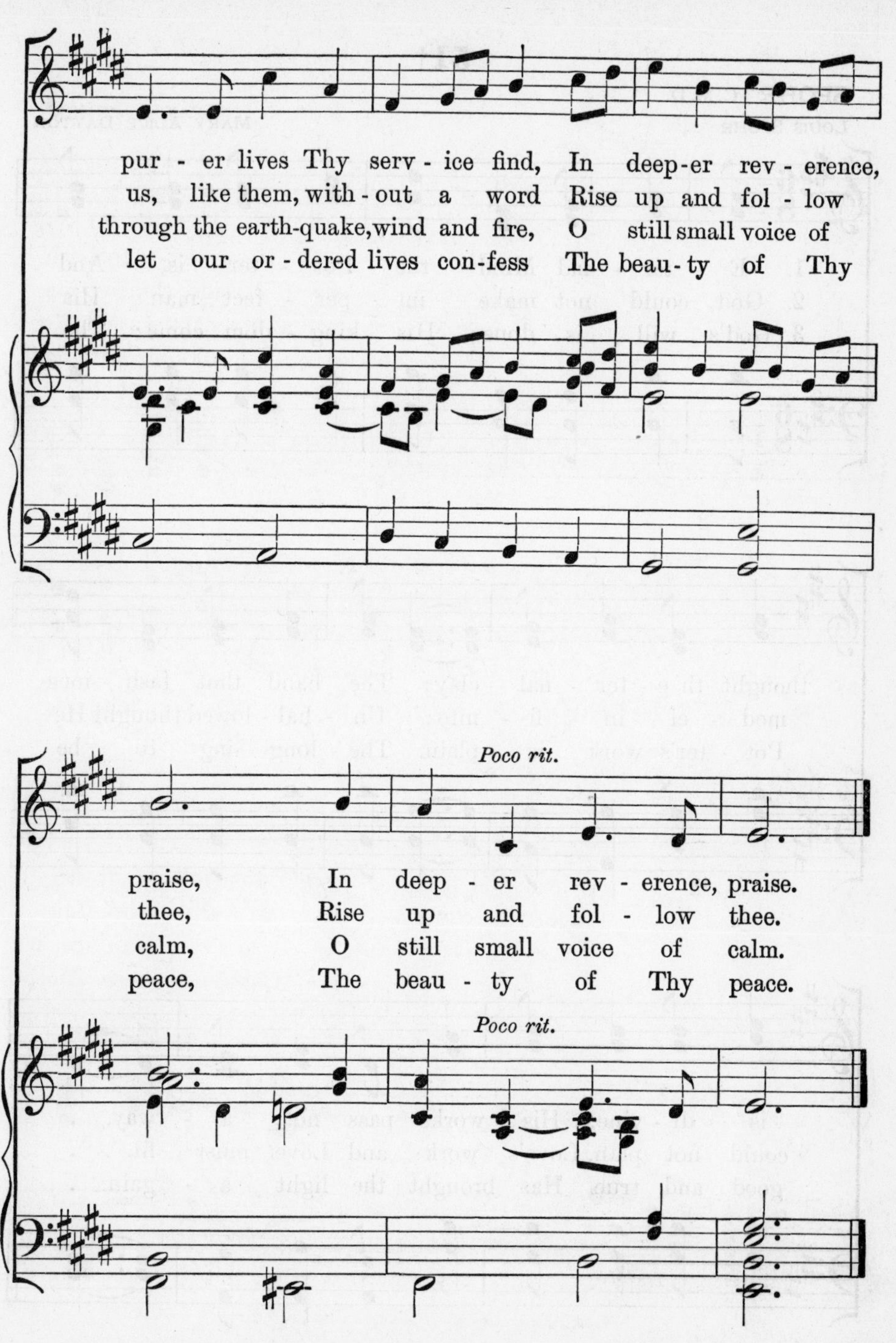
pur - er lives Thy serv - ice find, In deep-er rev - erence,
us, like them, with - out a word Rise up and fol - low
through the earth-quake, wind and fire, O still small voice of
let our or - dered lives con-fess The beau - ty of Thy
Poco rit.
praise, In deep - er rev - erence, praise.
thee, Rise up and fol - low thee.
calm, O still small voice of calm.
peace, The beau - ty of Thy peace.
Poco rit.

SPOHR C. M. D.

LOUIS SPOHR

MARY ALICE DAYTON

1. E - ter - nal Mind the Pot - ter is, And thought th'e - ter - nal clay: The hand that fash - ions is di - vine, His works pass not a - way. .
2. God could not make im - per - fect man His mod - el in - fi - nite; Un - hal - lowed thought He could not plan, Love's work and Love must fit. . .
3. God's will is done; His king - dom come; The Pot - ter's work is plain. The long - ing to be good and true Has brought the light a - gain. .

Man is the no - blest work of God, His
Life, Truth and Love the pat - tern make, Christ
And man does stand as God's own child, The

beau - ty, power and grace, Im - mor - tal; per - fect
is the per - fect heir; The clouds of sense roll
im - age of His love. Let glad - ness ring from

as his Mind Re - flect - ed face to face.
back, and show The form di - vine - ly fair.
ev - ery tongue, And heaven and earth ap - prove.

ST. MATTHEW C. M. D.

WILLIAM CROFT

Modern form of tune

MARY ALICE DAYTON

1. E - ter - nal Mind the Pot - ter is, And
2. God could not make im - per - fect man His
3. God's will is done; His king - dom come; The
thought th'e - ter - nal clay: The hand that fash - ions
mod - el in - fi - nite; Un - hal - lowed thought He
Pot - ter's work is plain. The long - ing to be
is ... di - vine, His works pass not a - way.
could not plan, Love's work and Love must fit.
good and true Has brought the light a - gain.

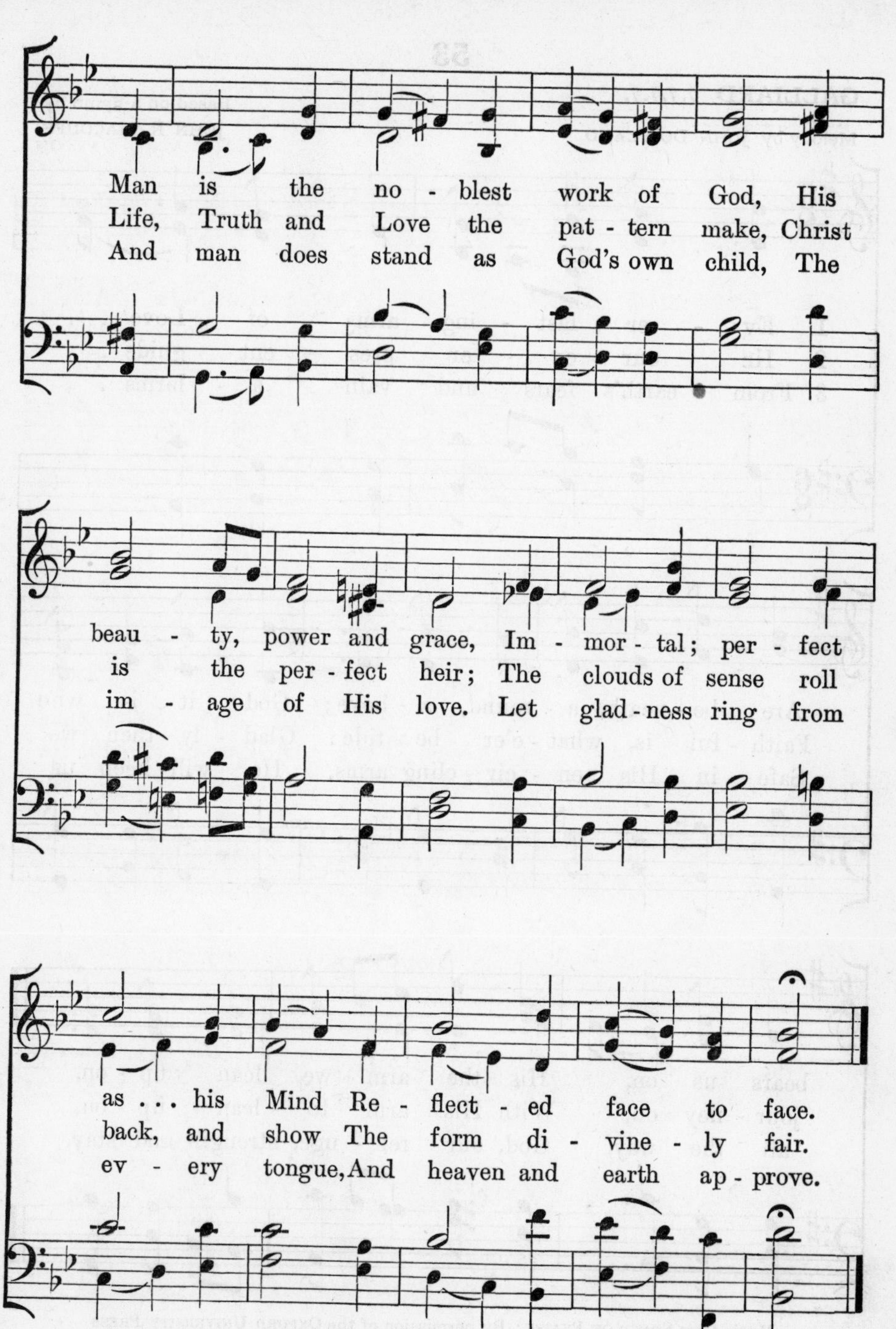
Man is the no - blest work of God, His
Life, Truth and Love the pat - tern make, Christ
And man does stand as God's own child, The
beau - ty, power and grace, Im - mor - tal; per - fect
is the per - fect heir; The clouds of sense roll
im - age of His love. Let glad - ness ring from
as . . . his Mind Re - flect - ed face to face.
back, and show The form di - vine - ly fair.
ev - ery tongue, And heaven and earth ap - prove.

53

GALLIARD 7.7.7.7.
Based on a hymn by
JOHN R. MACDUFF
Melody by JOHN DOWLAND
1. Ev - er - last - ing arms of Love . .
2. He our ev - er - pres - ent guide . .
3. From earth's fears and vain a - larms . .
Are be - neath, a - round, a - bove; God it is who
Faith - ful is, what - e'er be - tide; Glad - ly then we
Safe in His en - cir - cling arms, He will keep us
bears us on, His the arm we lean up - on.
jour - ney on, With His arm to lean up - on.
all the way, God, our ref - uge, strength and stay.

Music from SONGS OF PRAISE: By permission of the OXFORD UNIVERSITY PRESS

# 54

## WESTMINSTER C. M.

JAMES TURLE HARRIET MARTINEAU

1. Faith grasps the bless - ing she de - sires, Hope points the up - ward gaze; And Love, ce - les - tial Love, in - spires The el - o - quence of praise.
2. But sweet - er far the still small voice Un - heard by hu - man ear, When God has made the heart re - joice, And dried the bit - ter tear.
3. No ac - cents flow, no words as - cend; All ut - terance fail - eth there; But God Him - self doth com - pre - hend And an - swer si - lent prayer.

4 Words used by arrangement with the UNIVERSALIST PUBLISHING HOUSE

## GOTT WILL'S MACHEN 8.7.8.7.

J. Ludwig Steiner — Love M. Willis

1. Father, hear the prayer we offer;
Not for ease that prayer shall be,
But for strength, that we may ever
Live our lives courageously.

2. Not for ever in green pastures
Do we ask our way to be,
But the steep and rugged pathway
May we tread rejoicingly.

3. Not for ever by still waters
Would we idly quiet stay,
But would smite the living fountains
From the rocks along our way.

## 56

**CRISPINIAN** L. M.

JOHN W. IVIMEY — RAY PALMER

From the Latin. Adapted

1. Fa - ther, Thou joy of lov - ing hearts, Thou Fount of
2. Ev - er our long - ings turn to Thee, O Thou on
3. Thy truth un-changed hath ev - er stood; Thou sav - est
life, Thou Light of men, From all the best that
whom our care we cast; Re - joic - ing when Thy
those that on Thee call; To them that seek Thee
earth im - parts, We turn un - filled to Thee a - gain.
smile we see, And blest when faith can hold Thee fast.
Thou art good; To them that find Thee, All in all.

Music by permission of the composer, care of MARLBOROUGH COLLEGE

## 57

WELWYN 11. 10. 11. 10.
ALFRED SCOTT-GATTY
FREDERICK L. HOSMER
Adapted
1. Fa - ther, to Thee we turn a - way from sor - row, Thou art the foun - tain whence our heal - ing . . flows; . . .
2. Should fond hopes fail and skies seem dark be - fore us, Should the vain cares that vex our days in - crease, . . .
3. Naught shall af - fright us, on Thy good - ness lean - ing; Low in the heart faith sing - eth still her . . song; . . .

Music by permission of the proprietors of ARUNDEL HYMNS

Dark though the night, joy . . com - eth with the
Comes with its calm the . . thought that Thou art
Chas - tened and blessed we . . learn life's deep - er
mor - row; Safe - ly they
o'er us; Then we grow
mean - ing, Thus in our
rest . . who on Thy love re - pose.
qui - et, fold - ed in Thy peace.
meek - ness Thou dost make us strong.

**JOY** 8.7.8.7.D.

Arranged from
LUDWIG VAN BEETHOVEN

E. C. A.

1. Fa - ther, we Thy lov - ing chil - dren
2. Come we dai - ly then, dear Fa - ther,
3. In Thy house se - cure - ly dwell - ing,
Lift our hearts in joy to - day, Know - ing well that
O - pen hearts and will - ing hands, Ea - ger ears, ex -
Where Thy chil - dren live to bless, See - ing on - ly
Thou wilt keep us Ev - er in Thy bless - ed way.
pect - ant, joy - ful, Read - y for Thy right com - mands.
Thy cre - a - tion, We can share Thy hap - pi - ness,

Thou art Love and Thou art wis - dom,
We would hear no oth - er voi - ces,
Share Thy joy and spend it free - ly.

Thou art Life and Thou art All; In Thy Spir - it
We would heed no oth - er call; Thou a - lone art
Loy - al hearts can feel no fear; We Thy chil - dren

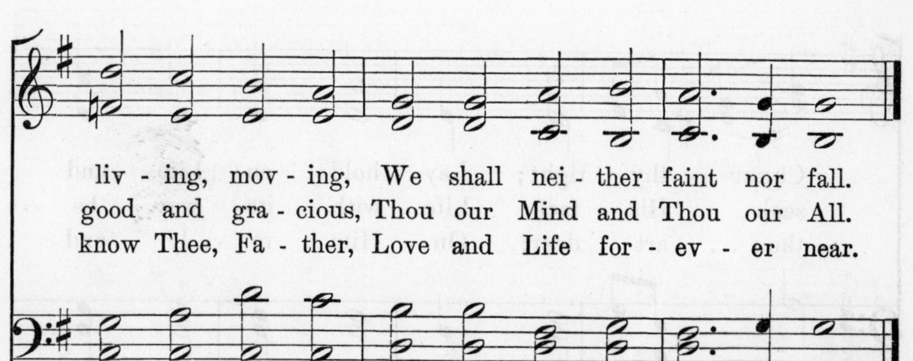
liv - ing, mov - ing, We shall nei - ther faint nor fall.
good and gra - cious, Thou our Mind and Thou our All.
know Thee, Fa - ther, Love and Life for - ev - er near.

## PARK STREET L. M.

FREDERICK M. A. VENUA
Arranged

JOHN S. B. MONSELL*

1. Fight the good fight . . with all . . thy might, Christ is thy strength, and . . Christ thy right; Lay hold on Life, and
2. Run the straight race . . through God's good grace, Lift up thine eyes, and . . seek . . His face; Life with its way be -
3. Faint not nor fear, . . His arms . . are near; He chang - eth not, and . . thou . . art dear; On Him re - ly and

it shall be Thy joy and crown e -
fore us lies, Christ is the path, and
thou shalt see That Christ is all in

ter - nal - ly, Thy joy and
Christ the prize, Christ is the
all . . to thee, That Christ is

crown . . e - ter - nal - ly.
path, . . and Christ the prize.
all . . . in all . . to thee.

## 60†

**PENTECOST** L. M.

WILLIAM BOYD — JOHN S. B. MONSELL*

1. Fight the good fight with all thy might, Christ is thy strength, and Christ thy right; Lay hold on Life, and it shall be Thy joy and crown e - ter - nal - ly.
2. Run the straight race through God's good grace, Lift up thine eyes, and seek His face; Life with its way be - fore us lies, Christ is the path, and Christ the prize.
3. Faint not nor fear, His arms are near; He chang-eth not, and thou art dear; On Him re - ly and thou shalt see That Christ is all in all to thee.

61†

VALOUR L. M.

HUGH P. ALLEN — JOHN S. B. MONSELL*

To be sung in unison
1. Fight the good fight with all thy might, Christ is thy strength, and Christ thy right; Lay hold on Life, and it shall be Thy joy and crown e - ter - nal - ly.
2. Run the straight race through God's good grace, Lift up thine eyes, and seek His face; Life with its way be - fore us lies, Christ is the path, and Christ the prize.
3. Faint not nor fear, His arms are near; He chang-eth not, and thou art dear; On Him re - ly and thou shalt see That Christ is all in all to thee.

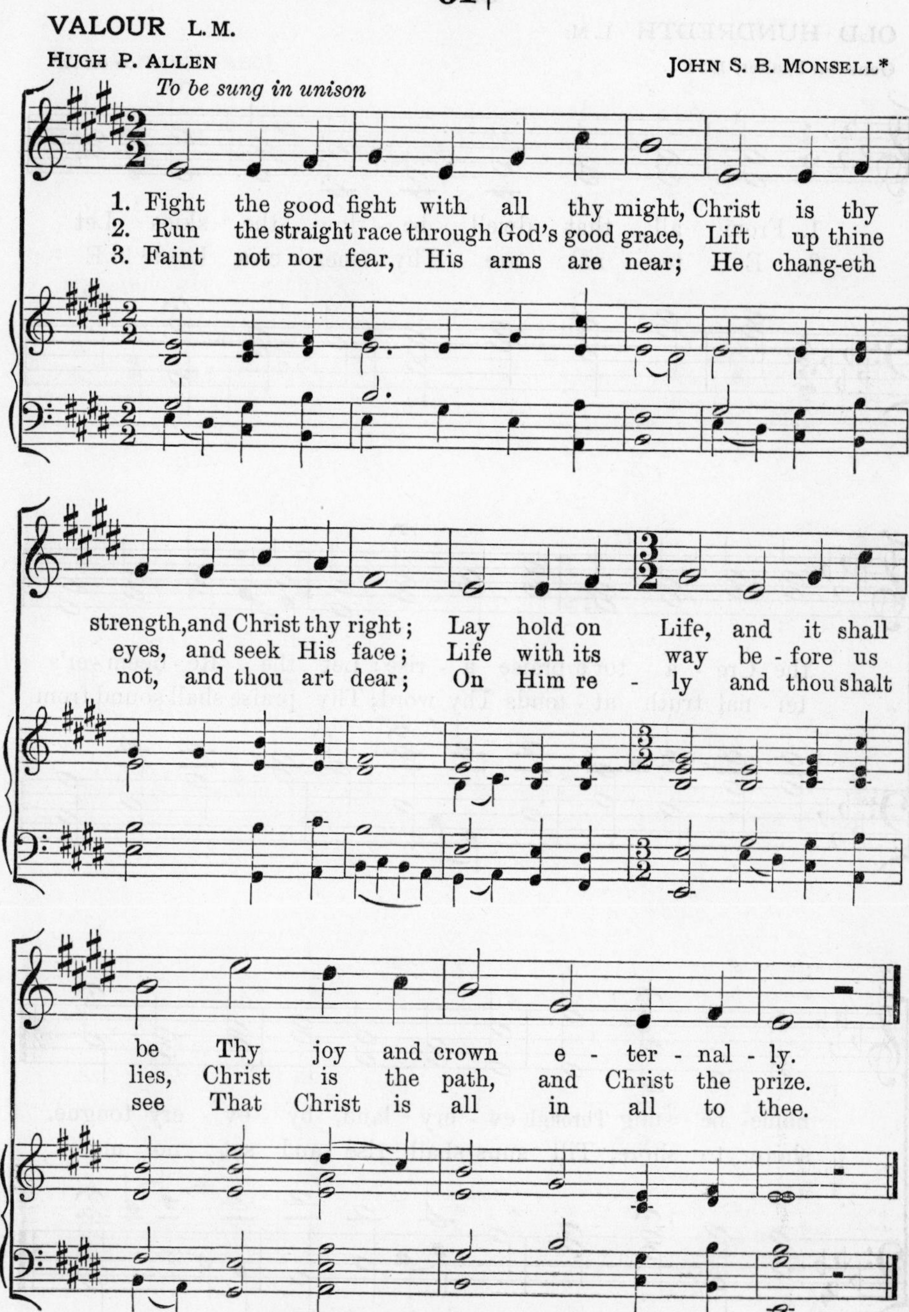

Music by permission of HUGH P. ALLEN

## OLD HUNDREDTH L. M.

Genevan Psalter, 1551 ISAAC WATTS*

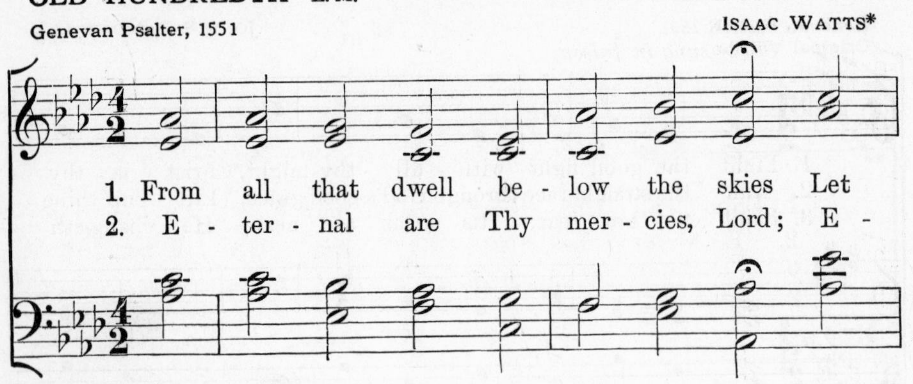
1. From all that dwell be - low the skies Let
2. E - ter - nal are Thy mer - cies, Lord; E -

the Cre - a - tor's praise a - rise; Let the Re - deem - er's
ter - nal truth at - tends Thy word; Thy praise shall sound from

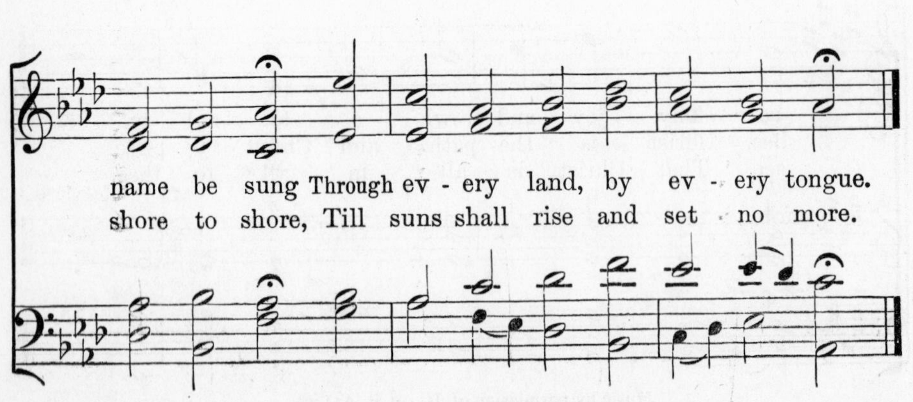
name be sung Through ev - ery land, by ev - ery tongue.
shore to shore, Till suns shall rise and set no more.

OLD HUNDREDTH L. M.

Genevan Psalter, 1551
Original Version

ISAAC WATTS*

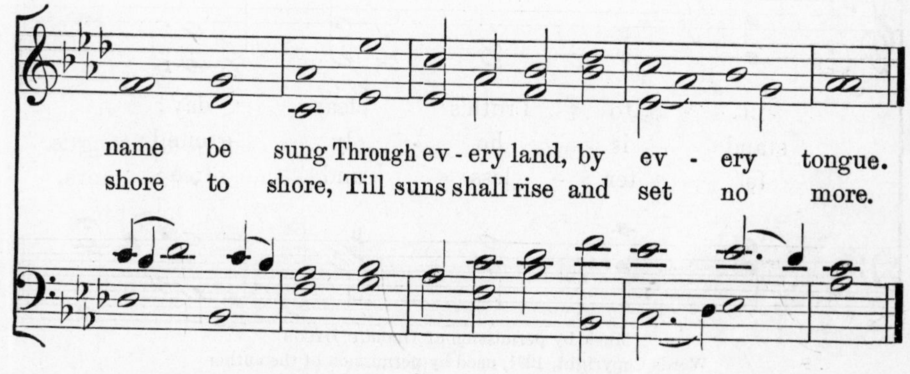

**ELGIN** 11. 10. 11. 10.

GEORGE DYSON — V. H.

1. From sense to Soul my path - way
2. I reach Mind's o - pen door, and
3. The way leads up - ward and its

lies be - fore me, From mist and shad - ow
at its por - tal I know that where I
goal draws near - er, Thought soars en - rap - tured,

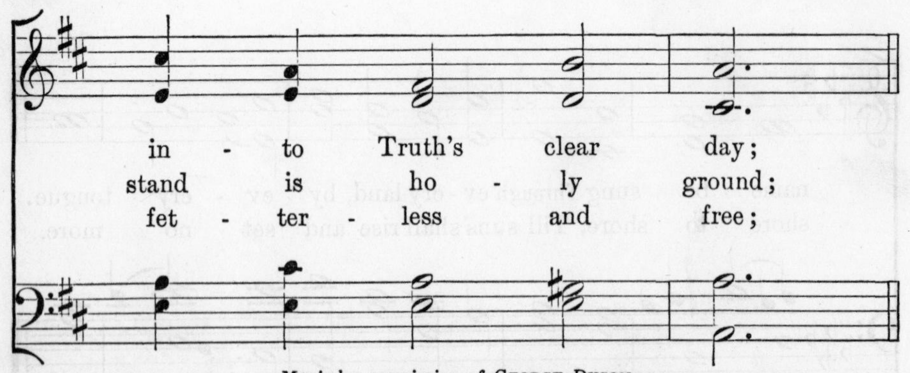
in - to Truth's clear day;
stand is ho - ly ground;
fet - ter - less and free;

Music by permission of GEORGE DYSON

The dawn of all things real is
I feel the calm and joy of
The vi - sion in - fi - nite to

break - ing o'er me, My heart is sing - ing:
things im - mor - tal, The love - li - ness of
me grows clear - er, I touch the frin - ges

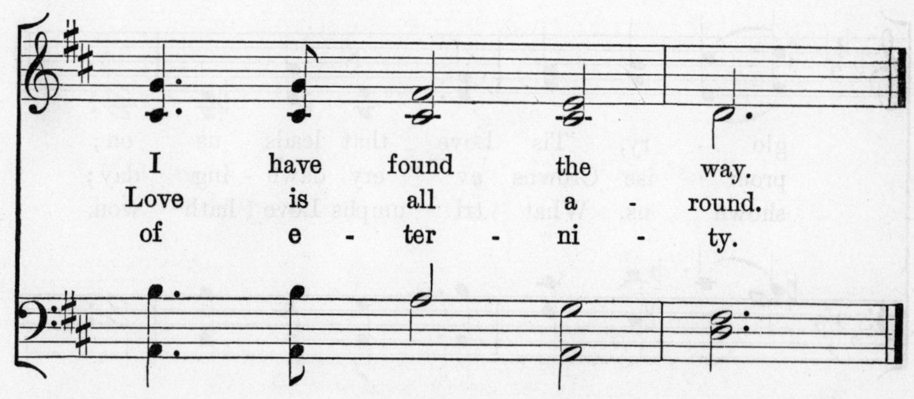
I have found the way.
Love is all a - round.
of e - ter - ni - ty.

ALFORD 76.76.76.86.

JOHN B. DYKES

FRANCES R. HAVERGAL
Adapted

1. From glo - ry un - to glo - ry, Be
2. The full - ness of His bless - ing En -
3. From glo - ry un - to glo - ry, What
this our joy - ous song; From glo - ry un - to
com - pass - eth our way; The full - ness of His
great things He hath done, What won - ders He hath
glo - ry, 'Tis Love that leads us on;
prom - ise Crowns ev - ery dawn - ing day;
shown us, What tri - umphs Love hath won.

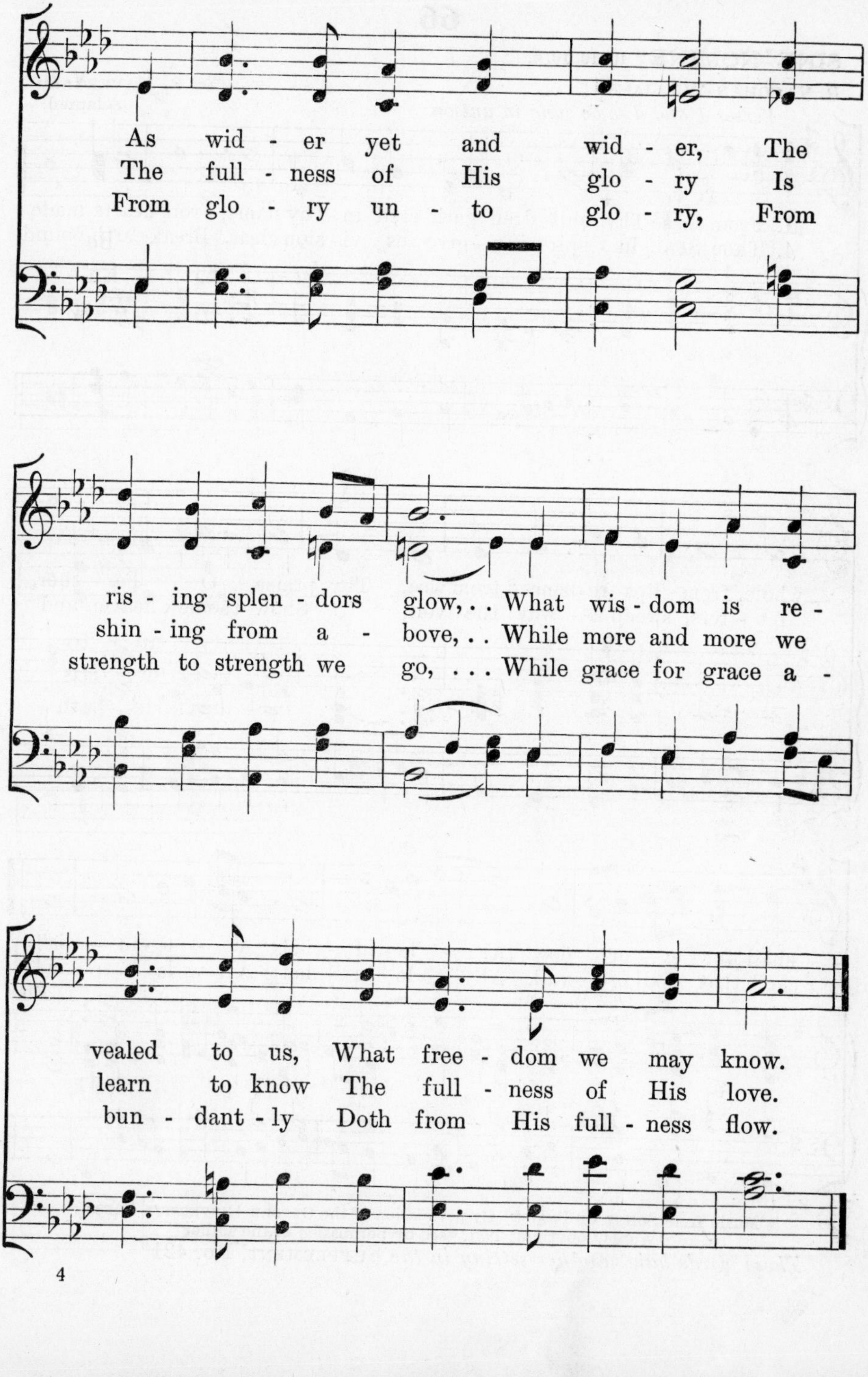

As wid - er yet and wid - er, The
The full - ness of His glo - ry Is
From glo - ry un - to glo - ry, From

ris - ing splen - dors glow, . . What wis - dom is re -
shin - ing from a - bove, . . While more and more we
strength to strength we go, . . . While grace for grace a -

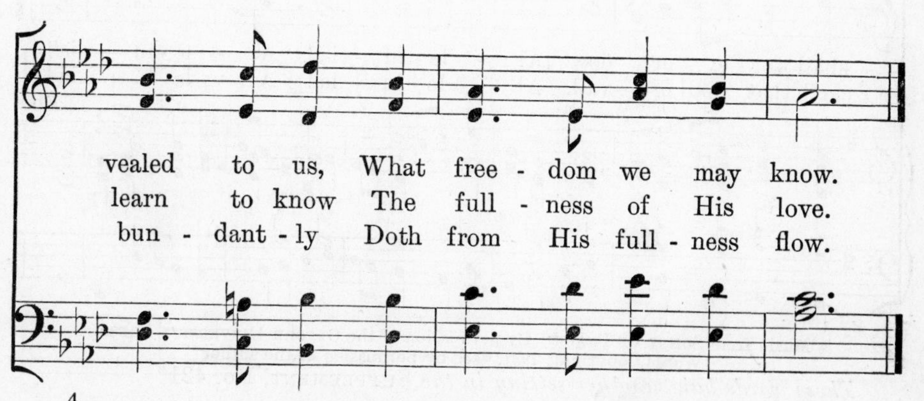
vealed to us, What free - dom we may know.
learn to know The full - ness of His love.
bun - dant - ly Doth from His full - ness flow.

# 66

SINE NOMINE 10. 10. 10. 4.
R. VAUGHAN WILLIAMS
V. H.
Verses 1 and 4 to be sung in unison
1. From these Thy chil - dren gath - ered in Thy name, From hearts made whole, from lips re-deemed from woe, Thy praise, O Fa - ther, shall for - ev - er flow. Al - le - lu - ia! Al - le - lu - ia!
4. Thou, Soul, in - spir - ing—give us vi - sion clear, Break earth-bound fet - ters, sweep a - way the veil, Show the new heaven and earth that shall pre - vail. Al - le - lu - ia! Al - le - lu - ia!
FINE

Music from SONGS OF PRAISE: By permission of the OXFORD UNIVERSITY PRESS

*These words have another setting in the* SUPPLEMENT, No. 421

Harmony, verses 2 and 3
2. O per - fect Life, in Thy com - plete - ness held, None can be - yond Thy om - ni - pres - ence stray;
3. O per - fect Mind, re - veal Thy like - ness true, That high - er self - hood which we all must prove,
Safe in Thy Love, we live and sing al - way Al - - le - lu - ia! Al - - - le - lu - ia!
Joy and do - min - ion, love re - flect - ing Love. Al - - le - lu - ia! Al - - - le - lu - ia!
D.C.

# 67†

**CAPETOWN** 7.7.7.3.

FRIEDRICH FILITZ — CHARLOTTE ELLIOTT, Adapted

1. Gird thy heaven - ly ar - mor on,
2. Hear the vic - tors who o'er - came;
3. Hear, a - bove all, hear thy Lord;
Wear it ev - er night and day; Am - bushed lies the
Still they mark each war - rior's way; All with warn - ing
Him thou lov - est to o - bey; Hide with - in thy
e - vil one: Watch . . and . . pray.
voice ex - claim, Watch . . and . . pray.
heart His word, Watch . . and . . pray.

# 68†

**VIGILATE** 7.7.7.3.

WILLIAM H. MONK
Slightly revised

CHARLOTTE ELLIOTT
Adapted

1. Gird thy heaven - ly ar - mor on,
2. Hear the vic - tors who o'er - came;
3. Hear, a - bove all, hear thy Lord;
Wear it . . . ev - er night and day;
Still they mark each war - rior's way;
Him thou lov - est to o - bey;
Am-bushed lies the e - vil one: Watch and pray.
All with warn - ing voice ex - claim, Watch and pray.
Hide with - in thy heart His word, Watch and pray.

SONG 24 10. 10. 10. 10.

ORLANDO GIBBONS JAMES J. ROME

1. Give me, O Lord, an un - der - stand - ing heart, That I may learn to know my - self in Thee, To spurn the wrong and choose the bet - ter part And thus from sin - ful bond - age be set free.
2. Give me, O Lord, a meek and con - trite heart, That I may learn to quell all self - ish pride, Bow - ing be - fore Thee, see Thee as Thou art And 'neath Thy shel-tering pres-ence safe - ly hide.
3. Give me, O Lord, a gen - tle, lov - ing heart, That I may learn to be more ten - der, kind, And with Thy heal-ing touch, each wound and smart With Christ-ly bands of Love and Truth to bind.

*These words have another setting in the* SUPPLEMENT, No. 423

# 70

MORNINGTON S.M.
GARRET WELLESLEY
E. C. A.
1. God giv - eth light to all Who . .
2. Plain shall His guid - ance be, If . . .
3. God is thy light and health; No . . .
ask with prayer sin - cere; He doth not fail to
thou but seek the right; Clear - ly thy path - way
death nor dark - ness there; Turn but to Him, ac -
hear that call; His Truth is . . ev - er near.
thou shalt see, A line of . . pur - est light.
cept His wealth, And all His glo - ry share.

**AUSTRIA** 8.7.8.7.D.

FRANZ JOSEPH HAYDN JOHN NEWTON*

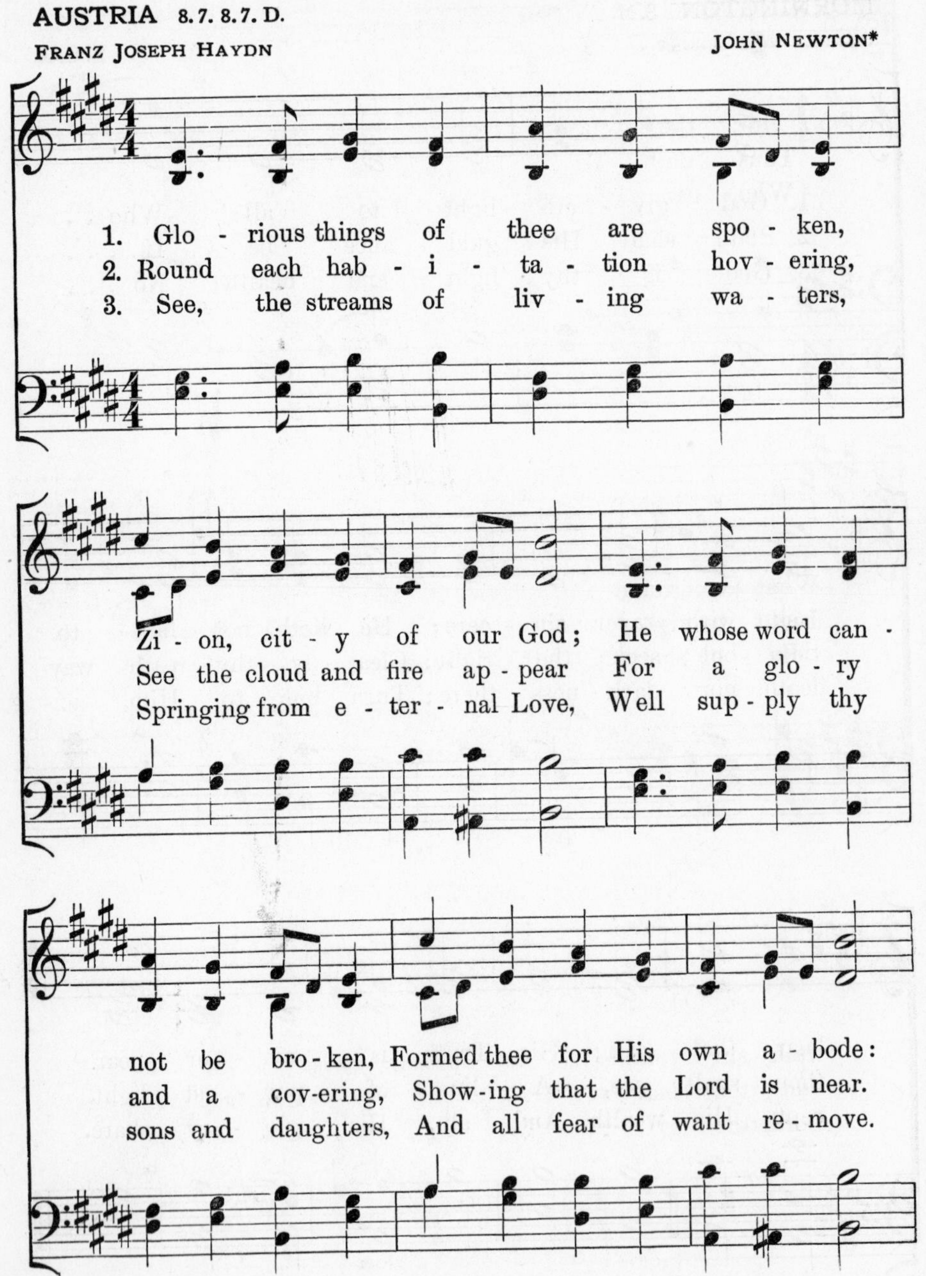
1. Glo - rious things of thee are spo - ken, Zi - on, cit - y of our God; He whose word can - not be bro - ken, Formed thee for His own a - bode:
2. Round each hab - i - ta - tion hov - ering, See the cloud and fire ap - pear For a glo - ry and a cov-ering, Show-ing that the Lord is near.
3. See, the streams of liv - ing wa - ters, Springing from e - ter - nal Love, Well sup - ply thy sons and daughters, And all fear of want re - move.

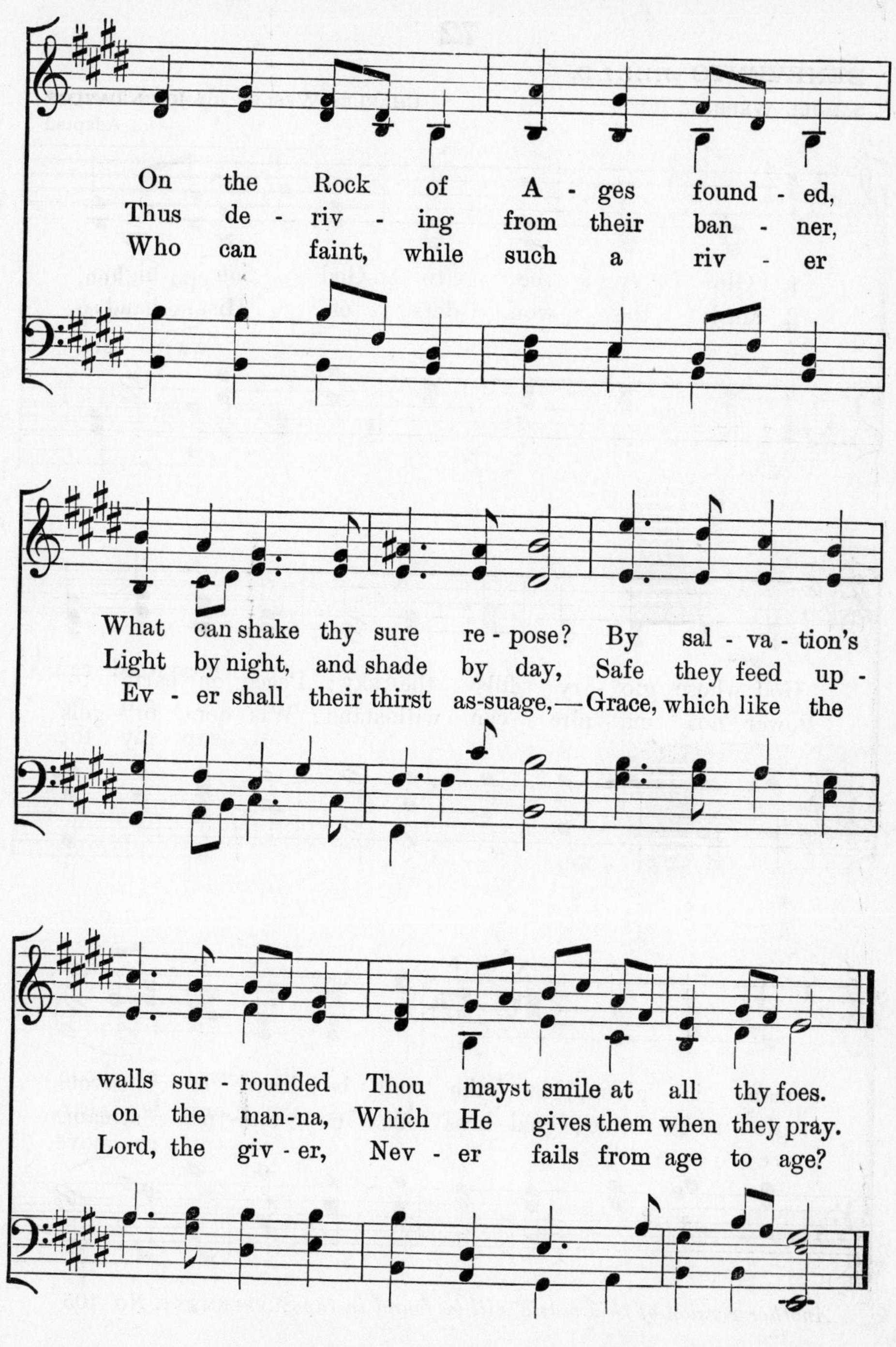
On the Rock of A - ges found - ed,
Thus de - riv - ing from their ban - ner,
Who can faint, while such a riv - er
What can shake thy sure re - pose? By sal - va - tion's
Light by night, and shade by day, Safe they feed up -
Ev - er shall their thirst as-suage,—Grace, which like the
walls sur - rounded Thou mayst smile at all thy foes.
on the man-na, Which He gives them when they pray.
Lord, the giv - er, Nev - er fails from age to age?

**BENEVENTO** 7.7.7.7.D.

SAMUEL WEBBE

CHARLES WESLEY and JOHN TAYLOR
Adapted

1. Glo - ry be to God on high,
2. Mark the won - ders of His hand:

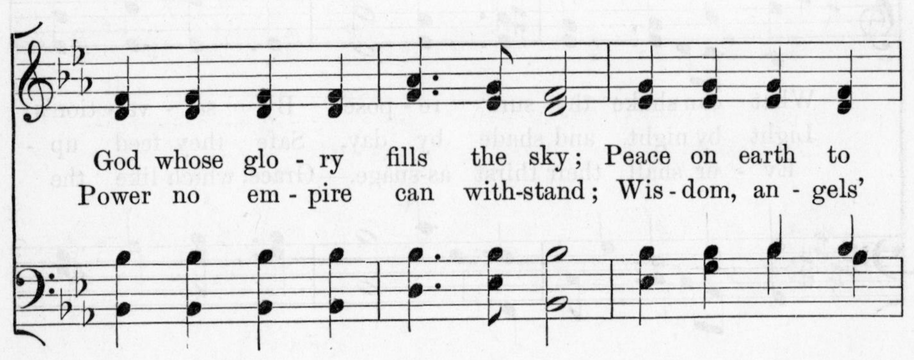
God whose glo - ry fills the sky; Peace on earth to
Power no em - pire can with-stand; Wis - dom, an - gels'

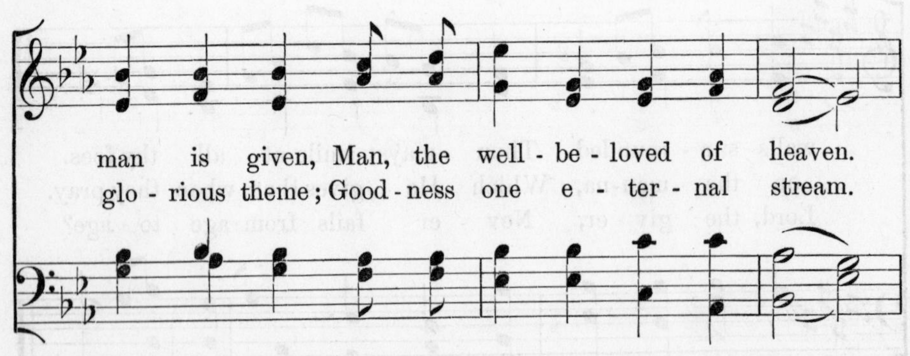
man is given, Man, the well - be - loved of heaven.
glo - rious theme; Good - ness one e - ter - nal stream.

*Another version of this music will be found in the* SUPPLEMENT, No. 405

Gra - cious Fa - ther, in Thy love,
All ye peo - ple, raise the song,

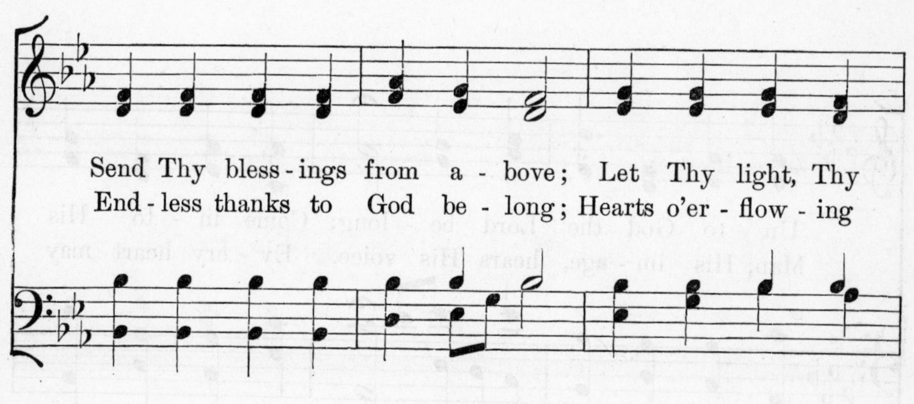
Send Thy bless - ings from a - bove; Let Thy light, Thy
End - less thanks to God be - long; Hearts o'er - flow - ing

truth, Thy peace Bid all strife and tu - mult cease. .
with His praise Join the hymns your voi - ces raise. .

## GRATITUDE 10 7. 10 7. 10 10. 7 7.

Eeuwig dank en eere
CANZUNS SPIRITUELAS, Celerina, 1765

Based on the Dutch
of ABRAHAM RUTGERS

1. Glo - ry, hon - or, praise and pure ob - la - tions
2. God is Mind and ho - ly thought is send - ing;
Un - to God the Lord be - long; Come in - to His
Man, His im - age, hears His voice. Ev - ery heart may
pres - ence with thanks - giv - ing, Come be - fore Him with a
un - der - stand His mes - sage, In His kind - ness may re -

song. In His hand is all the power of na - tions,
joice. Lo, He speaks, all con - dem - na - tion end - ing,

Sing to Him, ye joy - ous con - gre - ga - tions, Psalms of
Ev - ery true de - sire with Love's will blend - ing; Los - ing

grat - i - tude and praise Un - to God the Fa - ther raise.
self, in Him we find Joy, health, hope, for all man - kind.

# 74

## AUCH JETZT MACHT GOTT 86. 86. 88.

Koch's Choralbuch, 1816 EDMUND BEALE SARGANT

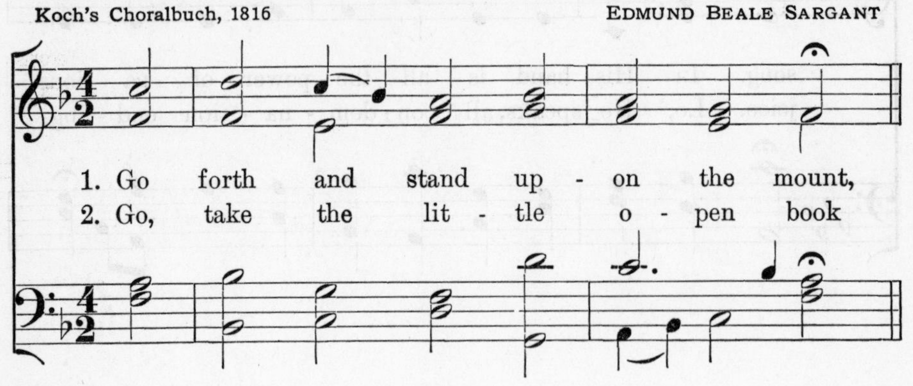
1. Go forth and stand up - on the mount,
2. Go, take the lit - tle o - pen book

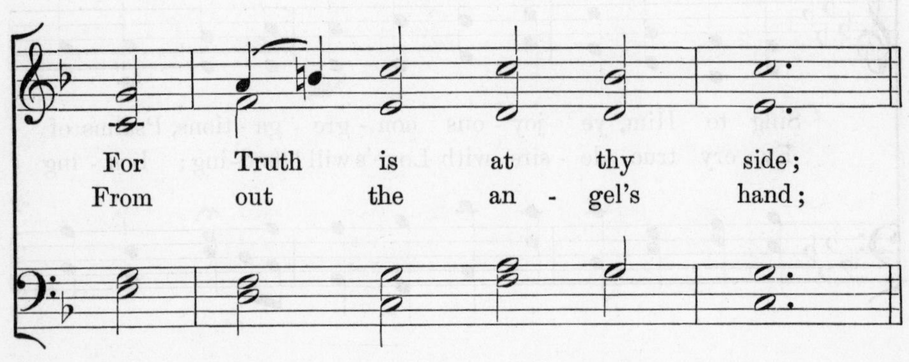
For Truth is at thy side;
From out the an - gel's hand;

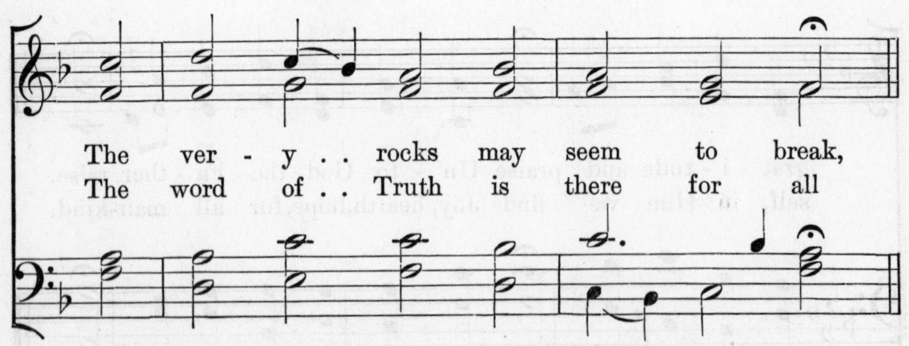
The ver - y . . rocks may seem to break,
The word of . . Truth is there for all

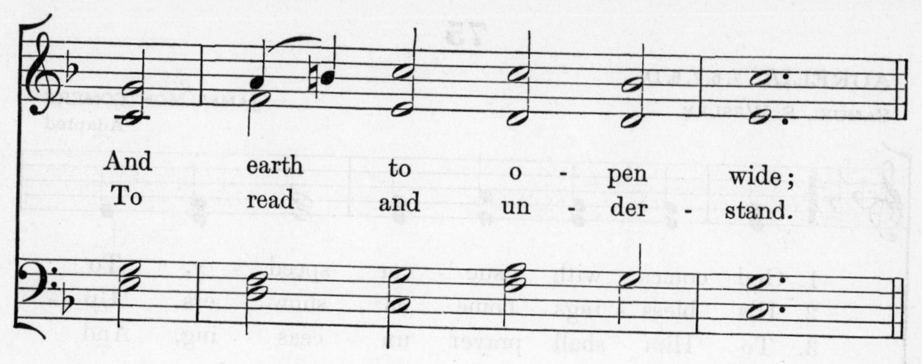
And earth to o - pen wide;
To read and un - der - stand.

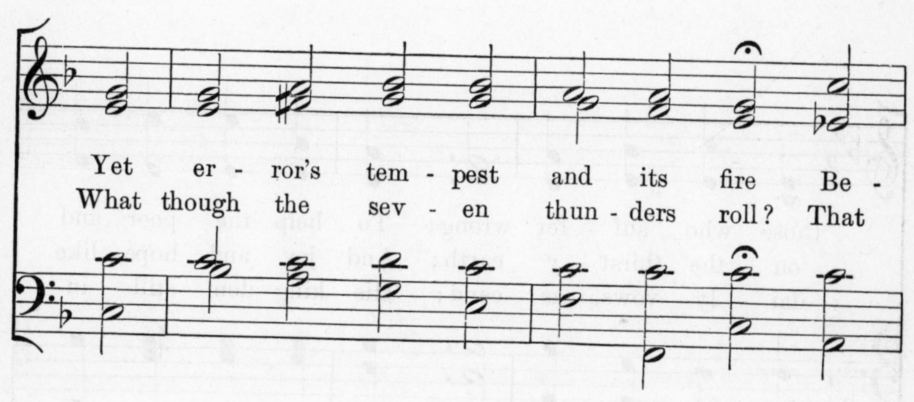
Yet er - ror's tem - pest and its fire Be -
What though the sev - en thun - ders roll? That

fore that still small voice re - tire.
still small voice shall make thee whole.

AURELIA 7. 6. 7. 6. D.

SAMUEL S. WESLEY

JAMES MONTGOMERY
Adapted

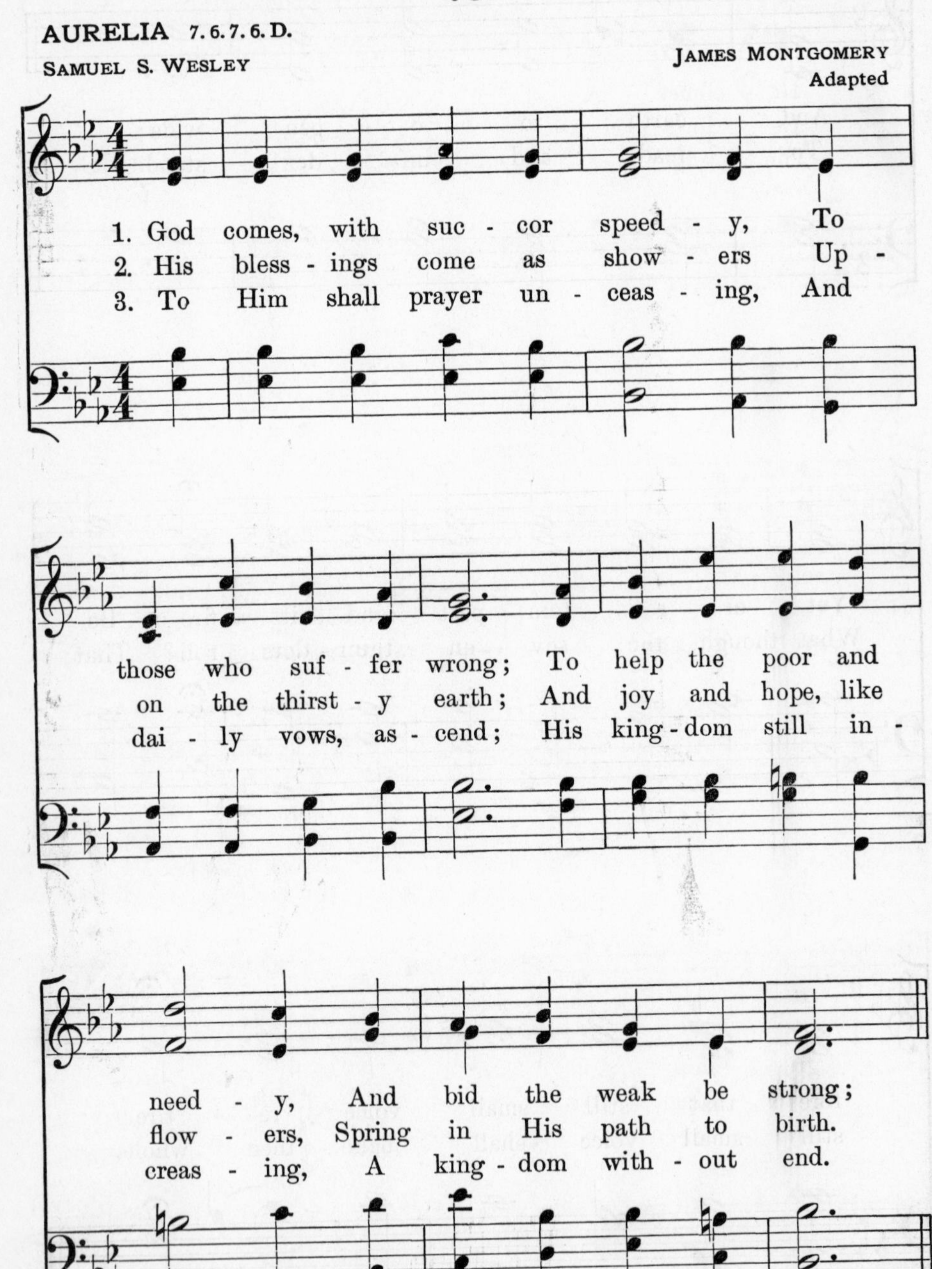
1. God comes, with suc - cor speed - y, To those who suf - fer wrong; To help the poor and need - y, And bid the weak be strong;
2. His bless - ings come as show - ers Up - on the thirst - y earth; And joy and hope, like flow - ers, Spring in His path to birth.
3. To Him shall prayer un - ceas - ing, And dai - ly vows, as - cend; His king - dom still in - creas - ing, A king - dom with - out end.

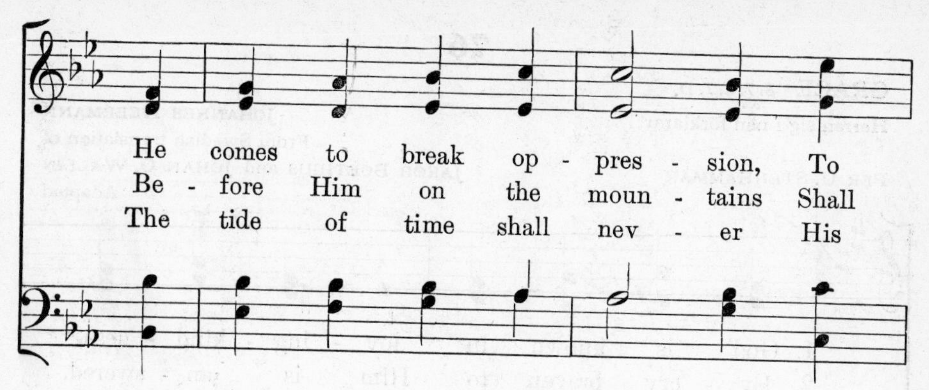
He comes to break op - pres - sion, To
Be - fore Him on the moun - tains Shall
The tide of time shall nev - er His

set the cap - tive free, To take a - way trans -
Peace, the her - ald, go; From hill to vale the
cov - e - nant re - move; His name shall stand for -

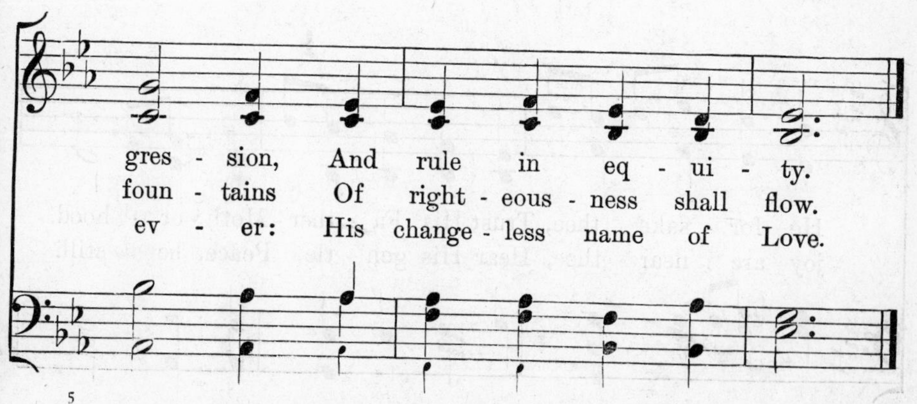
gres - sion, And rule in eq - ui - ty.
foun - tains Of right - eous - ness shall flow.
ev - er: His change - less name of Love.

# 76

**GRACE** 8.7.8.7.D.

Herren sig i nåd förklarar

PER U. STENHAMMAR

JOHANNES HEERMANN
From Swedish translation of
JAKOB BOËTHIUS and JOHAN O. WALLIN
Adapted

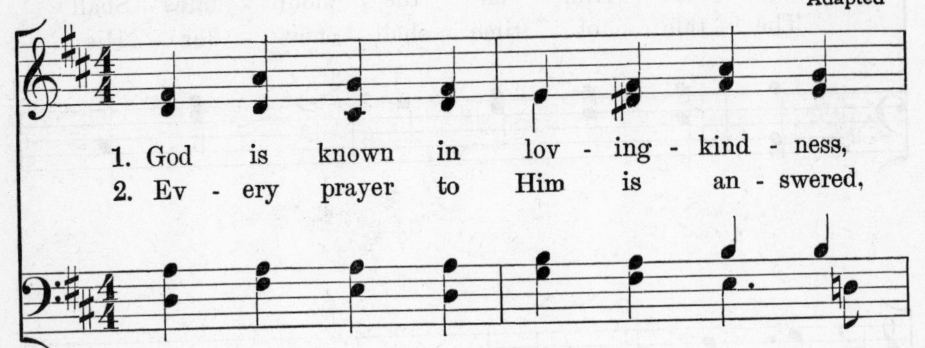
1. God is known in lov - ing - kind - ness,
2. Ev - ery prayer to Him is an - swered,

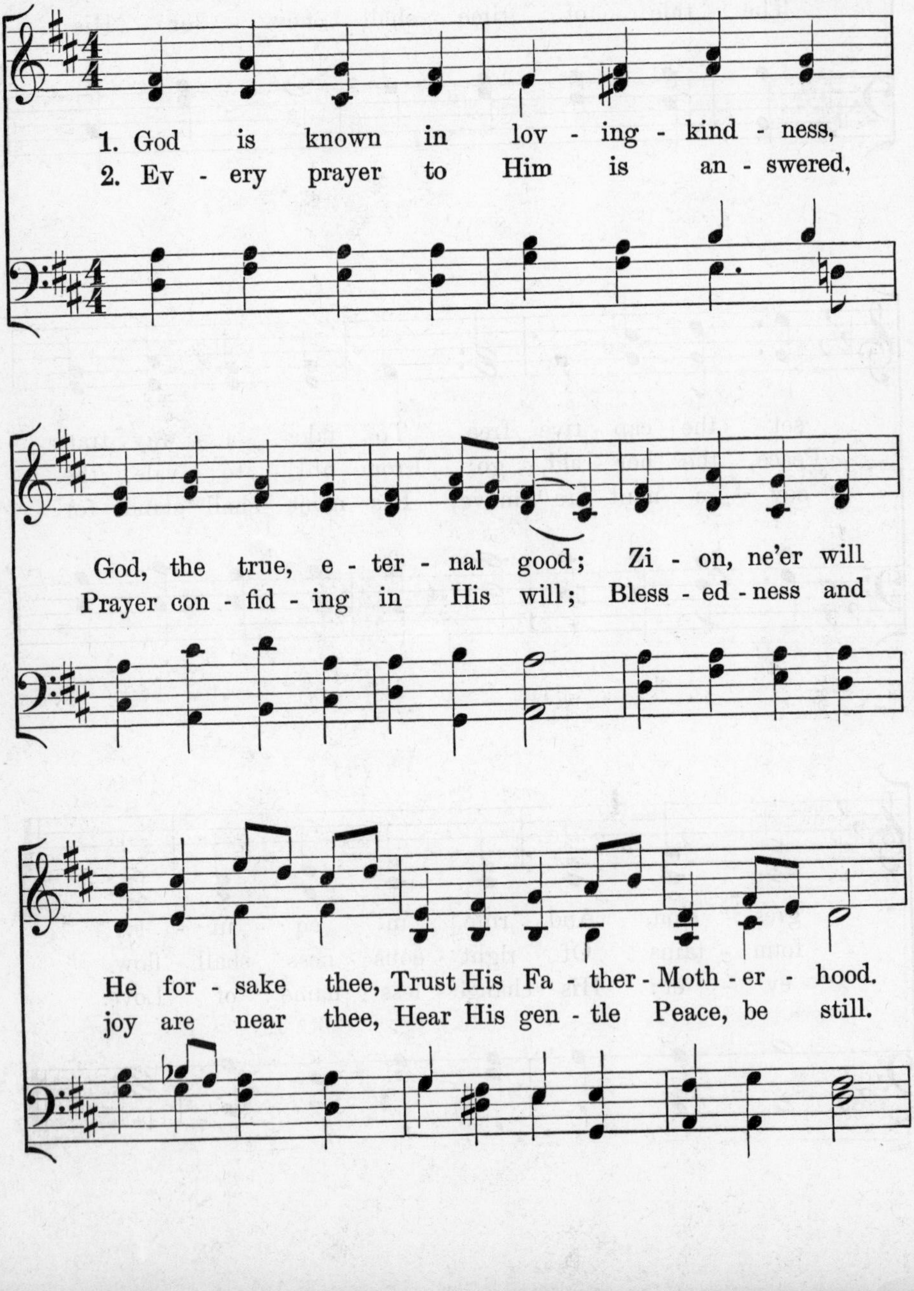

God, the true, e - ter - nal good; Zi - on, ne'er will
Prayer con - fid - ing in His will; Bless - ed - ness and

He for - sake thee, Trust His Fa - ther - Moth - er - hood.
joy are near thee, Hear His gen - tle Peace, be still.

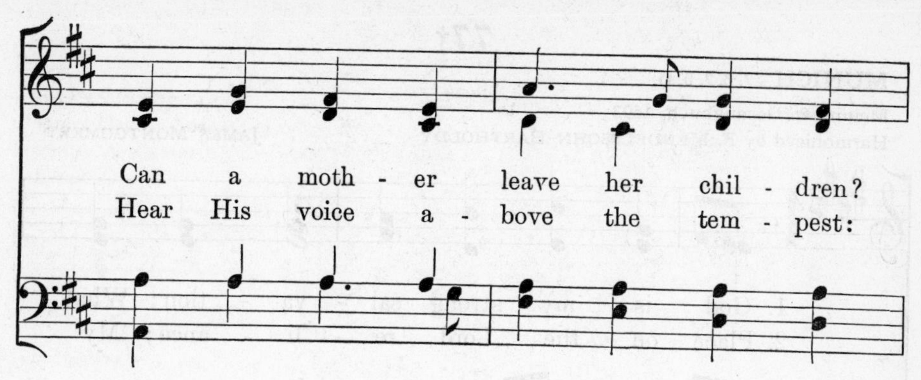
Can a moth - er leave her chil - dren?
Hear His voice a - bove the tem - pest:

Can un-chang-ing Love for - get? Though all earth - ly
I have not for - sak - en thee; In My hand thy

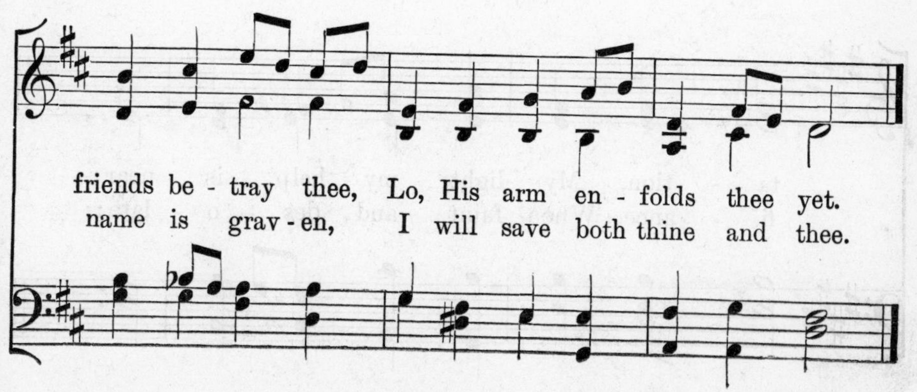
friends be - tray thee, Lo, His arm en - folds thee yet.
name is grav - en, I will save both thine and thee.

**MUNICH** 7. 6. 7. 6. D.

Meiningen Gesangbuch, 1693
Harmonized by F. MENDELSSOHN-BARTHOLDY

JAMES MONTGOMERY

1. God is my strong sal - va - tion; What
2. Place on the Lord re - li - ance; My
foe have I to fear? In dark - ness and temp -
heart, with cour - age wait; His truth be thine af -
ta - tion, My light, my help is near:
fi - ance, When faint and des - o - late:

Though hosts en - camp a - round me, Firm
His might thy heart shall strength - en, His

in the fight I stand; What ter - ror can con -
love thy joy in - crease; Thy day shall mer - cy

found me, With God at my right hand?
length - en: The Lord will give thee peace.

**KING'S LYNN** 7. 6. 7. 6. D.

English Traditional Melody | JAMES MONTGOMERY

*To be sung in unison*
1. God is my strong sal - va - tion; What foe have I to fear? In dark - ness and temp - ta - tion, My light, my help is near:
2. Place on the Lord re - li - ance; My heart, with cour - age wait; His truth be thine af - fi - ance, When faint and des - o - late:

Though hosts en - camp a - round me, Firm
His might thy heart shall strength - en, His

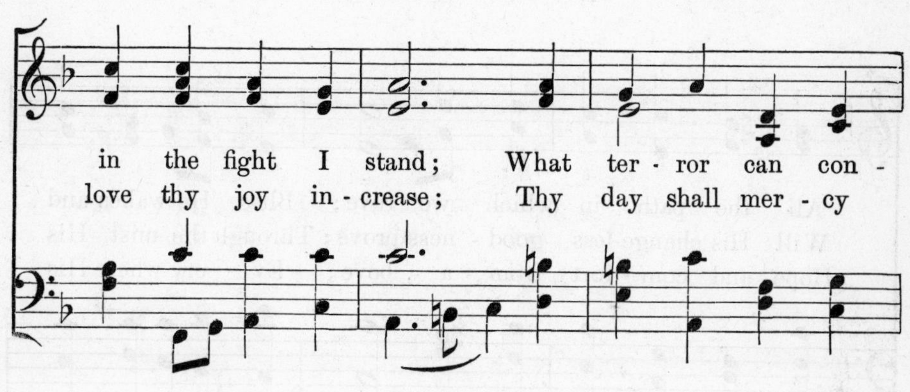
in the fight I stand; What ter - ror can con -
love thy joy in - crease; Thy day shall mer - cy

found me, With God at my right hand?
length - en: The Lord will give thee peace.

**MERTON** 8. 7. 8. 7.

WILLIAM H. MONK | JOHN BOWRING*

1. God is Love; His mer - cy bright - ens
2. E'en the hour that dark - est seem - eth,
3. He with earth - ly cares en - twin - eth
All the path in which we rove; Bliss He wakes and
Will His change-less good - ness prove; Through the mist His
Hope and com - fort from a - bove; Ev - ery-where His
woe He light - ens; God is wis - dom, God is Love.
bright-ness stream - eth; God is wis - dom, God is Love.
glo - ry shin - eth; God is wis - dom, God is Love.

# 80

**EISENACH** L. M.

Melody by JOHANN H. SCHEIN
Harmony from J. S. BACH

JAMES MONTGOMERY*

1. God is our ref - uge and de - fense, In
2. There is a riv - er pure and bright, Whose
3. Built by the word of His com - mand, With
trou - ble our un - fail - ing aid; Se - cure in His om -
streams make glad the heaven-ly plains; Where, in e - ter - ni -
His un - cloud-ed pres - ence blest, Firm as His throne the
nip - o - tence, What foe can make our heart a - fraid?
ty of light, The cit - y of our God re - mains.
bul - warks stand; There is our home, our hope, our rest.

## KINGLY VALE 87. 87. 47.

HUGH P. ALLEN — THEODORE C. WILLIAMS, Adapted

To be sung in unison
1. God is with me, gen - tly o'er me Are His wings of
2. God is with me, and His pres-ence Shall my per - fect

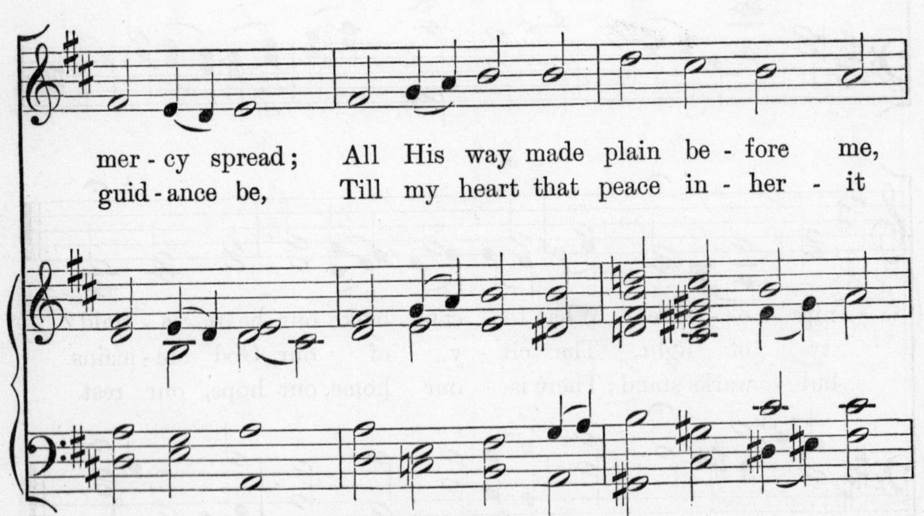
mer - cy spread; All His way made plain be - fore me,
guid - ance be, Till my heart that peace in - her - it

Music by permission of HUGH P. ALLEN

And His glo - ry round me shed. Safe - ly on -
God a - lone can give to me. His all - pow -

- - ward Shall my pil - grim feet be led.
- - er Helps and heals, and sets me free.

## PURPOSE C. M. D. (Irregular)

H. WALFORD DAVIES
ARTHUR C. AINGER
With dignity. To be sung in unison
1. God is . . . work - ing His pur - pose out As . . .
2. What can we do to . . . work God's work, To . . .
3. March we . . forth in the strength of God With the
year suc - ceeds to . . year, God is . . work - ing His
pros - per . and . . in - crease The . . broth - er - hood of . .
ban - ner of Christ un - furled, That the light of the glo - rious
pur - pose out And the time is . . draw - ing near;
all man - kind, The . . reign of the Prince of Peace?
Gos - pel of truth May . . shine through - out . . the world;

* This chord should be struck in 2nd and 3rd verses

Near - er and near - er draws . . the time, The . .
What can we do to has - ten the time, The . .
Fight we the fight with sor - row and sin, To . .
time that shall sure-ly be, When the earth shall be filled with the
time that shall sure-ly be, When the earth shall be filled with the
set their cap - tives free, That the earth may be filled with the
glo - ry of God As the wa - ters cov - er the sea.
glo - ry of God As the wa - ters cov - er the sea?
glo - ry of God As the wa - ters cov - er the sea.

83

INNOCENTS 7.7.7.7.
Old French Melody
Arranged by J. SMITH
JAMES MONTGOMERY
Adapted
1. God made all His crea - tures free; Life it - self is lib - er - ty; God or - dained no oth - er bands Than u - nit - ed hearts and hands.
2. One in fel - low - ship of Mind, We our bliss and glo - ry find In that end - less hap - py whole, Where our God is Life and Soul.
3. So shall all our slav - ery cease, All God's chil - dren dwell in peace, And the new - born earth re - cord Love, and Love a - lone, is Lord.

# 84

**REPENTANCE** 87. 87. 88.

Herre, jeg har handlet ille
LUDVIG M. LINDEMAN

Based on a hymn by
THEODOR V. OLDENBURG

1. God's e - ter - nal Word is spo-ken, Pierc-ing mists, a-round, a - bove; Of e - ter - nal might the to - ken, Em - blem of e - ter - nal Love; Out of dark - ness, world-en - thrall - ing, In - to Light, O hear it call - ing.
2. Word of God, O Word e - ter - nal, May we hear thy liv - ing voice, Learn the power of Love su - per - nal, Learn o - be - dience,—and re - joice; God's com - mands for - ev - er heed - ing, Fol - low where His love is lead - ing.

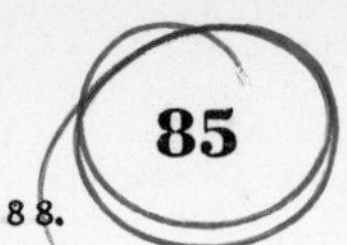
85

LIEBSTER JESU 78. 78. 88.

JOHANN R. AHLE
Arranged by J. S. BACH

EDITH GADDIS BREWER

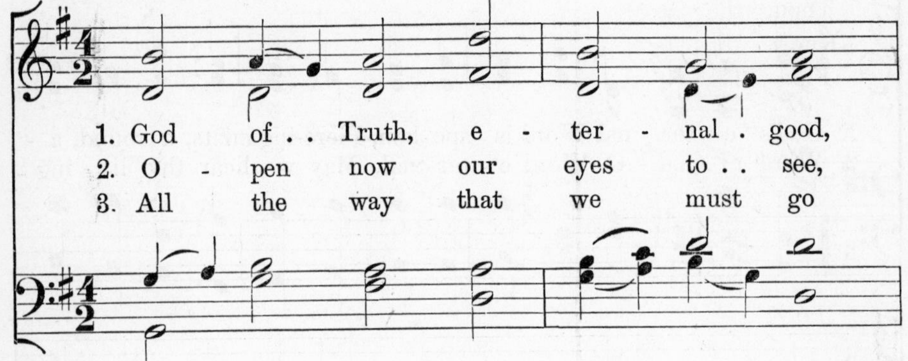
1. God of . . Truth, e - ter - nal . good,
2. O - pen now our eyes to . . see,
3. All the way that we must go

Lift our hearts to rev - e - la - tion,
As the clouds of sense are riv - en,
We will take at Thy di - rec - tion,

That Thou mayst be un - der - stood,
We be - hold re - al - i - ty,
Where the floods of trou - ble . . flow

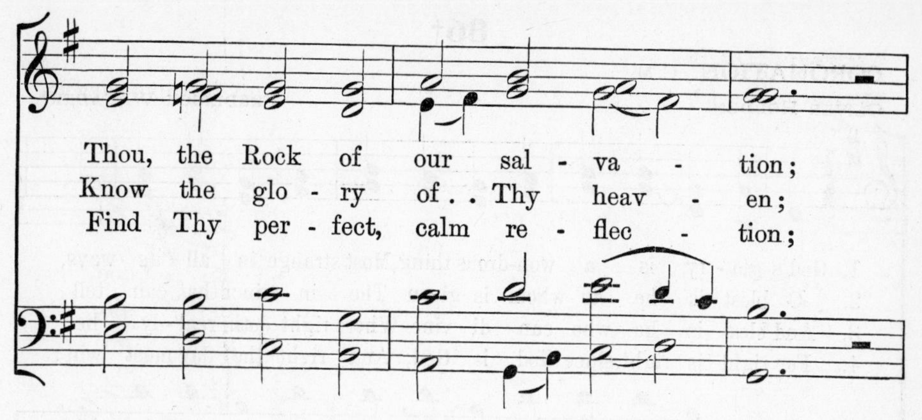
Thou, the Rock of our sal - va - tion;
Know the glo - ry of . . Thy heav - en;
Find Thy per - fect, calm re - flec - tion;

All Thy love we have for . . lov - ing,
So we seek Thy per - fect . . heal - ing
On the path that has no . . turn - ing,

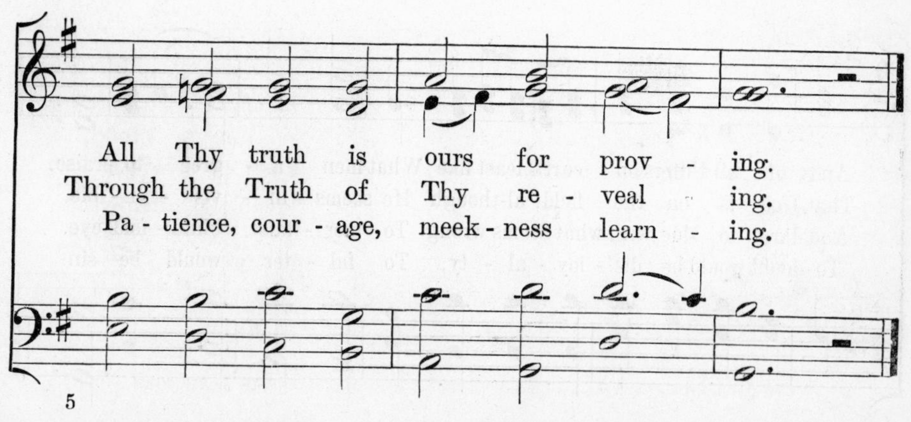
All Thy truth is ours for prov - ing.
Through the Truth of Thy re - veal - ing.
Pa - tience, cour - age, meek - ness learn - ing.

# 86†

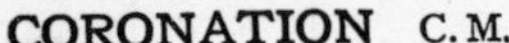

**CORONATION** C. M.

OLIVER HOLDEN — FREDERICK W. FABER*

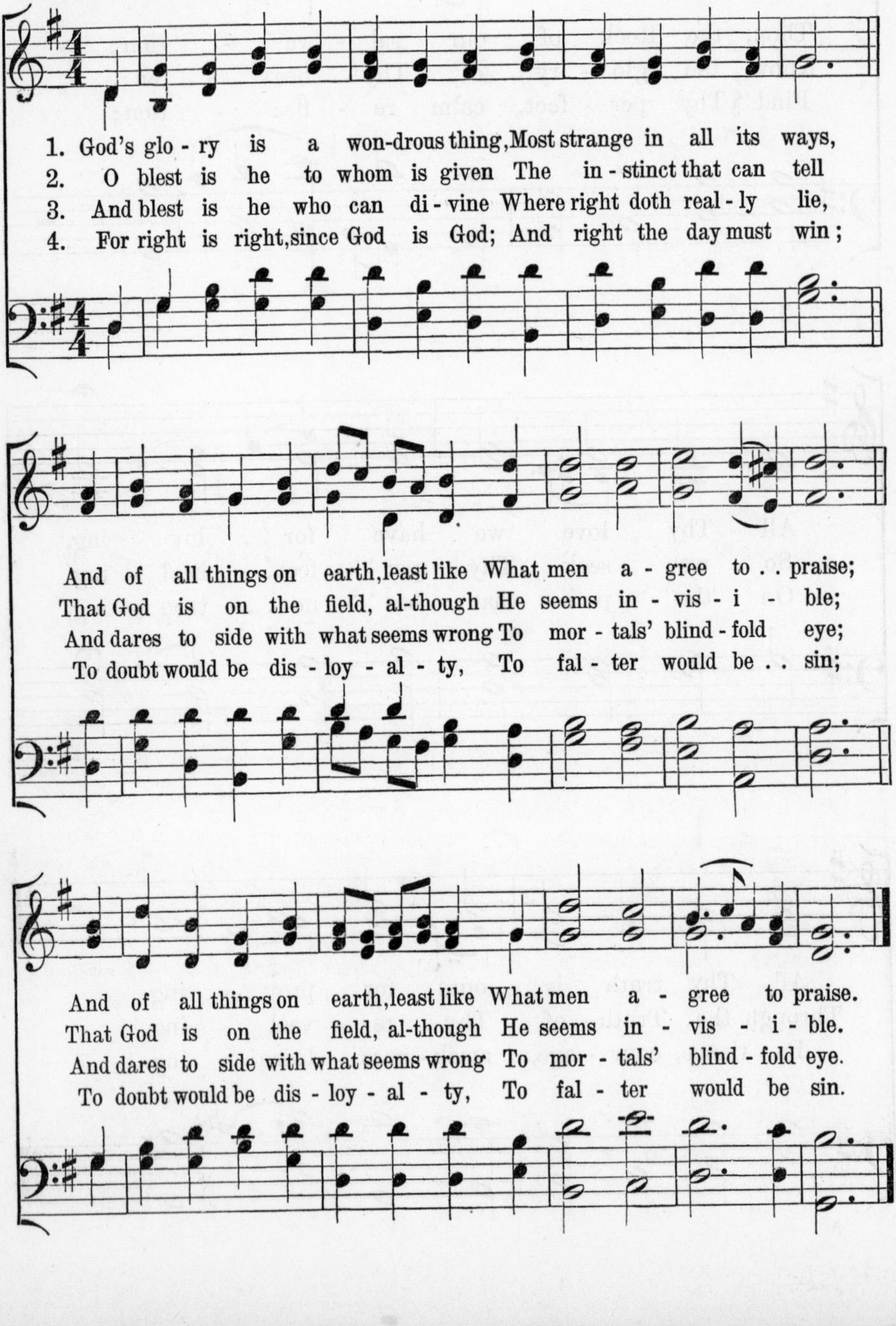

1. God's glo - ry is a won-drous thing, Most strange in all its ways,
2. O blest is he to whom is given The in - stinct that can tell
3. And blest is he who can di - vine Where right doth real - ly lie,
4. For right is right, since God is God; And right the day must win;

And of all things on earth, least like What men a - gree to . . praise;
That God is on the field, al-though He seems in - vis - i - ble;
And dares to side with what seems wrong To mor - tals' blind - fold eye;
To doubt would be dis - loy - al - ty, To fal - ter would be . . sin;

And of all things on earth, least like What men a - gree to praise.
That God is on the field, al-though He seems in - vis - i - ble.
And dares to side with what seems wrong To mor - tals' blind - fold eye.
To doubt would be dis - loy - al - ty, To fal - ter would be sin.

# 87†

**MENDIP** C. M.

English Traditional Melody — FREDERICK W. FABER*

1. God's glo - ry is a won - drous thing, Most
2. O blest is he to whom is given The
3. And blest is he who can di - vine Where
4. For right is right, since God is God; And
strange in all its ways, And of all things on
in - stinct that can tell That God is on the
right doth real - ly lie, And dares to side with
right the day must win; To doubt would be dis -
earth, least like What men a - gree to praise.
field, al - though He seems in - vis - i - ble.
what seems wrong To mor - tals' blind - fold eye.
loy - al - ty, . To fal - ter would be sin.

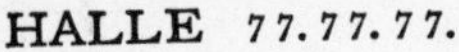
HALLE 77.77.77.

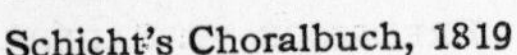
Schicht's Choralbuch, 1819

THOMAS T. LYNCH*

1. Gra - cious Spir - it, dwell . . with me:
2. Truth - ful Spir - it, dwell . . with me:
3. Might - y Spir - it, dwell . . with me:

I my - self . . would gra - cious be,
I my - self . . would truth - ful be,
I my - self . . would might - y be,

And with words that help . . and heal
And with wis - dom kind . . and clear
Might - y, that I may . . pre - vail

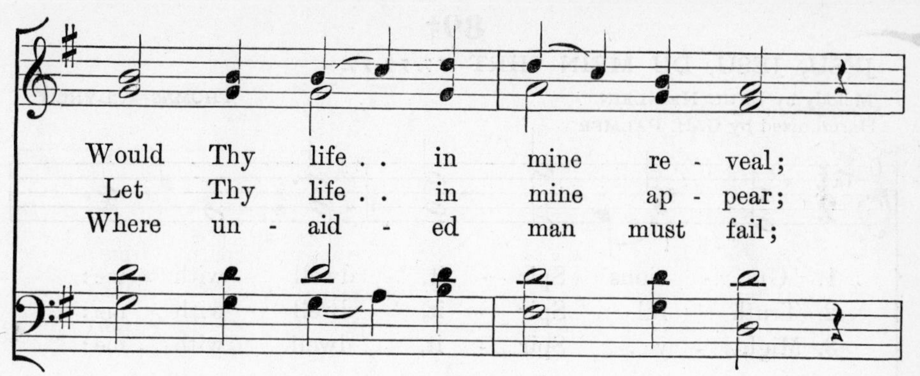
Would Thy life . . in mine re - veal;
Let Thy life . . in mine ap - pear;
Where un - aid - ed man must fail;

And . . with ac - tions bold . . and meek
And . . with ac - tions broth - er - ly
Ev - er by . . tri - um - phant hope

Christ's own gra - cious spir - it speak.
Fol - low Christ's sin - cer - i - ty.
Press - ing on . . and bear - ing up.

## JESU, JESU, DU MEIN HIRT 77.77.77.

Melody by PAUL HEINLEIN
Harmonized by G. H. PALMER

THOMAS T. LYNCH*

1. Gra - cious Spir - it, dwell with me:
2. Truth - ful Spir - it, dwell with me:
3. Might - y . . Spir - it, dwell with me:
I my - self would gra - cious be,
I my - self would truth - ful be,
I my - self would might - y be,
And with words that help . . and heal
And with wis - dom kind . . and clear
Might - y, . . that . . I . . may . . pre - vail

Music from SONGS OF SYON by permission of G. R. WOODWARD

Would Thy life . . in . . mine re - veal;
Let Thy life . . in . . mine ap - pear;
Where un - aid - ed . . man must fail;
And with ac - tions bold and meek
And with ac - tions broth - er - ly
Ev - er . . by tri - um - phant hope
Christ's own gra - cious spir - it speak.
Fol - low Christ's sin - cer - i - ty.
Press - ing on and bear - ing up.

# 90

**CORINTH** 87.87.87.

SAMUEL WEBBE'S
Motetts or Antiphons, 1792

WILLIAM WILLIAMS
From his hymn in Welsh
Adapted

1. Guide me, O Thou great Je - ho - vah,
2. O - pen is the crys - tal foun - tain,
Pil - grim through this bar - ren land:
Whence the heal - ing wa - ters flow;
I am Thine, and Thou art might - y,
And the fi - ery cloud - y pil - lar

Hold me with Thy power - ful hand.
Leads me all my jour - ney through.

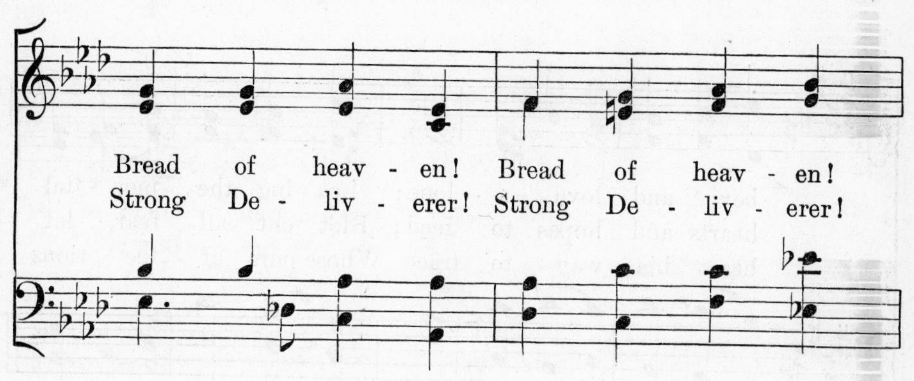
Bread of heav - en! Bread of heav - en!
Strong De - liv - erer! Strong De - liv - erer!

Feed me now and ev - er - more.
Still Thou art my strength and shield.

# 91

**BIRLING** L. M.

From an early 19th Century MS. — Nemi Robertson

1. Grace for to - day, O Love di - vine, Thee to o -
2. Grace for to - day, Thou Love di - vine, Fam - ish - ing
3. Grace for to - day, Thou Love di - vine, Pa - tient of

bey and love a - lone; Los - ing the mor - tal
hearts and hopes to feed; Blot out all fear, let
heart his way to trace Whose pure af - fec - tions

will in Thine, Find we a joy be - fore un-known.
Thy light shine With ten - der warmth on all our need.
Thee de - fine In ten - der love and per - fect grace.

*These words have another setting in the* Supplement, No. 422

**DOMINICA** S. M.

HERBERT S. OAKELEY

THOMAS COGSWELL UPHAM
Adapted

1. Hap - py the man who knows His Mas - ter to o - bey; Whose life of love and la - bor flows, Where God points out the way.
2. Ris - ing to ev - ery task, Soon as the word is given, He doth not wait nor ques - tion ask When or - ders come from heaven.
3. God's will he makes his own, And noth - ing can him stay; His feet are shod for God a - lone, And God a - lone o - bey.
4. Give us, O God, this mind, Which waits but Thy com - mand, And doth its high - est pleas - ure find In Thy great work to stand.

Music by permission of Major E. F. OAKELEY

93

**PEACE** L. M.

Arranged from
WOLFGANG AMADEUS MOZART

WILLIAM P. McKENZIE

1. Hap - py the man whose heart can rest, As - sured God's
2. God keep-eth him, and God is one, One Life, for -
3. Dwell-ing in Love that can - not change, From anx - ious
4. In per-fect peace, with tu - mult stilled, En - ha - vened
good - ness ne'er will cease; Each day, com - plete, with
ev - er - more the same, One Truth un - changed while
fear man finds re - lease; No more his home - less
where no storms a - rise, There man can work what
joy is blessed, God keep - eth him in per - fect peace.
a - ges run; E - ter - nal Love His ho - liest name.
long - ings range, God keep - eth him in per - fect peace.
God hath willed; The joy of per - fect work his prize.

**UFFINGHAM** L. M.

JEREMIAH CLARK

STEPHEN G. BULFINCH
Adapted

1. Hath not thy heart with - in . . thee burned At eve-ning's
2. It was the voice of God that spake In si - lence
3. O voice of God, for - ev - er near, In low, sweet
calm and ho - ly hour, As if its in - most
to thy si - lent heart, And bade each wor - thier
ac - cents whis-pering peace, Make us Thy har - mo -
depths dis-cerned The pres - ence of a loft - ier power?
thought a - wake, And ev - ery dream of earth de - part.
nies to hear Whose heaven-ly ech - oes nev - er cease.

## 95

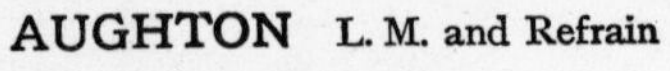

**AUGHTON** L. M. and Refrain

WILLIAM B. BRADBURY — JOSEPH H. GILMORE

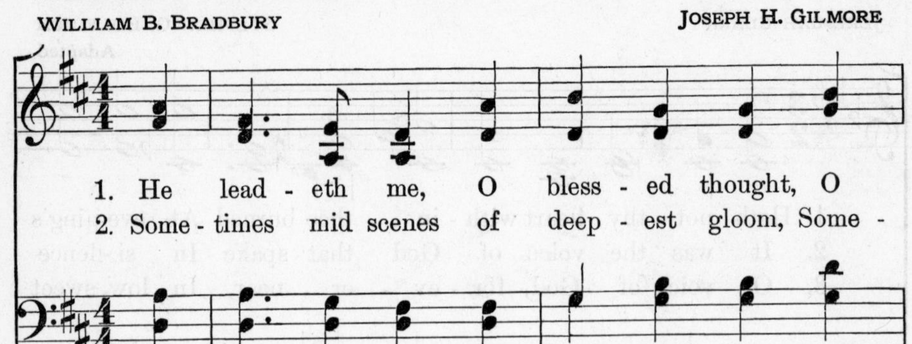
1. He lead - eth me, O bless - ed thought, O
2. Some - times mid scenes of deep - est gloom, Some -

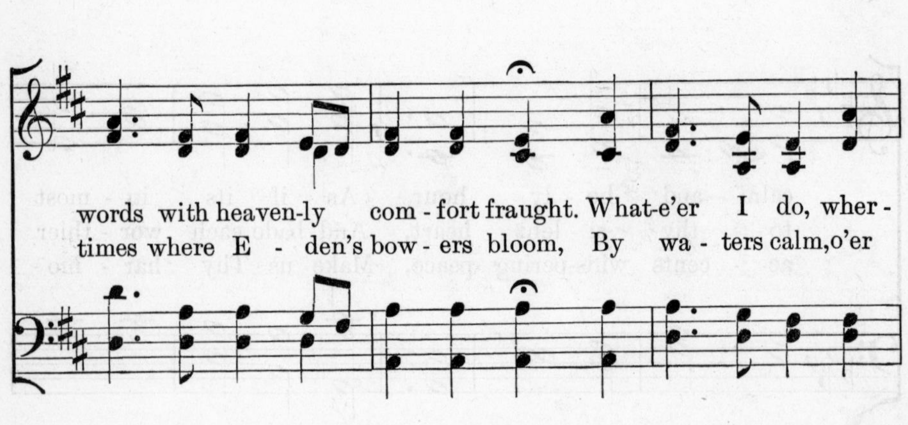
words with heaven-ly com - fort fraught. What-e'er I do, wher -
times where E - den's bow - ers bloom, By wa - ters calm, o'er

e'er I be, Still 'tis God's hand that lead - eth me.
trou - bled sea, Still 'tis His hand that lead - eth me.

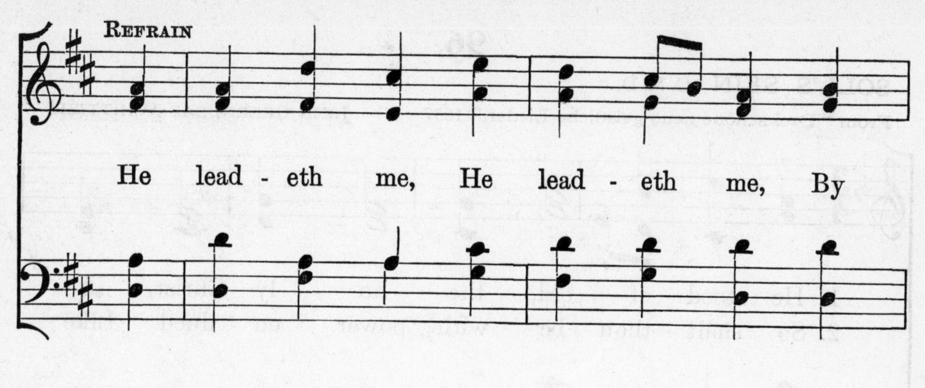
Refrain
He lead - eth me, He lead - eth me, By

His own hand He lead - eth me. His faith - ful fol - lower

I would be, For by His hand He lead - eth me.

## SOLL'S SEIN C. M. D.

From "Drei schöne neue geistliche Lieder," 1637 — JOHN GREENLEAF WHITTIER*

1. He stood of old, the holy Christ, Amid the suffering throng,
With whom his lightest touch sufficed To make the weakest strong.

2. So shalt thou be with power endued Like him who went about
The Syrian hillsides doing good And casting demons out.

That heal - ing gift God gives to them Who
The Great Phy - si - cian liv - eth yet Thy

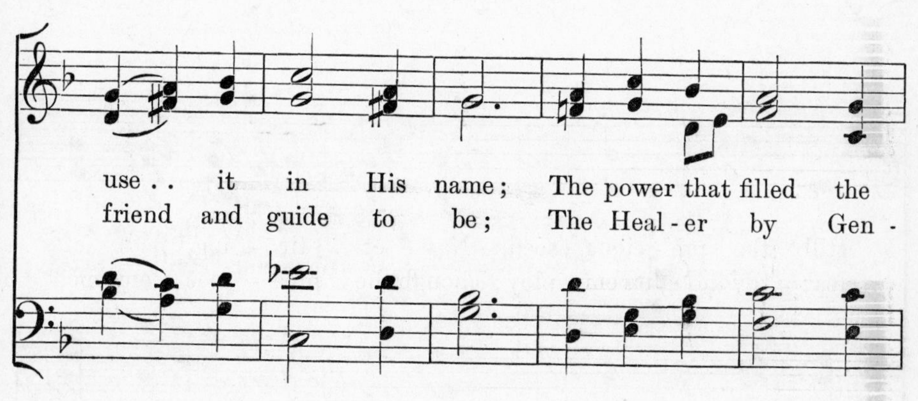
use . . it in His name; The power that filled the
friend and guide to be; The Heal - er by Gen -

gar - ment's hem Is ev - - er - more the same.
nes - ar - et Shall walk . . . the rounds with thee.

ILSLEY 8. 7. 8. 7. D.

FRANK G. ILSLEY

THOMAS HASTINGS
Adapted

1. He that go - eth forth with weep - ing, Bear - ing
2. Sow thy seed, be nev - er wea - ry, Let not
still the pre - cious seed, Nev - er tir - ing, nev - er
fear thy thoughts em - ploy; Though the pros - pect seem most
sleep - ing, Soon shall see his toil suc - ceed; Showers of
drear - y, Thou shalt reap the fruits of joy: Lo, the

Music by permission of BEEKMAN F. ILSLEY

rain will fall from heav - en, Then the
scene of ver - dure bright - ening, See the

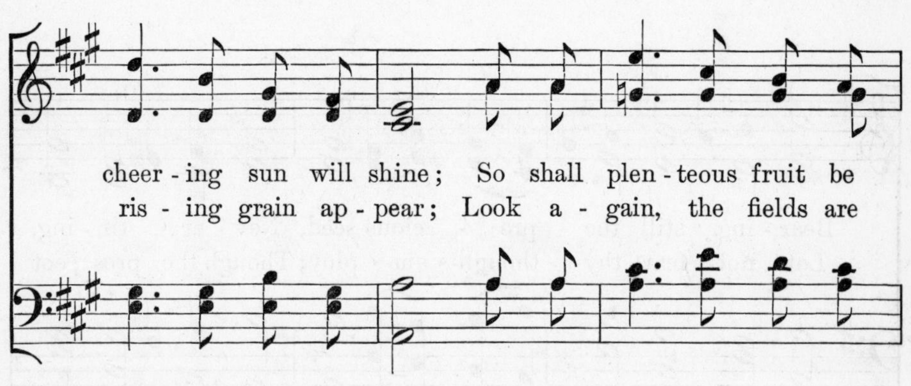
cheer - ing sun will shine; So shall plen - teous fruit be
ris - ing grain ap - pear; Look a - gain, the fields are

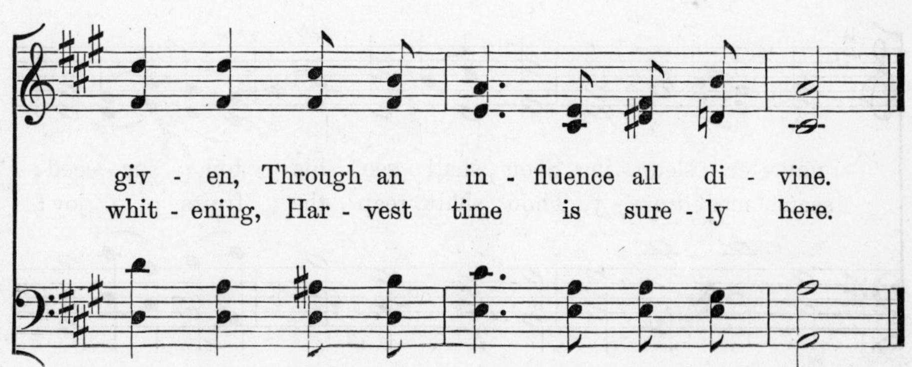
giv - en, Through an in - fluence all di - vine.
whit - ening, Har - vest time is sure - ly here.

**IN BABILONE** 8. 7. 8. 7. D.

Dutch Traditional Melody

THOMAS HASTINGS
Adapted

1. He that . . go - eth forth with weep - ing,
2. Sow thy . . seed, be nev - er . . wea - ry,
Bear - ing still the pre - cious seed, Nev - er . . tir - ing,
Let not fear thy thoughts em - ploy; Though the pros - pect
nev - er sleep - ing, Soon shall see his toil suc - ceed;
seem most drear - y, Thou shalt reap the fruits of joy:

Music by permission of DR. JULIUS RÖNTGEN

Showers of . . rain will fall from heav - en,
Lo, the scene of ver - dure bright - ening,

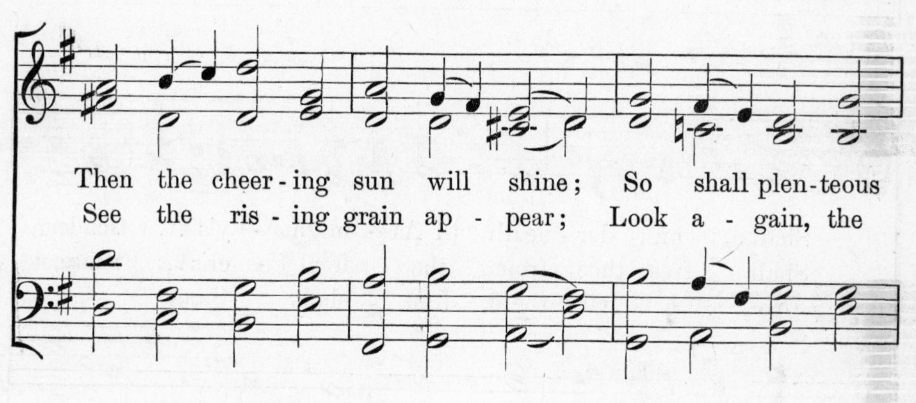
Then the cheer - ing sun will shine; So shall plen - teous
See the ris - ing grain ap - pear; Look a - gain, the

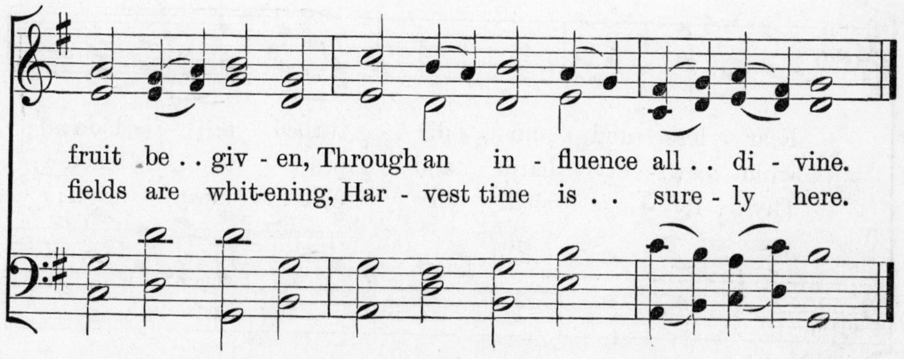
fruit be . . giv - en, Through an in - fluence all . . di - vine.
fields are whit-ening, Har - vest time is . . sure - ly here.

BERA 88. 8. 88. 8.

JOHN E. GOULD
Arranged by WALTER E. YOUNG

NINETY-FIRST PSALM 1
Adapted from TATE and BRADY

1. He that hath God his guard - ian made,
2. His ten - der love and watch - ful care
3. He gives His an - gels charge o'er thee,
Shall un - der - neath th' Al - might - y's . . shade
Shall free thee from the fowl - er's . . snare,
No e - vil there - fore shalt thou see;
Fear - less and un - dis - turbed a - bide;
From ev - ery harm and pes - ti - lence.
Thy ref - uge shall be God . . most high;

Thus to my - self of . . Him I'll . . say,
He o - ver thee His wings shall spread
Dwell - ing with - in His se - cret place,
He is my for - tress, shield and . . stay,
To cov - er thy un - guard - ed . . head.
Thou shalt be - hold His . . power and . . grace,
My . . God; in Him I will . . con - fide.
His . . truth shall be thy strong de - fense.
See . . His sal - va - tion ev - er . . nigh.

# 100

**DAVID'S HARP** 88. 88. 88.

NINETY-FIRST PSALM II

ROBERT KING in "The Divine Companion," 1772

Varied from TATE and BRADY

1. He that hath God his guar - dian . made Shall
2. His ten - der love and watch - ful . . care Shall
3. He gives His an - gels charge o'er . thee, No
dwell be - neath th' Al - might - y's shade;
free thee from the fowl - er's snare.
e - vil there - fore shalt thou see.
Thus of the Lord I now will say,
He o - ver thee His wings shall spread,
Dwell - ing with - in His se - cret place,

He is my for - tress, shield and stay,
To cov - er thy un - guard - ed head,
Thou shalt be - hold His power and grace;

My God; in Him I will con - fide And
And from the noi - some pes - ti - lence His
Thy ref - uge shall be God most high, See

in His se - cret place . . a - bide.
truth shall be thy . . strong . de - fense.
His sal - va - tion ev - er nigh.

# 101

LOBT GOTT 86. 86. 6.
NICOLAS HERMAN
Harmonized by J. S. BACH
M. DE V. N.
1. He sent His Word, His ho - ly Word, And griev - ing hearts were healed; Up - lift - ed they be - held in light Man's her - it - age re - vealed; . . For this we bless Thee, Lord.
2. He sent His Word, His shin - ing Word Of Truth, for - ev - er one, And sons of men re - joice to know The dream of sor - row done; . . For this we bless Thee, Lord.
3. He sent His Word, His faith - ful Word, And hosts who toil in vain Re - ject the false - hood a - ges taught And rise to Life a - gain; . . For this we bless Thee, Lord.

# 102†

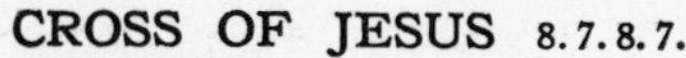
CROSS OF JESUS 8.7.8.7.

JOHN STAINER — FLORENCE L. HEYWOOD

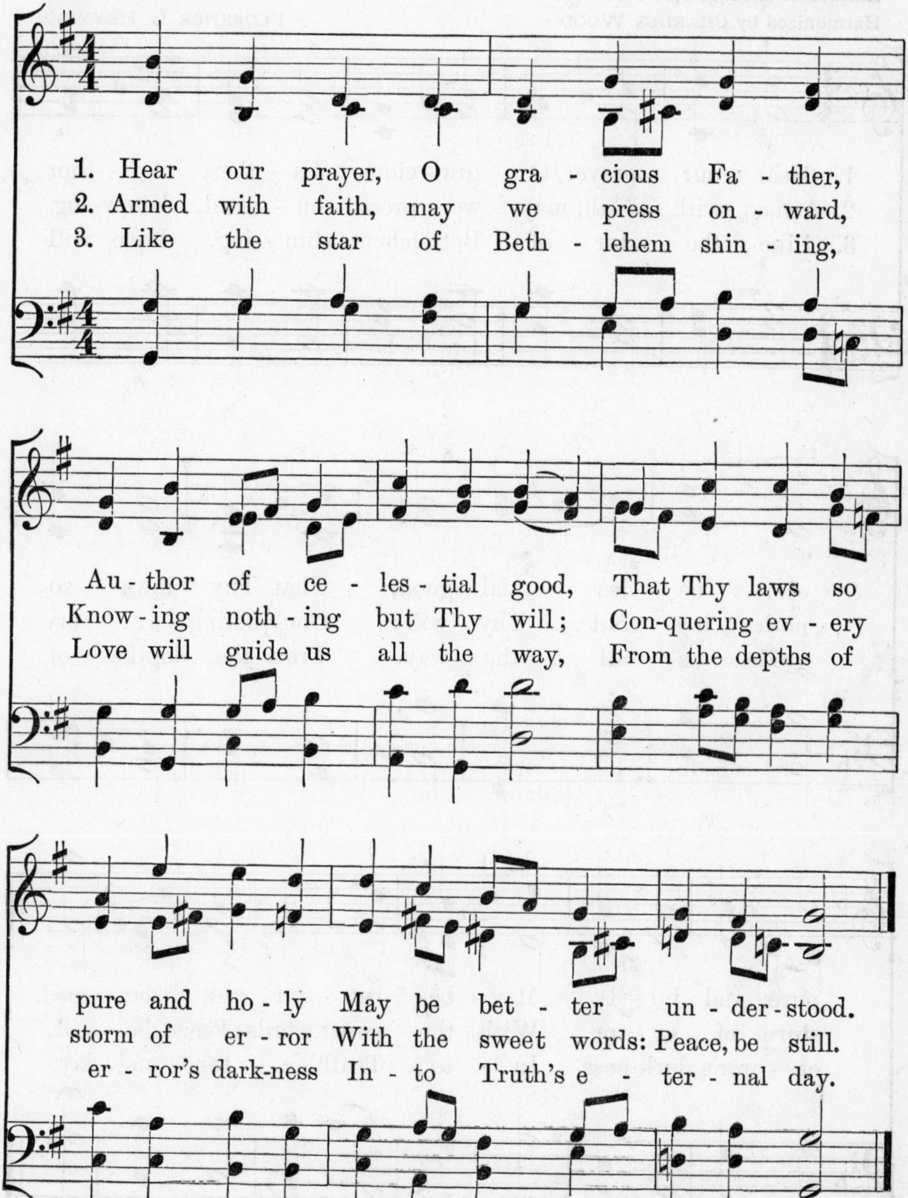

1. Hear our prayer, O gra - cious Fa - ther,
Au - thor of ce - les - tial good,
That Thy laws so pure and ho - ly
May be bet - ter un - der - stood.

2. Armed with faith, may we press on - ward,
Know - ing noth - ing but Thy will;
Con - quering ev - ery storm of er - ror
With the sweet words: Peace, be still.

3. Like the star of Beth - lehem shin - ing,
Love will guide us all the way,
From the depths of er - ror's dark - ness
In - to Truth's e - ter - nal day.

Music by permission of NOVELLO & Co. Ltd.

## 103†

**GLÜCK ZU KREUZ** 8.7.8.7.

Darmstadt Gesangbuch, 1698
Harmonized by CHARLES WOOD
FLORENCE L. HEYWOOD
1. Hear our prayer, O gra - cious Fa - ther, Au - thor of . . ce - les - tial good, That Thy laws so pure and ho - ly May be bet - ter un - der - stood.
2. Armed with faith, may we press on - ward, Know - ing noth - ing but . . Thy will; Con-quering ev - ery storm of er - ror With the sweet words: Peace, be still.
3. Like the star of Beth-lehem shin - ing, Love will guide us all . . the way, From the depths of er - ror's dark-ness In - to Truth's e - ter - nal day.

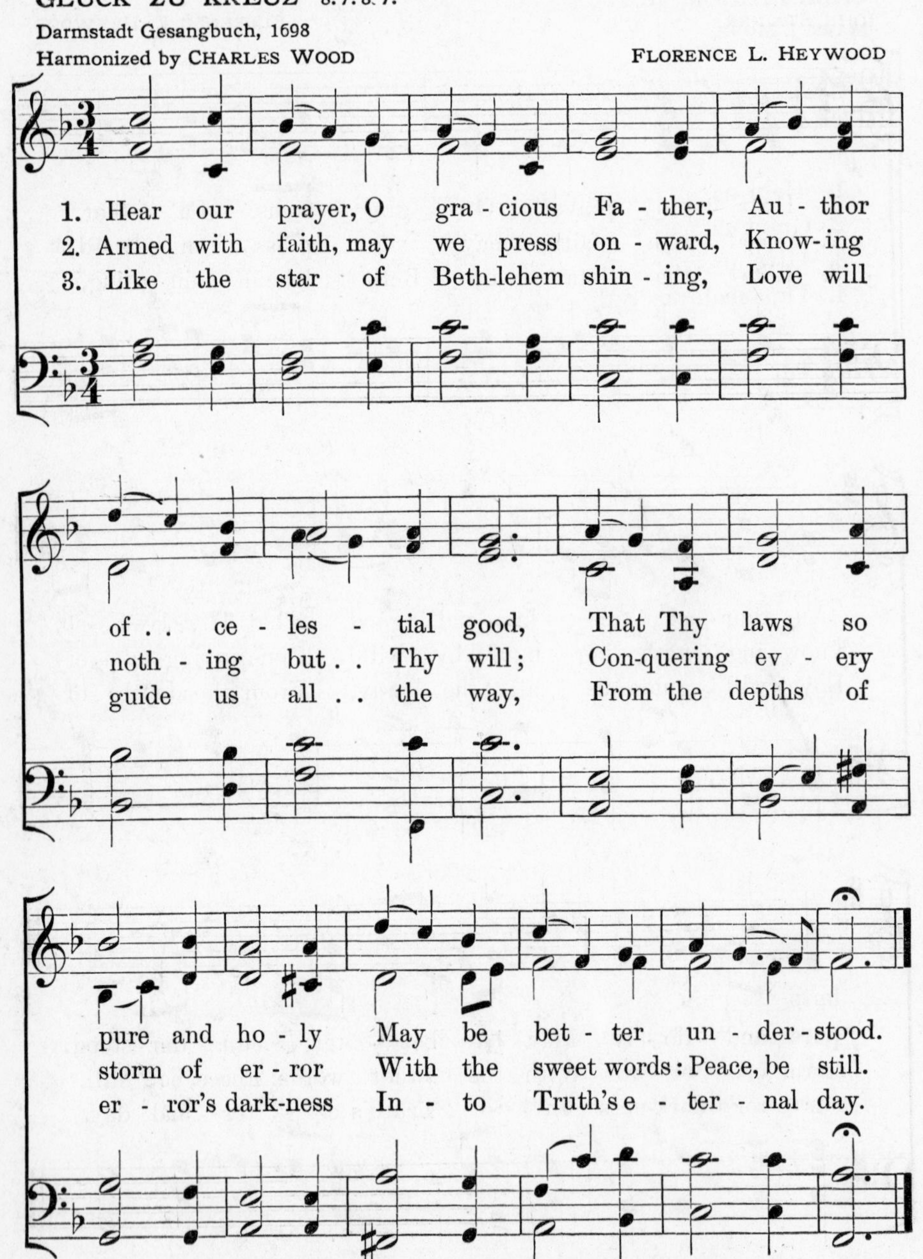

Music from SONGS OF SYON by permission of G. R. WOODWARD

# 104

**CAMPFIELDS** 86. 886.

MARK J. MONK

D. S.

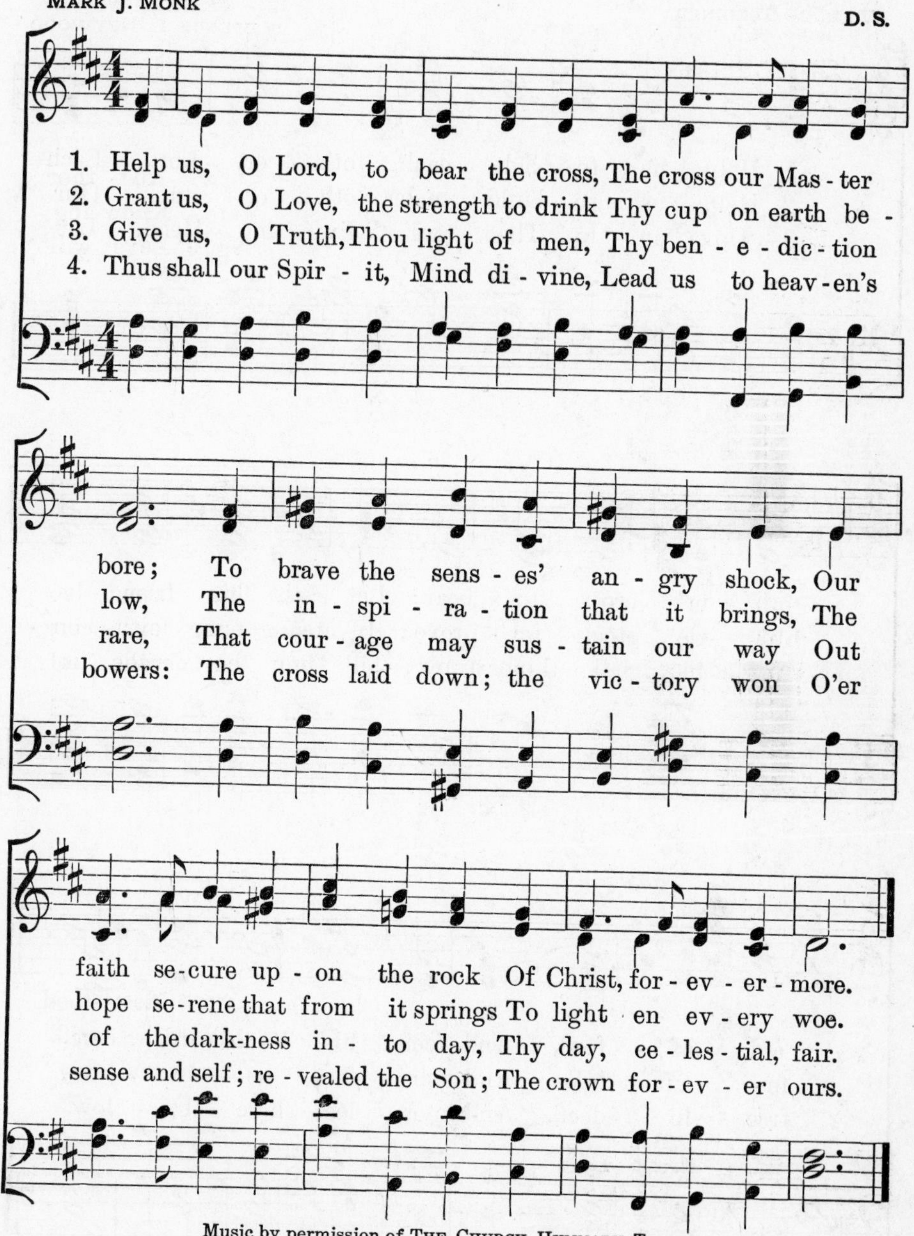
1. Help us, O Lord, to bear the cross, The cross our Mas-ter bore; To brave the sens-es' an-gry shock, Our faith se-cure up-on the rock Of Christ, for-ev-er-more.
2. Grant us, O Love, the strength to drink Thy cup on earth be-low, The in-spi-ra-tion that it brings, The hope se-rene that from it springs To light en ev-ery woe.
3. Give us, O Truth, Thou light of men, Thy ben-e-dic-tion rare, That cour-age may sus-tain our way Out of the dark-ness in-to day, Thy day, ce-les-tial, fair.
4. Thus shall our Spir-it, Mind di-vine, Lead us to heav-en's bowers: The cross laid down; the vic-tory won O'er sense and self; re-vealed the Son; The crown for-ev-er ours.

Music by permission of THE CHURCH HYMNARY TRUST

## 105†

**DEDHAM** C. M.

WILLIAM GARDINER — CHARLES WESLEY

1. Help us to help each oth - er, Lord, Each
2. Help us to build each oth - er up, Our
3. Up un - to Thee, our liv - ing Head, Let
oth - er's cross to bear; Let each his friend - ly
lit - tle . . stock im - prove; In - crease our faith, con -
us in . . all things grow; Till Thou hast made us
aid af - ford, And feel his broth - er's . care.
firm our . . hope, And per - fect us in . . love.
free in - deed, And spot - less here be - low.

# 106†

BROMSGROVE C. M.

Psalmodia Evangelica, 1789

CHARLES WESLEY

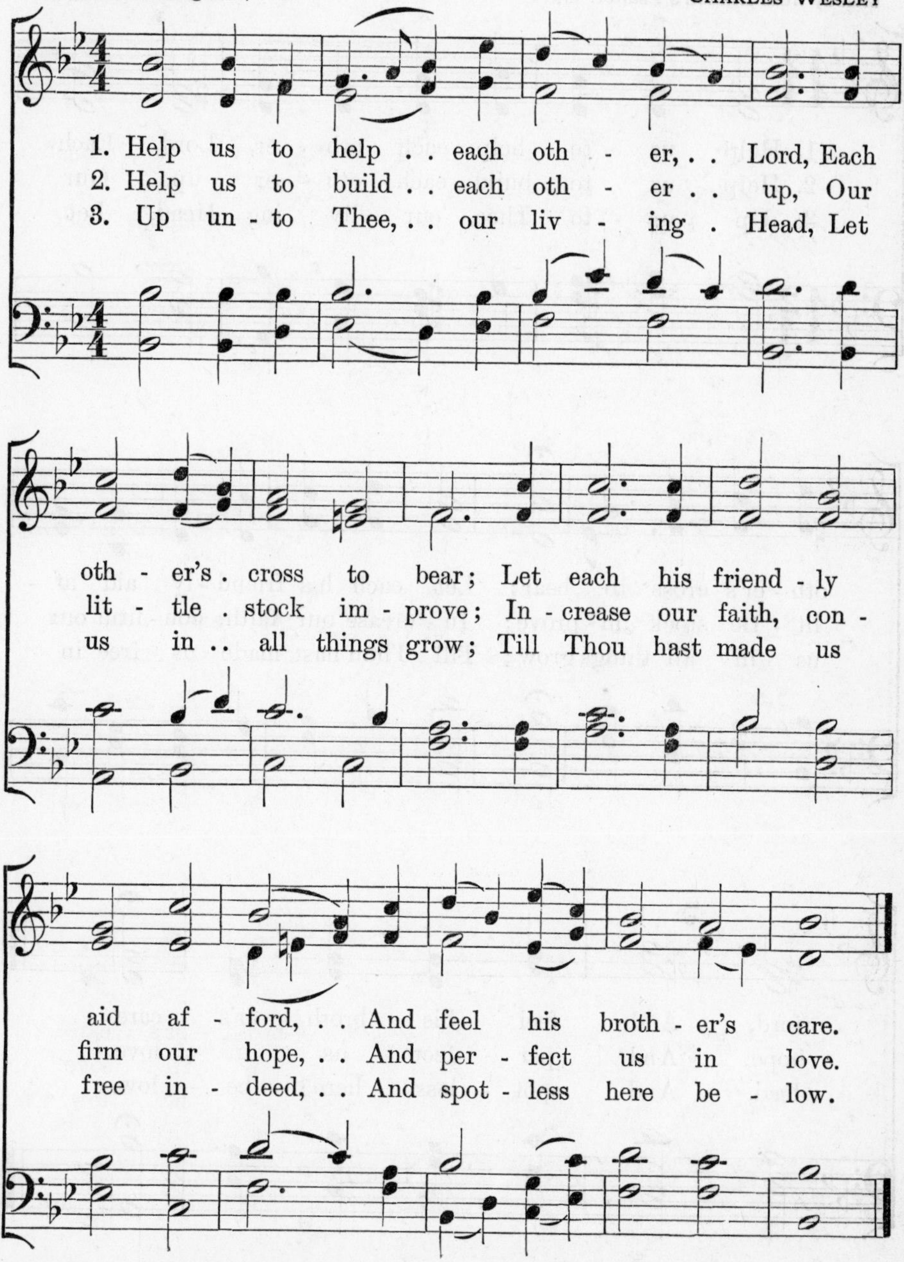

1. Help us to help . . each oth - er, . . Lord, Each
2. Help us to build . . each oth - er . . up, Our
3. Up un - to Thee, . . our liv - ing . Head, Let

oth - er's . cross to bear; Let each his friend - ly
lit - tle . stock im - prove; In - crease our faith, con -
us in . . all things grow; Till Thou hast made us

aid af - ford, . . And feel his broth - er's care.
firm our hope, . . And per - fect us in love.
free in - deed, . . And spot - less here be - low.

## 107†

**WINDSOR** C. M.

Melody from Damon's Psalter, 1591 — CHARLES WESLEY

1. Help us to help each oth - er, Lord, Each oth - er's cross to bear; Let each his friend - ly aid af - ford, And feel his broth - er's care.
2. Help us to build each oth - er up, Our lit - tle stock im - prove; In - crease our faith, con - firm our hope, And per - fect us in love.
3. Up un - to Thee, our liv - ing Head, Let us in all things grow; Till Thou hast made us free in - deed, And spot - less here be - low.

# 108

**TOULON** (OLD 124th) 10. 10. 10. 10.

Arranged from the
Genevan Psalter, 1551

HORATIUS BONAR*

1. Here, O my Lord, I'd see Thee face to face; Here would I
2. Here would I feed up - on the bread of God; Here drink a -
3. And as we rise, the sym-bols dis - ap - pear; The feast, though
4. Feast af - ter feast thus comes and pass - es by; Yet pass - ing,

touch and han - dle things un - seen; Here grasp with firm - er
new the roy - al wine of heaven; Here would I lay a -
not the love, is past and gone; The bread and wine re -
points to the glad feast a - bove, Giv - ing sweet fore - taste

hand th' e-ter - nal grace, And all my wea - ri - ness up - on Thee lean.
side each earth-ly load, Here taste a - fresh the calm of sin for - given.
move, but Thou art here, Near - er than ev - er, still my shield and sun.
of the fes - tal joy, The Lamb's great brid-al feast of bliss and love.

# 109†

**ELLESDIE** 8.7.8.7.D.

WOLFGANG AMADEUS MOZART
Arranged by H. P. MAIN

MARIA LOUISE BAUM

1. Here, O God, Thy heal - ing pres - ence
2. Rev - erent lives un - veil Thy beau - ty,
Lifts our thoughts from self and sin, Fills with light their
Faith - ful wit - ness bear of Thee; Bind - ing up the
hid - den pla - ces, When Thy love is wel - comed in.
bro - ken - heart-ed, We re - flect Thy ra - dian - cy.

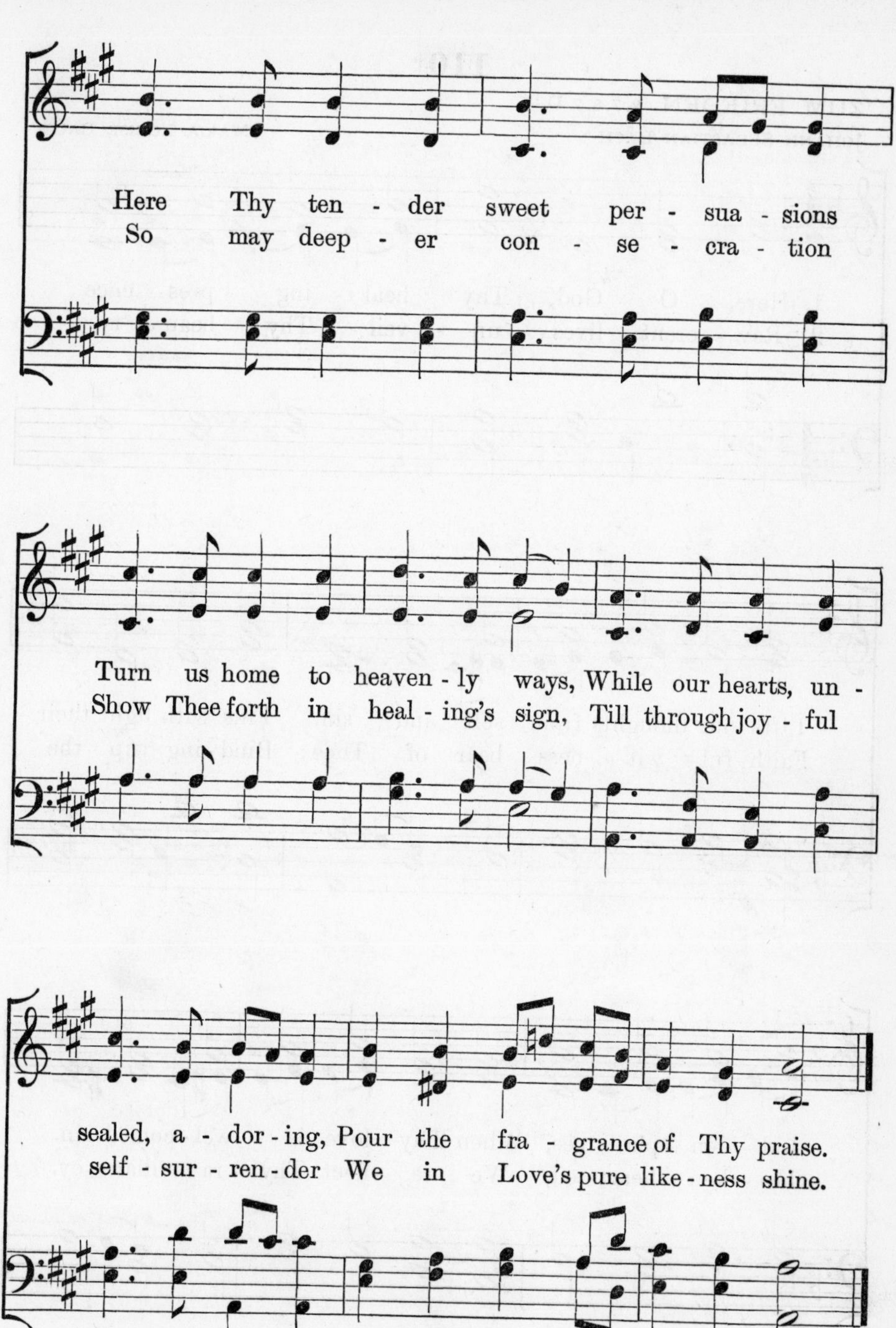
Here Thy ten - der sweet per - sua - sions
So may deep - er con - se - cra - tion
Turn us home to heaven - ly ways, While our hearts, un -
Show Thee forth in heal - ing's sign, Till through joy - ful
sealed, a - dor - ing, Pour the fra - grance of Thy praise.
self - sur - ren - der We in Love's pure like - ness shine.

# 110†

ZUM FRIEDEN 8. 7. 8. 7. D.
JOHANN SEBASTIAN BACH
MARIA LOUISE BAUM
1. Here, O God, Thy healing presence
Lifts our thoughts from self and sin,
Fills with light their hidden places,
When Thy love is welcomed in.
2. Reverent lives unveil Thy beauty,
Faithful witness bear of Thee;
Binding up the broken-hearted,
We reflect Thy radiancy.

Here Thy ten - der sweet per - sua - sions
So may deep er con - se - cra - tion

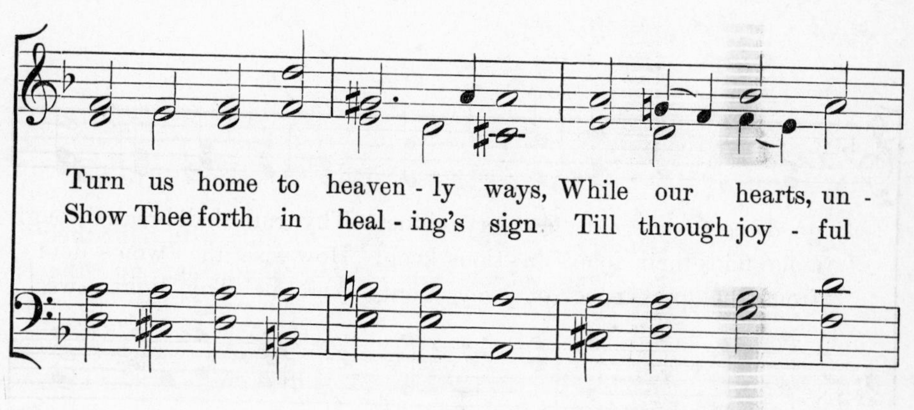
Turn us home to heaven - ly ways, While our hearts, un -
Show Thee forth in heal - ing's sign Till through joy - ful

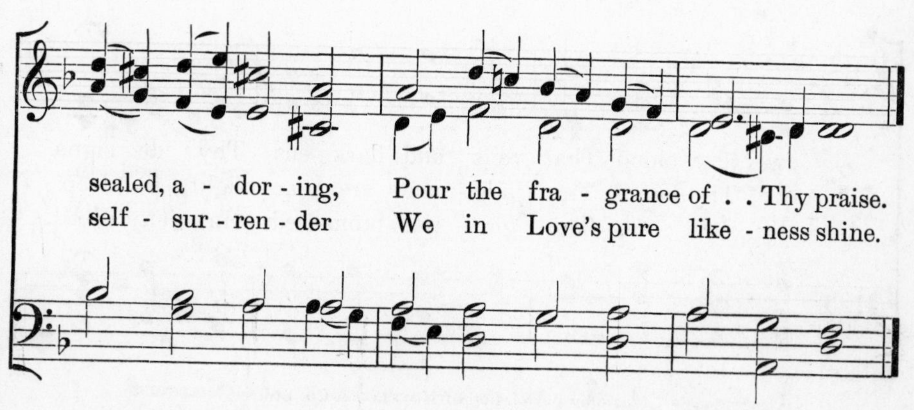
sealed, a - dor - ing, Pour the fra - grance of . . Thy praise.
self - sur - ren - der We in Love's pure like - ness shine.

## 111

**ESCHOL** L. M.

GEORGE M. GARRETT

ISAAC WATTS*

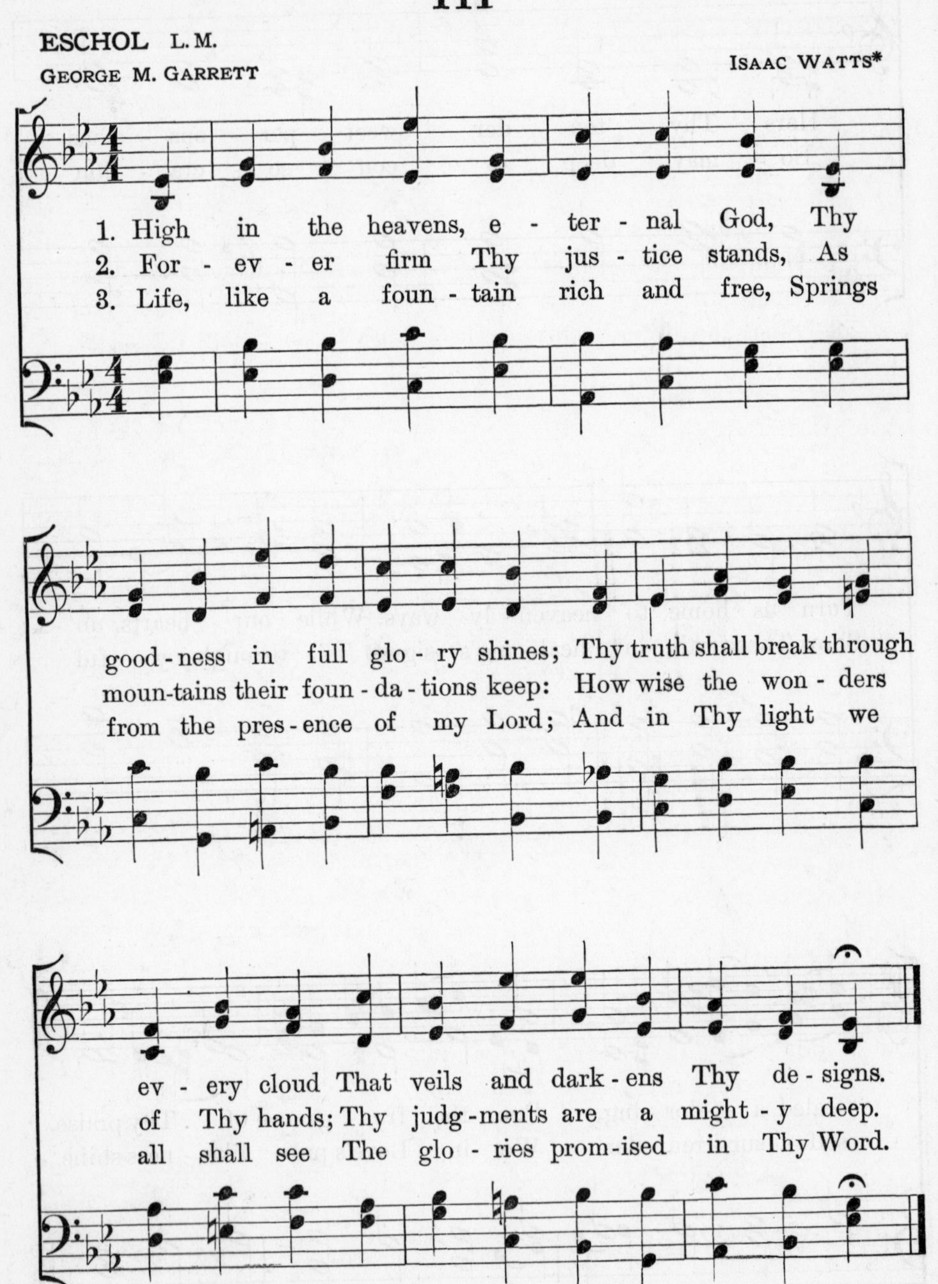
1. High in the heavens, e - ter - nal God, Thy
2. For - ev - er firm Thy jus - tice stands, As
3. Life, like a foun - tain rich and free, Springs
good - ness in full glo - ry shines; Thy truth shall break through
moun-tains their foun - da - tions keep: How wise the won - ders
from the pres - ence of my Lord; And in Thy light we
ev - ery cloud That veils and dark - ens Thy de - signs.
of Thy hands; Thy judg - ments are a might - y deep.
all shall see The glo - ries prom - ised in Thy Word.

Music by permission of NOVELLO & Co. Ltd.

# 112

SECURITY 8.8.8.8.
Tryggare kan ingen vara
IVAR WIDÉEN
MARIA LOUISE BAUM
Not slow
1. High to heaven let song be . . soar-ing, Borne on
2. Sing, till all the world re - joi - ces, Sing! for
3. Sing the Word, whose power su - per - nal Love - li -
faith's tri - um - phant pin - ion; Free from sin, our hearts a -
fear no more en - slaves us. From th' ac - cus - er's mock-ing
ness and joy un - fold - eth; Man who lives in Life e -
dor - ing Yield them - selves to Love's do - min - ion.
voi - ces Christ, our might - y Coun - sel, saves us.
ter - nal Ev - er - more the light be - hold - eth.

# 113

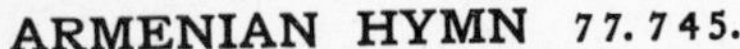

## ARMENIAN HYMN 77.745.

From the Armenian Liturgy
Translated by LEON TOURIAN
Adapted

*To be sung in unison*

1. Ho - li - ness be - comes Thy house, 'Tis Thou who dost dwell in light; Thou be - girt with maj - es - ty, Gird us with Truth, And with Thy great might.
2. Send Thou forth Thy power and love, In beau - ty of ho - li - ness; We would here com-mune with Thee, E - ter - nal God, Be . . Thou near to . . bless.
3. O su - preme and per - fect One, O Lord, praise to Thee is due; Clothe us in the grace of . . love, Main - tain Thy church To . . Thy serv - ice . . true.

# 114

**ORIENTIS PARTIBUS** 7.7.7.7.

Old French Melody
PIERRE DE CORBEIL (?)
Arranged

JOHN BURTON
Adapted

To be sung in unison
1. Ho - ly Bi - ble, book di - vine, Pre - cious treas - ure, thou art mine: Mine to tell me whence I came; Mine to tell me what I am;
2. Mine to chide me when I rove, Mine to show a Sav - iour's love; Mine thou art to guide and guard; Mine to give a rich re - ward;
3. Mine to com - fort in dis - tress, With a Sav - iour's ten - der - ness; Mine to show, by liv - ing faith, Man can tri - umph o - ver death.

# 115†

**LUX EOI** 8.7.8.7.D.

**ARTHUR SULLIVAN**

**JOHN M. NEALE**
**Adapted**

1. Ho - ly Fa - ther, Thou hast taught us
2. We would trust in Thy pro - tect - ing,
We should live to Thee a - lone; Year by year, Thy
Whol - ly rest up - on Thine arm, Fol - low whol - ly
hand hath brought us On through dan - gers oft un - known.
Thy di - rect - ing, Thou our on - ly guard from harm.

Music by permission of NOVELLO & Co. Ltd.

When we wan - dered, Thou hast found us;
Keep us from our own un - do - ing,

When we doubt-ed, sent us light; Still Thine arm has
Help us turn to Thee when tried, Still our strength in

been a - round us, All our paths were in Thy sight.
Thee re - new - ing, Keep us ev - er at Thy side.

# 116†

**LLANSANNAN** 8.7.8.7.D.
Welsh Hymn Melody

JOHN M. NEALE
Adapted

1. Ho - ly Fa - ther, Thou hast taught us
2. We would trust in Thy pro - tect - ing,

We should live to Thee a - lone; Year by year, Thy
Whol - ly rest up - on Thine arm, Fol - low whol - ly

hand hath brought us On through dan - gers oft un - known.
Thy di - rect - ing, Thou our on - ly guard from harm.

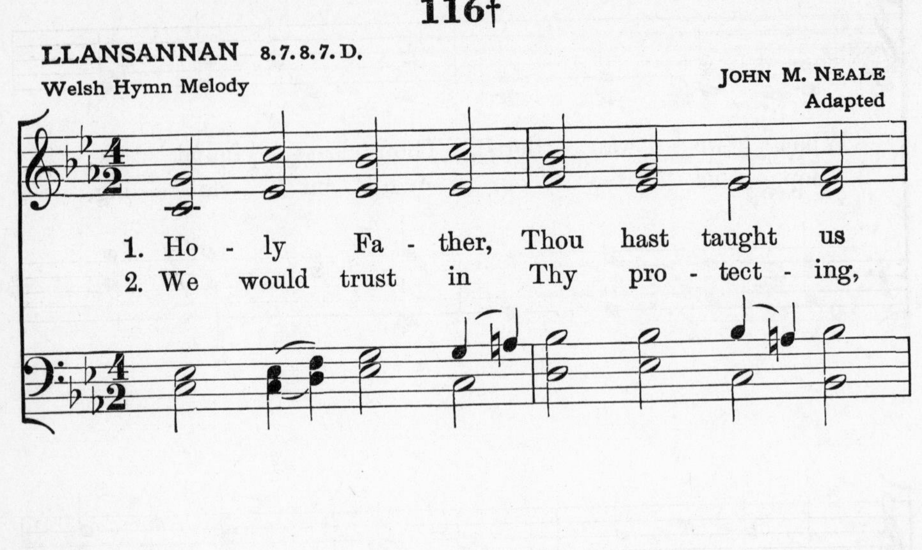

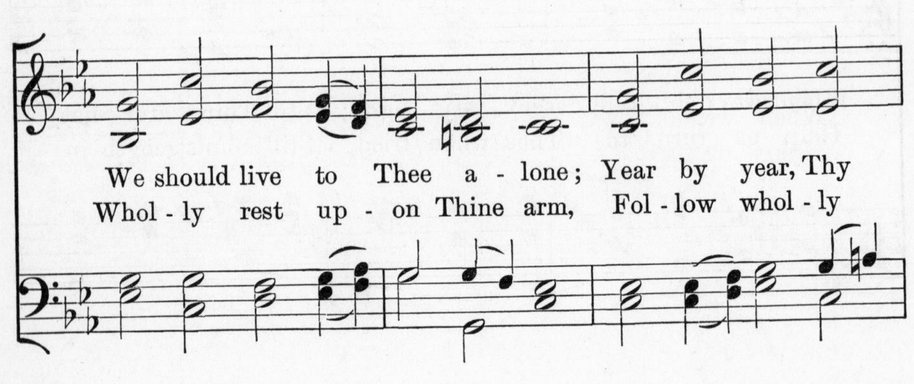

When we wan - dered, Thou hast . . found us;
Keep us from our own un - do - ing,

When we doubt - ed, sent us light; Still Thine arm has
Help us turn to Thee when tried, Still our strength in

been a - round us, All our paths were in Thy sight.
Thee re - new - ing, Keep us ev - er . . at Thy side.

# 117

NICAEA 11. 12. 12. 10.

JOHN B. DYKES REGINALD HEBER*

1. Ho - ly, Ho - ly, Ho - ly, . .
2. Ho - ly, Ho - ly, Ho - ly, . .
3. Ho - ly, Ho - ly, Ho - ly, . .
Lord . . God Al - might - y, Ear - ly in the
dark - ness can - not hide Thee, Though the eyes of
Lord . . God Al - might - y, All Thy works shall
morn - ing our song shall rise to Thee.
sin - ful men Thy glo - ry can - not see.
praise Thy name in earth, and sky and sea;

Ho - ly, Ho - ly, Ho - ly, . .
Thou a - lone art ho - ly, . .
Ho - ly, Ho - ly, Ho - ly, . .
mer - ci - ful and might - y, Which wert, and
there is none be - side Thee, Per - fect in
mer - ci - ful and might - y, Which wert, and
art, and . . ev - er - more shalt be.
power, in . . . love and pu - ri - ty.
art, and . . ev - er - more shalt be.

# 118

**ELIJAH** 7.7.7.7.

Arranged from
FELIX MENDELSSOHN-BARTHOLDY

ANDREW REED and
SAMUEL LONGFELLOW
Adapted

1. Ho - ly Spir - it, Light di - vine, Shine up -
2. Ho - ly Spir - it, Peace di - vine, Still this
3. Ho - ly Spir - it, all di - vine, Dwell with -

on this heart of . . mine; Kin - dle . . ev - ery
rest - less heart of . . mine; Speak to . . calm the
in this heart of . . mine; Bid my . . trou - bled

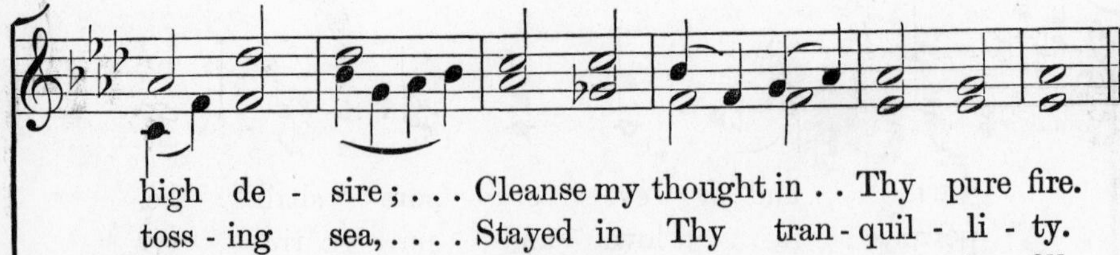
high de - sire; . . . Cleanse my thought in . . Thy pure fire.
toss - ing sea, . . . . Stayed in Thy tran - quil - li - ty.
thoughts be still; . . . With Thy peace my spir - it fill.

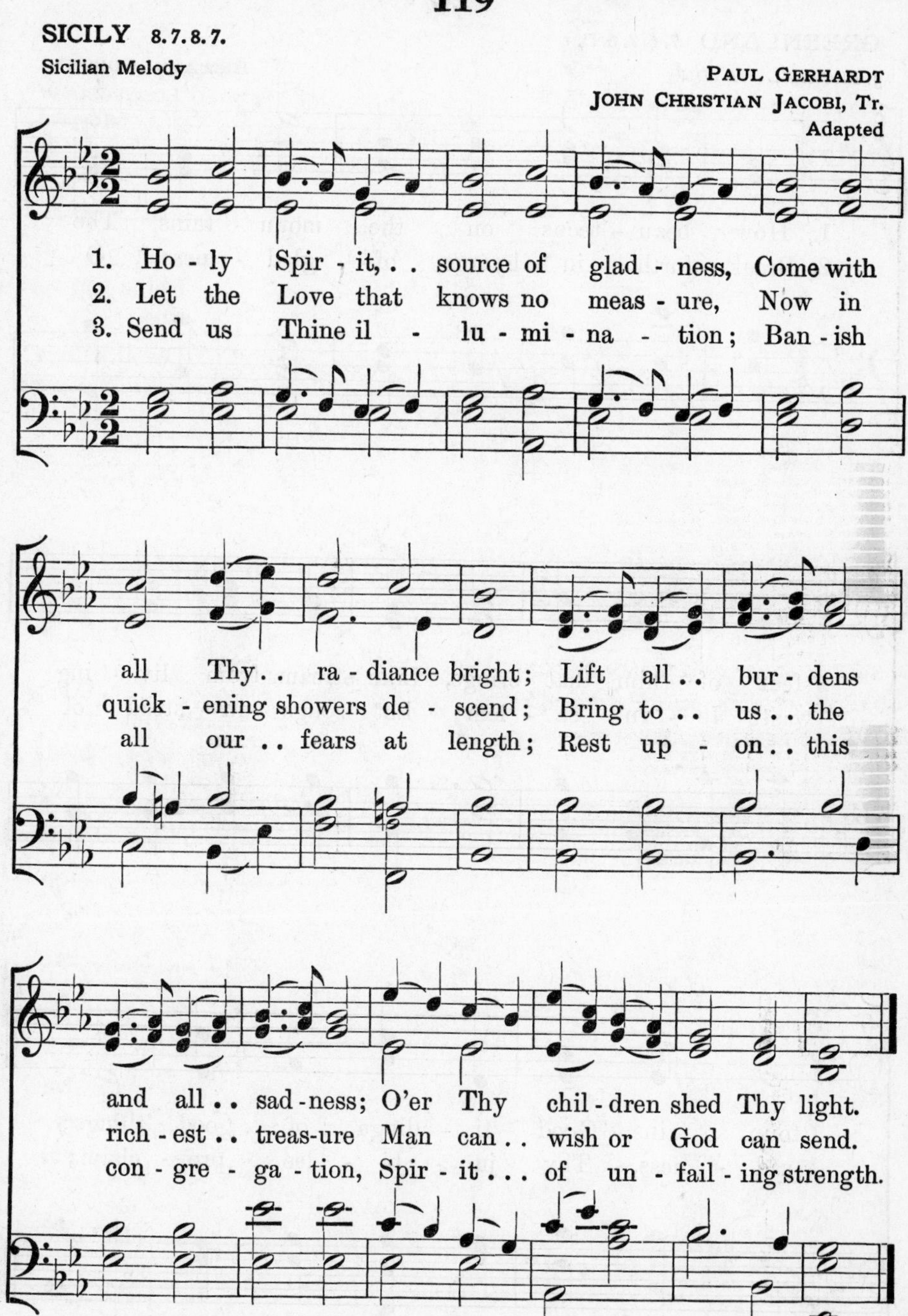
119
SICILY 8.7.8.7.
Sicilian Melody
PAUL GERHARDT
JOHN CHRISTIAN JACOBI, Tr.
Adapted
1. Ho - ly Spir - it, . . source of glad - ness, Come with all Thy . . ra - diance bright; Lift all . . bur - dens and all . . sad - ness; O'er Thy chil - dren shed Thy light.
2. Let the Love that knows no meas - ure, Now in quick - ening showers de - scend; Bring to . . us . . the rich - est . . treas - ure Man can . . wish or God can send.
3. Send us Thine il - lu - mi - na - tion; Ban - ish all our . . fears at length; Rest up - on . . this con - gre - ga - tion, Spir - it . . . of un - fail - ing strength.

## 120

GREENLAND 7.6.7.6.D.
J. MICHAEL HAYDN
BENJAMIN GOUGH*
1. How beau - teous on the moun - tains The
2. Break forth in hymns of glad - ness, O
feet of him that brings, Like streams from liv - ing
waste Je - ru - sa - lem; Let songs in - stead of
foun - tains, Good ti - dings of good things;
sad - ness, Thy ju - bi - lee pro - claim;

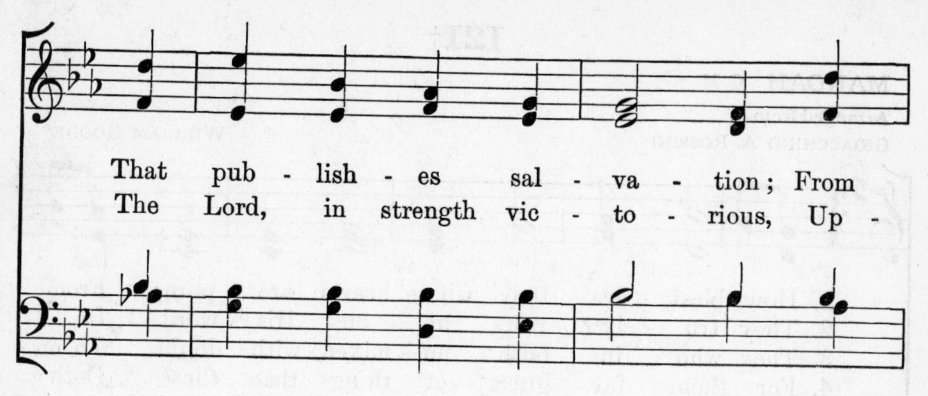
That pub - lish - es sal - va - tion ; From
The Lord, in strength vic - to - rious, Up -
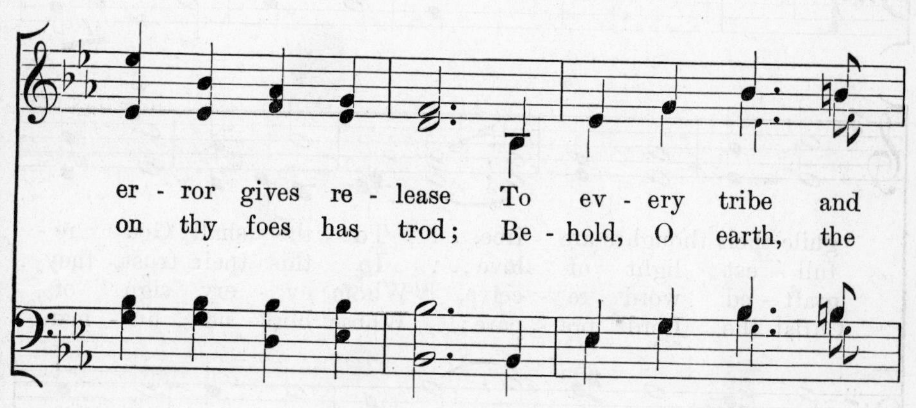
er - ror gives re - lease To ev - ery tribe and
on thy foes has trod ; Be - hold, O earth, the

na - tion : God's reign of joy and peace.
glo - rious Sal - va - tion of our God.

# 121†

**MANOAH** C. M.

Arranged from
GIOACCHINO A. ROSSINI

WILLIAM GOODE*

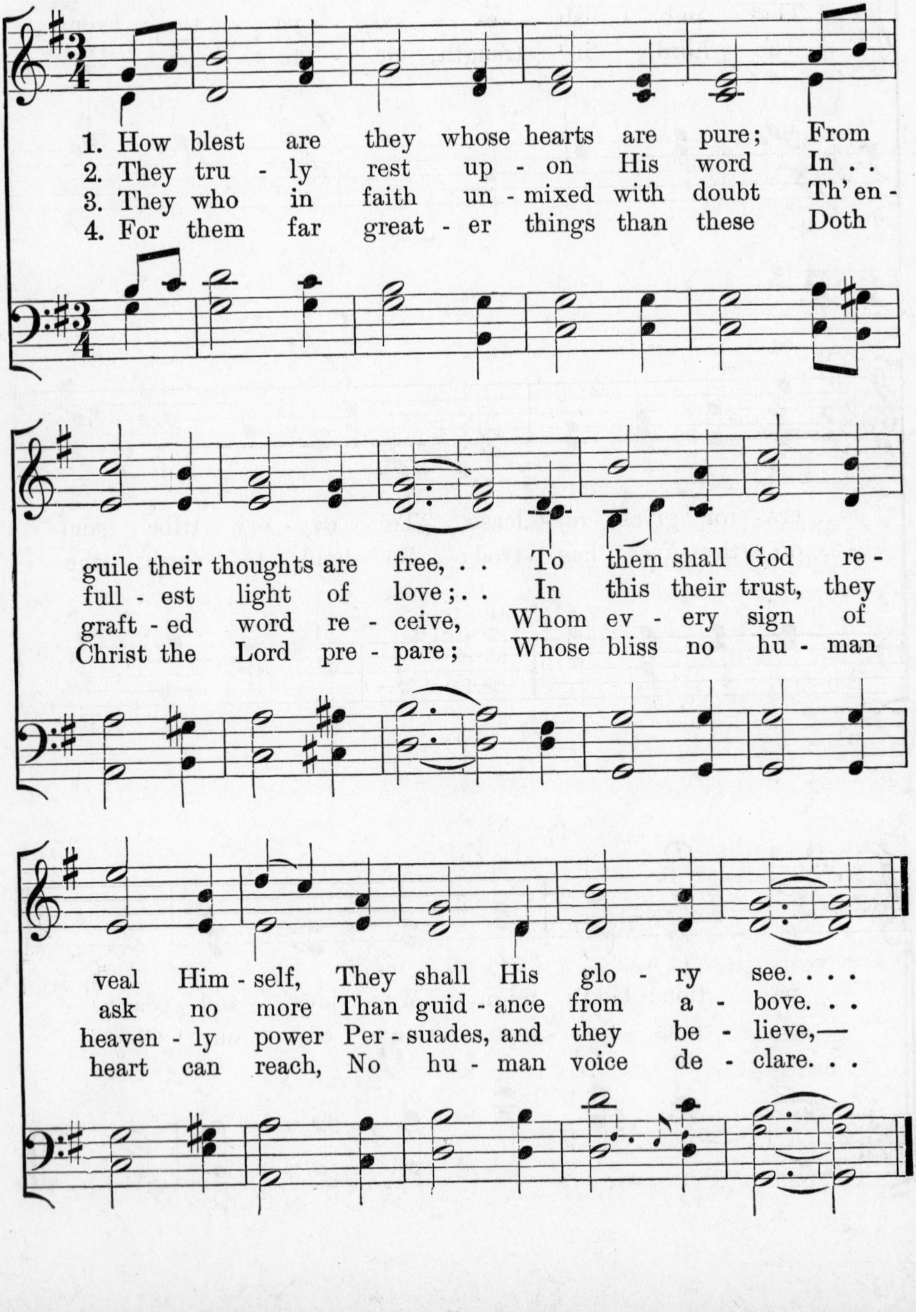

1. How blest are they whose hearts are pure; From guile their thoughts are free, . . To them shall God re - veal Him - self, They shall His glo - ry see. . . .
2. They tru - ly rest up - on His word In . . full - est light of love; . . In this their trust, they ask no more Than guid - ance from a - bove. . .
3. They who in faith un - mixed with doubt Th' en - graft - ed word re - ceive, Whom ev - ery sign of heaven - ly power Per - suades, and they be - lieve,—
4. For them far great - er things than these Doth Christ the Lord pre - pare; Whose bliss no hu - man heart can reach, No hu - man voice de - clare. . .

# 122†

## WINCHESTER OLD C.M.

Este's Psalter, 1592

WILLIAM GOODE*

1. How blest are they whose hearts are pure;
From guile their thoughts are free,
To them shall God reveal Himself,
They shall His glory see.

2. They truly rest upon His word
In fullest light of love;
In this their trust, they ask no more
Than guidance from above.

3. They who in faith unmixed with doubt
Th'engrafted word receive,
Whom every sign of heavenly power
Persuades, and they believe,—

4. For them far greater things than these
Doth Christ the Lord prepare;
Whose bliss no human heart can reach,
No human voice declare.

# 123

**ADESTE FIDELES** 11. 11. 11. 11.

Composer Unknown
Probably 18th Century

"K"
in Rippon's Selection, 1787
Adapted

1. How firm a foun - da - tion, ye saints of the Lord, . . Is laid . . for your faith in His ex - cel - lent Word. What more can He
2. Fear not, I am with thee, O be . . not dis - mayed, . For I . . . am thy God, I will still give thee aid; I'll strength - en thee,
3. When through fi - ery tri - als thy path - way shall lie, . . . My grace, all suf - fi - cient, shall be thy sup - ply; The flame shall not

say . . than to you . . He hath said, . . .
help . thee, and cause . thee to stand, . .
hurt . thee; I on - ly de - sign . . .
Unison
To you who to God for your ref - uge have fled, . .
Up - held by My gra - cious, om - nip - o - tent hand, .
Thy dross to con - sume and thy gold to re - fine, . .
Without pedals
Harmony
To you who to God for your ref - uge have fled:
Up - held by My gra - cious, om - nip - o - tent hand;
Thy dross to con - sume and thy gold to re - fine.
Pedals

**CAMBERWELL** S. M.

European Psalmist, 1872

PHILIP DODDRIDGE
Adapted

1. How gen - tle God's com - mands, How kind His pre - cepts are; Come, cast your bur - dens on the Lord, And trust His con - stant care.
2. Be - neath His watch - ful . . eye His saints se - cure - ly dwell; That hand which bears cre - a - tion up Shall guard His chil - dren well.
3. His good - ness stands ap - proved, Un - changed from day to day: I drop my bur - den at His feet, And bear a song a - way.

*These words have another setting in the* SUPPLEMENT, No. 402

# 125

**ST. PETER** C. M.

ALEXANDER R. REINAGLE

JOHN MILTON
Adapted

1. How love - ly are Thy dwell - ings, Lord, From
2. Lord God of Hosts, that reigns on high, They
3. For God the Lord, both sun and shield, Gives
noise and trou - ble free; How beau - ti - ful the
are the tru - ly blest Who on Thee on - ly
grace and glo - ry bright; No good from him shall
sweet ac - cord Of those who pray to Thee.
will re - ly, In Thee a - lone will rest.
be with - held Whose ways are just and right.

# 126†

BALLERMA C.M.
Spanish Melody
JOSEPH SWAIN
Adapted
1. How sweet, how heaven - ly is the sight, When
2. When, free from en - vy, scorn, and pride, Our
3. Let love, in one de - light - ful stream, Through
4. Love is the gold - en chain that binds The
those who love the Lord In one an - oth - er's
wish - es all a - bove, Each can his broth - er's
ev - ery bos - om flow; And un - ion sweet, and
hearts that faith - ful prove; And he's an heir of
peace de - light, And so ful - fill His word;
fail - ings hide, And show a broth-er's love.
dear es - teem In ev - ery ac - tion glow.
heaven who finds His bos - om glow with love.

*Another version of this music will be found in the* Supplement, No. 403

## 127†

**LIVERPOOL** C. M.

ROBERT WAINWRIGHT
Harmonized by S. S. WESLEY

JOSEPH SWAIN
Adapted

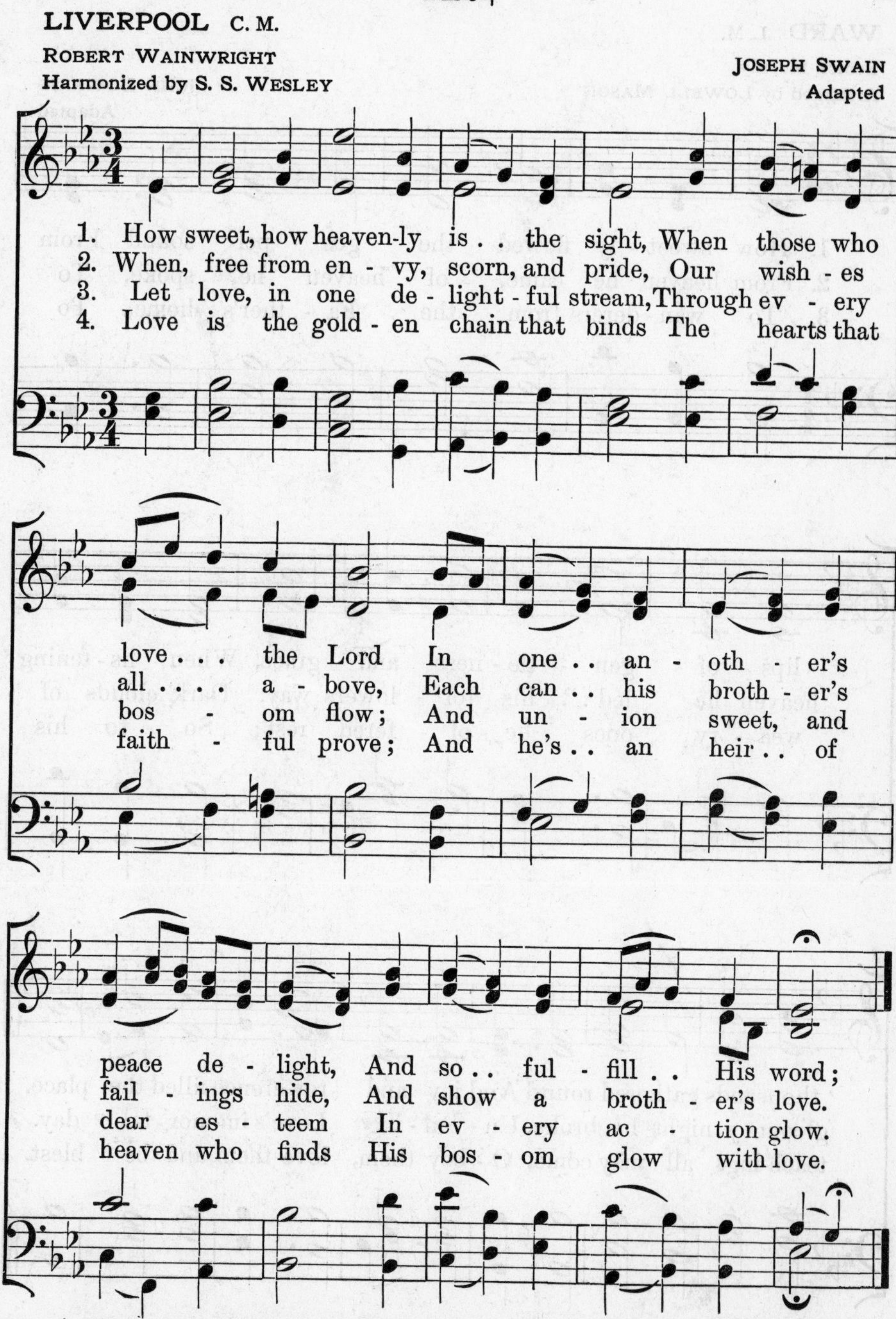

1. How sweet, how heaven-ly is . . the sight, When those who love . . . the Lord In one . . an - oth er's peace de - light, And so . . ful - fill . . His word;
2. When, free from en - vy, scorn, and pride, Our wish - es all . . . . a - bove, Each can . . his broth - er's fail - ings hide, And show a broth - er's love.
3. Let love, in one de - light - ful stream, Through ev - ery bos - om flow; And un - ion sweet, and dear es - teem In ev - ery ac - tion glow.
4. Love is the gold - en chain that binds The hearts that faith - ful prove; And he's . . an heir . . of heaven who finds His bos - om glow with love.

*Another version of this music will be found in the* SUPPLEMENT, No. 403

## WARD L. M.

Scotch Melody
Arranged by LOWELL MASON

JOHN BOWRING
Adapted

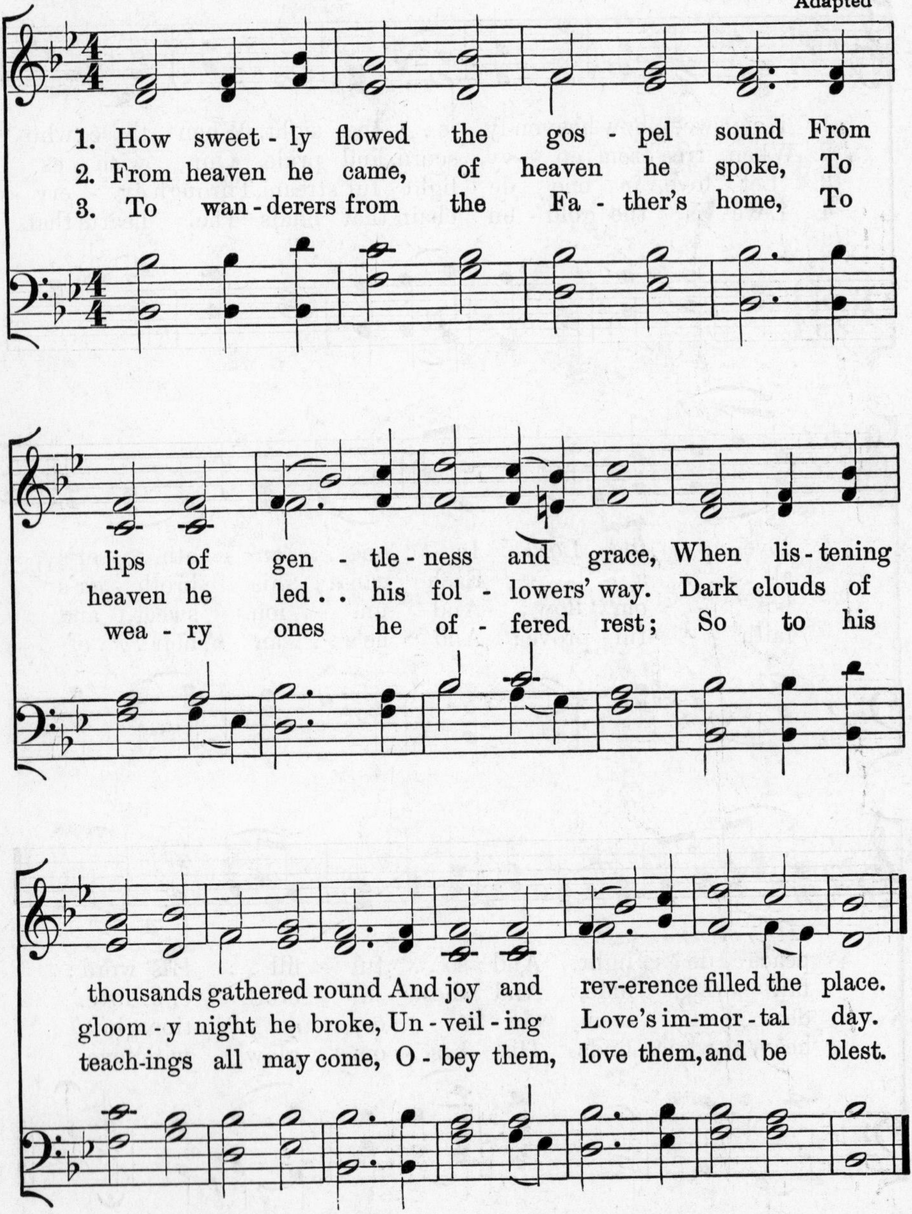

1. How sweet - ly flowed the gos - pel sound From
2. From heaven he came, of heaven he spoke, To
3. To wan - derers from the Fa - ther's home, To

lips of gen - tle - ness and grace, When lis - tening
heaven he led . . his fol - lowers' way. Dark clouds of
wea - ry ones he of - fered rest; So to his

thousands gathered round And joy and rev - erence filled the place.
gloom - y night he broke, Un - veil - ing Love's im - mor - tal day.
teach - ings all may come, O - bey them, love them, and be blest.

ILLSLEY L. M.

JOHN BISHOP

JOHN BOWRING
Adapted

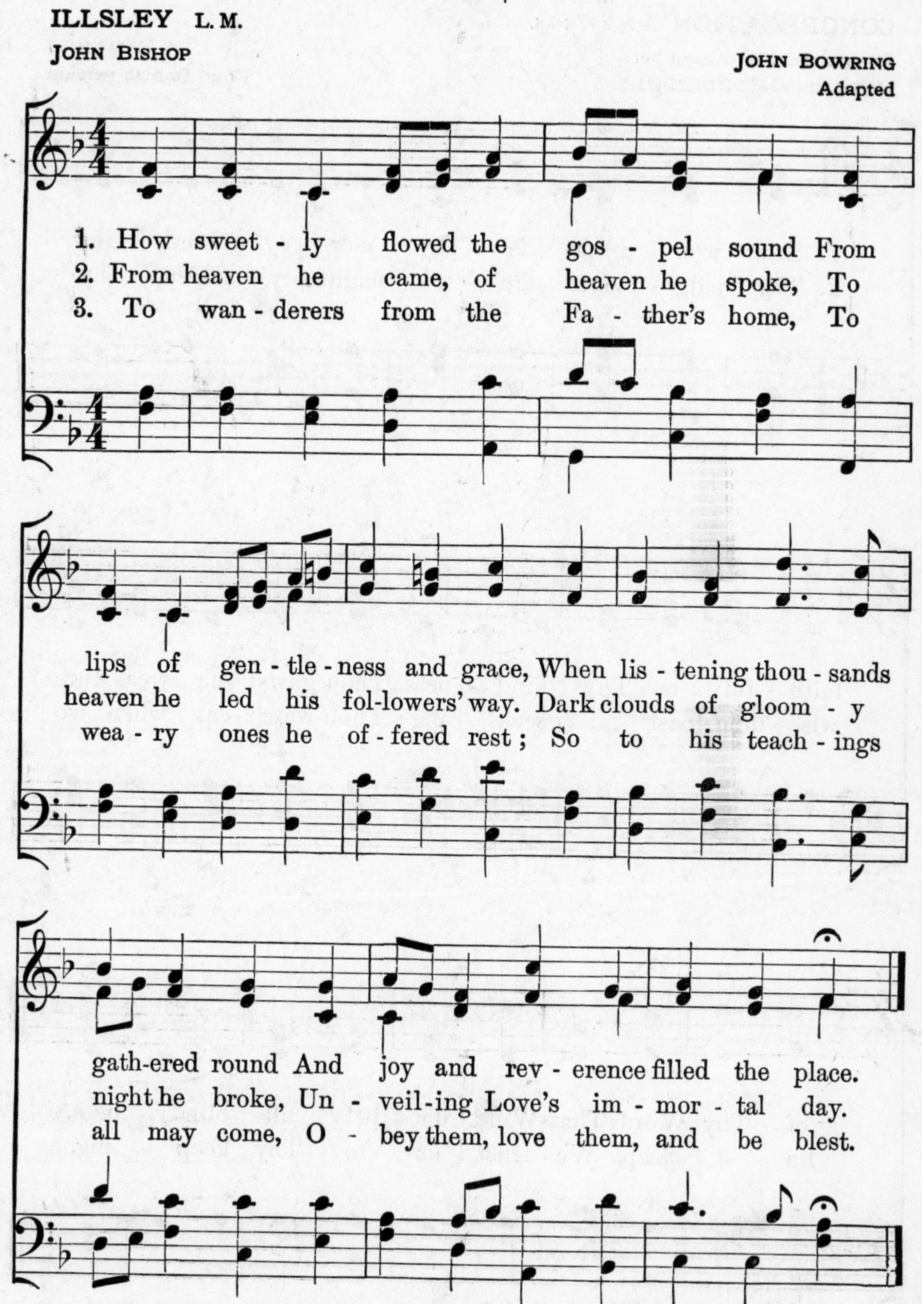
1. How sweet - ly flowed the gos - pel sound From lips of gen - tle - ness and grace, When lis - tening thou - sands gath-ered round And joy and rev - erence filled the place.
2. From heaven he came, of heaven he spoke, To heaven he led his fol-lowers' way. Dark clouds of gloom - y night he broke, Un - veil-ing Love's im - mor - tal day.
3. To wan - derers from the Fa - ther's home, To wea - ry ones he of - fered rest; So to his teach - ings all may come, O - bey them, love them, and be blest.

# 130

**CONGREGATION** 87. 87. 888.

Vi samles for dit Aasyn her

HARNACK O. C. ZINCK (?)

PSALM 36

From Danish version

1. How won - drous is Thy mer - cy, Lord, How
2. Thy judg - ments are a might - y deep, Thy
faith - ful is Thy kind - ness. Thou gav'st the treas - ure
wis - dom past all seek - ing; Thou watch - est when we
of Thy Word; That Word dis - pels all blind - ness.
lie a - sleep, We trust us to Thy keep - ing.

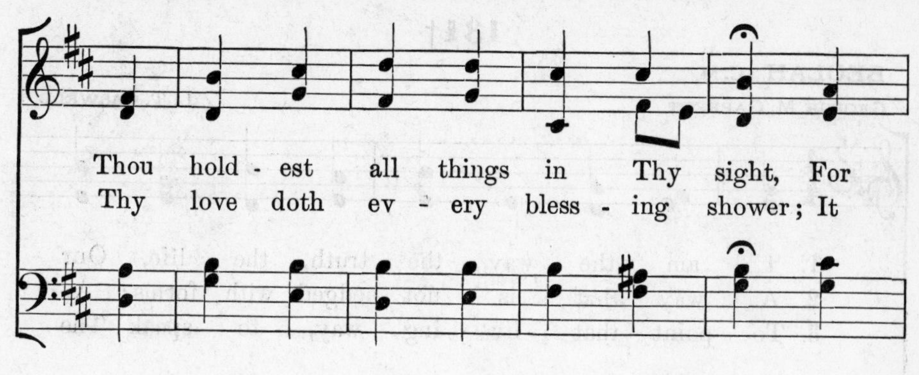
Thou hold - est all things in Thy sight, For
Thy love doth ev - ery bless - ing shower; It

in Thy pres - ence is no night,
rests a - like on man and flower:

And in Thy light shall we see light.
The whole cre - a - tion owns Thy power.

131†

BEULAH C. M.
GEORGE M. GARRETT
L. T. CASWELL
1. I am the way, the truth, the life, Our blessed Master said; And whoso to the Father comes, Must in my pathway tread:
2. A way that is not hedged with forms; A truth, too large for creeds; A life, indwelling, deep and broad, That meets the heart's great needs.
3. To point that living way, to speak The truth that makes men free, To bring that quick-'ning life from heaven, Is highest ministry.

# 132†

**ETHERINGTON** C. M.

H. Walford Davies — L. T. Caswell

*To be sung in unison*

1. I am the way, the truth, the life, Our
2. A way that is not hedged with forms; A
3. To point that liv - ing way, to speak The

bless - ed . . Mas - ter said; And who - so to . . the
truth, too large for creeds; A life, in - dwell - ing,
truth that makes men free, To bring that quick - 'ning

Fa - ther comes, Must in my path - way tread:
deep and broad, That meets the heart's great needs.
life from heaven, Is high - est min - is - try.



Music from A Students' Hymnal (Hymns of the Kingdom)
By permission of the Oxford University Press

# 133

**ABENDS** L. M.

HERBERT S. OAKELEY

JOHN BOWRING*

1. I can-not al - ways trace the way Where Thou, Al - might - y One, dost move; But I can al - ways, al - ways say That God is Love, that God is Love.
2. When mys-tery clouds my dark - ened path, I con - quer dread and doubts re - prove; In this my heart sweet com - fort hath, That God is Love, that God is Love.
3. Yes, God is Love: a thought like this Can ev - ery gloom - y thought re - move, And turn all tears, all woes, to bliss, For God is Love, for God is Love.

Music by permission of Major E. F. OAKELEY

*These words have another setting in the* SUPPLEMENT, No. 424

# 134

**WESSEX** 86. 86. 88.

EDWARD J. HOPKINS — SAMUEL LONGFELLOW*

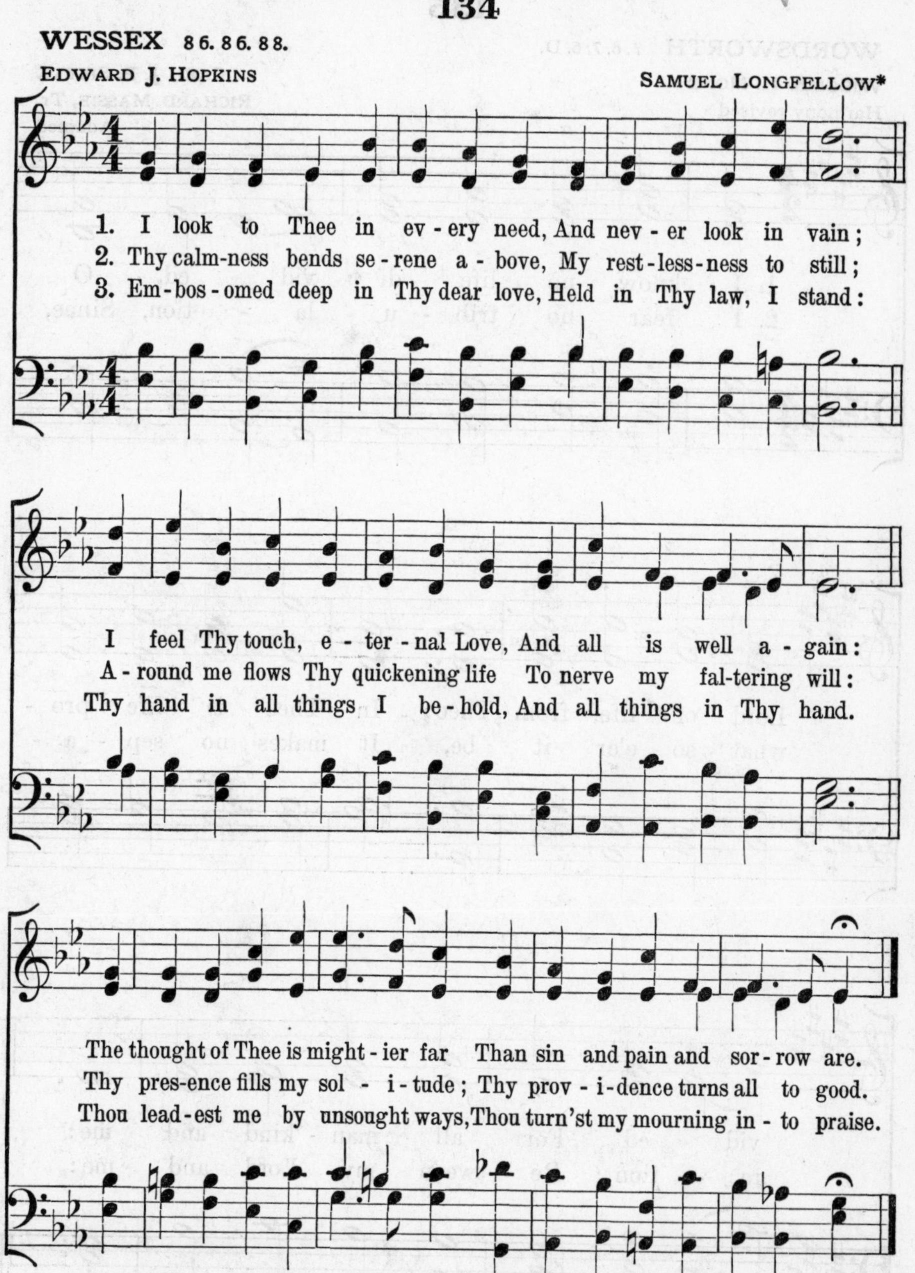
1. I look to Thee in ev - ery need, And nev - er look in vain;
2. Thy calm-ness bends se - rene a - bove, My rest-less-ness to still;
3. Em - bos - omed deep in Thy dear love, Held in Thy law, I stand:
I feel Thy touch, e - ter - nal Love, And all is well a - gain:
A - round me flows Thy quickening life To nerve my fal-tering will:
Thy hand in all things I be - hold, And all things in Thy hand.
The thought of Thee is might - ier far Than sin and pain and sor - row are.
Thy pres-ence fills my sol - i - tude; Thy prov - i - dence turns all to good.
Thou lead - est me by unsought ways, Thou turn'st my mourning in - to praise.

# 135

**WORDSWORTH** 7.6.7.6.D.

WILLIAM H. MONK
Harmony revised

CARL J. P. SPITTA
RICHARD MASSIE, Tr.
Adapted

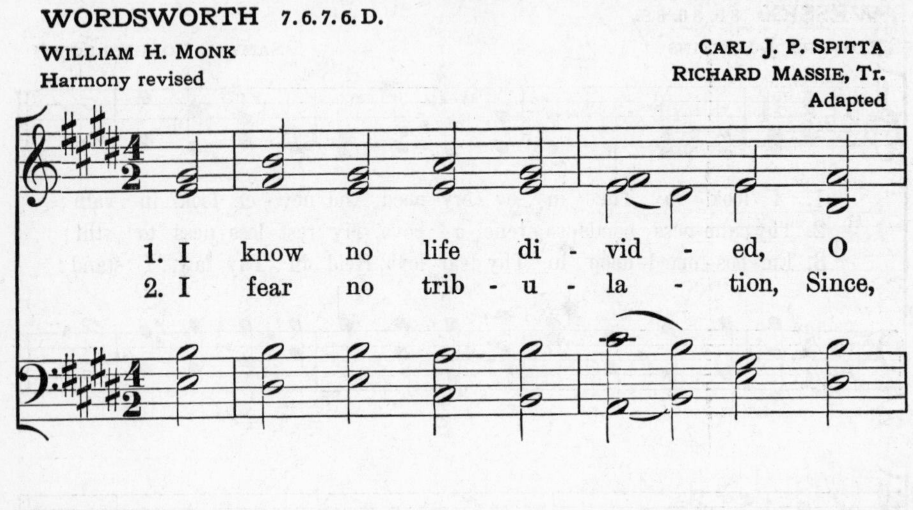
1. I know no life di - vid - ed, O
2. I fear no trib - u - la - tion, Since,

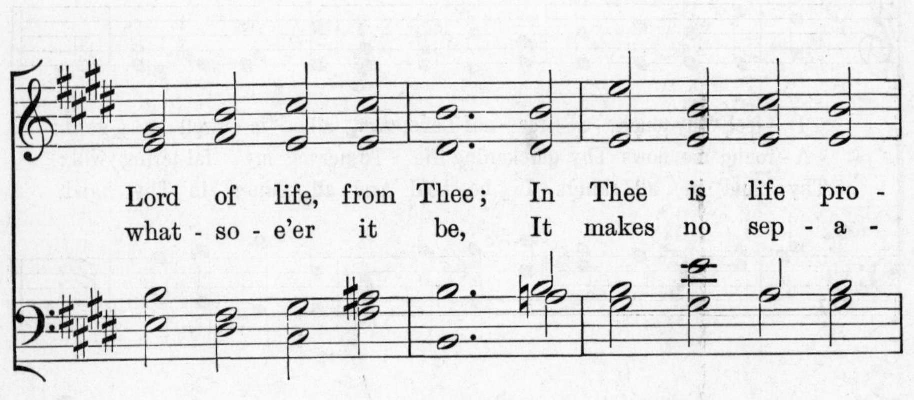
Lord of life, from Thee; In Thee is life pro -
what - so - e'er it be, It makes no sep - a -

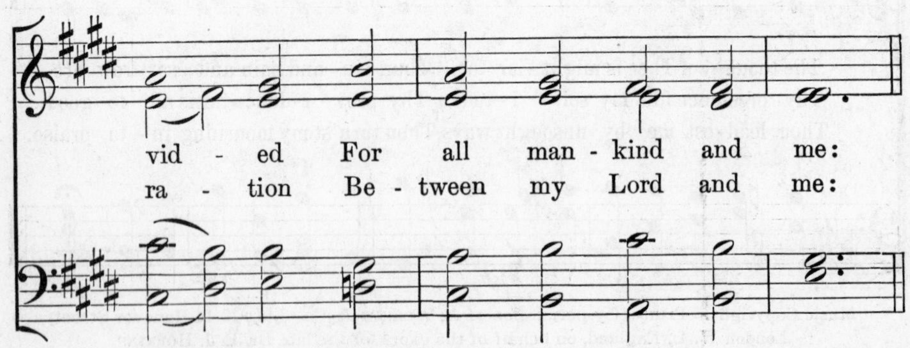
vid - ed For all man - kind and me:
ra - tion Be - tween my Lord and me:

I know no death, O Fa - ther, Be -
Since Thou, my God and Fa - ther, Dost

cause I live in Thee; Thy life it is that
claim me as Thine own, I rich - ly shall in -

frees us From death e - ter - nal - ly.
her - it All good, from Thee a - lone.

# 136

**HEAVENWARD** C. M. D.

Irish Melody
Arranged by H. WALFORD DAVIES
V. H.
To be sung in unison
1. I love Thy way .. of ... free - dom, Lord, To
2. Though storm or dis - cord .. cross my path Thy
3. I climb, with joy, .. the .. heights of Mind, To
serve Thee is .. my .. choice, In Thy clear light of ..
power is still my .. stay, Though hu - man will and
soar o'er time and space; I yet shall know as ..
Truth I rise And, lis - tening for .. Thy voice, I
woe would check My up - ward - soar - ing way; All
I am known And see Thee face to .. face. Till

Music by permission of H. WALFORD DAVIES
Words Copyright, 1931, used by permission of the author

hear Thy prom - ise old and new, That
un - a - fraid I wait, the while Thy
time and space and fear are naught My
Poco rit.
bids all fear to cease: My pres - ence still shall
an - gels bring re - lease, For still Thy pres - ence
quest shall nev - er cease, Thy pres - ence ev - er . .
Poco rit.
go with thee And I will give thee peace.
is with me, And Thou dost give me peace.
goes with me And Thou dost give me peace.

# 137

NEED 6. 4. 6. 4. and Refrain
ROBERT LOWRY
ANNIE S. HAWKS*
1. I need Thee ev - ery hour, Most gra - cious Lord;
2. I need Thee ev - ery hour; Stay Thou near - by;
3. I need Thee every hour; Teach me.. Thy will;
No ten - der voice like Thine Can peace af - ford.
Temp - ta - tions lose their power When Thou art nigh.
And Thy rich prom - ise, Lord, In me.. ful - fill.
REFRAIN
I need Thee, O, I need Thee; Ev - ery hour I need Thee; O
bless me now, my Sav - iour, I come.. to Thee.

# 138

**FESTUS** L. M.

From a German Chorale

SAMUEL JOHNSON
Adapted

1. I praise Thee, Lord, for bless - ings sent To
2. I take Thy hand and fears grow still; Be -
3. That Truth gives prom - ise of a dawn Be -
break the dream of hu - man power; For now, my shal - low
hold Thy face and doubts re - move; Who would not yield his
neath whose light I am to see, When all these blind-ing
cis - tern spent, I find Thy font and thirst no more.
wav - ering will To per - fect Truth and bound-less Love?
veils are drawn, Thy love has al - ways guid - ed me.

# 139

**SURREY** 88. 88. 88.

HENRY CAREY — MINNY M. H. AYERS

1. I walk with Love a - long the way,
2. Who walks with Love a - long the way,
3. Come, walk with Love a - long the way,
And O, it is a ho - ly day;
Shall talk with Love and Love o - bey;
Let child - like trust be yours to - day;
No more I suf - fer cru - el fear,
God's heal - ing truth is free to all,
Up - lift . . your thought, with cour - age go,

*These words have another setting in the* SUPPLEMENT, No. 427

I feel God's pres - ence with .. me here;
Our Fa - ther an - swers ev - ery call;
Give of .. your heart's rich o - ver - flow,
The joy .. that none can take .. a - way
'Tis He .. dis - pels .. the clouds of .. gray
And peace shall crown your joy - filled day.
Is mine; I walk with Love to - day.
That all may walk with Love to - day.
Come, walk with Love a - long the way.

# 140

**ST. OLAVE** L. M.

ROBERT HUDSON
Harmonized by S. S. WESLEY

JOHN KEBLE
Adapted

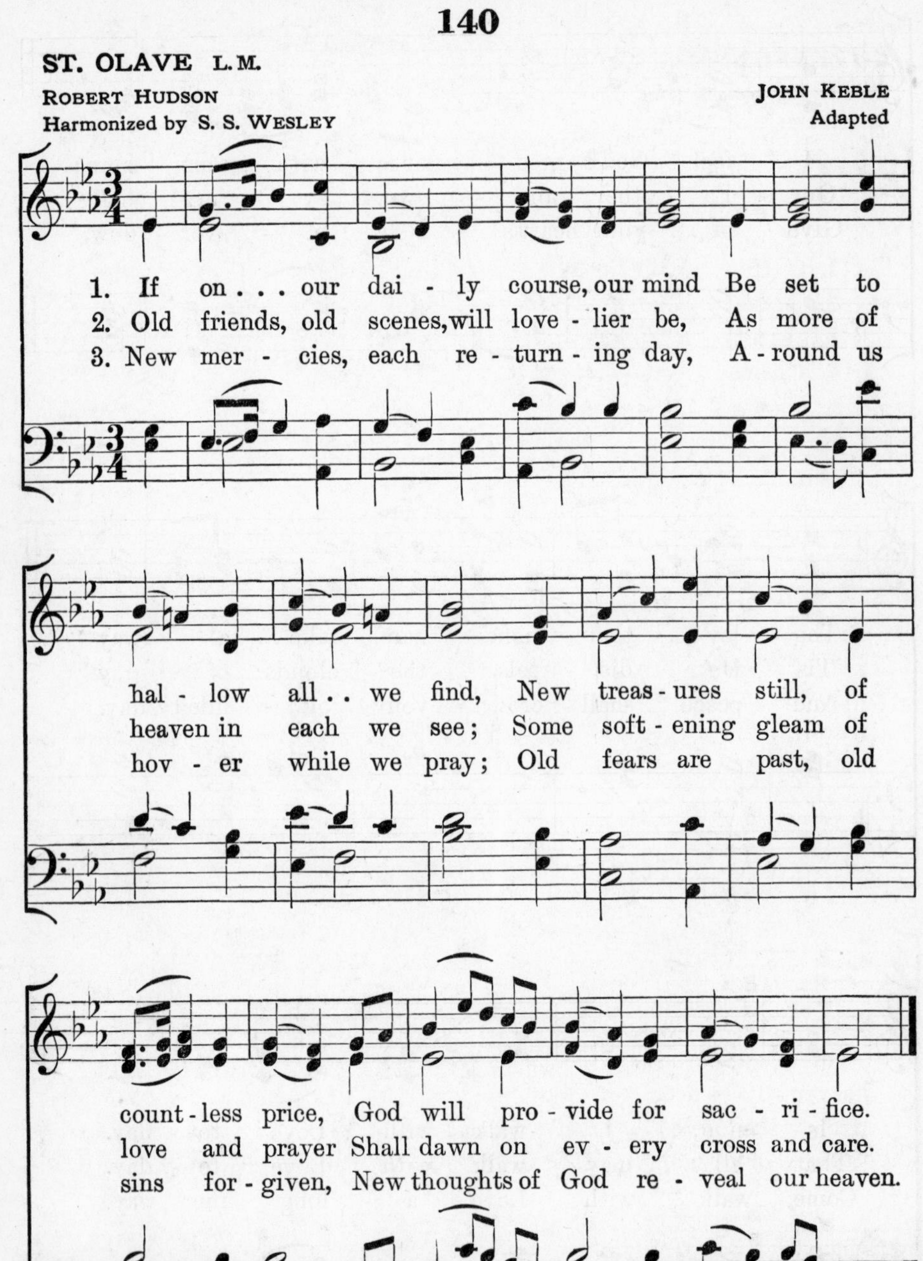

1. If on . . . our dai - ly course, our mind Be set to
2. Old friends, old scenes, will love - lier be, As more of
3. New mer - cies, each re - turn - ing day, A - round us
hal - low all . . we find, New treas - ures still, of
heaven in each we see; Some soft - ening gleam of
hov - er while we pray; Old fears are past, old
count - less price, God will pro - vide for sac - ri - fice.
love and prayer Shall dawn on ev - ery cross and care.
sins for - given, New thoughts of God re - veal our heaven.

CHEERFULNESS 7.7.7.7.

Altid frejdig, naar du gaar

CHRISTOPH E. F. WEYSE

MARIA LOUISE BAUM

1. If the Lord build not the house
2. Make our plant - ing time - ly, true,
3. Fruit - ful shall our till - age be,
4. Cleans - ing men of fear and hate,
They that la - bor build in vain; Fa - ther, may our
Gov - erned by a power be - nign; Nour - ish by a
Known the work of per - fect Mind, Leaves be gath - ered
Lift - ing hope a - bove the sod, Truth will sum - mon,
cor - ner stone Stand four - square, with - out a stain.
heaven - ly dew All.. the.. branch - es and the vine.
from the tree For.. the.. heal - ing of man - kind.
soon or late, All.. the.. earth to wor - ship God.

# 142

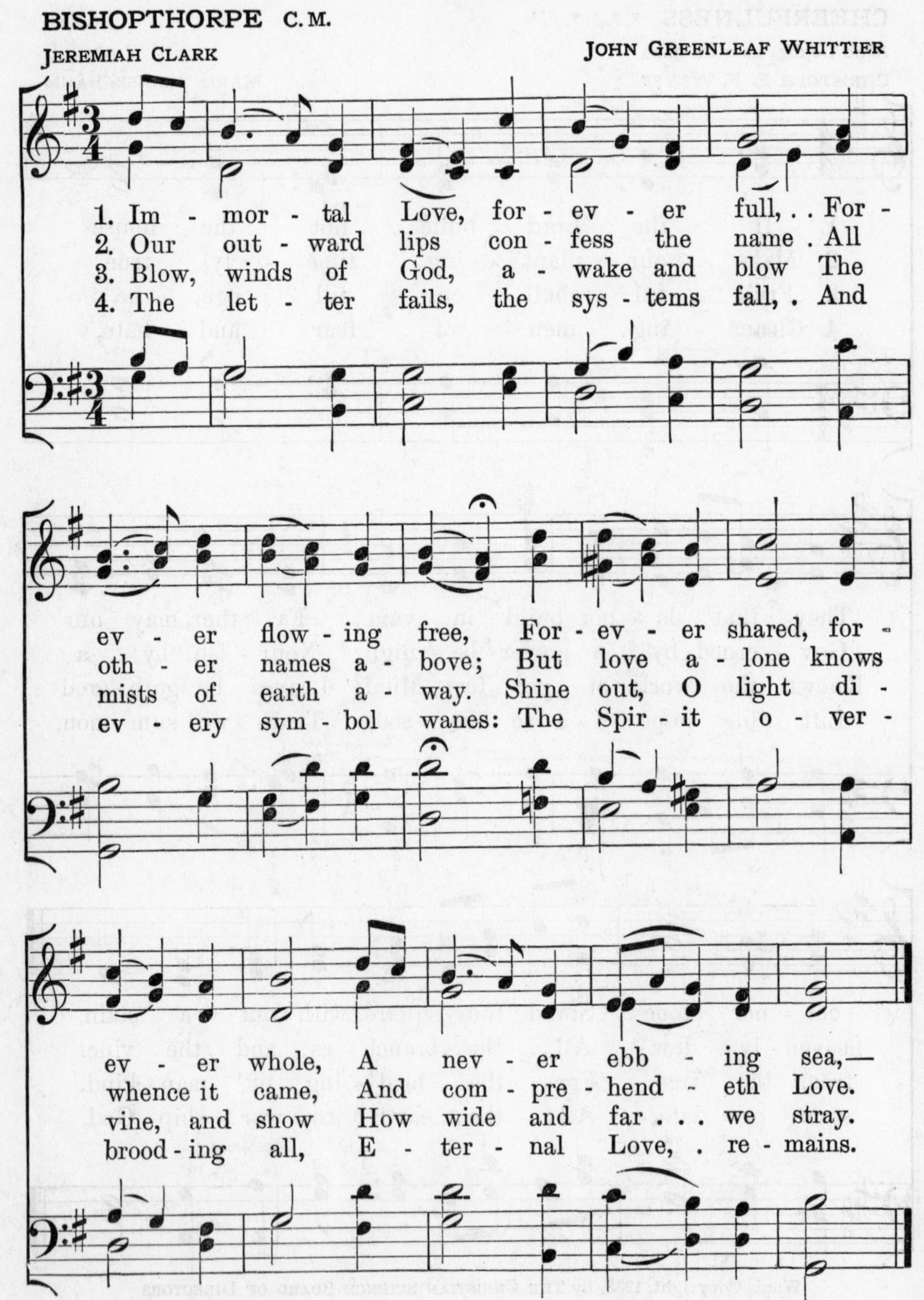
BISHOPTHORPE C. M.
JEREMIAH CLARK
JOHN GREENLEAF WHITTIER
1. Im - mor - tal Love, for - ev - er full, . . For -
2. Our out - ward lips con - fess the name . All
3. Blow, winds of God, a - wake and blow The
4. The let - ter fails, the sys - tems fall, . And
ev - er flow - ing free, For - ev - er shared, for -
oth - er names a - bove; But love a - lone knows
mists of earth a - way. Shine out, O light di -
ev - ery sym - bol wanes: The Spir - it o - ver -
ev - er whole, A nev - er ebb - ing sea,—
whence it came, And com - pre - hend - eth Love.
vine, and show How wide and far . . . we stray.
brood - ing all, E - ter - nal Love, . re - mains.

WINDERMERE S. M

ARTHUR SOMERVELL

THOMAS SCOTT
Adapted

1. Im - pos - ture shrinks from light, And
2. With un - der - stand - ing . . blest, Cre -
3. The truth Thou dost im - part May

dreads the pierc - ing eye; But sa - cred truths the
at - ed to be . . free, Our faith, O God, on
we with firm - ness own, Ab - hor - ring each e -

test in - vite, They bid us search and try.
Thee we rest, O - bey - ing none but Thee.
va - sive art, And lov - ing Thee a - lone.

Music by permission of ARTHUR SOMERVELL

## 144†

MOUNT CALVARY C.M.
ROBERT P. STEWART
H.
Adapted
1. In atmosphere of Love divine, We live, and move, and breathe; Though mortal eyes may see it not, 'Tis sense that would deceive.
2. The mortal sense we must destroy, If we would bring to light The wonders of eternal Mind, Where sense is lost in sight.
3. For God, immortal Principle, Is with us everywhere; He holds us perfect in His love, And we His image bear.

Music by permission of ASSOCIATION FOR PROMOTING CHRISTIAN KNOWLEDGE

# 145†

**IRISH** C. M.

Irish Melody, 1749

H.
Adapted

1. In at - mos - phere of Love di - vine, We live, and move, and breathe; Though mor - tal eyes may see . . . it not, 'Tis sense . . that would de - ceive.
2. The mor - tal sense we must de - stroy, If we would bring to light The won - ders of . . e - ter - nal Mind, Where sense . . is lost . . in sight.
3. For God, im - mor - tal Prin - ci - ple, Is with us ev - ery - where; He holds us per - fect in . . . . His love, And we . . . His im - age bear.

# 146†

**NEWBURY** C. M.

English Traditional Melody — V. K. S.

1. In God I find a pre - cious gift That
2. It bright - ens all the paths of earth, Re -
3. With con - fi - dence it hails each task, With
4. In seam - less grat - i - tude I weave A
knows no fear, no feud, That glows so still, se -
flect - ing Truth and right, For grat - i - tude doth
cour - age un - dis - mayed, For naught a - gainst In -
si - lent, heal - ing prayer, With shin - ing threads of
rene and pure: The gift of grat - i - tude.
stead - fast - ly A - bide in heaven - ly light.
fin - i - ty Can ev - er be ar - rayed.
cease - less joy; For man is God's great heir.

# 147†

**HOLY TRINITY** C. M.

JOSEPH BARNBY — V. K. S.

1. In God I find a pre - cious gift That
2. It bright - ens all the paths of earth, Re -
3. With con - fi - dence it hails each task, With
4. In seam - less grat - i - tude I weave A
knows no fear, no feud, . . That glows so still, se -
flect - ing Truth and right, . For grat - i - tude doth
cour - age un - dis - mayed, . For naught a - gainst In -
si - lent, heal - ing prayer, With shin - ing threads of
rene and pure: The gift of grat - i - tude.
stead - fast - ly A - bide in heaven - ly light.
fin - i - ty Can ev - er be ar - rayed.
cease - less joy; For man is God's great heir.

## 148

**EWING** 7. 6. 7. 6. D.

ALEXANDER EWING | ANNA L. WARING*

1. In heaven - ly Love a - bid - ing, No
2. Wher - ev - er He may guide me, No
3. Green pas - tures are be - fore me, Which
change my heart shall fear; And safe is such con -
want shall turn me back; My Shep - herd is be -
yet I have not seen; Bright skies will soon be
fid - ing, For noth - ing chan - ges here.
side me, And noth - ing can I lack.
o'er me, Where dark - est clouds have been.

The storm may roar with - out me, My
His wis - dom ev - er wak - eth, His
My hope I can - not meas - ure, My
heart may low be laid; But God is round a -
sight is nev - er dim; He knows the way He
path in life is free; My Fa - ther has my
bout me, And can I be dis - mayed?
tak - eth, And I will walk with Him.
treas - ure, And He will walk with me.

# 149

**ST. BARNABAS** 11. 10. 11. 10.

PERCY C. BUCK — S. F. C.

*To be sung in unison*

1. In Love di - vine all earth - born fear and
2. And as on wings of faith we soar and
3. Then in this ra - diant light of ad - o -

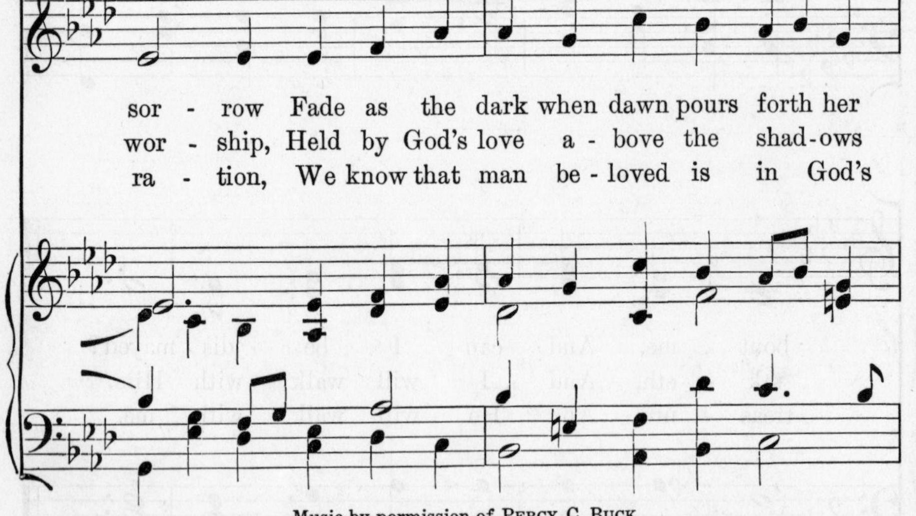
sor - row Fade as the dark when dawn pours forth her
wor - ship, Held by God's love a - bove the shad - ows
ra - tion, We know that man be - loved is in God's

Music by permission of PERCY C. BUCK

*These words have another setting in the* SUPPLEMENT, No. 426

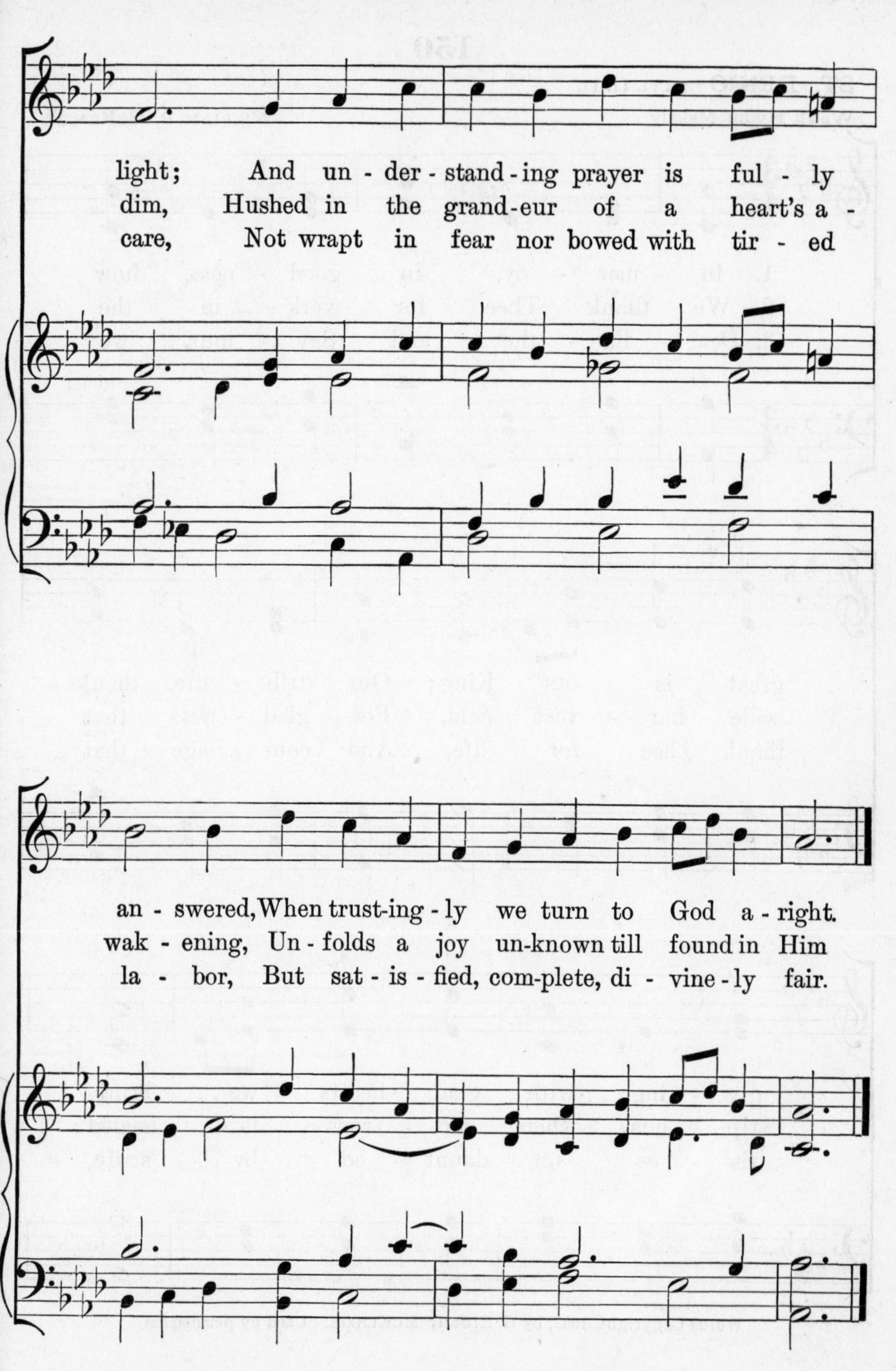
light; And un - der - stand - ing prayer is ful - ly
dim, Hushed in the grand - eur of a heart's a -
care, Not wrapt in fear nor bowed with tir - ed
an - swered, When trust - ing - ly we turn to God a - right.
wak - ening, Un - folds a joy un - known till found in Him
la - bor, But sat - is - fied, com - plete, di - vine - ly fair.

# 150

ST. DENIO 11. 11. 11. 11.
Welsh Hymn Melody
WILLIAM P. McKENZIE
1. In mer - cy, in good - ness, how great is our King; Our trib - ute, thanks - giv - ing, with glad hearts we . . bring.
2. We thank Thee for work in the wide har - vest field, For glad - ness that rip - ens when sor - row is . . . healed;
3. Dear Fa - ther and Sav - iour, we thank Thee for life, And cour - age that ris - es un - daunt - ed by . . strife,

Thou art the Re - new - er, the
Made strong with Thy good - ness that
For con - fi - dent giv - ing and
An - cient of Days, Who giv - est, for
meets ev - ery need, We gath - er the
giv - ing's re - ward, For beau - ty and
mourn - ing, the gar - ment of . . praise.
fruit of the Sow - er's good seed.
love in the life of our Lord.

151†
RUTHERFORD 76. 76. 676.
Arranged from CHRÉTIEN URHAN
E. J. G.
1. In speech - less prayer and rev - erence, Dear
2. To do Thy will is great - er Than
Lord, I come to Thee; My heart with love Thou
sac - ri - fice can be; O give me need - ed
fill - est, Yea, with hu - mil - i - ty.
cour - age Sweet with sin - cer - i - ty.

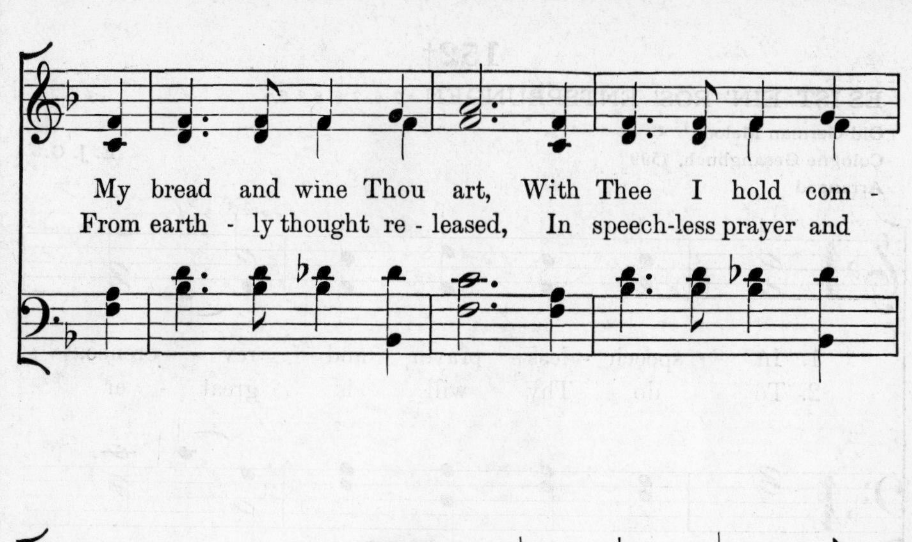

My bread and wine Thou art, With Thee I hold com -
From earth - ly thought re - leased, In speech-less prayer and

mun - ion; Thy pres - ence heal - eth
rev - erence, Dear Lord, I come to

me, Thy pres - ence heal - eth me.
Thee; Dear Lord, I come to Thee.

# 152†

## ES IST EIN' ROS' ENTSPRUNGEN 7 6. 7 6. 6 7 6.

Old German Melody
Cologne Gesangbuch, 1599
Arranged

E. J. G.

1. In speech - less prayer and rev - erence,
2. To do Thy will is great - er
Dear Lord, I come . . . to Thee; My
Than sac - ri - fice . . . . can be; O
heart with love Thou fill - est, Yea, with hu -
give me need - ed cour - age Sweet with sin -

mil - - - - - i - ty. My
cer - - - - - i - ty. From
bread and wine Thou art, . . With Thee I hold com -
earth - ly thought re - leased, . In speech - less prayer and
mun - ion; Thy pres - ence heal - eth me.
rev - erence, Dear Lord, I come to Thee.

153

ST. THEODULPH 76. 76. 86. 76. 76.
MELCHIOR TESCHNER
Arranged by J. S. BACH
LUKE I: 46
MARIA LOUISE BAUM
1. In Thee, my God and Sav - iour, For - ev - er - more the same, My spir - it hath re - joic - ing, For ho - ly is Thy name. My soul doth mag - ni - fy . . the Lord, Sing
2. Thou who a - lone art might - y Hast done to me great things, Re - mem-brance of Thy mer - cy Sure help to Is - rael brings. Thy power, O Lord, will I . . . ex - tol, Who

all in glad ac - cord! Praise Him who lifts the
hast re - deemed my soul; I praise Thee, Lord, with

low - ly, For faith - ful is His word. I
glad - ness, For Thou hast made me whole. I
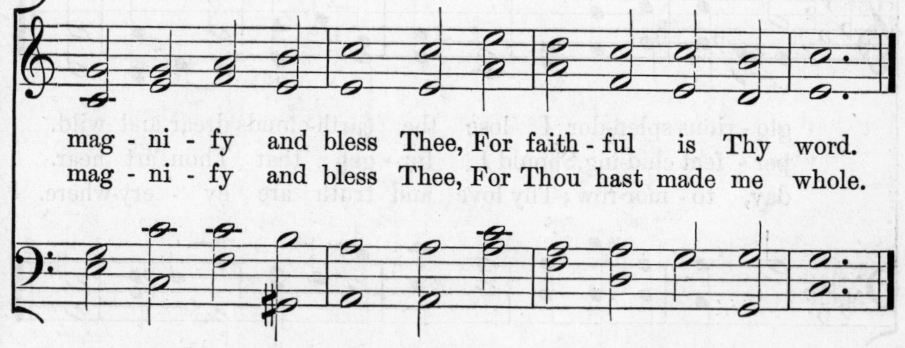
mag - ni - fy and bless Thee, For faith - ful is Thy word.
mag - ni - fy and bless Thee, For Thou hast made me whole.

## 154†

ALMA 9. 8. 9. 8.
LYMAN BRACKETT
FRANCES A. FOX
1. In Thee, O Spir - it true and ten-der, I find my life . . as God's own child; With - in Thy light of glo - rious splen-dor I lose the earth-clouds drear and wild.
2. With - in Thy love is safe a - bid-ing From ev - ery thought that giv - eth fear; With - in Thy truth a per - fect chid-ing, Should I for - get that Thou art near.
3. In Thee I have no pain or sor-row, No anx-ious thought, no load of care. Thou art the same to-day, to - mor-row; Thy love and truth are ev - ery-where.

## 155†

**ST. VINCENT** 9. 8. 9. 8.

From SIGISMUND NEUKOMM
Arranged by J. UGLOW

FRANCES A. FOX

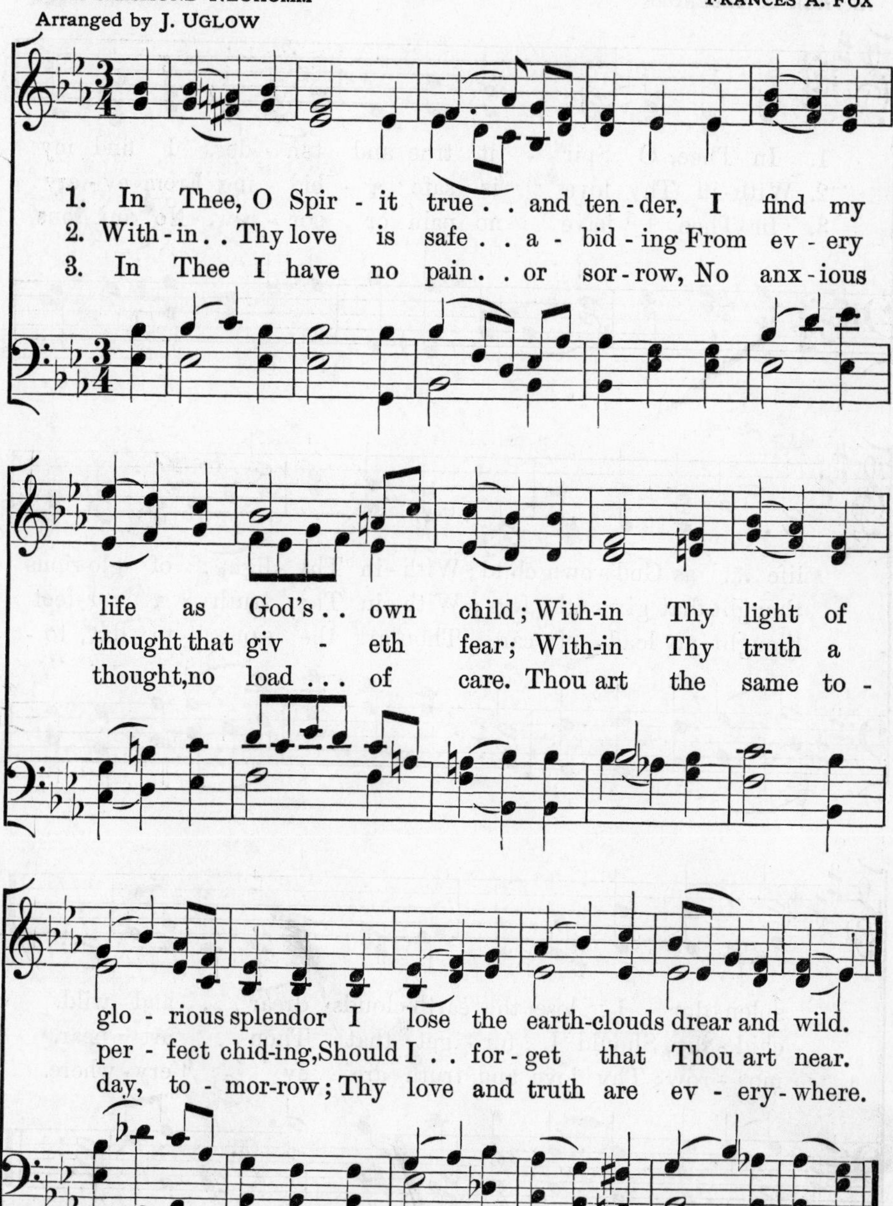
1. In Thee, O Spir - it true . . and ten - der, I find my
2. With - in . . Thy love is safe . . a - bid - ing From ev - ery
3. In Thee I have no pain . . or sor - row, No anx - ious
life as God's . . own child; With - in Thy light of
thought that giv - eth fear; With - in Thy truth a
thought, no load . . . of care. Thou art the same to -
glo - rious splendor I lose the earth-clouds drear and wild.
per - fect chid - ing, Should I . . for - get that Thou art near.
day, to - mor - row; Thy love and truth are ev - ery - where.

## 156†

**EVENSONG** 9. 8. 9. 8.

ARTHUR C. HEBERDEN | FRANCES A. FOX

1. In Thee, O Spir - it true and ten - der, I find my life . . as God's own child; With - in Thy light . . of glo-rious splen - dor I lose the earth-clouds drear . . . and wild.
2. With - in Thy love is safe a - bid - ing From ev - ery thought that giv - eth fear; With - in Thy truth a per - fect chid - ing, Should I for - get that Thou . . . art near.
3. In Thee I have no pain or sor - row, No anx - ious thought, no load of care. Thou art the same . . to - day, to - mor - row; Thy love and truth are ev - ery - where.

Music by permission of MARLBOROUGH COLLEGE

157

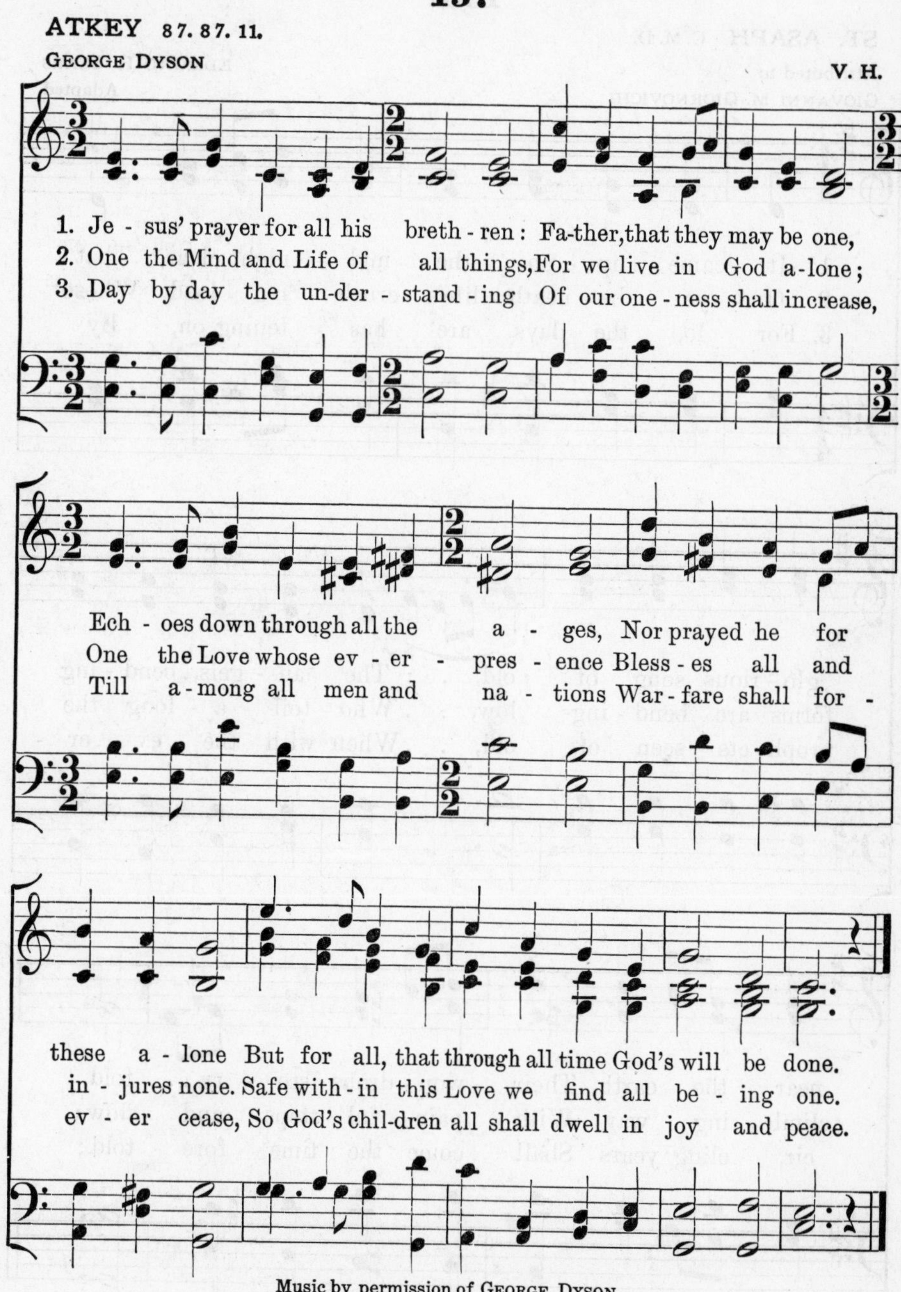
ATKEY 87. 87. 11.
GEORGE DYSON
V. H.
1. Je - sus' prayer for all his breth - ren : Fa-ther, that they may be one,
2. One the Mind and Life of all things, For we live in God a-lone;
3. Day by day the un-der - stand - ing Of our one - ness shall increase,
Ech - oes down through all the a - ges, Nor prayed he for
One the Love whose ev - er - pres - ence Bless - es all and
Till a - mong all men and na - tions War-fare shall for -
these a - lone But for all, that through all time God's will be done.
in - jures none. Safe with - in this Love we find all be - ing one.
ev - er cease, So God's chil-dren all shall dwell in joy and peace.

Music by permission of GEORGE DYSON
Words Copyright, 1931, used by permission of the author

## 158†

**ST. ASAPH** C. M. D.

Attributed to
GIOVANNI M. GIORNOVICHI

EDMUND H. SEARS
Adapted

1. It came up - on the mid - night clear, That glo - rious song of old, . . The an - gels, bend - ing near the earth, Their won - drous sto - ry . . told
2. O ye be - neath life's crush - ing load Whose forms are bend - ing low, . . Who toil a - long the climb - ing way With pain - ful steps and slow;
3. For lo, the days are has - tening on, By proph - ets seen of old, . . When with the ev - er - cir - cling years Shall come the time fore - told;

Of peace on earth, good will to . . . men, From
Look now, for glad and gold - en . . . hours Come
When the new heaven and earth shall own The
heaven's all - gra - cious King; The world in sol - emn
swift - ly on the wing; O rest be - side the
Prince of Peace their King, And all the world send
still - ness lay To hear the an - gels sing.
wea - ry . . road, And hear the an - gels sing.
back the song Which now the an - gels sing.

## 159†

PENTATONE C. M. D.
H. WALFORD DAVIES
EDMUND H. SEARS
Adapted
1. It came up - on the mid - night clear, That glo - rious song of old, The an - gels, bend - ing near the earth, Their won - drous sto - ry told Of
2. O ye be - neath life's crush - ing load Whose forms are bend - ing low, Who toil a - long the climb - ing way With pain - ful steps and slow; Look
3. For lo, the days are has - tening on, By proph - ets seen of old, When with the ev - er - cir - cling years Shall come the time fore - told; When

Music from A STUDENTS' HYMNAL (HYMNS OF THE KINGDOM)
By permission of the OXFORD UNIVERSITY PRESS

peace on .. earth, good will to men, From
now, for .. glad and gold - en hours Come
the new heaven and earth shall own The

heaven's all - gra - cious King; The world in sol - emn
swift - ly .. on the wing; O .. rest be - side the
Prince of . Peace their King, And all the world send

still - ness lay To hear the an - gels sing.
wea - ry road, And hear the an - gels sing.
back the song Which now the an - gels sing.

**GLOAMING** 8. 4. 8. 4. D.

JOHN STAINER

**SATISFIED**

MARY BAKER EDDY

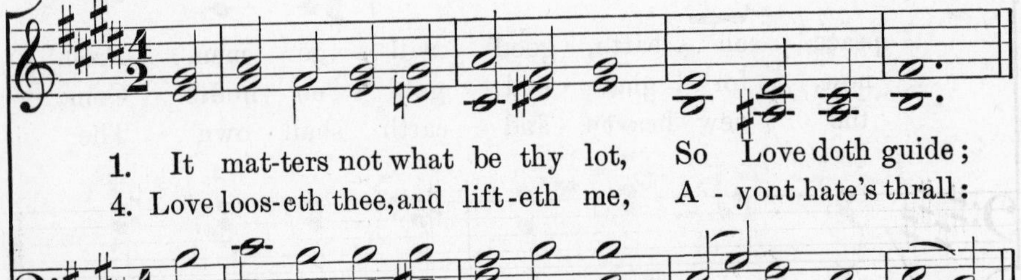
1. It mat-ters not what be thy lot, So Love doth guide;
4. Love loos-eth thee, and lift-eth me, A - yont hate's thrall:

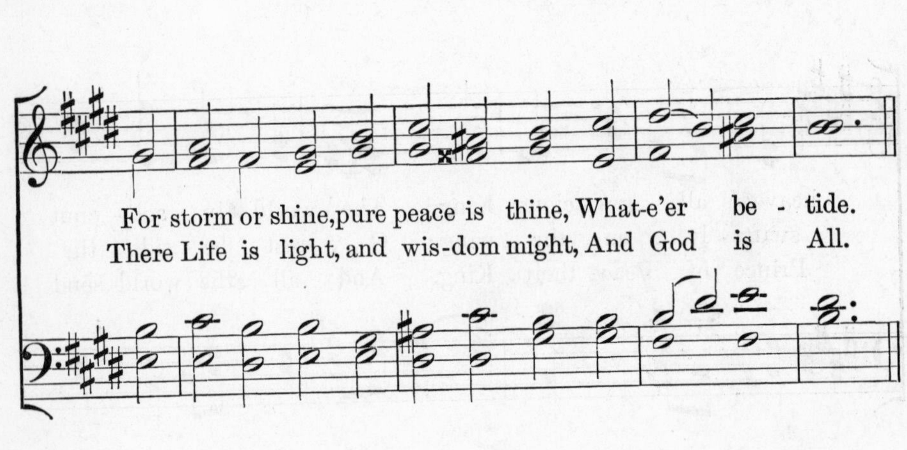
For storm or shine, pure peace is thine, What-e'er be - tide.
There Life is light, and wis-dom might, And God is All.

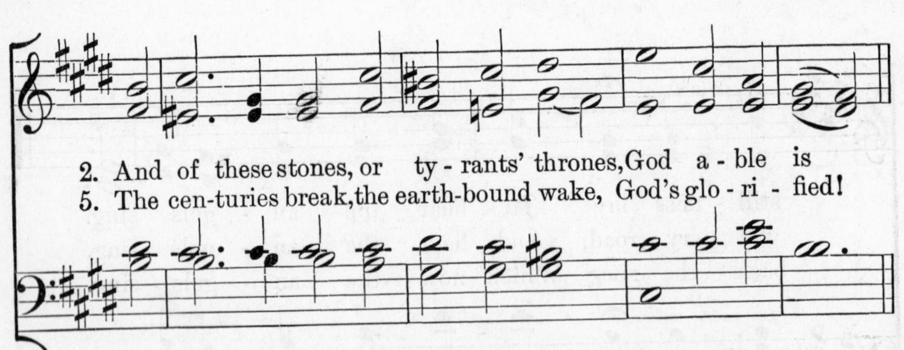
2. And of these stones, or ty - rants' thrones, God a - ble is
5. The cen-turies break, the earth-bound wake, God's glo - ri - fied!

Fine
To raise up seed—in thought and deed—To faith - ful His.
Who doth His will—His like - ness still—Is sat - is - fied.
3. Aye, dark-ling sense, a - rise, go hence! Our God is good.
D.C.
False fears are foes—truth tat-ters those, When un - der - stood.

## 161†

**FORTITUDE** 8. 4. 8. 4. — **SATISFIED**

WALTER E. YOUNG — MARY BAKER EDDY

1. It mat - ters not what be thy lot, So
2. And of these stones, or ty - rants' thrones, God
3. Aye, dark - ling sense, a - rise, go hence! Our
4. Love loos - eth thee, and lift - eth me, A -
5. The cen - turies break, the earth - bound wake, God's
Love doth . . guide; For storm or shine, pure
a - ble . . . is To raise up seed— in
God is . . . good. False fears are foes— truth
yont hate's thrall: There Life is light, and
glo - ri - fied! Who doth His will— His
peace is . . thine, What - e'er be - tide.
thought and deed— To faith - ful His.
tat - ters those, When un - der - stood.
wis - dom might, And God is All.
like - ness still— Is sat - is - fied.

# 162†

**SATIS** 8. 4. 8. 4. — **SATISFIED**

PERCY WHITLOCK — MARY BAKER EDDY

1. It mat - ters not what be thy lot, So Love doth guide; For storm or shine, pure peace is thine, What - e'er . . . be - tide.
2. And of these stones, or ty - rants' thrones, God a - ble . . is To raise up seed — in thought and deed — To faith - - ful His.
3. Aye, dark - ling sense, a - rise, go hence! Our God is . . good. False fears are foes — truth tat - ters those, When un - - der - stood.
4. Love loos - eth thee, and lift - eth me, A - yont hate's thrall: There Life is light, and wis - dom might, And God . . . is All.
5. The cen - turies break, the earth-bound wake, God's glo - ri - - fied! Who doth His will — His like - ness still — Is sat - - is - fied.

# 163

**WARRINGTON** L. M.

RALPH HARRISON

MARY A. LIVERMORE
Adapted

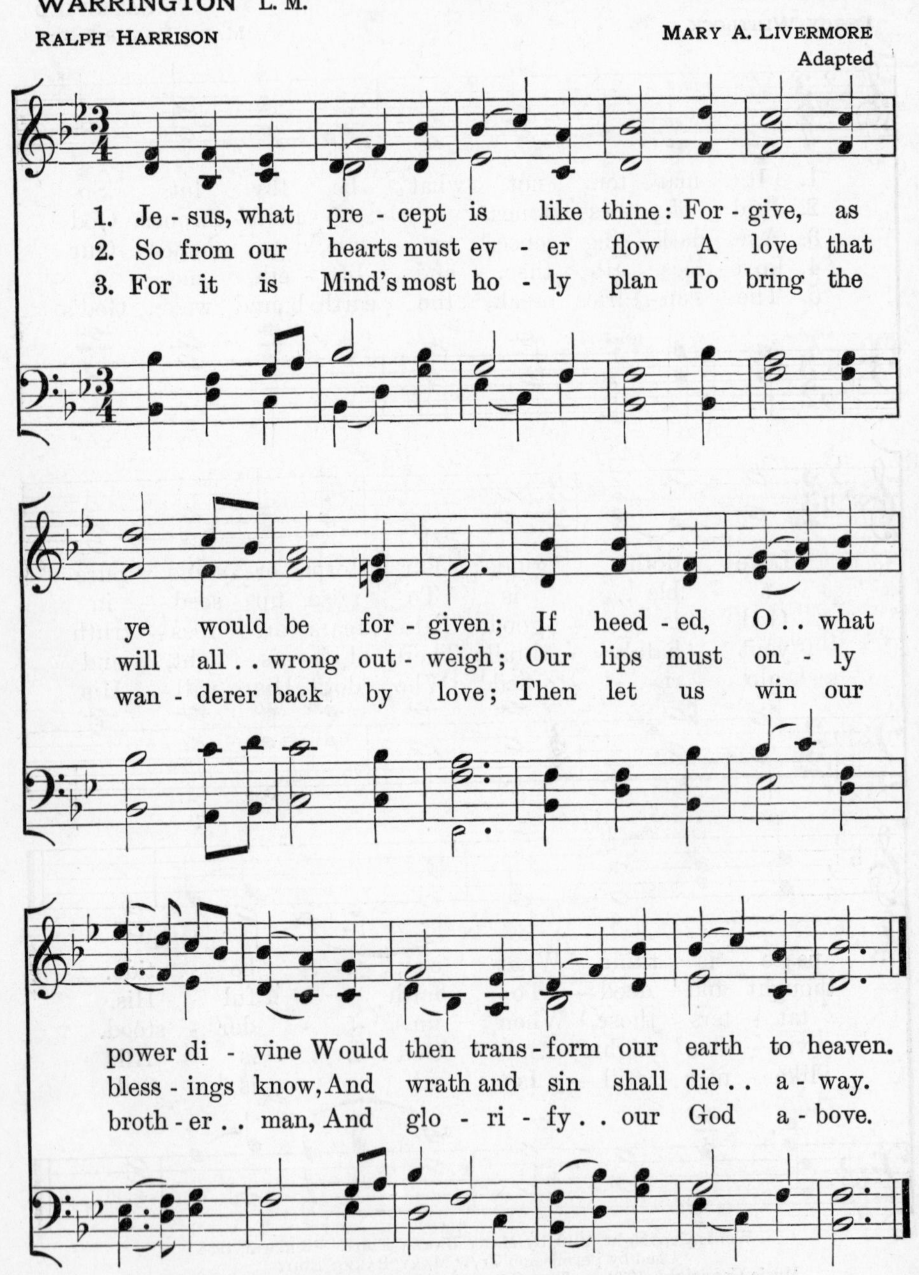
1. Je - sus, what pre - cept is like thine: For - give, as
2. So from our hearts must ev - er flow A love that
3. For it is Mind's most ho - ly plan To bring the
ye would be for - given; If heed - ed, O . . what
will all . . wrong out - weigh; Our lips must on - ly
wan - derer back by love; Then let us win our
power di - vine Would then trans - form our earth to heaven.
bless - ings know, And wrath and sin shall die . . a - way.
broth - er . . man, And glo - ri - fy . . our God a - bove.

Words used by arrangement with the UNIVERSALIST PUBLISHING HOUSE

# 164†

**NATIVITY** C. M.

HENRY LAHEE

ISAAC WATTS
Adapted

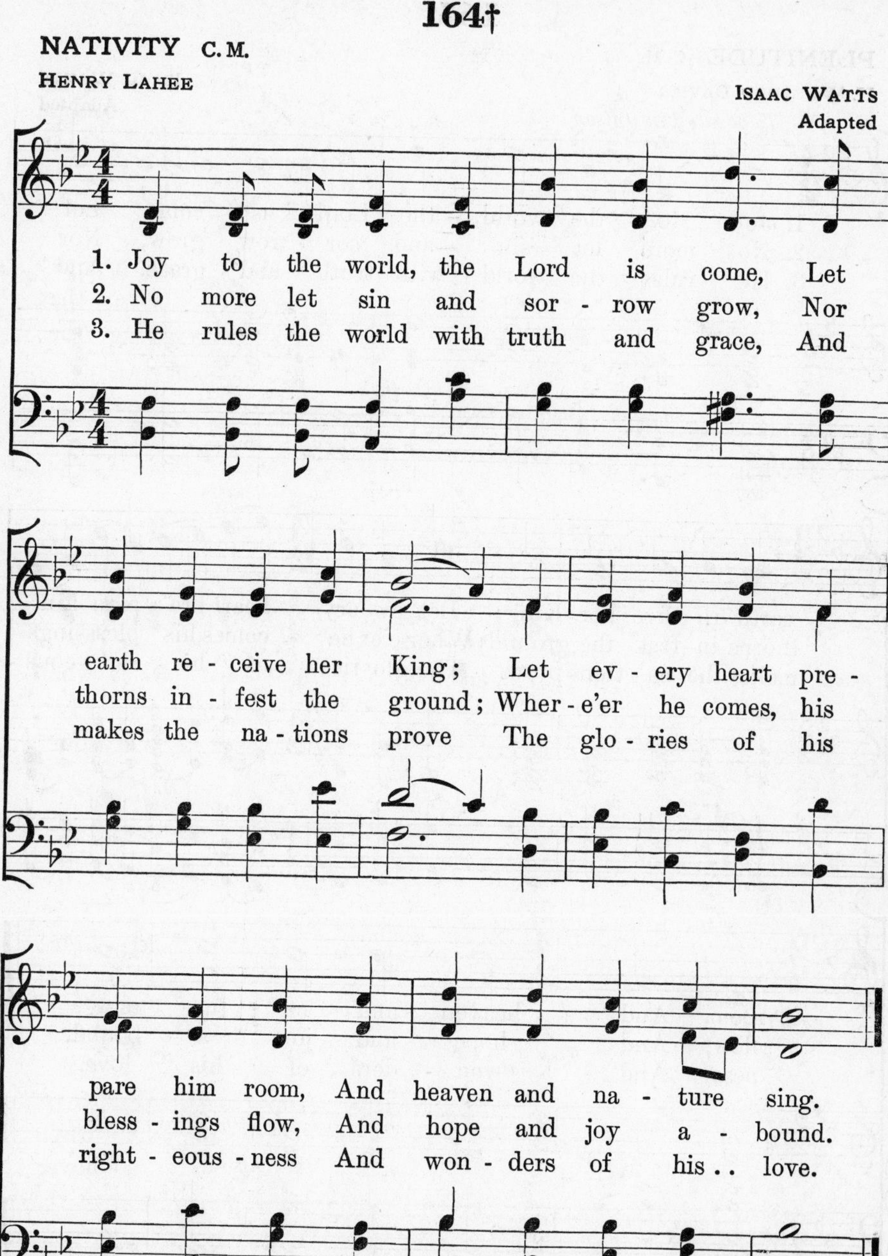

1. Joy to the world, the Lord is come, Let earth re - ceive her King; Let ev - ery heart pre - pare him room, And heaven and na - ture sing.
2. No more let sin and sor - row grow, Nor thorns in - fest the ground; Wher - e'er he comes, his bless - ings flow, And hope and joy a - bound.
3. He rules the world with truth and grace, And makes the na - tions prove The glo - ries of his right - eous - ness And won - ders of his . . love.

Music by permission of the Misses HORDER

*These words have another setting in the* SUPPLEMENT, No. 417

# 165†

PLENITUDE C. M.
H. WALFORD DAVIES
ISAAC WATTS
Adapted
To be sung in unison
1. Joy to the world, the Lord is come, Let earth re-ceive her King; Let ev-ery heart pre-pare him room, And heaven and na - ture sing.
2. No more let sin and sor - row grow, Nor thorns in-fest the ground; Wher-e'er he comes, his bless-ings flow, And hope and joy a - bound.
3. He rules the world with truth and grace, And makes the na - tions prove The glo-ries of his right-eous - ness And won - ders of his love.

Music from A STUDENTS' HYMNAL (HYMNS OF THE KINGDOM)
By permission of the OXFORD UNIVERSITY PRESS

*These words have another setting in the* SUPPLEMENT, No. 417

# 166†

**GOTT DES HIMMELS** 8. 7. 8. 7.

HEINRICH ALBERT — HENRY FRANCIS LYTE

Simpler Version — Adapted

1. Know, O child, thy full sal - va - tion;
2. Think what spir - it dwells with - in thee;
3. Haste thee on . . from grace to glo - ry,
4. So ful - fill . . thy ho - ly mis - sion,
Rise o'er sin and fear and care; Joy to find, in
Think what Fa - ther's smiles are thine; Think what Je - sus
Armed with faith and winged with prayer; Heaven's e - ter - nal
Swift shall pass thy pil - grim days, Hope shall change to
ev - ery sta - tion, Some - thing still to do, or bear.
did to . . win thee; Child of heaven, can'st thou re - pine?
day be - fore thee, God's own hand shall guide thee there.
glad fru - i - tion, Faith to sight and prayer to praise.

# 167†

**GOTT DES HIMMELS** 8.7.8.7.

HEINRICH ALBERT
Harmonized by J. S. BACH

HENRY FRANCIS LYTE
Adapted

*With breadth*

1. Know, O child, thy full sal - va - tion; Rise o'er sin and fear and care; Joy to find, in ev - ery sta - tion, Some-thing still to do, or bear.
2. Think what spir - it dwells with - in thee; Think what Fa-ther's smiles are thine; Think what Je - sus did to . . win thee; Child of heaven, can'st thou re - pine?
3. Haste thee on . . from grace to . . glo - ry, Armed with faith and winged with prayer; Heaven's e - ter - nal day be - fore thee, God's own hand shall guide thee there.
4. So ful - fill . . thy ho - ly . . mis - sion, Swift shall pass thy pil - grim-days, Hope shall change to glad fru - i - tion, Faith to sight and prayer to praise.

# 168

**VOM HIMMEL HOCH** L. M.

GEISTLICHE LIEDER, Leipzig, 1539
Harmony from J. S. BACH

10th Century
RICHARD MANT, Tr.
Adapted

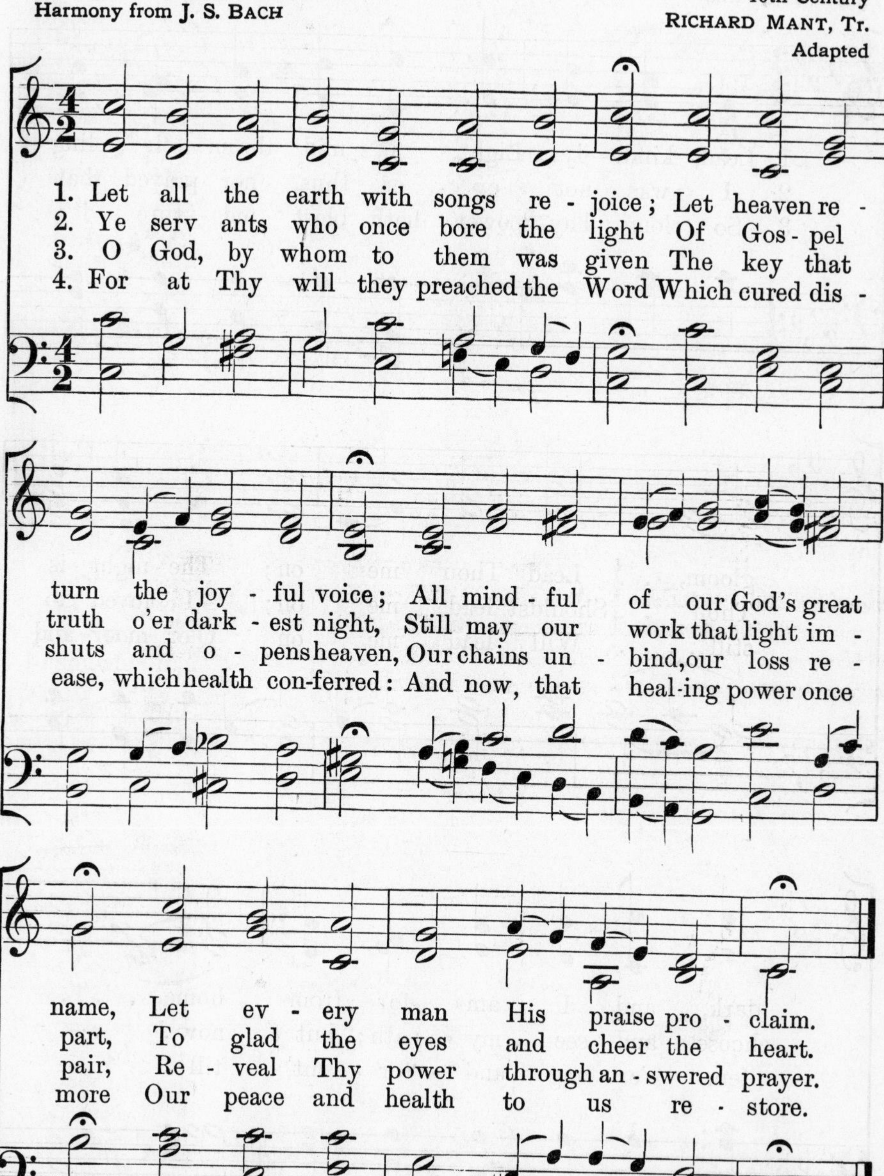
1. Let all the earth with songs re - joice; Let heaven re - turn the joy - ful voice; All mind - ful of our God's great name, Let ev - ery man His praise pro - claim.
2. Ye serv ants who once bore the light Of Gos - pel truth o'er dark - est night, Still may our work that light im - part, To glad the eyes and cheer the heart.
3. O God, by whom to them was given The key that shuts and o - pens heaven, Our chains un - bind, our loss re - pair, Re - veal Thy power through an - swered prayer.
4. For at Thy will they preached the Word Which cured dis - ease, which health con-ferred: And now, that heal-ing power once more Our peace and health to us re - store.

LUX BENIGNA 10 4. 10 4. 10 10.

JOHN B. DYKES

JOHN HENRY NEWMAN

1. Lead, kind - ly Light, a - mid the en - cir - cling
2. I was not ev - er thus, nor prayed that
3. So long Thy power hath blest me, sure it
gloom, . . Lead Thou me on; The night is
Thou . . . Shouldst lead me on; I loved to
still . . . Will lead me on O'er moor and
dark, and I am far from home, . . .
choose and see my path; but now . . .
fen, o'er crag and tor - rent, till . . .

Lead Thou me on. . Keep Thou my feet; I
Lead Thou me on. . I loved the gar - ish
The night is gone,. And with the morn those

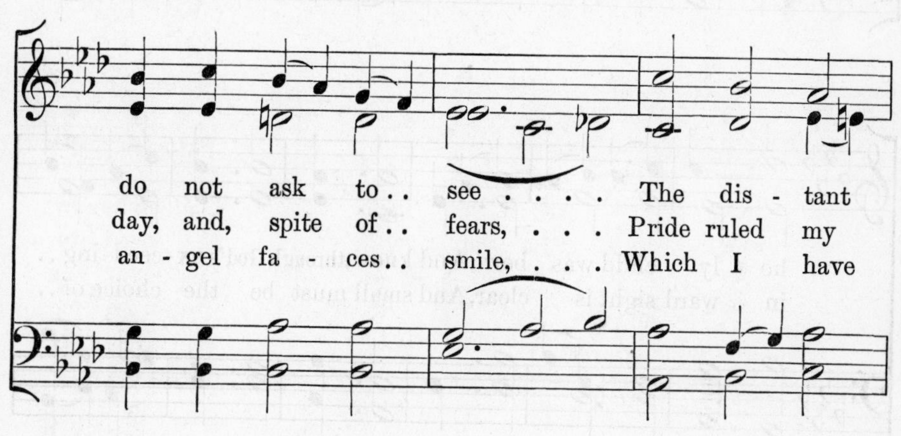
do not ask to . . see . . . The dis - tant
day, and, spite of . . fears, . . . Pride ruled my
an - gel fa - ces . . smile, . . Which I have

scene; one step e - nough . . for me. . .
will: re - mem - ber not . . . past years. .
loved long since, and lost . . . a - while. .

# 170

**CREATION** L. M. D.

FRANZ JOSEPH HAYDN

JOHN GREENLEAF WHITTIER
Adapted

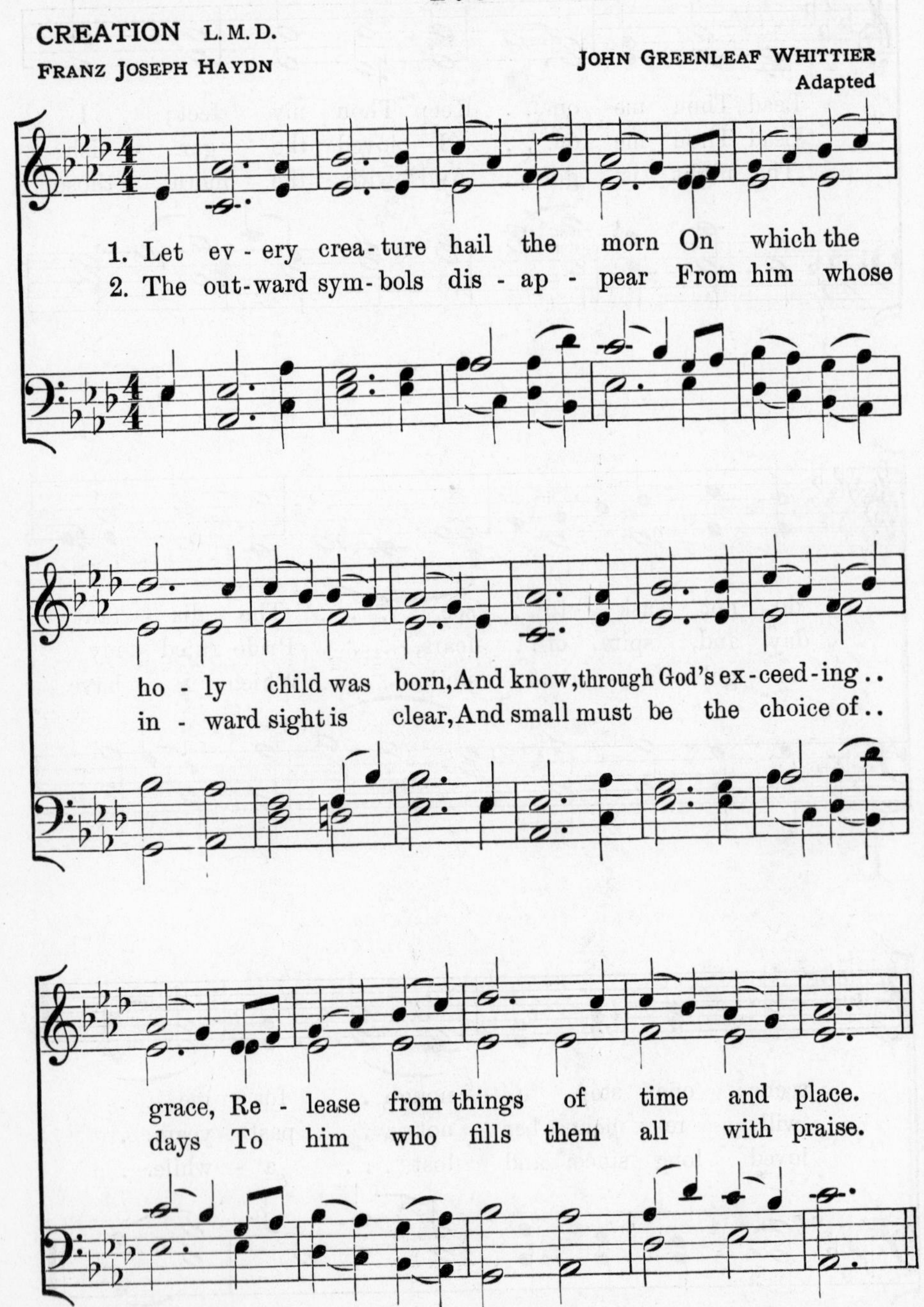
1. Let ev - ery crea - ture hail the morn On which the
2. The out - ward sym - bols dis - ap - pear From him whose
ho - ly child was born, And know, through God's ex - ceed - ing ..
in - ward sight is clear, And small must be the choice of ..
grace, Re - lease from things of time and place.
days To him who fills them all with praise.

I lis - ten, from no mor - tal tongue, To hear the
Keep while ye need it, broth - ers mine, With hon - est
song the an - gels sung, And wait with - in . . my -
zeal your Christ-mas sign, But judge not him who
self to know The Christ-mas lil - ies bud and blow.
ev - ery morn Feels in . . his heart the Lord Christ born.

# 171

**ALLELUIA** 8.7.8.7.D.

SAMUEL S. WESLEY F. T. H.

1. Let us sing of Eas - ter glad - ness
2. When we touch Truth's heal - ing gar - ment
3. Liv - ing meek - ly as the Mas - ter,
That re - joi - ces ev - ery day, Sing of hope and
And be - hold Life's pu - ri - ty, When we find in
Who of God was glo - ri - fied, Look - ing ev - er
faith up - lift - ed; Love has rolled the stone a - way.
Love the ref - uge That is man's se - cu - ri - ty,
to the ra - diance Of his won - drous Eas - ter - tide;

*These words have another setting in the* SUPPLEMENT, No. 413

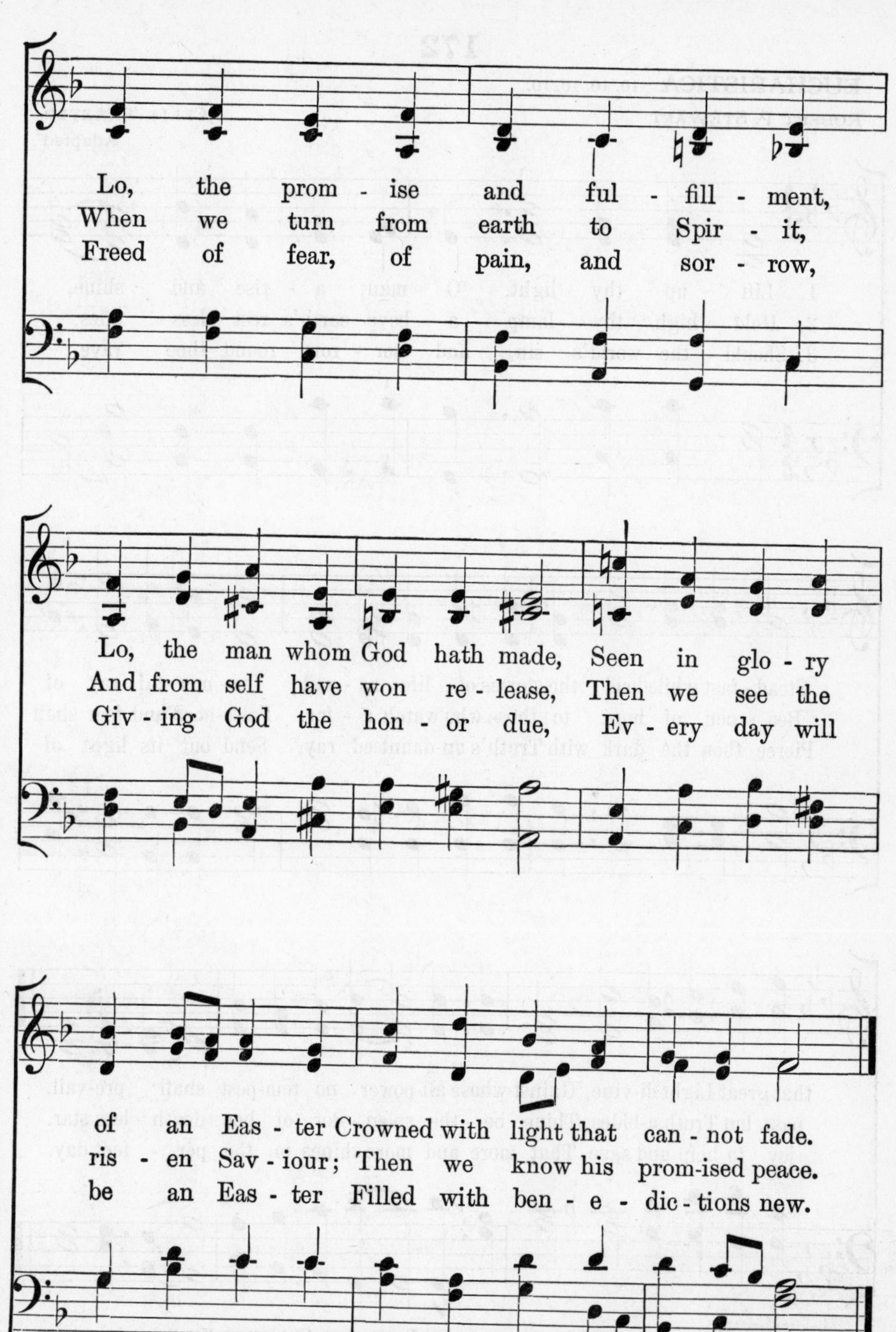
Lo, the prom - ise and ful - fill - ment,
When we turn from earth to Spir - it,
Freed of fear, of pain, and sor - row,
Lo, the man whom God hath made, Seen in glo - ry
And from self have won re - lease, Then we see the
Giv - ing God the hon - or due, Ev - ery day will
of an Eas - ter Crowned with light that can - not fade.
ris - en Sav - iour; Then we know his prom - ised peace.
be an Eas - ter Filled with ben - e - dic - tions new.

# 172

**EUCHARISTICA** 10. 10. 10. 10.

ROBERT P. STEWART — CELIA THAXTER, Adapted

1. Lift up thy light, O man, a - rise and shine,
2. Hold high thy lamp a - bove earth's rest - less tides,
3. Should the world's sin and sor - row round thee rave,

Stead - fast while loud the storms of life as - sail; Im - mor - tal ray of
Bea - con of hope to those who watch a - far. False-hood and fear shall
Pierce thou the dark with Truth's un - daunt - ed ray, Send out its light of

that great Light di - vine, 'Gainst whose all-power no tem - pest shall pre - vail.
pass, but Truth a - bides; Thine be the splen - dor of her death - less star.
joy to help and save, That more and more shines to the per - fect day.

Music by permission of ASSOCIATION FOR PROMOTING CHRISTIAN KNOWLEDGE

# 173

**HUDDERSFIELD** 7.7.7.5.

WALTER PARRATT — CHRISTOPHER WORDSWORTH
Adapted

1. Love is kind and suf - fers long, Love is meek and thinks no wrong, Love than death it - self more strong; There - fore give . . . us love.
2. Proph - e - cy will fade a - way, Melt - ing in the light of day; Love will ev - er with us stay; There - fore give . . . us love.
3. Faith will van - ish in - to sight; Hope shall be ful - filled in light; Love will ev - er shine more bright; There - fore give . . . us love.
4. Faith and hope and love we see Join - ing hand in hand a - gree; But the great - est of the three, And the best, . . . is love.

Music by permission of the family of the late Sir WALTER PARRATT

**CONSOLATION** 12. 10. 11. 10.

FELIX MENDELSSOHN-BARTHOLDY
Arranged

MARIA LOUISE BAUM

To be sung in unison
1. Like as a moth - er, God
2. Love is true sol - ace and
3. O ho - ly pres - ence, that
com - fort - eth His chil - dren; Com - fort is
giv - eth joy for sor - row,— O, in that
stills all our de - mand - ing, O love of
calm, that bids all tu - mult cease;
light, all earth - ly loss is gain;
God, that needs but to be known!

Com - fort is hope and
Joy must en - dure, Love's
Heaven is at hand, when

cour - age for en - deav - or, Com - fort is
giv - ing is for - ev - er; Life is of
thy pure touch per - suades us, Com - fort of

love, whose home a - bides in peace.
God, whose ra - diance can - not wane.
God, that seeks and finds His own.

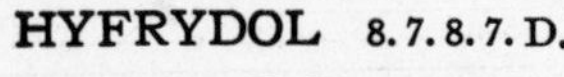
HYFRYDOL 8.7.8.7.D.

ROWLAND H. PRICHARD — V. H.

1. Lo, He sent His Word and healed them, Still that
2. Love di - vine, that fail - eth nev - er, Still Thy

Word of God . . is here. Still its ten - der
pres - ence and . . Thy power Might - y are . . to

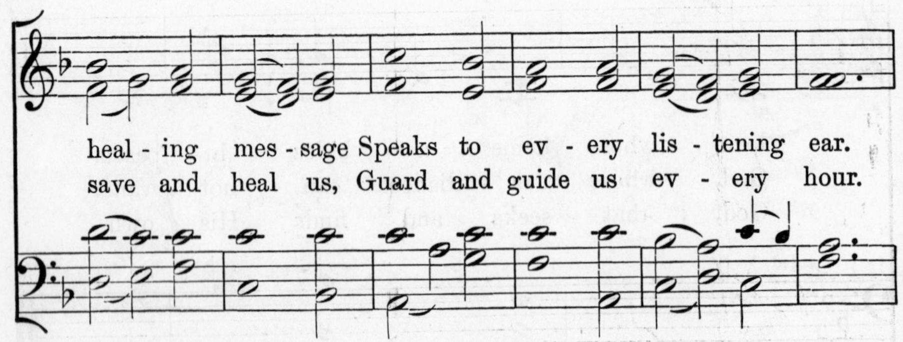
heal - ing mes - sage Speaks to ev - ery lis - tening ear.
save and heal us, Guard and guide us ev - ery hour.

Truth di - vine, that o - ver - com - eth All . . the
Life di - vine, Thy Word pro - claim - eth All . . true

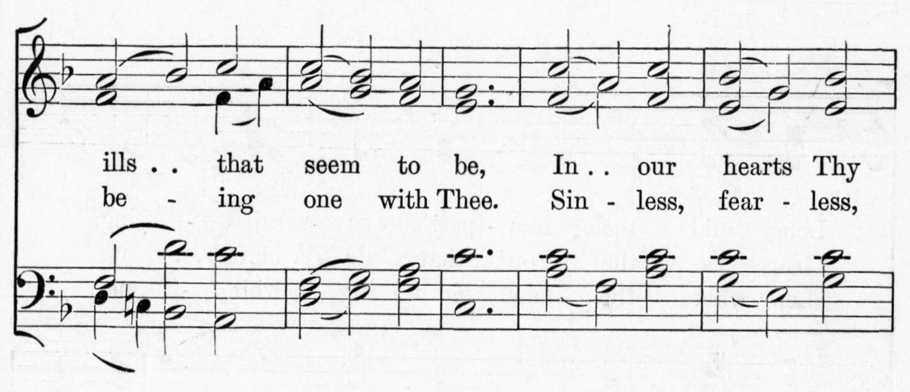
ills . . that seem to be, In . . our hearts Thy
be - ing one with Thee. Sin - less, fear - less,

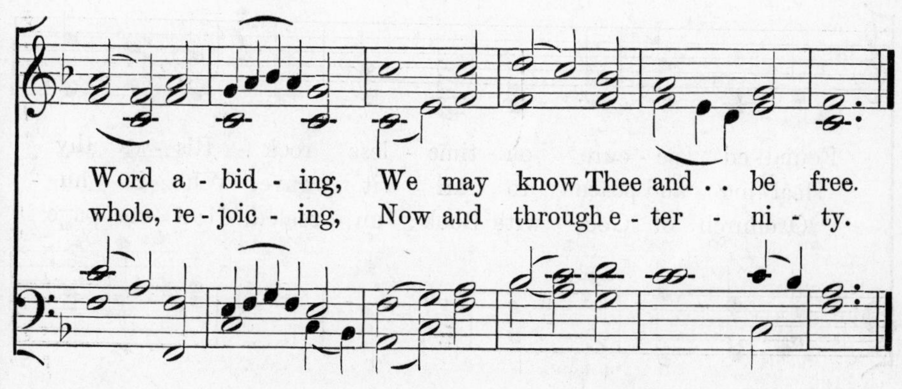
Word a - bid - ing, We may know Thee and . . be free.
whole, re - joic - ing, Now and through e - ter - ni - ty.

176

CHURCH 88. 88. 888.
Kirken den er et gammelt hus
LUDVIG M. LINDEMAN
Based on the Danish of
NIKOLAJ F. S. GRUNDTVIG
1. Long hast thou stood, O church of God,
2. Let there be light, and light was there,
3. Let there be light, the Word shines forth,
Long mid the tem - pest's as - sail - ing,
Clear as the Word that de - clared . . it;
Lo, where the new morn - ing whit - ens;
Found - ed se - cure on time - less rock Ris - es thy
Heal - ing and peace to all it gave, Who in hu -
O church of God, with Book un - sealed, How its page

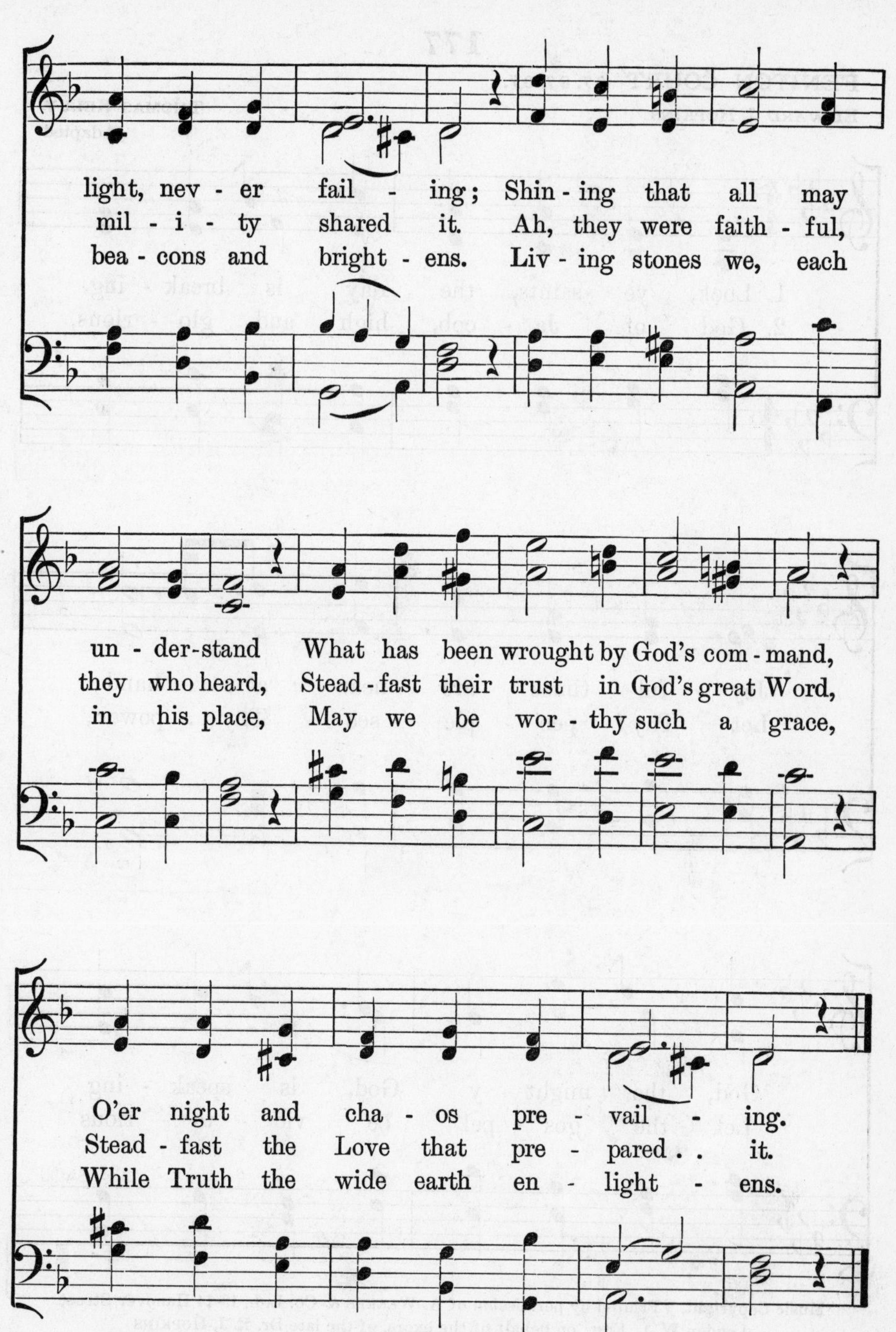
light, nev - er fail - ing; Shin - ing that all may
mil - i - ty shared it. Ah, they were faith - ful,
bea - cons and bright - ens. Liv - ing stones we, each
un - der-stand What has been wrought by God's com - mand,
they who heard, Stead - fast their trust in God's great Word,
in his place, May we be wor - thy such a grace,
O'er night and cha - os pre - vail - ing.
Stead - fast the Love that pre - pared . . it.
While Truth the wide earth en - light - ens.

**FENITON COURT** 87.87.87.

EDWARD J. HOPKINS

THOMAS KELLY
Adapted

1. Look, ye saints, the day is break - ing,
2. God of Ja - cob, high and glo - rious,
Joy - ful times are near at . . hand;
Let Thy peo - ple see Thy . . power;
God, the might - y God, is speak - ing
Let the gos - pel be vic - to - rious

By His Word in.. ev - ery... land:
Through the world for - ev - er - more:

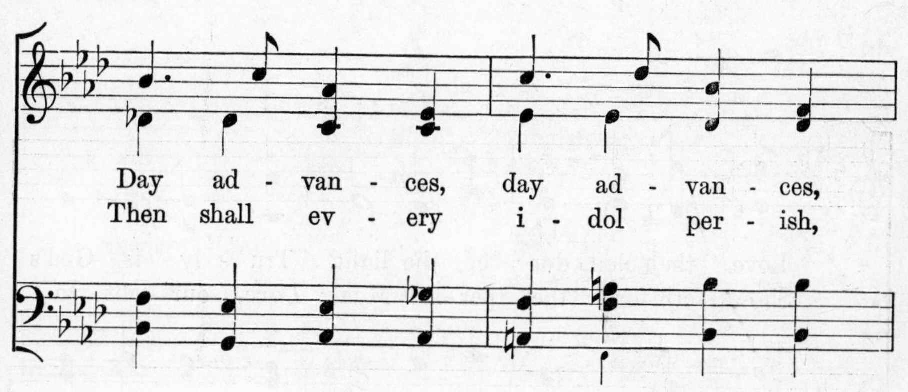
Day ad - van - ces, day ad - van - ces,
Then shall ev - ery i - dol per - ish,

Dark - ness flees at... His com - mand.
While Thy faith - ful.. saints a - dore.

# 178

**LIGHT** 87. 87. 88. 77.

Kjærlighet er lysets kilde
LUDVIG M. LINDEMAN

Based on the Danish of
NIKOLAJ F. S. GRUNDTVIG

1. Love is life's true crown and glo - ry,
2. Love, the Gold - en Rule of liv - ing,
Love the splen - dor of the light, Tru - ly is God's
Show - eth forth the per - fect Mind; Love, our debt to
coun - sel gen - tle, Tru - ly all His ways are bright;
God who gives it, All com - pas - sion is, and kind;

Je - sus knew the law of kind - ness,
Char - i - ty the law ful - fill - eth,

Heal - ing mind and heart of blind-ness; And in heaven - ly
Mid the na - tions ran - cor still - eth; Lov - ing hearts in
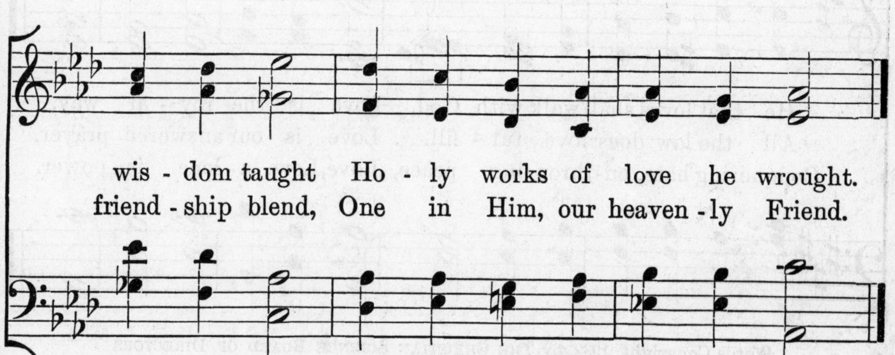
wis - dom taught Ho - ly works of love he wrought.
friend - ship blend, One in Him, our heaven - ly Friend.

INTEGER VITAE 11. 12. 6. 7. 6.

FRIEDRICH F. FLEMMING — M. M.

1. Love one an - oth - er,—word of rev - e - la - tion; Love frees from
2. Love knows no e - vil, nei-ther shade of sad - ness; Love casts out
3. Love now is dawn - ing o - ver ev - ery na - tion; Show - ing true

er-ror's thrall,—Love is lib - er - a - tion. Love's way the Mas-ter trod;
ev - ery fear, lifts the heart to glad-ness. Love heals our ev - ery ill,
broth - er-hood, pub-lish-ing sal - va - tion, Love bids all dis-cord cease.

He that loves shall walk with God. Love is the roy - al way.
All the law does love ful - fill. . . Love is our answered prayer.
Conquering hate, en-thron -ing peace, Love, Love a - lone is power.

# 180

**CHARITY** 556.866.

Kærlighed fra Gud
C. F. JÆHNIGEN

Based on the Danish of
JENS N. L. SCHJØRRING

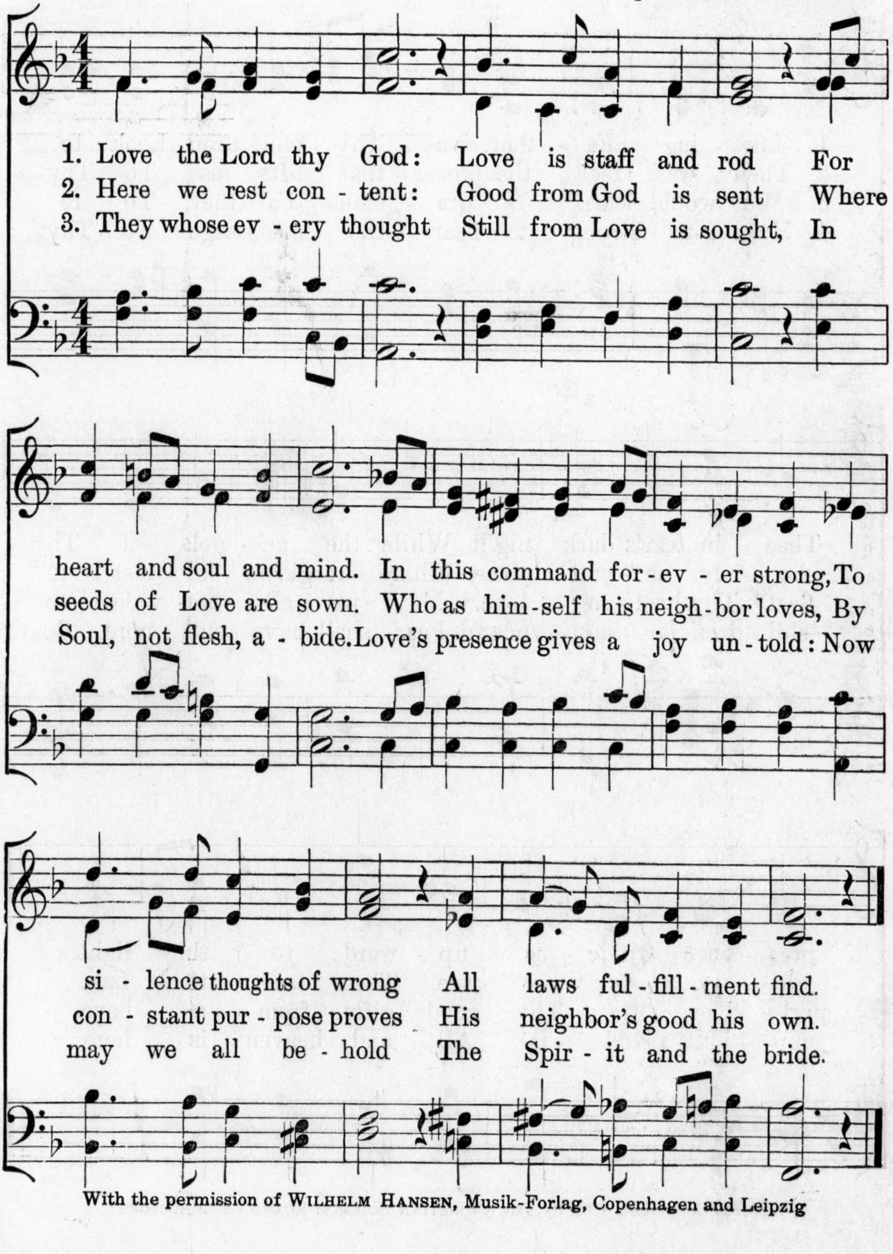

1. Love the Lord thy God: Love is staff and rod For
2. Here we rest con - tent: Good from God is sent Where
3. They whose ev - ery thought Still from Love is sought, In
heart and soul and mind. In this command for - ev - er strong, To
seeds of Love are sown. Who as him - self his neigh - bor loves, By
Soul, not flesh, a - bide. Love's presence gives a joy un - told: Now
si - lence thoughts of wrong All laws ful - fill - ment find.
con - stant pur - pose proves His neighbor's good his own.
may we all be - hold The Spir - it and the bride.


With the permission of WILHELM HANSEN, Musik-Forlag, Copenhagen and Leipzig

# 181

**SARDIS** 8.7.8.7.

Arranged from
LUDWIG VAN BEETHOVEN

ROSEMARY B. HACKETT

1. Lov - ing Fa - ther, we Thy chil - dren Look to
2. Then we feel the power that lifts us To Thy
3. We would learn, O gra - cious Fa - ther, To re
4. Make us strong to bear the mes - sage To Thy
Thee in fear's dark night While the an - gels of Thy
ho - ly se - cret place, Where our gloom is lost in
flect Thy heal - ing love. May we all a - wake to
chil - dren far and near: Fear shall have no more do -
pres - ence Guide us up - ward to the light.
glo - ry As we see Thee face to face.
praise Thee For Thy good gifts from a - bove.
min - ion. God is All, and heaven is here.

# 182

COLCHESTER C.M.

HENRY PURCELL

RICHARD C. TRENCH*

1. Make chan - nels for . . the streams of Love, Where they may broad - ly run; And Love has o - ver - flow - ing streams, To fill . . them ev - ery one.
2. But if . . at an - y time . . we cease Such chan - nels to pro - vide, The ver - y founts of love for us Will then seem parched and dried.
3. For we . . must share, if we . . . would keep That bless - ing from a - bove; They cease to have who cease to give: Such is . . the law of Love.

# 183†

**HEATH** S. M.

MASON and WEBB'S Cantica Laudis, 1850

HORATIUS BONAR Adapted

1. Make haste, O man, to do What - ev - er must be done; Thou hast no time to lose in sloth, When all to Truth must come.
2. The use - ful and the great, The thing that nev - er dies, The si - lent toil that is not lost,— Set these be - fore thine eyes.
3. Up, face the task and work; Fling ease and self a - way; This is no time for thee to sleep; Up, watch, and work, and pray.

# 184†

English Traditional Carol
Sandys' Collection, 1833

HORATIUS BONAR
Adapted

1. Make haste, O man, to . . do What -
2. The use - ful and the . . great, The
3. Up, face the task and . . work; Fling

ev - er must be done; Thou hast no time to
thing that nev - er dies, The si - lent toil that
ease and self a - way; This is no time for

lose in sloth, When all to Truth must come.
is not lost,— Set these be - fore thine eyes.
thee to sleep; Up, watch, and work, and pray.

## 185

**BOWEN** 9. 8. 8. 8.

Arranged from
FRANZ JOSEPH HAYDN

B. S. P.

1. Mas - ter and Lord, 'tis good to be here, Guid - ed by thee to joy - crowned height Where we man's per - fect son - ship see Safe and se - cure in ra - diant light.
2. Light of the world, 'tis good to hold fast To the clear vi - sion thou hast shown; So shall this vi - sion gen - tly mold Our lives more close - ly to thine own.
3. Thou art the Way, we know that the truth Shown on the moun - tain here a - bove, Still in thy light's tri - um - phant glow Through all earth's val - leys we can prove.

# 186†

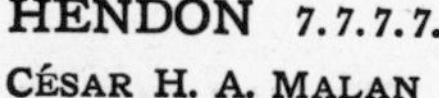

**HENDON** 7.7.7.7.

CÉSAR H. A. MALAN

WILLIAM GASKELL
Adapted

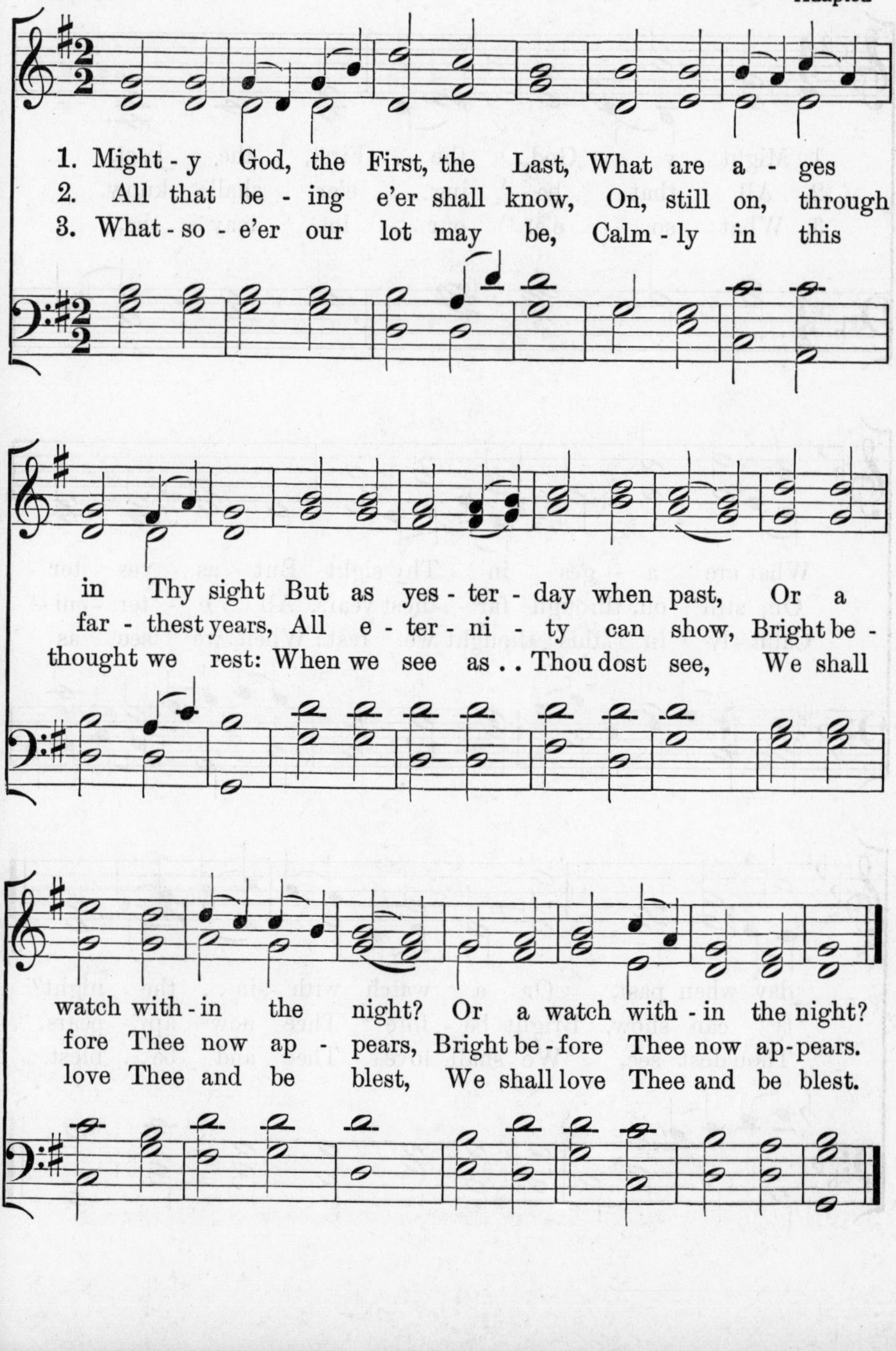

1. Might - y God, the First, the Last, What are a - ges
2. All that be - ing e'er shall know, On, still on, through
3. What - so - e'er our lot may be, Calm - ly in this

in Thy sight But as yes - ter - day when past, Or a
far - thest years, All e - ter - ni - ty can show, Bright be -
thought we rest: When we see as . . Thou dost see, We shall

watch with - in the night? Or a watch with - in the night?
fore Thee now ap - pears, Bright be - fore Thee now ap - pears.
love Thee and be blest, We shall love Thee and be blest.

## 187†

**TUNBRIDGE** 7.7.7.7.

JEREMIAH CLARK

WILLIAM GASKELL
Adapted

1. Might - y . . . God, the . . First, the Last,
2. All that be - ing . . e'er shall know,
3. What - so - e'er our . . lot may be,
What are a - ges in Thy sight But as yes - ter -
On, still on, through far - thest years, All e - ter - ni -
Calm - ly in this thought we rest: When we see as
day when past, Or a watch with - in . . the night?
ty can show, Bright be - fore Thee now ap - pears.
Thou dost see, We shall love Thee and be . . blest.

**ROCKINGHAM** L. M.

EDWARD MILLER

E. C. A.

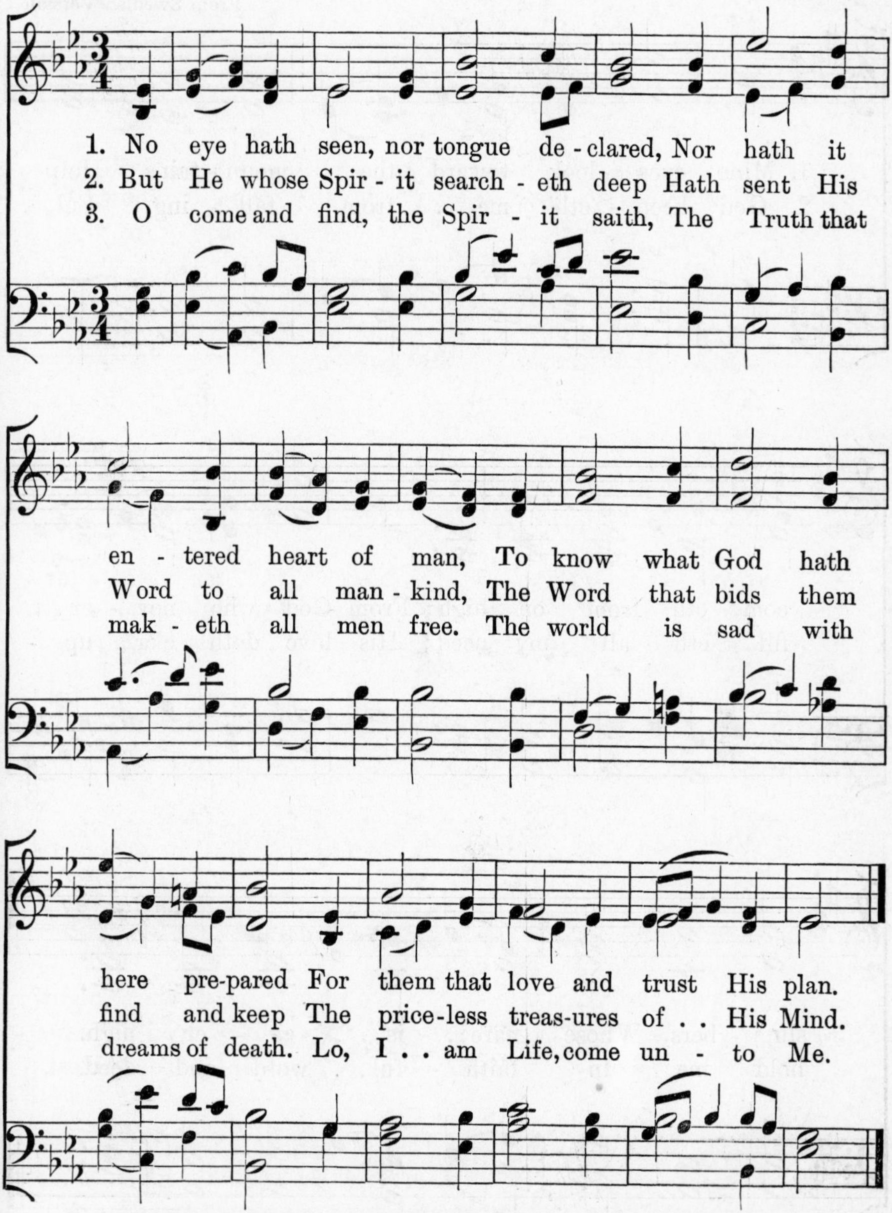

1. No eye hath seen, nor tongue de - clared, Nor hath it
2. But He whose Spir - it search - eth deep Hath sent His
3. O come and find, the Spir - it saith, The Truth that

en - tered heart of man, To know what God hath
Word to all man - kind, The Word that bids them
mak - eth all men free. The world is sad with

here pre-pared For them that love and trust His plan.
find and keep The price-less treas-ures of . . His Mind.
dreams of death. Lo, I . . am Life, come un - to Me.

# 189

**BOHEMIAN HYMN** 7. 6. 7. 6. D.

Bohemian Brethren

PSALM 121
From Swedish Version

1. Mine eyes look toward the . . moun - tains, Help
2. God keep - eth me . . from fall - ing, Ful -
com - eth from on high; From God who nev - er . .
fill - eth all my need; His love doth e'er up -
slum - bers, Whose care . . is . . ev - er nigh.
hold me In faith - ful . . word and deed.

My foot shall not be mov - ed, My keep - er is the
He keep - eth me from e - vil, My on - ward way doth

Lord, He nev - er shall . . for -
trace, My go - ing and . . my . .

sake me; I trust me . . to His Word.
com - ing He crown - eth . . with His grace.

# 190†

**ALMSGIVING** 8. 8. 8. 4.

JOHN B. DYKES

FREDERIC MANN
Adapted

1. My God, my Fa - ther, make me strong,
2. With con - fi - dent and hum - ble mind,
3. Things deemed im - pos - si - ble I dare,
4. Heaven's mu - sic chimes the glad days in,
When tasks of life seem hard and long, To greet them
My joy in serv - ice I . . would find, My prayer through
Thine is the call and Thine the care, Thy wis - dom
Hope soars be - yond death, pain and sin, Faith sings in
with this tri - umph song, Thy will be done.
ev - ery task . . as - signed, Thy will be done.
shall the way . . pre - pare; Thy will be done.
tri - umph, Love doth win; Thy will is done.

Words by permission of A. W. RIDLEY & Co.

# 191†

**ES IST KEIN TAG** 8. 8. 8. 4.

JOHANN D. MEYER | FREDERIC MANN, Adapted

1. My .. God, my .. Fa - ther, make me strong,
2. With con - fi - dent and hum - ble mind,
3. Things deemed im - pos - si - ble .. I dare,
4. Heaven's mu - sic .. chimes the glad days in,
When tasks of .. life seem hard and long, To
My .. joy .. in .. serv - ice I would find, My
Thine is .. the call and Thine the care, Thy
Hope soars be - yond death, pain and sin, Faith
greet them with this tri - umph song, Thy will be done.
prayer through ev - ery task as - signed, Thy will be done.
wis - dom shall the way pre - pare; Thy will be done.
sings in tri - umph, Love doth win; Thy will is done.

Words by permission of A. W. RIDLEY & Co.

# 192†

**BETHANY** 64. 64. 66. 64.

LOWELL MASON | SARAH F. ADAMS

Not too slow
1. Near - er, my God, to Thee,
2. Though like the wan - der - er,
3. There let the way ap - pear,
Near - er to Thee: E'en though it be a cross
The sun gone down, Dark - ness be o - ver me,
Steps un - to heaven; All that Thou send - est me
That rais - eth me; Still all my song shall be,
My rest a stone; Yet in my dreams I'd be
In . . mer - cy given; An - gels to beck - on me

Near - er, my God, to Thee, Near - er, my

God, to Thee, Near - er to Thee.

4. Then, with my waking thoughts
   Bright with Thy praise,
Out of my stony griefs
   Bethel I'll raise;
So by my woes to be
Nearer, my God, to Thee,
   Nearer to Thee.

5. Or if on joyful wing
   Cleaving the sky,
Sun, moon, and stars forgot,
   Upward I fly,
Still all my song shall be,
Nearer, my God, to Thee,
   Nearer to Thee

# 193†

HORBURY 64. 64. 664.
JOHN B. DYKES
SARAH F. ADAMS
1. Near - er, my God, to Thee,
2. Though like the wan - der - er,
3. There let the way ap - pear,
Near - er . . to Thee: E'en though it
The sun gone down, Dark - ness . . be
Steps un - to heaven; All that . . Thou
be a cross That rais - eth me; . . .
o - ver me, My rest a stone; .
send - est me In mer - cy given; .

Still all my song shall be, Near - er, my . .
Yet in my dreams I'd be . . Near - er, my . .
An - gels to beck - on me Near - er, my . .

God, to Thee, Near - er . . to Thee.

4. Then, with my waking thoughts
   Bright with Thy praise,
Out of my stony griefs
   Bethel I'll raise;
So by my woes to be
Nearer, my God, to Thee,
   Nearer to Thee.

5. Or if on joyful wing
   Cleaving the sky,
Sun, moon, and stars forgot,
   Upward I fly,
Still all my song shall be,
Nearer, my God, to Thee,
   Nearer to Thee.

**CONTEMPLATION** (CONSOLATION) C. M.

Arranged from
LUDWIG VAN BEETHOVEN

SAMUEL GREENWOOD

1. No mor - tal sense can still or stay The
2. The heart's own long - ing lifts it high Where
3. The voi - ces that are world - ly wise, With
flight of si - lent prayer, Un - ceas - ing, voice - less,
words can nev - er reach, Though hu - man lips may
mor - tal modes in tune, Are mute in that tran -
heart - de - sire That seeks God ev - ery - where.
nev - er form That glo - ry in - to speech.
scend - ent hour When God and man com - mune.

*These words have another setting in the* SUPPLEMENT, No. 410

# 195

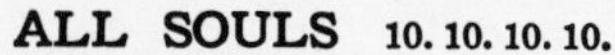

**ALL SOULS** 10. 10. 10. 10.

JOHN YOAKLEY — HORATIUS BONAR*

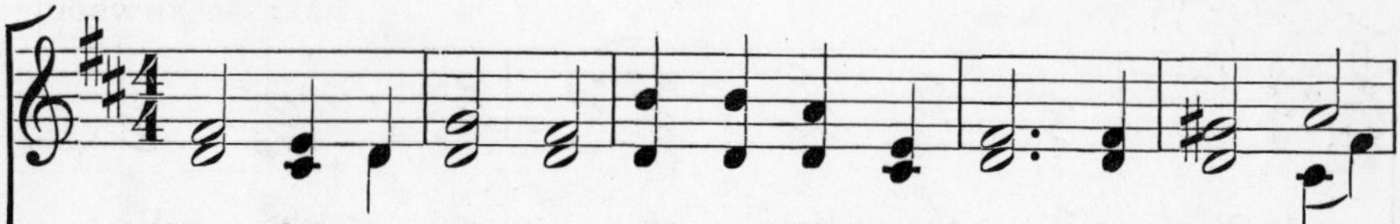

1. Not what I am, O Lord, but what Thou art; That, that a -
2. Girt with the love of God, on ev - ery side, I breathe that
3. 'Tis what I know of Thee, my Lord and God, That fills my

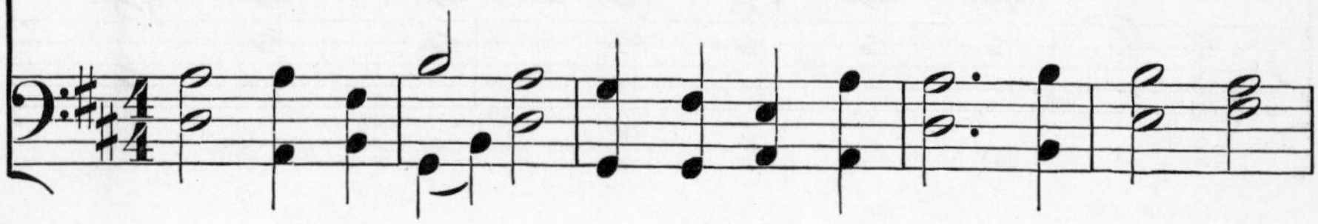

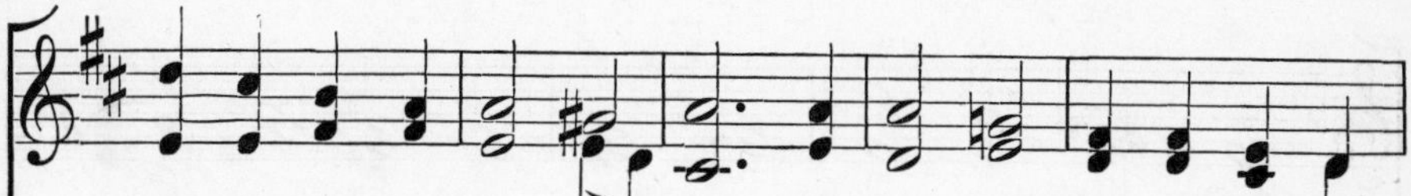

lone can be my soul's true rest; Thy love, not mine, bids fear and
love as heaven's own heal - ing air; I work and pray, and fol - low
soul with peace, my lips with song; Thou art my health, my joy, my

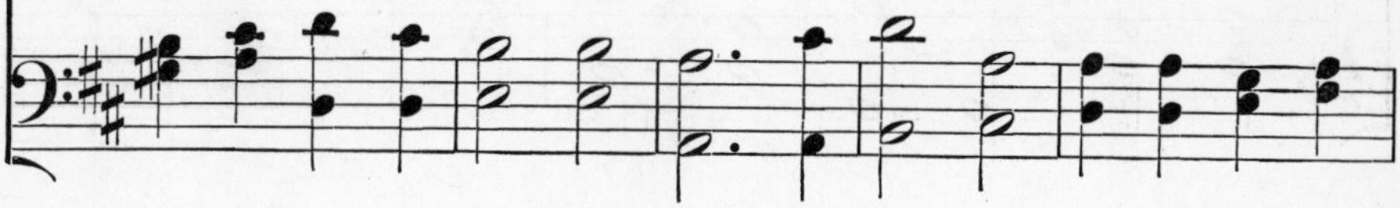

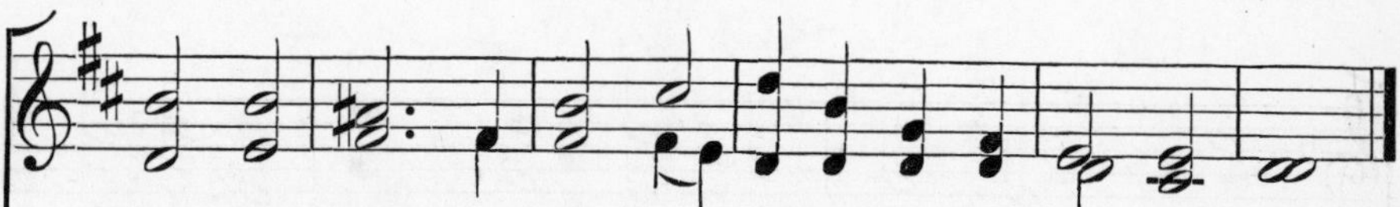

doubt de - part, And stills the tu - mult of my trou - bled breast.
still my guide, And fear no foe, es - cap - ing ev - ery snare.
staff, my rod; I lean on Thee, in weak - ness I am strong.

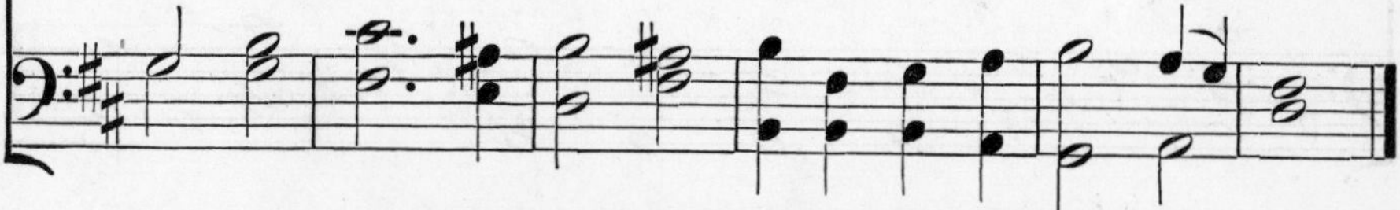

Music by permission of JOHN N. YOAKLEY

# 196

## DAY OF REST 7.6.7.6.D.

JAMES W. ELLIOTT — JANE BORTHWICK

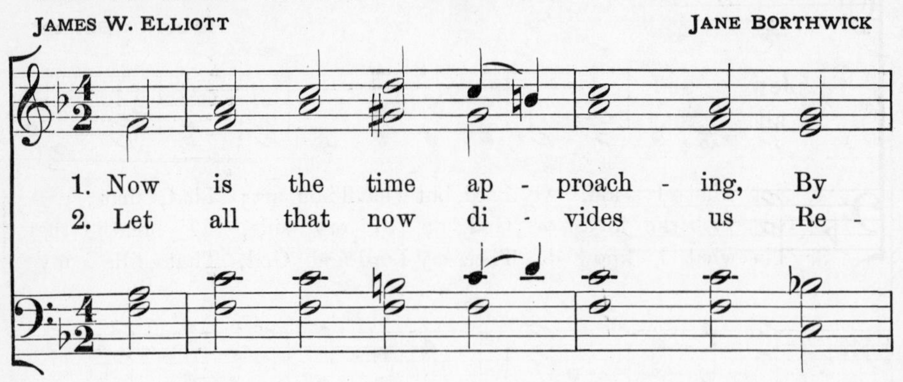
1. Now is the time ap - proach - ing, By
2. Let all that now di - vides us Re -

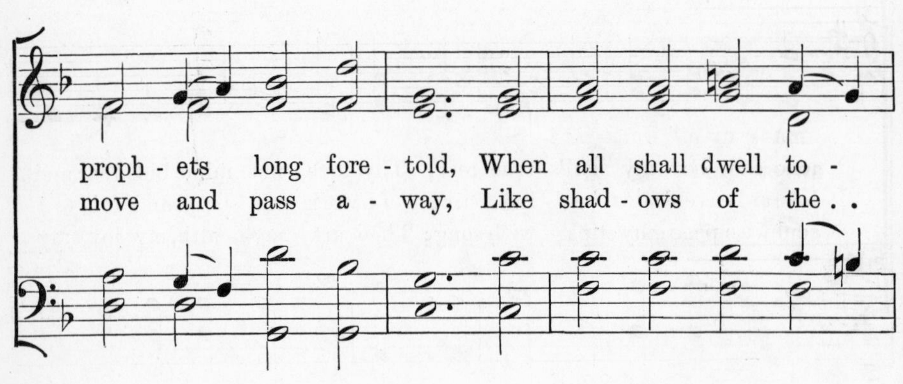
proph - ets long fore - told, When all shall dwell to -
move and pass a - way, Like shad - ows of the . .

geth - er, One Shep - herd and one fold. Now
morn - ing Be - fore the blaze of day. Let

Jew and Gen - tile, meet - ing From
all that now u - nites us More

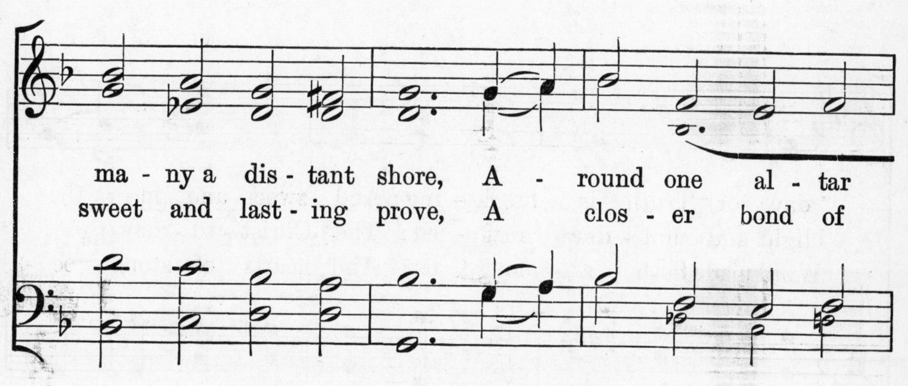
ma - ny a dis - tant shore, A - round one al - tar
sweet and last - ing prove, A clos - er bond of

kneel - ing, One com - mon Lord a - dore.
un - ion, In a blest land of love.

# 197†

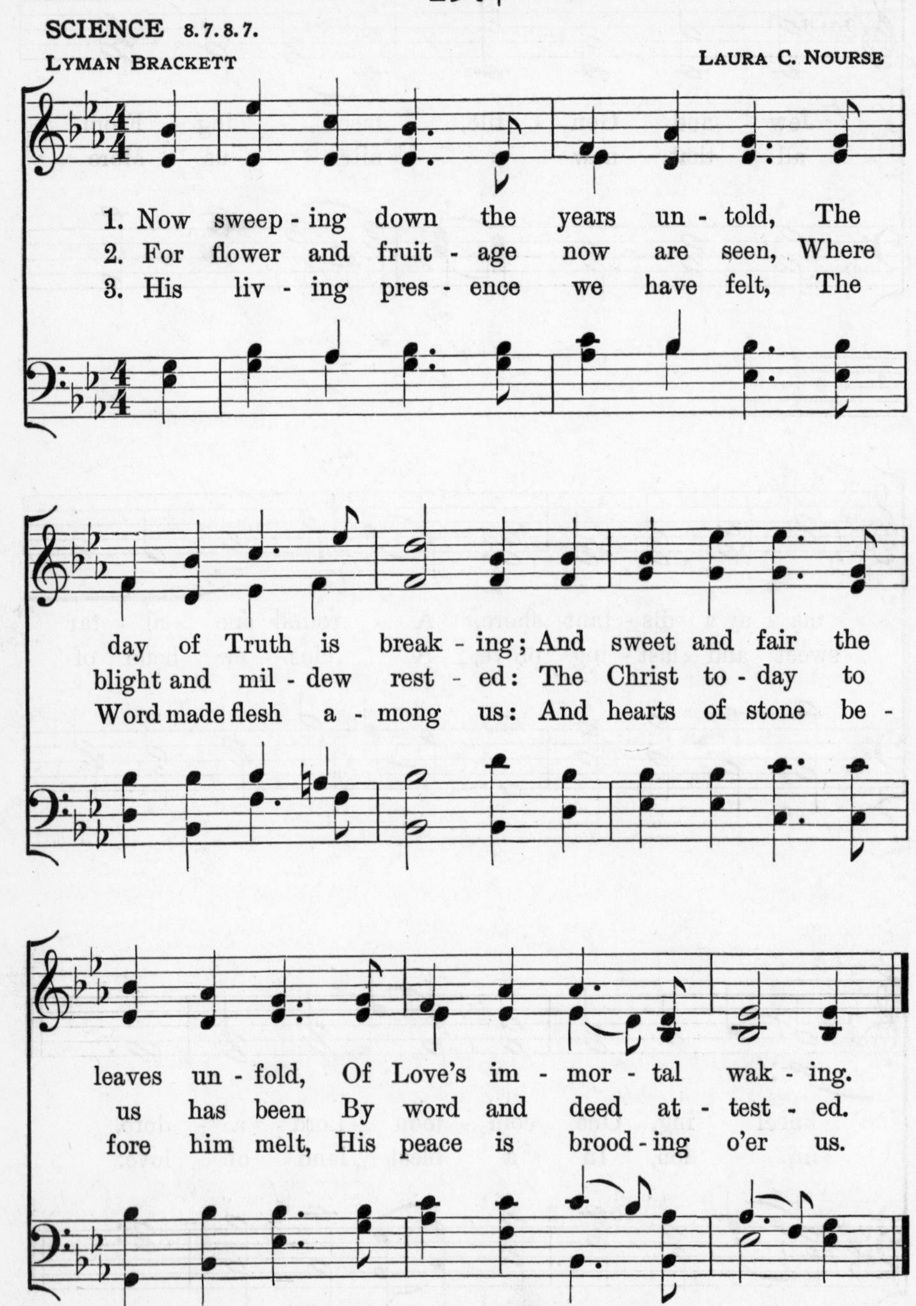
SCIENCE 8.7.8.7.
LYMAN BRACKETT
LAURA C. NOURSE
1. Now sweep - ing down the years un - told, The day of Truth is break - ing; And sweet and fair the leaves un - fold, Of Love's im - mor - tal wak - ing.
2. For flower and fruit - age now are seen, Where blight and mil - dew rest - ed: The Christ to - day to us has been By word and deed at - test - ed.
3. His liv - ing pres - ence we have felt, The Word made flesh a - mong us: And hearts of stone be - fore him melt, His peace is brood - ing o'er us.

# 198†

WISDOM 8.7.8.7.
G. THALBEN-BALL
LAURA C. NOURSE
1. Now sweep - ing down the years un - told, The
2. For flower and fruit - age now are seen, Where
3. His liv - ing pres - ence we have felt, The
day of Truth is break - ing; And sweet and fair the
blight and mil - dew rest - ed: The Christ to - day to
Word made flesh a - mong us: And hearts of stone be -
leaves un - fold, Of Love's im - mor - tal wak - ing.
us has been By word and deed at - test - ed.
fore him melt, His peace is brood - ing o'er us.

Music by permission of G. THALBEN-BALL

# 199

NUN DANKET 67. 67. 66. 66.
JOHANN CRÜGER
Harmonized by F. MENDELSSOHN-BARTHOLDY
MARTIN RINKART
CATHERINE WINKWORTH, Tr.
Adapted
1. Now thank we all our . . God With . . grateful hearts and voi - ces Who won-drous things hath done, In whom the world re - joi - ces;
2. We know our gra - cious . God Through all our life is near us, To fill our thoughts with light, To strength - en . . us and cheer . . us;

Who from the . . days of yore Hath
From His e - ter - nal care We

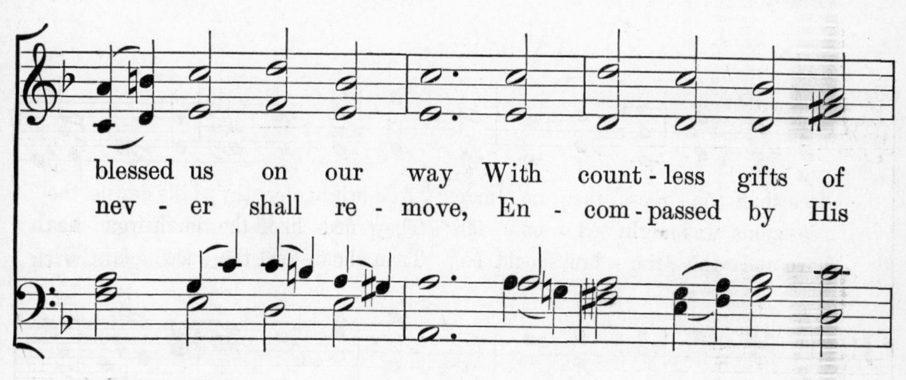
blessed us on our way With count - less gifts of
nev - er shall re - move, En - com - passed by His

love And still is . . ours to - day.
grace, En - fold - ed . . in His love.

## 200

**SWANAGE** 12. 11. 12. 11.

E. N. G. — Author Unknown*

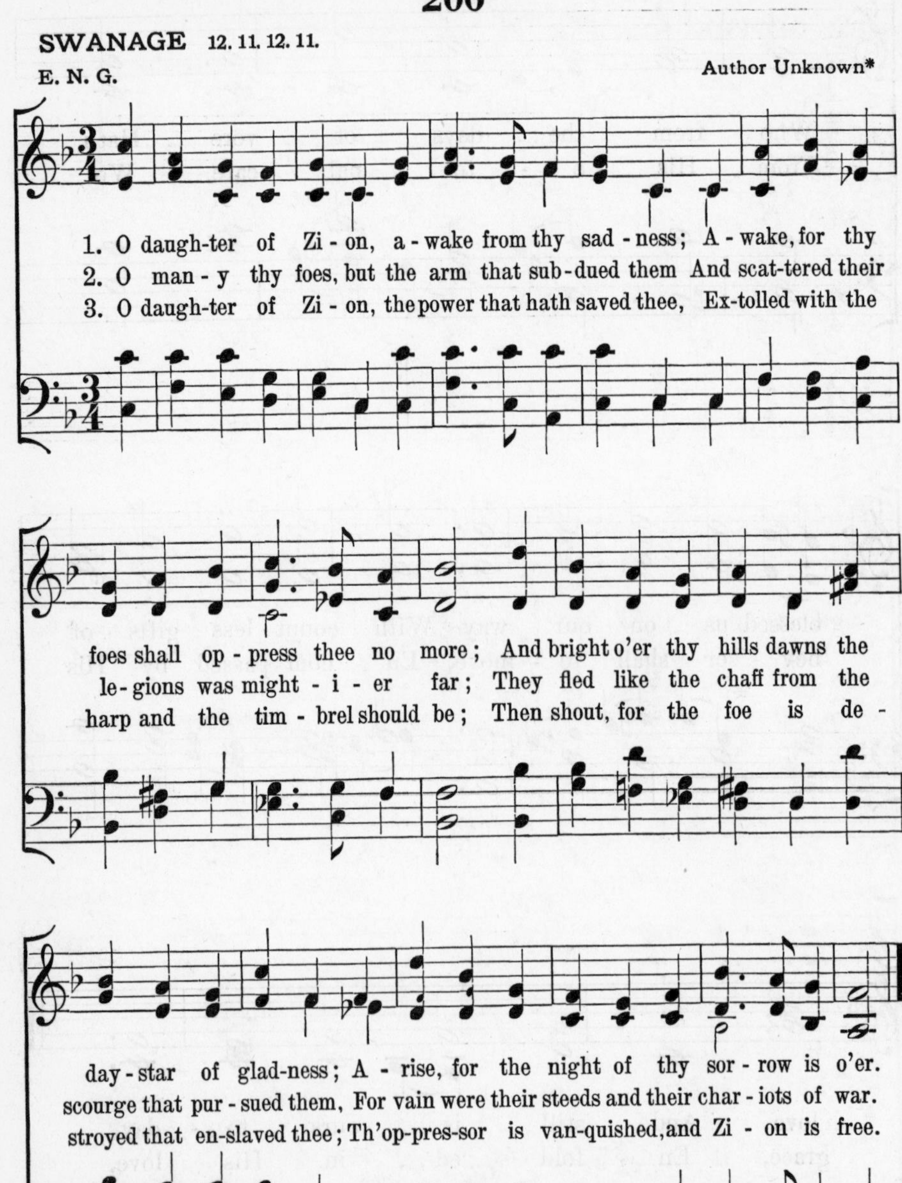
1. O daugh-ter of Zi - on, a - wake from thy sad - ness; A - wake, for thy
2. O man - y thy foes, but the arm that sub - dued them And scat-tered their
3. O daugh-ter of Zi - on, the power that hath saved thee, Ex-tolled with the
foes shall op - press thee no more; And bright o'er thy hills dawns the
le - gions was might - i - er far; They fled like the chaff from the
harp and the tim - brel should be; Then shout, for the foe is de -
day - star of glad-ness; A - rise, for the night of thy sor - row is o'er.
scourge that pur - sued them, For vain were their steeds and their char - iots of war.
stroyed that en-slaved thee; Th'op-pres-sor is van-quished, and Zi - on is free.

## 201

**ST. GEORGE** S.M.

HENRY J. GAUNTLETT | CHARLES PARSONS

1. O do not bar your mind A - gainst the light of good; But o - pen wide, let in the Word, And Truth will be your food.
2. Truth will from er - ror free Your long en - slav - ed mind, And bring the light of lib - er - ty Where it shall be en - shrined.
3. Hid treas - ures it re - veals To all who know its power; And all who will may light re - ceive In this most gra - cious hour.
4. Then o - pen wide your heart To Truth and Light and Love; You then shall know your life is hid With Christ in God a - bove.

*These words have another setting in the* SUPPLEMENT, No. 404

## ANCIENT OF DAYS 11. 10. 11. 10.

HORATIO W. PARKER | ROSA M. TURNER

1. O dream - er, leave thy dreams for joy - ful wak - ing, O cap - tive, rise and sing, for thou . . art . . . free; . . .
2. He comes to bless thee on his wings of heal - ing; To ban - ish pain, and wipe all tears . . a - way; . . .
3. He comes to give thee joy for des - o - la - tion, Beau - ty for ash - es of the van - ished years; . .
4. He comes to call the dumb to joy - ful sing - ing; The deaf to hear; the blind - ed eyes . . to . . . see; . . . .

*These words have another setting in the* SUPPLEMENT, No. 412

The Christ is here, all dreams of er - - ror break - ing, Un - loos - ing bonds of all cap - tiv - i - ty.
He comes a - new, to hum - ble hearts.... re - veal - ing The mount - ing foot - steps of the up - ward way.
For ev - ery tear to bring full com - pen - sa - tion, To give thee con - fi - dence for all thy fears.
The glo - rious ti - dings of sal - va - tion bring - ing. O cap - tive, rise, thy Sav - iour comes to thee.

**FIRMAMENT** L. M. D.

H. WALFORD DAVIES — LEWIE PRITTIE CASTELLAIN

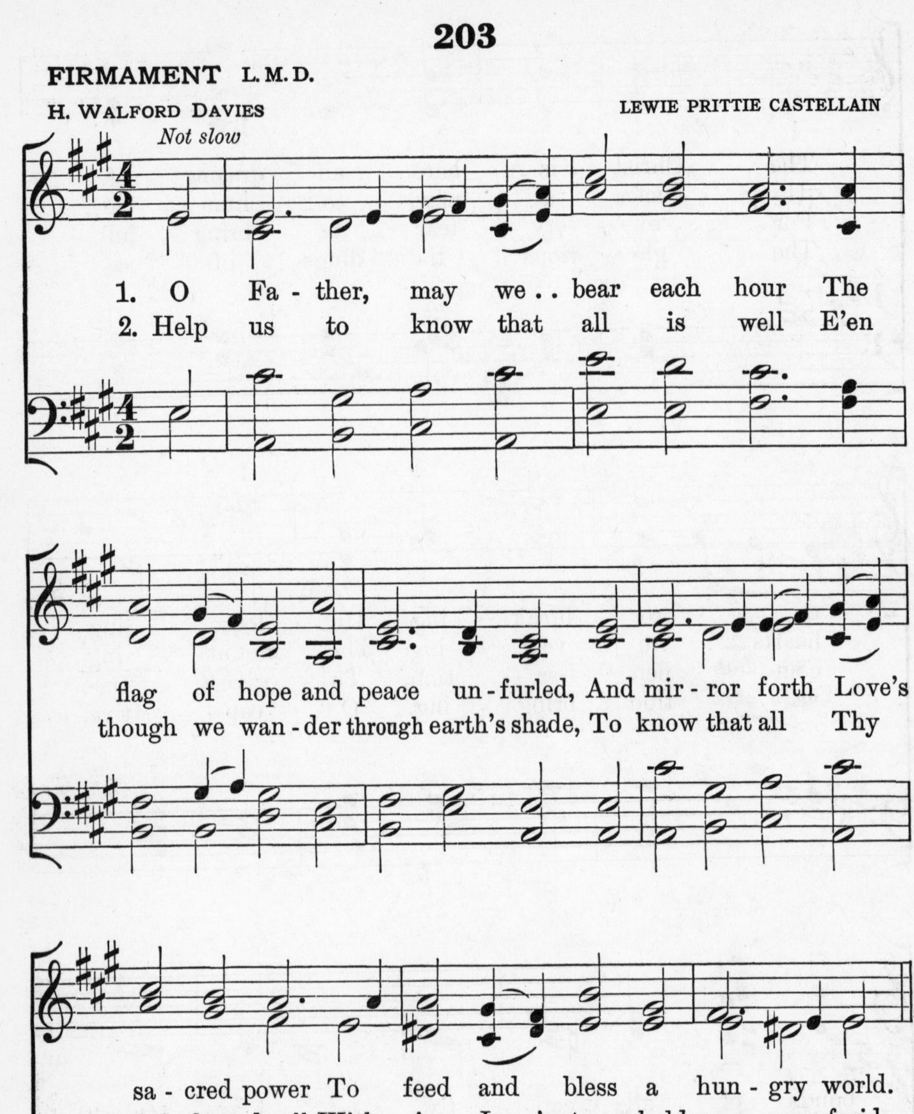
Not slow
1. O Father, may we.. bear each hour The flag of hope and peace unfurled, And mirror forth Love's sacred power To feed and bless a hungry world.
2. Help us to know that all is well E'en though we wander through earth's shade, To know that all Thy children dwell Within Love's stronghold unafraid.

Music from A STUDENTS' HYMNAL (HYMNS OF THE KINGDOM)
By permission of the OXFORD UNIVERSITY PRESS

We shall not fal - ter by the way If
Teach us to fol - low fear - less - ly The
we but place our trust in Thee, O - bey - ing glad - ly . .
way our gen - tle Mas - ter trod, 'Twill lead us safe - ly . .
day by day The liv - ing Truth that makes men free.
home to Thee, O lov - ing Fa - ther-Moth - er, God.

# 204

**THY KINGDOM COME** 11 9. 11 9. 9 9.

Tillkomme ditt rike
GUNNAR WENNERBERG

Based on the Swedish of
LINA SANDELL BERG

To be sung in unison
1. O Fa - ther, Thy king - dom is come up - on earth, Thou
2. They lift up a light a - mid shad - ows of fear, And
3. They go in Thy strength, and they speak in Thy name, With
rul - est in all Thy cre - a - - tion; Thou
Love is Thy ban - ner a - bove . . . . them; No
power of Thy prom - ise forth far - - ing, And
send - est Thy wit - ness - es, tell - ing Thy worth,
trou - ble shall touch them, no foes that ap - pear
dur - ing the bat - tle the vic - to - ry claim,—

By permission of EVANGELISKA FOSTERLANDS-STIFTELSENS BOKFÖRLAG

To call and en - treat ev - ery na - tion, With
Shall e'er from their loy - al - ty move them; 'Tis
Their trust in Thy truth is their dar - ing, Sal -
news of Thy might - y sal - va - tion, With
Thou dost up - hold and ap - prove . . them, 'Tis
va - tion to all men de - clar - ing, Sal -
news of Thy might - y sal - va - - tion.
Thou dost up - hold and ap - prove . . . them.
va - tion to all men de - clar - - ing.

## BELMONT C.M.

Gardiner's Sacred Melodies, 1812
Reharmonized by G. THALBEN–BALL

WILLIAM H. BATHURST*

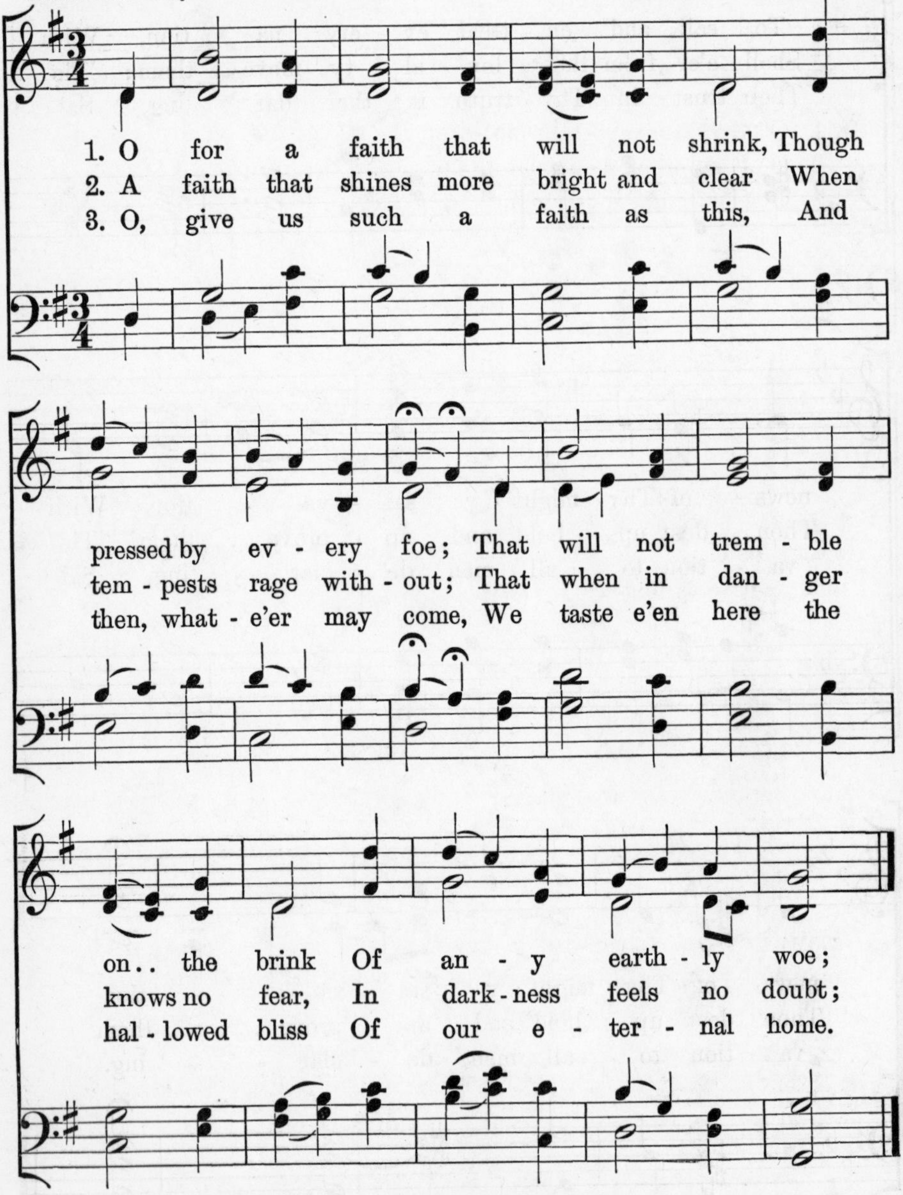

1. O for a faith that will not shrink, Though
pressed by ev - ery foe; That will not trem - ble
on.. the brink Of an - y earth - ly woe;

2. A faith that shines more bright and clear When
tem - pests rage with - out; That when in dan - ger
knows no fear, In dark - ness feels no doubt;

3. O, give us such a faith as this, And
then, what - e'er may come, We taste e'en here the
hal - lowed bliss Of our e - ter - nal home.

Music by permission of G. THALBEN–BALL

# 206

**NEWCASTLE** 86. 886.

HENRY L. MORLEY D. S.

1. O God, our Fa - ther-Moth - er, Love, Purge Thou our hearts from
2. O God, our Fa - ther-Moth - er, Truth, Send forth Thy light sub -
3. O God, our Fa - ther-Moth - er, Life, Re - veal in us Thy
sin, That in Thy ra - dian - cy di - vine We
lime, That in its pure and cleans - ing rays We
might, That hence - forth we may live to Thee, In
may with eyes un-dimmed de-fine Thy will, re - al - i - ty.
may, with thought at-tuned to praise, Be - hold re - al - i - ty.
all our ways re - flect-ing Thee, And know re - al - i - ty.

*These words have another setting in the* SUPPLEMENT, No. 428

# 207†

**MORECAMBE** 10. 10. 10. 10.

FREDERICK C. ATKINSON

Arranged by ALBERT F. CONANT

**MOTHER'S EVENING PRAYER**

MARY BAKER EDDY

1. O gen - tle pres - ence, peace and joy and power;
2. Love is our ref - uge; on - ly with mine eye
3. O make me glad for ev - ery scald - ing tear,
O Life di - vine, that owns each wait - ing hour,
Can I be - hold the snare, the pit, the fall:
For hope de - ferred, in - grat - i - tude, dis - dain!
Thou Love that guards the nest - ling's fal - tering flight!
His hab - i - ta - tion high is here, and nigh,..
Wait, and love more for ev - ery hate, and fear...

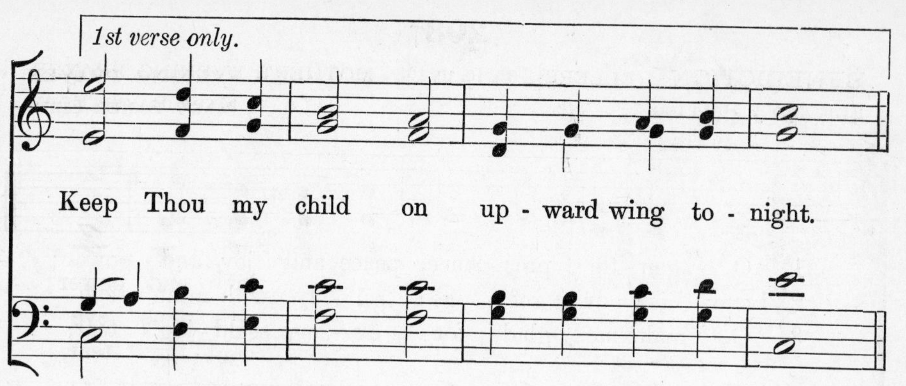
1st verse only.
Keep Thou my child on up - ward wing to - night.

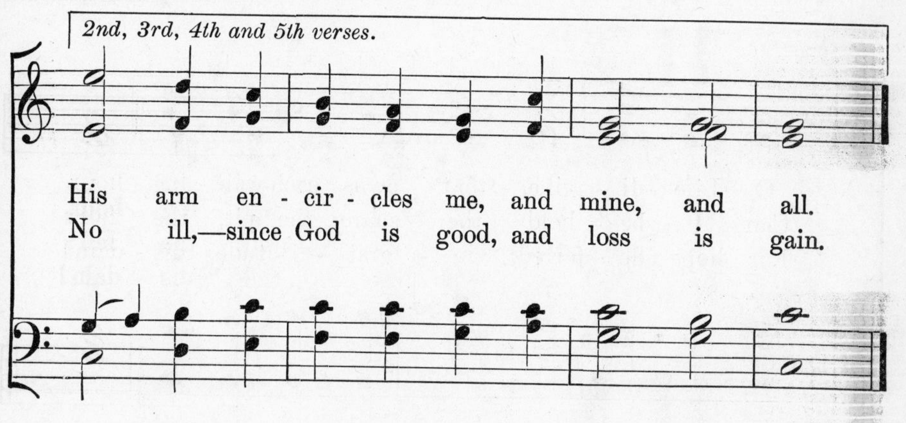
2nd, 3rd, 4th and 5th verses.
His arm en - cir - cles me, and mine, and all.
No ill,—since God is good, and loss is gain.

4. Beneath the shadow of His mighty wing;
In that sweet secret of the narrow way,
Seeking and finding, with the angels sing:
"Lo, I am with you alway,"—watch and pray.

5. No snare, no fowler, pestilence or pain;
No night drops down upon the troubled breast,
When heaven's aftersmile earth's tear-drops gain,
And mother finds her home and heav'nly rest.

# 208†

**BENEDICTION** (ELLERS) 10. 10. 10. 10. **MOTHER'S EVENING PRAYER**

EDWARD J. HOPKINS — MARY BAKER EDDY

1. O gen - tle pres - ence, peace and joy and power;
2. Love is our ref - uge; on - ly with mine eye
3. O make me glad for ev - ery scald - ing tear,
O Life di - vine, that owns each wait - ing hour,
Can I be - hold the snare, the pit, the fall:
For hope de - ferred, in - grat - i - tude, dis - dain!
Thou Love that guards the nest - ling's fal - tering flight!
His hab - i - ta - tion high is here, and nigh,
Wait, and love more for ev - ery hate, and fear

Keep Thou my child on up - ward wing to - night.
His arm en - cir - cles me, and mine, and all.
No ill,—since God is good, and loss is gain.

4. Beneath the shadow of His mighty wing;
   In that sweet secret of the narrow way,
Seeking and finding, with the angels sing:
   "Lo, I am with you alway," — watch and pray.

5. No snare, no fowler, pestilence or pain;
   No night drops down upon the troubled breast,
When heaven's aftersmile earth's tear-drops gain,
   And mother finds her home and heav'nly rest.

# 209†

**EXPECTATION** 10. 10. 10. 10.

Tænk, naar engang
ANDREAS P. BERGGREEN

**MOTHER'S EVENING PRAYER**

MARY BAKER EDDY

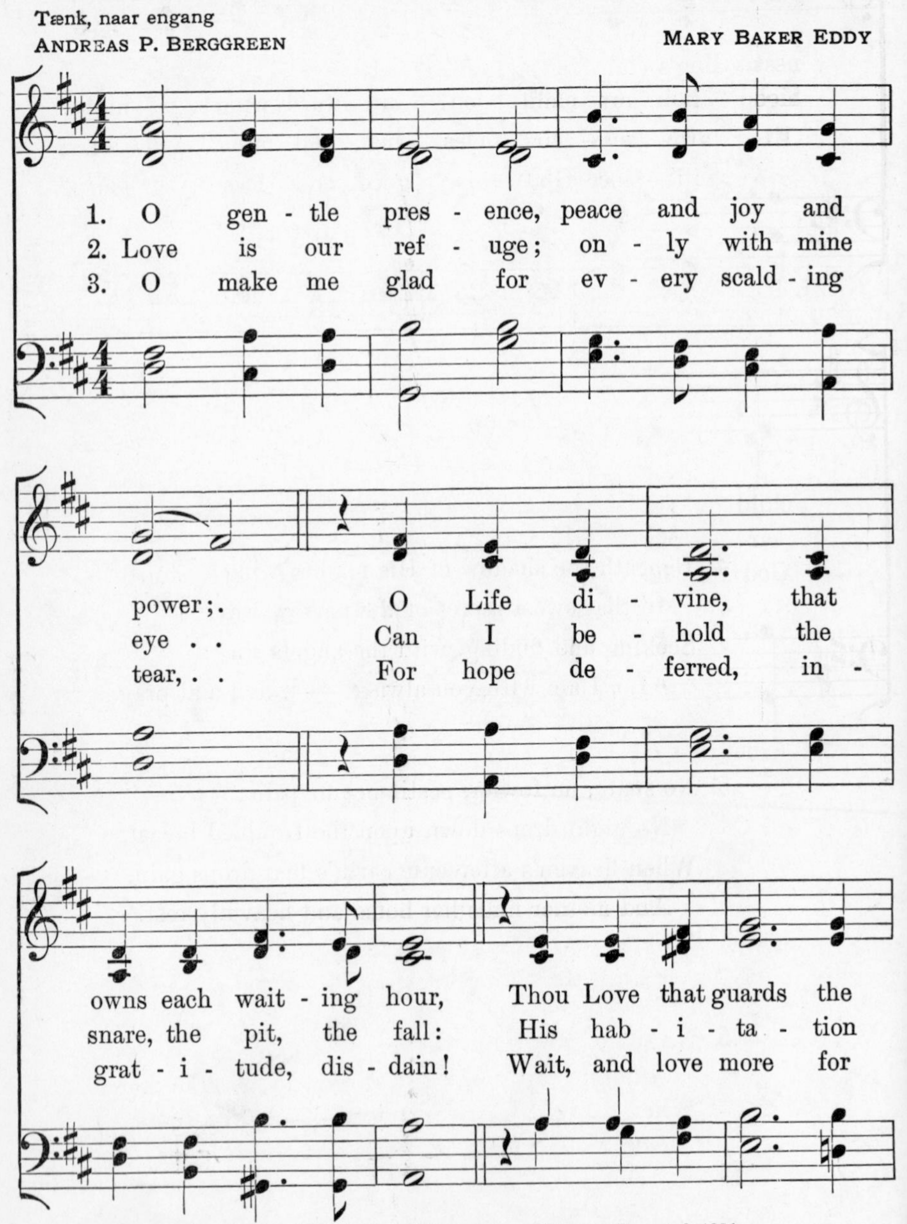
1. O gen - tle pres - ence, peace and joy and
2. Love is our ref - uge; on - ly with mine
3. O make me glad for ev - ery scald - ing
power; . . O Life di - vine, that
eye . . Can I be - hold the
tear, . . For hope de - ferred, in -
owns each wait - ing hour, Thou Love that guards the
snare, the pit, the fall: His hab - i - ta - tion
grat - i - tude, dis - dain! Wait, and love more for

nest - ling's fal - tering flight! . Keep Thou my
high is here, and nigh, . . His arm en -
ev - ery hate, and fear . . No ill, — since
child on up - ward wing to - night.
cir - cles me, and mine, and all.
God is good, and loss is gain.

4. Beneath the shadow of His mighty wing;
   In that sweet secret of the narrow way,
Seeking and finding, with the angels sing:
   "Lo, I am with you alway," — watch and pray.

5. No snare, no fowler, pestilence or pain;
   No night drops down upon the troubled breast,
When heaven's aftersmile earth's tear-drops gain,
   And mother finds her home and heav'nly rest.

**LIMPSFIELD** 10. 10. 10. 10. **MOTHER'S EVENING PRAYER**

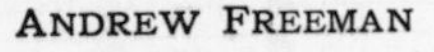

ANDREW FREEMAN MARY BAKER EDDY

*To be sung in unison*

1. O gen - tle pres - ence, peace and joy and
2. Love is our ref - uge; on - ly with mine
3. O make me glad for ev - ery scald - ing
4. Be - neath the shad - ow of His might - y
5. No snare, no fowl - er, pes - ti - lence or

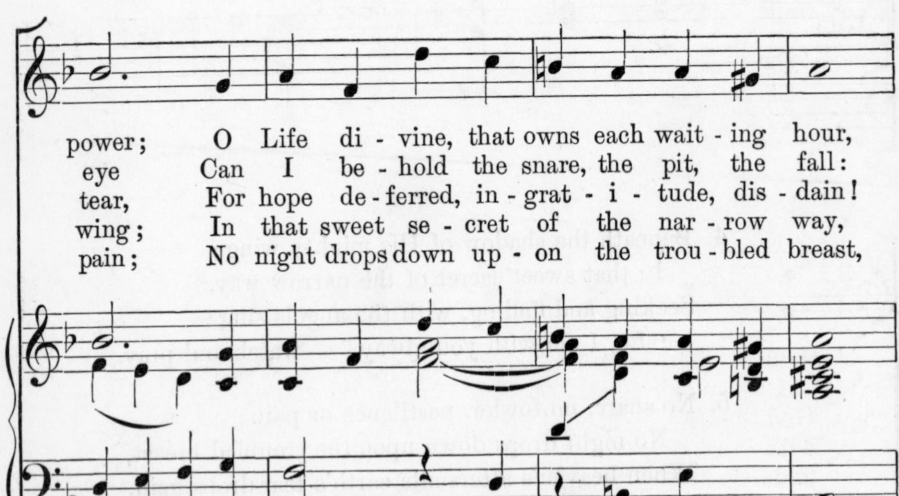
power; O Life di - vine, that owns each wait - ing hour,
eye Can I be - hold the snare, the pit, the fall:
tear, For hope de - ferred, in - grat - i - tude, dis - dain!
wing; In that sweet se - cret of the nar - row way,
pain; No night drops down up - on the trou - bled breast,

To be sung in harmony
Thou Love that guards . . . the nest - ling's fal - tering flight! . . Keep Thou my child on up - ward wing to - night.
His hab - i - ta - - - tion high is here, and nigh, . . . His arm en - cir - cles me, and mine, and all.
Wait, and love more . . . . for ev - ery hate, and fear . . . . . . No ill,—since God is good, and loss is gain.
Seek - ing and find - - ing, with the an - gels sing: . . . "Lo, I am with you al - way,"—watch and pray.
When heav - en's aft - - - er - smile earth's tear - drops gain, . . . And moth - er finds her home and heav'n - ly rest.

# 211†

**PRESENCE** 10. 10. 10. 10. **MOTHER'S EVENING PRAYER**

PERCY WHITLOCK MARY BAKER EDDY

Original Key G♭

With free rhythm
1. O gentle presence, peace and joy and power;
O Life divine, that owns each waiting hour,
Thou Love that guards the nestling's faltering flight!
2. Love is our refuge; only with mine eye
Can I behold the snare, the pit, the fall:
His habitation high is here, and nigh,
3. O make me glad for every scalding tear,
For hope deferred, ingratitude, disdain!
Wait, and love more for every hate, and fear

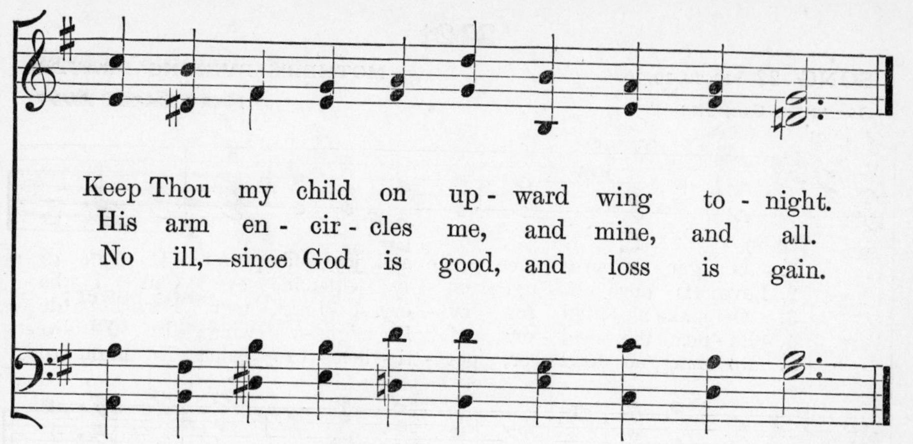


4. Beneath the shadow of His mighty wing;
   In that sweet secret of the narrow way,
Seeking and finding, with the angels sing:
   "Lo, I am with you alway,"—watch and pray.

5. No snare, no fowler, pestilence or pain;
   No night drops down upon the troubled breast,
When heaven's aftersmile earth's teardrops gain,
   And mother finds her home and heavenly rest.

## 212†

**SONG 22** 10. 10. 10. 10. — **MOTHER'S EVENING PRAYER**

ORLANDO GIBBONS — MARY BAKER EDDY

1. O gen-tle pres-ence, peace and joy and power; O Life di-
2. Love is our ref-uge; on-ly with mine eye Can I be-
3. O make me glad for ev-ery scald-ing tear, For hope de-
4. Be-neath the shad-ow of His might-y wing; In that sweet
5. No snare, no fowl-er, pes-ti-lence or pain; No night drops
vine, that owns each wait-ing hour, Thou Love that guards the
hold the snare, the pit, the fall: His hab-i-ta-tion
ferred, in-grat-i-tude, dis-dain! Wait, and love more for
se-cret of the nar-row way, Seek-ing and find-ing,
down up-on the trou-bled breast, When heav-en's aft-er-
nestling's faltering flight! Keep Thou my child on upward wing to-night.
high is here, and nigh, His arm en-cir-cles me, and mine, and all.
ev-ery hate, and fear No ill,—since God is good, and loss is gain.
with the an-gels sing: "Lo, I am with you alway,"—watch and pray.
smile earth's tear-drops gain, And moth-er finds her home and heav'nly rest.

# 213

**ST. ANNE** C.M.

WILLIAM CROFT

ISAAC WATTS*

1. O God, our help in a - ges past, Our
2. Be - fore the hills in or - der stood, Or
3. A thou - sand a - ges in Thy sight Are
4. O God, our help in a - ges past, Our

hope for time to come, Our shel - ter from the
earth re - ceived her frame, From ev - er - last - ing
like an eve - ning gone, Short as the watch that
hope for time to come, Thou art our guard while

storm - y blast, And our e - ter - nal home.
Thou art God, To end - less years the same.
ends the night Be - fore the ris - ing sun.
a - ges last, And our e - ter - nal home.

# 214

ANGELUS L. M.
Cantica Spiritualia, 1847
Founded on a Melody by G. JOSEPH
NATHANIEL L. FROTHINGHAM
Adapted
1. O God, whose pres - ence glows in all, With - in, a - round us, and a - bove, Thy Word we bless, Thy name we call, Whose Word is Truth, whose name is Love.
2. May Love its ho - ly in - fluence pour To keep us meek, and make us free; And bind its ten - der bless - ing more Round each with all, and all with Thee.
3. O send its an - gel to our side, Its ho - ly calm up - on the breast; For we would know no oth - er guide, And we can need no oth - er rest.

# 215

**CAITHNESS** C. M.

Scottish Psalter, 1635

MICHAEL BRUCE

1. O hap - py is the man who hears In - struc - tion's warn - ing voice; And who ce - les - tial wis - dom makes His ear - ly, on - ly choice.
2. For she has treas - ures great - er far Than east or west un - fold; And her re - wards more pre - cious are Than all their stores of gold.
3. Ac - cord - ing as her la - bors rise, So her re - wards in - crease; Her ways are ways of pleas - ant - ness, And all her paths are peace.

# 216

**NEUMARK** 98. 98. 88.

GEORG NEUMARK
Harmonized by J. S. BACH

From the German of
GEORG NEUMARK

*To be sung in unison*

1. O he who trusts in God's pro - tec - tion . . And hopes in
2. O wait on Him with ven - er - a - tion, . Be si - lent

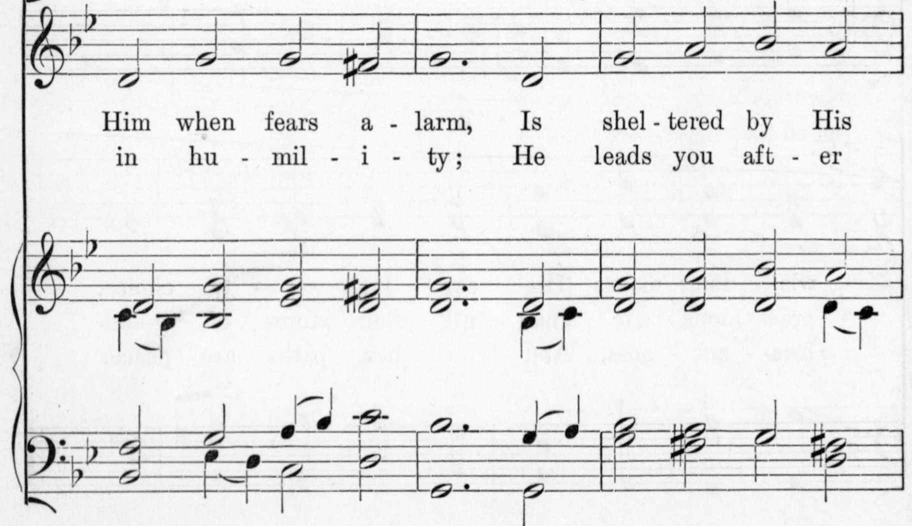

Him when fears a - larm, Is shel - tered by His
in hu - mil - i - ty; He leads you aft - er

lov - ing - kind - ness, . De - liv- ered by His might- y arm ; If
His own coun - sel, . . His will is done and still shall be ; All

ye God's law can un-der-stand, Ye have not build-ed on the sand.
good for you His wis-dom planned; O trust in God and un - der - stand.

# 217

**SECCOMB** 11. 10. 11. 10.

CHARLES H. MORSE — JOHN GREENLEAF WHITTIER

1. O, he whom Je - sus loved has tru - ly spo - ken,That ho - lier
2. Then,broth-er man, fold to thy heart thy broth-er, For where love
3. Fol - low with rev - erent steps the great ex - am - ple Of him whose

wor - ship, which God deigns to bless, Re-stores the lost, and
dwells, the peace of God is there: To wor - ship right - ly
ho - ly work was do - ing good; So shall the wide earth

heals the spir- it bro - ken,And feeds the wid-ow and the fa - ther - less.
is to love each oth - er; Each smile a hymn,each kindly deed a prayer.
seem our Father's tem-ple,Each lov - ing life a psalm of grat - i - tude.

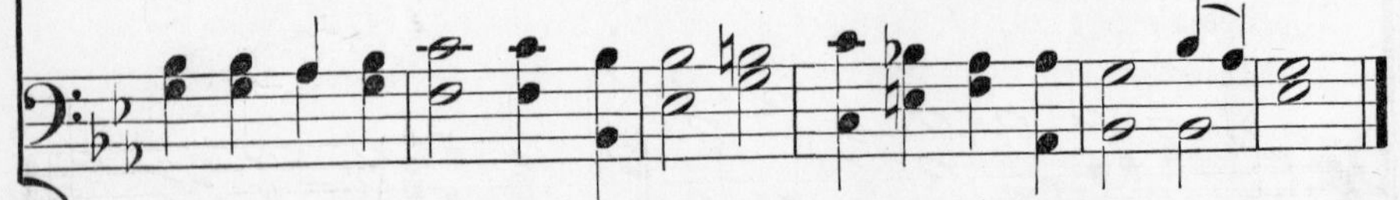

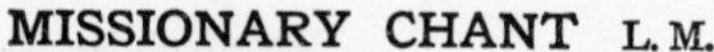

## MISSIONARY CHANT L. M.

HEINRICH C. ZEUNER — SAMUEL LONGFELLOW

1. O Life that mak-eth all things new, The bloom-ing earth, the thoughts of men; Our pil-grim feet, wet with Thy dew, In glad-ness hith-er turn a-gain.

2. From hand to hand the greet-ing flows, From eye to eye the sig-nals run, From heart to heart the bright hope glows, The seek-ers of the Light are one:

3. One in the free-dom of the truth, One in the joy of paths un-trod, One in the heart's per-en-nial youth, One in the larg-er thought of God;—

4. The fre-er step, the full-er breath, The wide ho-ri-zon's grand-er view; The sense of Life that knows no death,— The Life that mak-eth all things new.

# 219†

AFFECTION L. M.

Greenwood's Psalmody, Halifax, 1838

SAMUEL LONGFELLOW

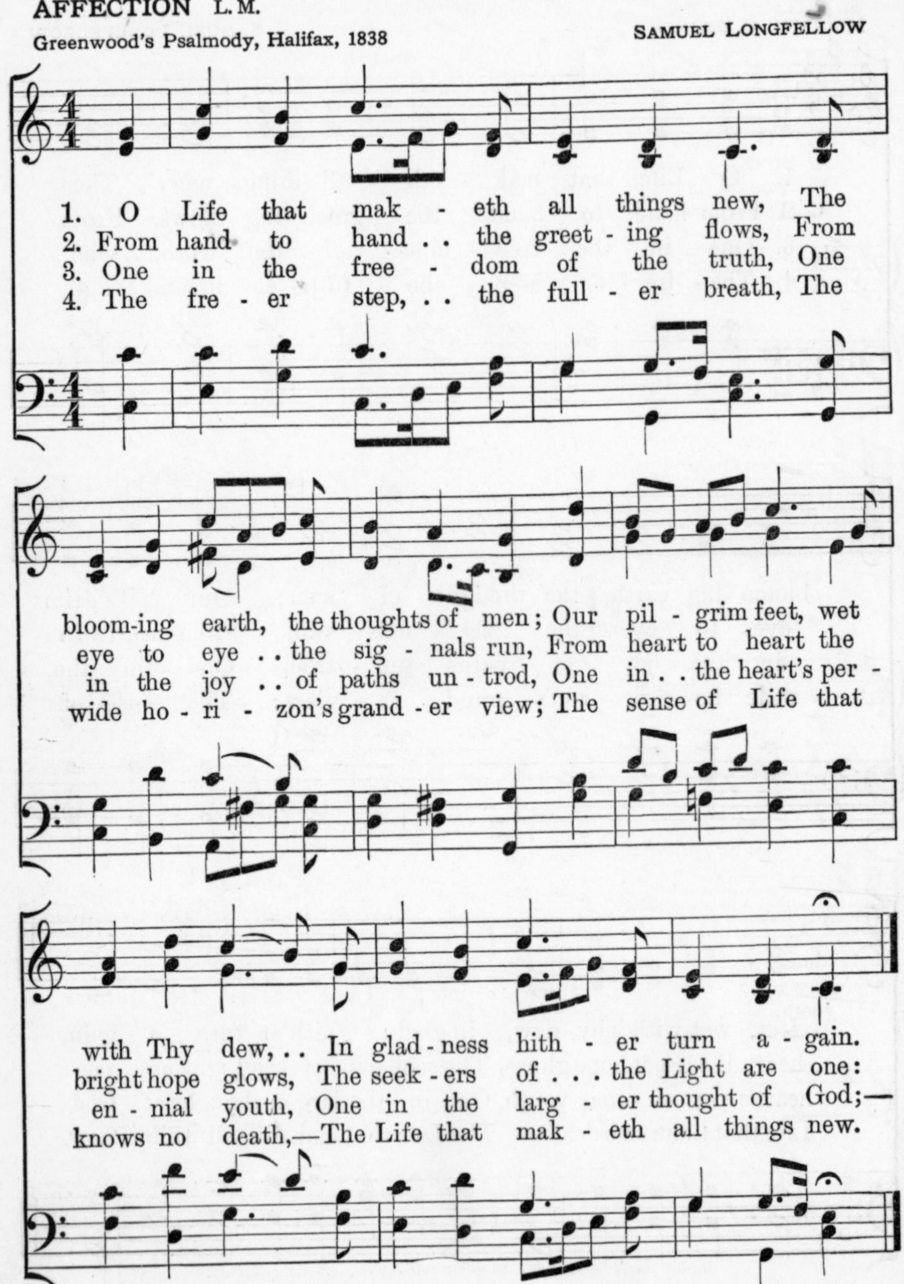

1. O Life that mak - eth all things new, The
2. From hand to hand . . the greet - ing flows, From
3. One in the free - dom of the truth, One
4. The fre - er step, . . the full - er breath, The
bloom-ing earth, the thoughts of men; Our pil - grim feet, wet
eye to eye . . the sig - nals run, From heart to heart the
in the joy . . of paths un - trod, One in . . the heart's per -
wide ho - ri - zon's grand - er view; The sense of Life that
with Thy dew, . . In glad - ness hith - er turn a - gain.
bright hope glows, The seek - ers of . . . the Light are one:
en - nial youth, One in the larg - er thought of God;—
knows no death,—The Life that mak - eth all things new.

# 220†

LANSDOWNE L. M.
E. N. G.
SAMUEL LONGFELLOW
To be sung in unison
1. O Life that mak - eth all things new, The blooming earth, the thoughts of men; Our pil - grim feet, wet with Thy dew, In glad - ness hith - er turn a - gain.
2. From hand to hand the greet - ing flows, From eye to eye the sig - nals run, From heart to heart the bright hope glows, The seek - ers of the Light are one:
3. One in the free - dom of the truth, One in the joy of paths un - trod, One in the heart's per - en - nial youth, One in the larg - er thought of God; —
4. The fre - er step, the full - er breath, The wide ho - ri - zon's grand - er view; The sense of Life that knows no death, — The Life that mak - eth all things new.

# 221

ST. HILDA 7.6.7.6.D.
JUSTIN H. KNECHT
M. G. M.
1. O Je - sus, our dear Mas - ter, Thy works, now un - der - stood, Re - veal their full ef - ful - gence Through love and broth - er - hood.
2. The Christ, e - ter - nal man - hood, As God's own Son be - loved, A ten - der ev - er - pres - ence With - in each heart is proved.
3. O Sci - ence, God - sent mes - sage To tired hu - man - i - ty, Thou art Love's rev - e - la - tion Of Truth that makes us free.

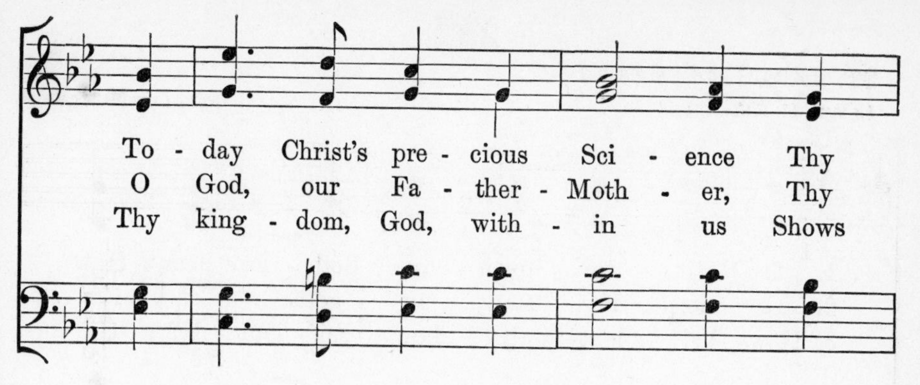

To - day Christ's pre - cious Sci - ence Thy
O God, our Fa - ther - Moth - er, Thy
Thy king - dom, God, with - in us Shows


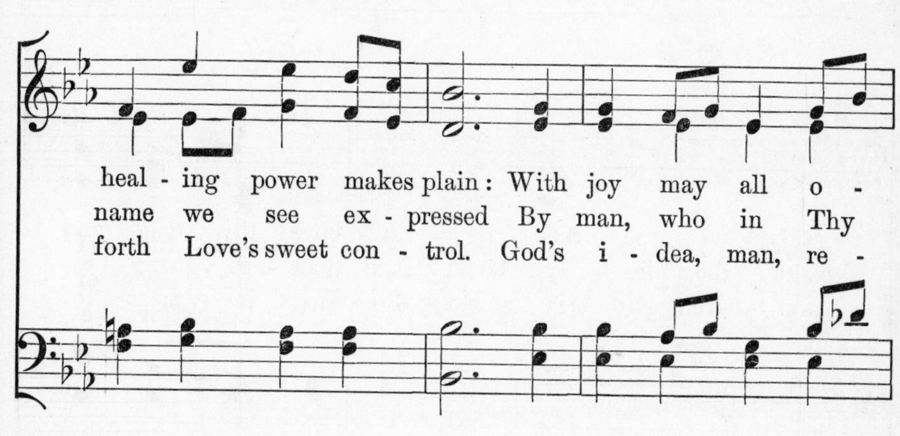

heal - ing power makes plain: With joy may all o -
name we see ex - pressed By man, who in Thy
forth Love's sweet con - trol. God's i - dea, man, re -


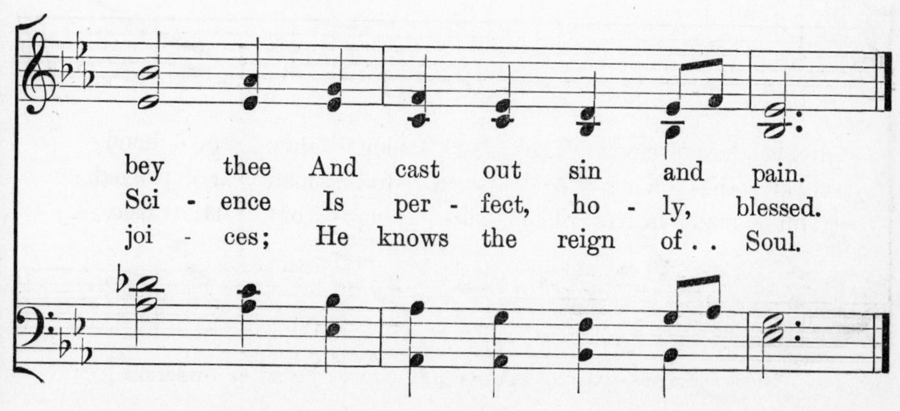

bey thee And cast out sin and pain.
Sci - ence Is per - fect, ho - ly, blessed.
joi - ces; He knows the reign of . . Soul.

222†

ST. LOUIS 86. 86. 76. 86.
Lewis H. Redner
Phillips Brooks
1. O lit - tle town of Beth - le - hem, How still we see thee lie; A - bove thy deep and dream - less sleep The si - lent stars go by;
2. O morn - ing stars, to - geth - er Pro - claim the ho - ly birth, And prais - es sing to God the King, And peace to . . men on earth;
3. How si - lent - ly, how si - lent - ly, The won - drous gift is given; So God im - parts to hu - man hearts The bless - ings of His heaven.

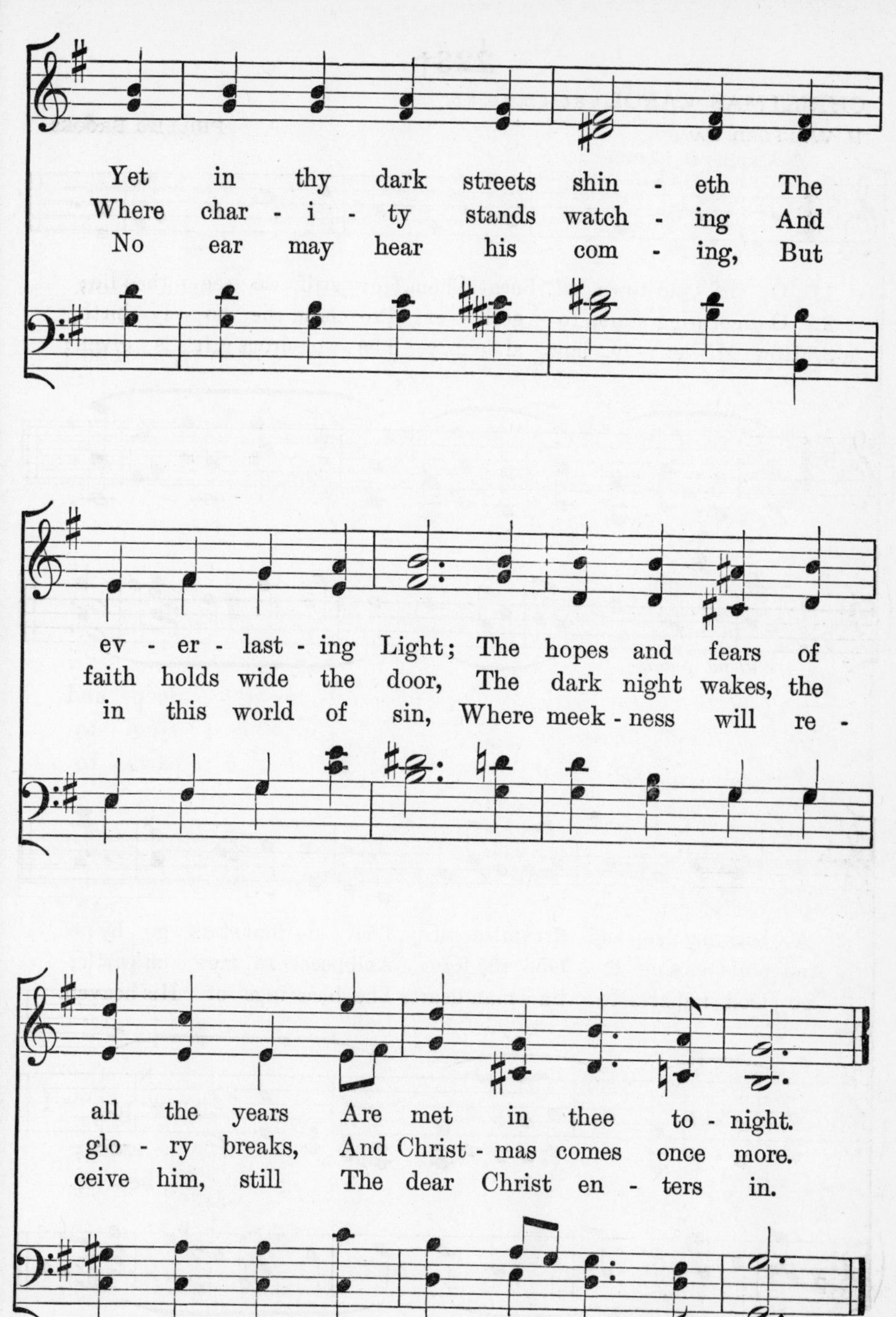
Yet in thy dark streets shin - eth The
Where char - i - ty stands watch - ing And
No ear may hear his com - ing, But
ev - er - last - ing Light; The hopes and fears of
faith holds wide the door, The dark night wakes, the
in this world of sin, Where meek - ness will re -
all the years Are met in thee to - night.
glo - ry breaks, And Christ - mas comes once more.
ceive him, still The dear Christ en - ters in.

# 223†

## CHRISTMAS CAROL 86. 86. 76. 86.

H. WALFORD DAVIES — PHILLIPS BROOKS

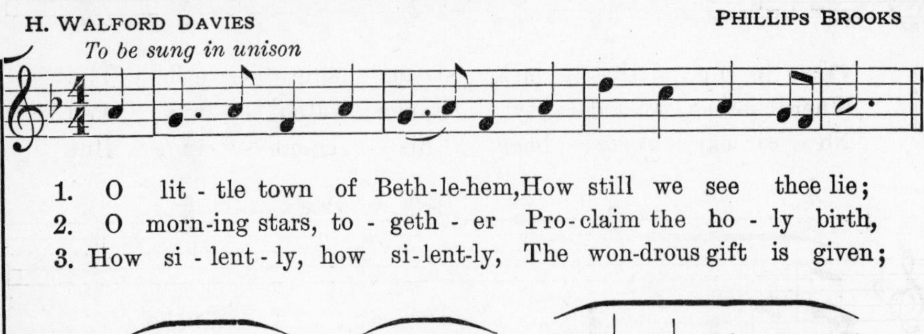

To be sung in unison
1. O lit - tle town of Beth-le-hem, How still we see thee lie;
2. O morn-ing stars, to - geth - er Pro-claim the ho - ly birth,
3. How si - lent - ly, how si-lent-ly, The won-drous gift is given;

Without pedals

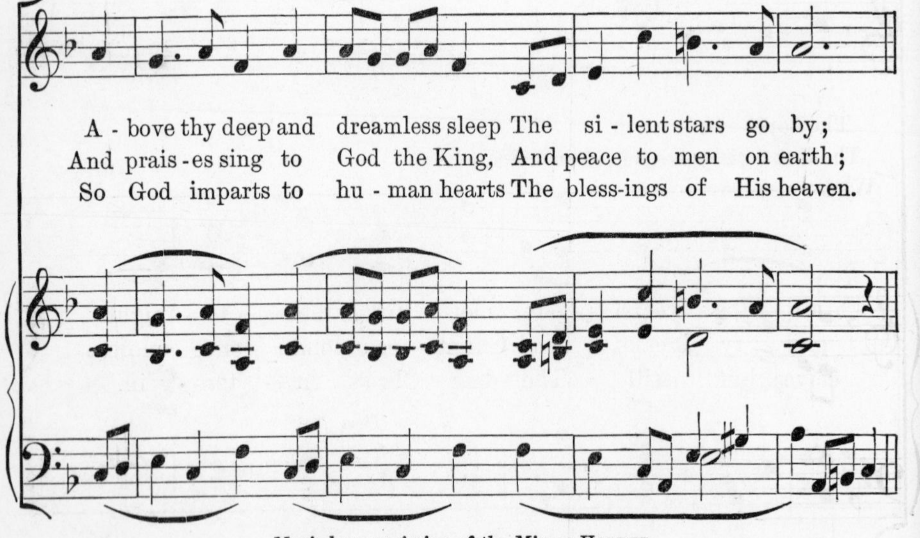

A - bove thy deep and dreamless sleep The si - lent stars go by;
And prais - es sing to God the King, And peace to men on earth;
So God imparts to hu - man hearts The bless-ings of His heaven.

Music by permission of the Misses HORDER

Yet in thy dark streets shin-eth The ev - er - last - ing Light;
Where char-i - ty stands watching And faith holds wide the door,
No ear may hear his com - ing, But in this world of sin,

The hopes and fears of all the years Are met . . in thee to - night.
The dark night wakes, the glo-ry breaks, And Christ - mas comes once more.
Where meekness will re-ceive him, still The dear Christ en - ters in.

# 224†

**ST. LEONARD** C. M. D.

HENRY HILES

JOHN RYLAND
Adapted

1. O Lord, I would de - light in Thee, And
2. All good, wher - e'er it may be found, Its
3. He that has made my heaven se - cure, Will

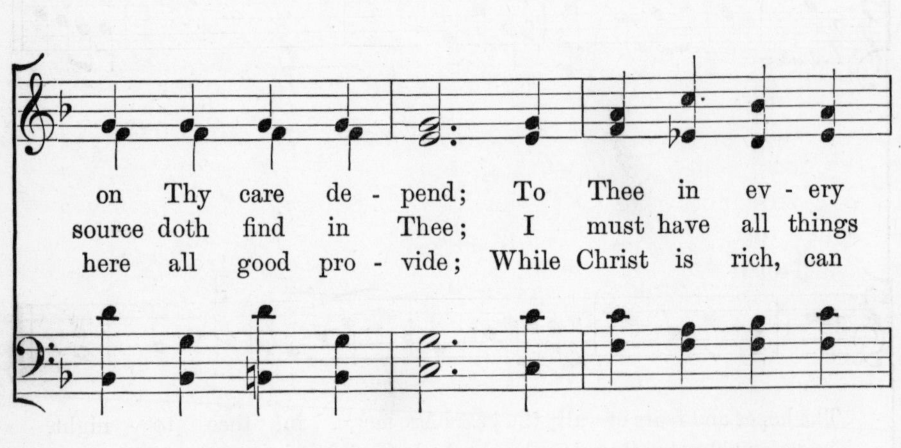

on Thy care de - pend; To Thee in ev - ery
source doth find in Thee; I must have all things
here all good pro - vide; While Christ is rich, can

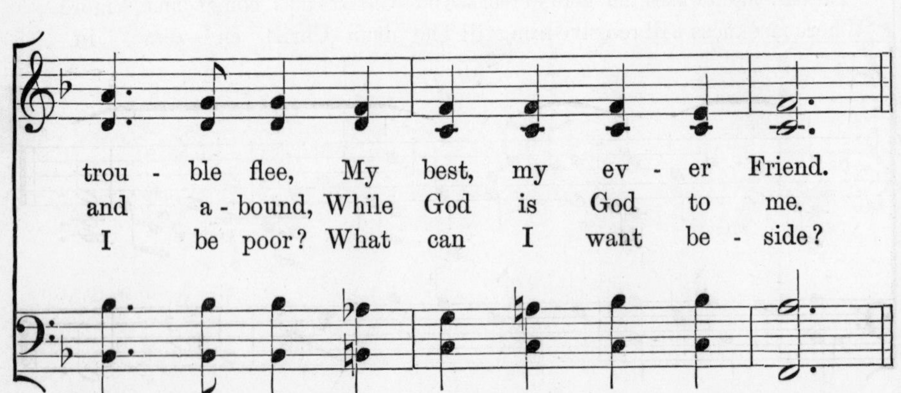

trou - ble flee, My best, my ev - er Friend.
and a - bound, While God is God to me.
I be poor? What can I want be - side?

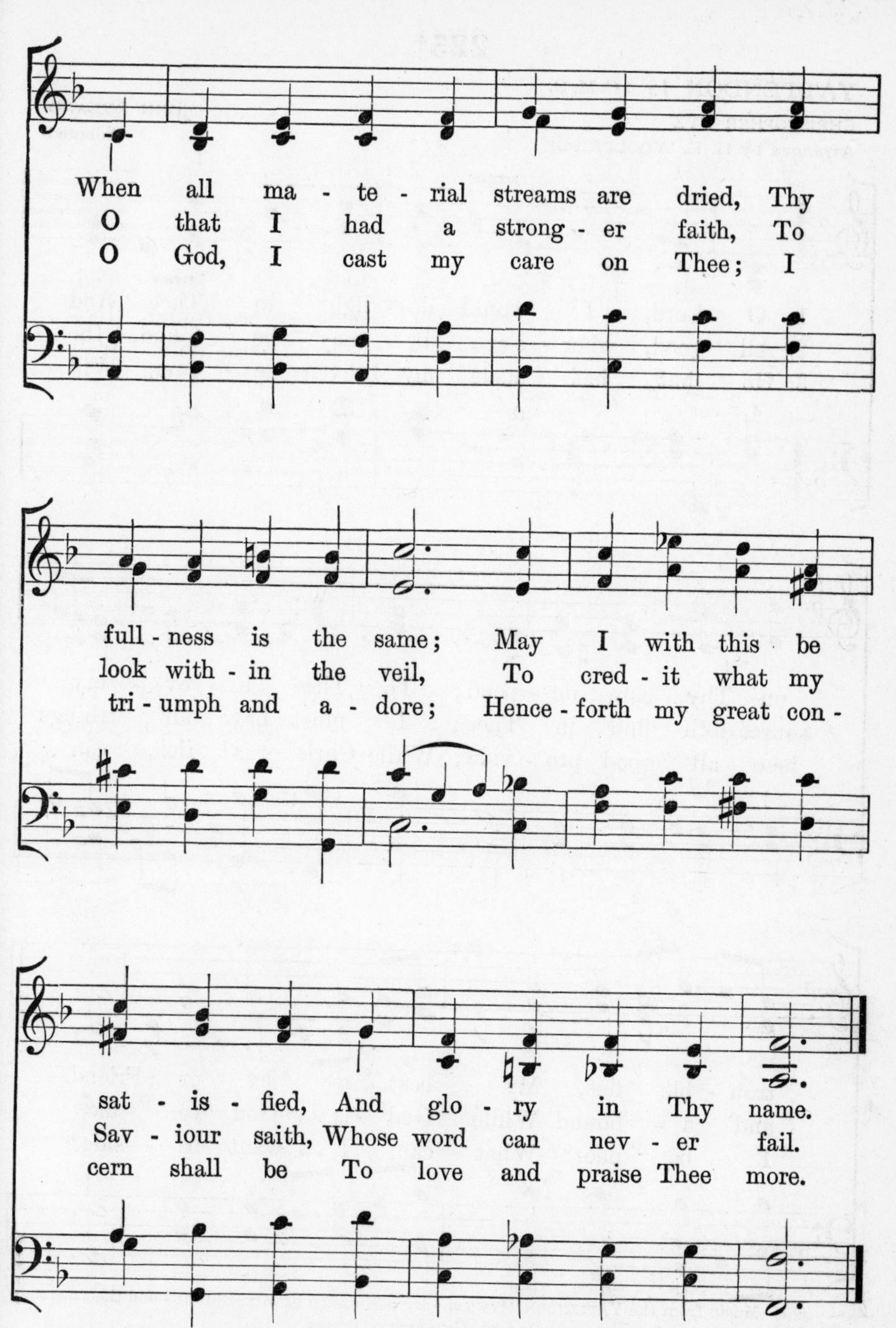
When all ma - te - rial streams are dried, Thy
O that I had a strong - er faith, To
O God, I cast my care on Thee; I
full - ness is the same; May I with this be
look with - in the veil, To cred - it what my
tri - umph and a - dore; Hence - forth my great con -
sat - is - fied, And glo - ry in Thy name.
Sav - iour saith, Whose word can nev - er fail.
cern shall be To love and praise Thee more.

# 225†

**YATTENDON 15** C. M. D.

CHRISTOPHER TYE
Arranged by H. E. WOOLDRIDGE

JOHN RYLAND
Adapted

1. O Lord, I would de - light in Thee, And
2. All good, wher - e'er .. it may be found, Its
3. He that has made my heaven se - cure, Will
on Thy care de - pend; To Thee in ev - ery
source doth find in Thee; I must have all things
here all good pro - vide; While Christ is rich, can
trou - ble flee, My best, my ev - er Friend.
and a - bound, While God is .. God to me.
I be poor? What can I .. want be - side?

Music from the YATTENDON HYMNAL: By permission of Mrs. BRIDGES and the OXFORD UNIVERSITY PRESS

When all ma - te - rial streams are . . dried, Thy
O that I had a . . strong - er . . faith, To
O God, I cast my care on . . Thee ; I
full - ness is the same ; May I with this be
look with - in the veil, To cred - it what my
tri - umph and a - dore ; Hence - forth my great con -
sat - is - fied, And glo - ry in Thy name.
Sav - iour saith, Whose word can nev - er fail.
cern shall be . . To . . love and praise Thee more.

## 226

**ELLACOMBE** C. M. D.

Mainz Gesangbuch, 1833 WASHINGTON GLADDEN*

1. O Lord of .. life, to Thee we .. lift Our
2. Shine forth, O .. Light, that we may see, With
3. Light up Thy word; the fet - tered page From
hearts in praise for those, Thy proph - ets, who have
hearts all un - a - fraid, The mean - ing and the
dark - ened bond - age free: Light up our way; lead
shown Thy gift Of grace that ev - er grows,
maj - es - ty Of things that Thou hast made:
forth this age In love's large lib - er - ty.

Of truth that spreads from shore to shore, Of
Shine forth, and let the dark - ling past Be -
O Light of light, with - in us dwell, Through
wis - dom's wid - ening ray, Of light that shin - eth
neath Thy beam grow bright; Shine forth, and touch the
us Thy ra - diance pour, That word and deed Thy
more and more Un - to .. Thy per - fect day.
fu - ture vast With Thine un - trou - bled light.
truths may tell, And praise Thee ev - er - more.

**HURSLEY** L. M.

Schicht's Choralbuch, 1819

WILLIAM COWPER
Adapted

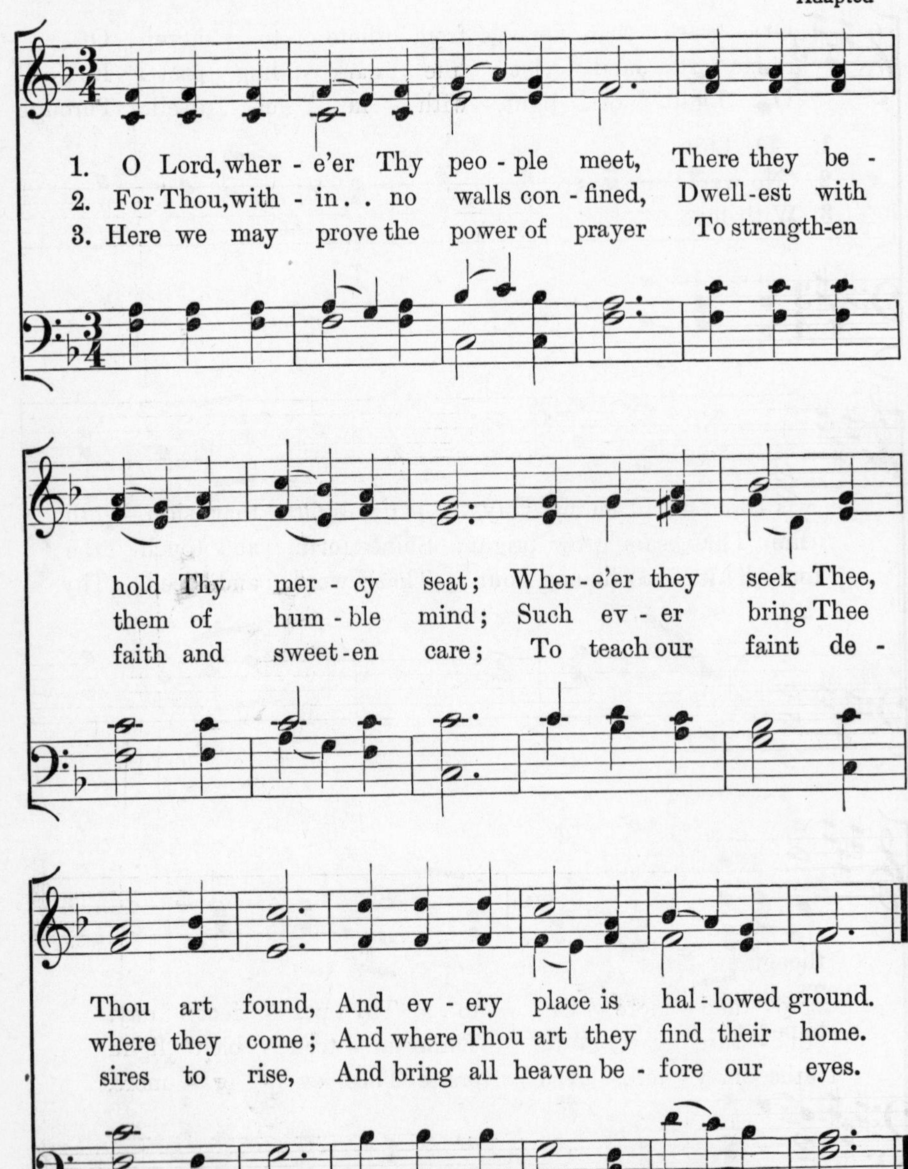
1. O Lord, wher - e'er Thy peo - ple meet, There they be -
2. For Thou, with - in . . no walls con - fined, Dwell-est with
3. Here we may prove the power of prayer To strength-en
hold Thy mer - cy seat; Wher - e'er they seek Thee,
them of hum - ble mind; Such ev - er bring Thee
faith and sweet - en care; To teach our faint de -
Thou art found, And ev - ery place is hal - lowed ground.
where they come; And where Thou art they find their home.
sires to rise, And bring all heaven be - fore our eyes.

## MENDON L. M.

Old German Melody
Arranged by SAMUEL DYER

WILLIAM P. McKENZIE

1. O Love di - vine, that dwells se - rene, Whose light of
2. No words our hid - den joy can tell, A well-ing
3. With love we meet the low de - spite Of such as

life has no.. e - clipse, We feel Thy com - fort,
fount, it fills the heart; Not in the flesh, in
hate our Mas-ter's way. With pa-tience he main -

though un - seen, And lay our hand up - on .. our lips.
Thee we dwell, In Thee our life, for Life Thou art.
tained the right; So may we tri - umph day.. by day.

# 229

**CONSTANCY** L. M. D.

FELIX MENDELSSOHN-BARTHOLDY
Arranged

JOHN GREENLEAF WHITTIER
Adapted

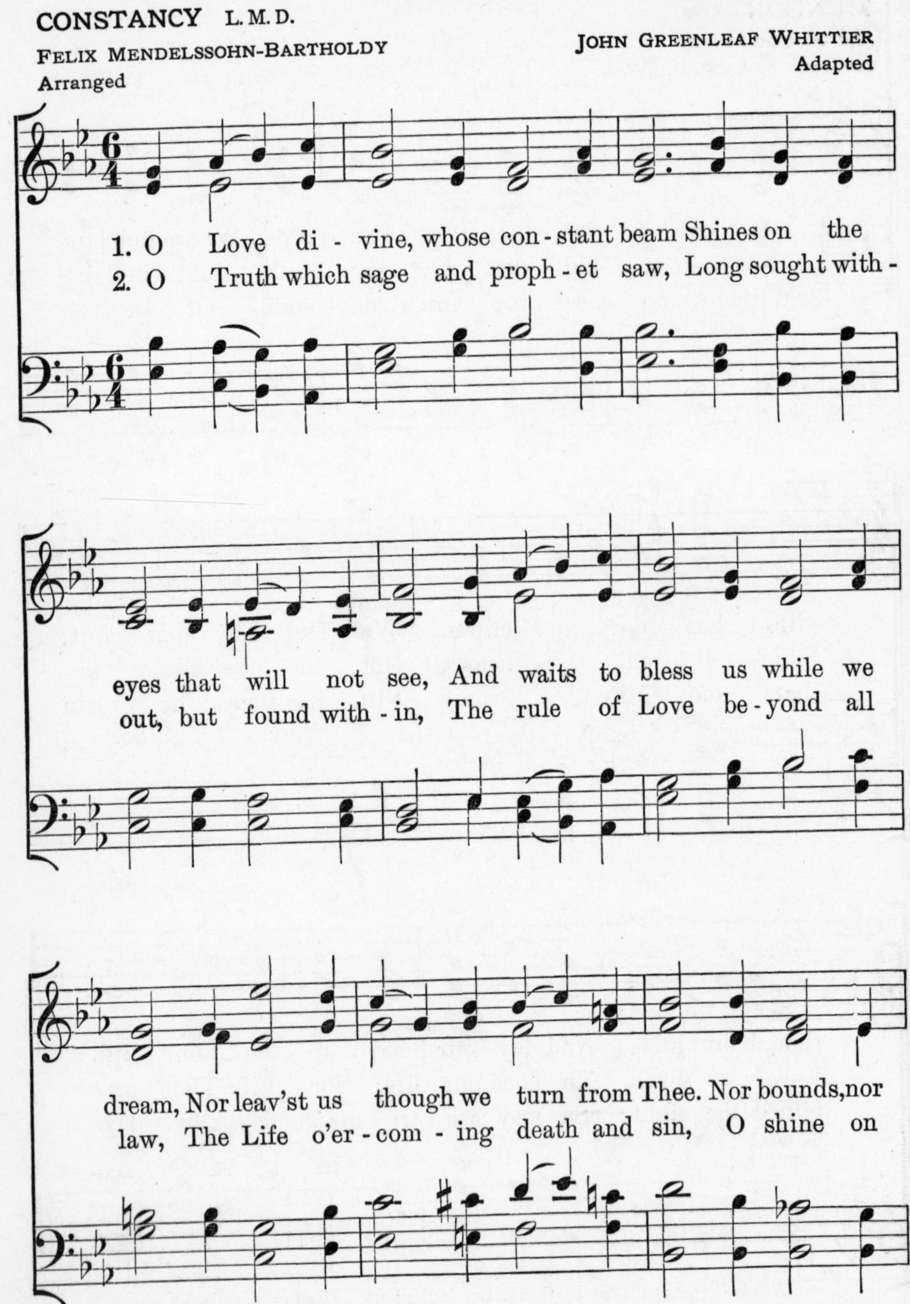
1. O Love di - vine, whose con - stant beam Shines on the
2. O Truth which sage and proph - et saw, Long sought with -
eyes that will not see, And waits to bless us while we
out, but found with - in, The rule of Love be - yond all
dream, Nor leav'st us though we turn from Thee. Nor bounds, nor
law, The Life o'er - com - ing death and sin, O shine on

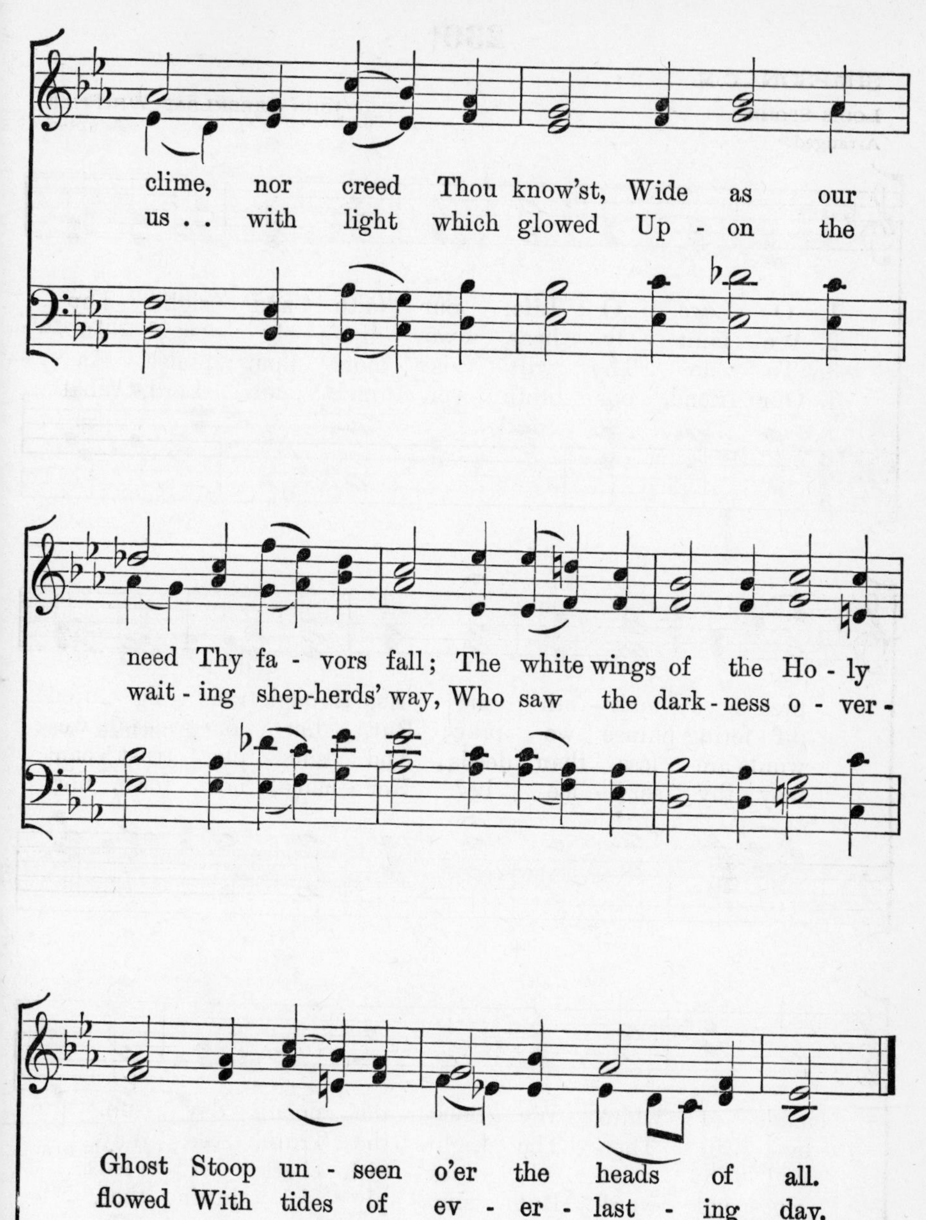
clime, nor creed Thou know'st, Wide as our
us . . with light which glowed Up - on the
need Thy fa - vors fall; The white wings of the Ho - ly
wait - ing shep-herds' way, Who saw the dark - ness o - ver -
Ghost Stoop un - seen o'er the heads of all.
flowed With tides of ev - er - last - ing day.

# 230†

**SIMPSON** C. M.

LOUIS SPOHR
Arranged

JOHN GREENLEAF WHITTIER

1. O Love, O Life, our faith and sight Thy
2. We faint - ly hear, we dim - ly see, In
3. To do Thy will is more than praise, As
4. Our friend, our broth - er, and our Lord, What
pres - ence mak - eth one; As, through trans - fig - ured
dif - fering phrase we pray; But, dim or clear, we
words are less than deeds; And sim - ple trust can
may thy serv - ice be? Nor name, nor form, nor
clouds of white, We trace the noon - day sun.
own in Thee The Light, the Truth, the Way.
find Thy ways We miss with chart of creeds.
rit - ual word, But sim - ply fol - lowing thee.

231†
RADLETT C.M.
E. N. G.
JOHN GREENLEAF WHITTIER
1. O Love, O . . Life, our faith and sight Thy presence mak - eth one; As, through trans - fig - ured clouds of white, We trace the noon - day sun.
2. We faint - ly . . hear, we dim - ly see, In dif - fering phrase we pray; But, dim or clear, we own in Thee The Light, the Truth, the Way.
3. To do Thy will is more than praise, As words are less than deeds; And sim - ple trust can find Thy ways We miss with chart of creeds.
4. Our friend, our broth - er, and our Lord, What may thy serv - ice be? Nor name, nor form, nor rit - ual word, But sim - ply fol - lowing thee.

# 232

**HAMPSTEAD** 88. 886.

H. Walford Davies — M. G. M.

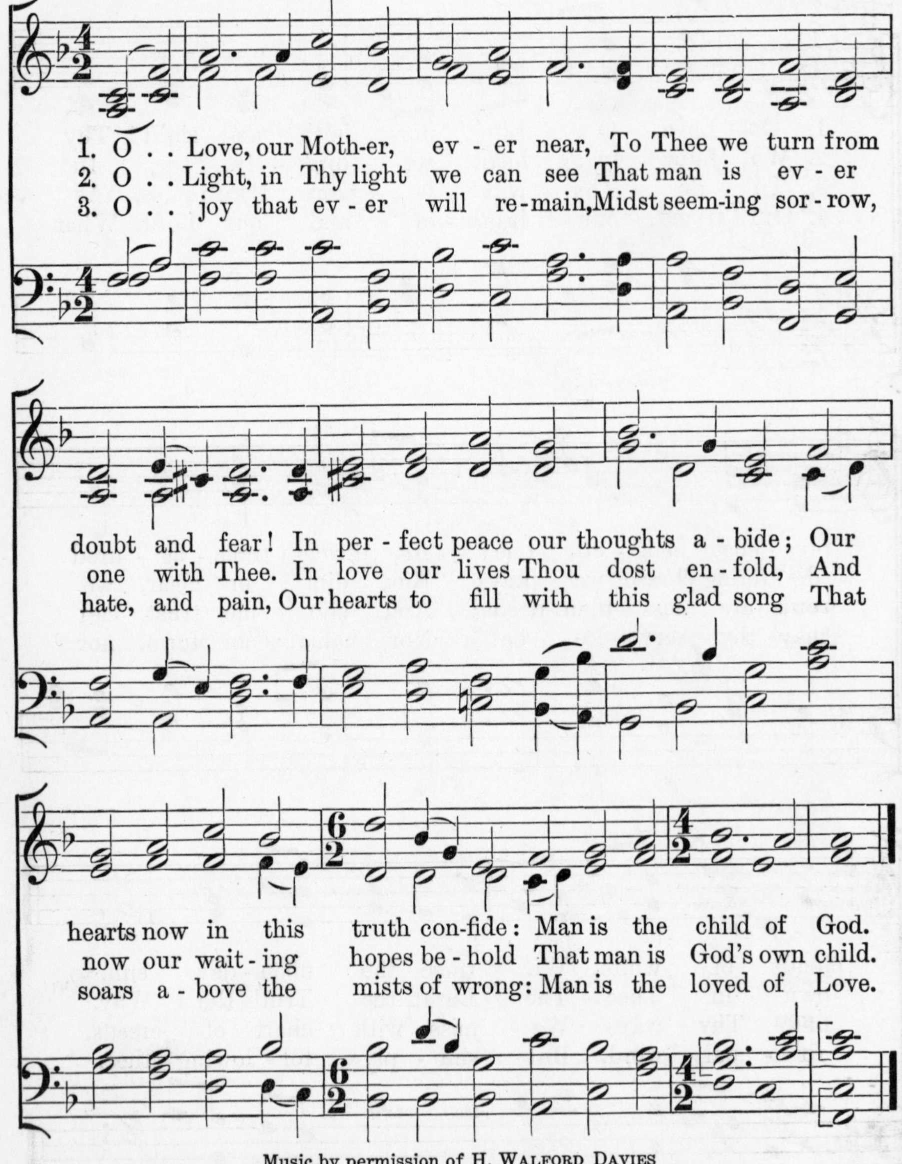
1. O . . Love, our Moth-er, ev - er near, To Thee we turn from
2. O . . Light, in Thy light we can see That man is ev - er
3. O . . joy that ev - er will re-main, Midst seem-ing sor - row,
doubt and fear! In per - fect peace our thoughts a - bide; Our
one with Thee. In love our lives Thou dost en - fold, And
hate, and pain, Our hearts to fill with this glad song That
hearts now in this truth con-fide: Man is the child of God.
now our wait - ing hopes be - hold That man is God's own child.
soars a - bove the mists of wrong: Man is the loved of Love.

*These words have another setting in the* Supplement, No. 406

# 233

**DAS WALT' GOTT** L. M.

DANIEL VETTER
Harmony from J. S. BACH

R. E. K.

1. O Love whose per - fect path is known To
2. Thy ra - diance is so pure, so free, So
3. And ev - ery sa - cred shrine shall burn With
all who walk the ways of God, Whose mys - teries are so
beau - ti - ful and swift to bless, That by . . re - flec - tion
flames of Truth di - vine - ly bright, And ev - ery wea - ry
clear - ly . . shown To pil - grims with the gos - pel shod;
con - stant - ly We man - i - fest Thy ten - der - ness:
child shall turn In grat - i - tude toward Thee, the Light.

*These words have another setting in the* SUPPLEMENT, No. 419

# 234†

MARYTON L. M.

H. PERCY SMITH

WASHINGTON GLADDEN*

1. O Mas - ter, let me walk with thee In low - ly paths of serv - ice free; Tell me thy se - cret; help me bear The strain of toil, the fret.. of care.

2. Help me the slow of heart to move By some clear win - ning word of love; Teach me the way - ward feet to stay, And guide them in the home - ward way.

3. Teach me thy pa - tience; still with thee In clos - er, dear - er com - pa - ny, In work that keeps faith sweet and strong, In trust that tri - umphs o - ver wrong.

4. In hope that sends a shin - ing ray Far down the fu - ture's broad - ening way; In peace that God a - lone can give, With thee, O Mas - ter, let.. me live.

Music by permission of the Misses HORDER

# 235†

**BROCKHAM** L. M.

JEREMIAH CLARK — WASHINGTON GLADDEN*

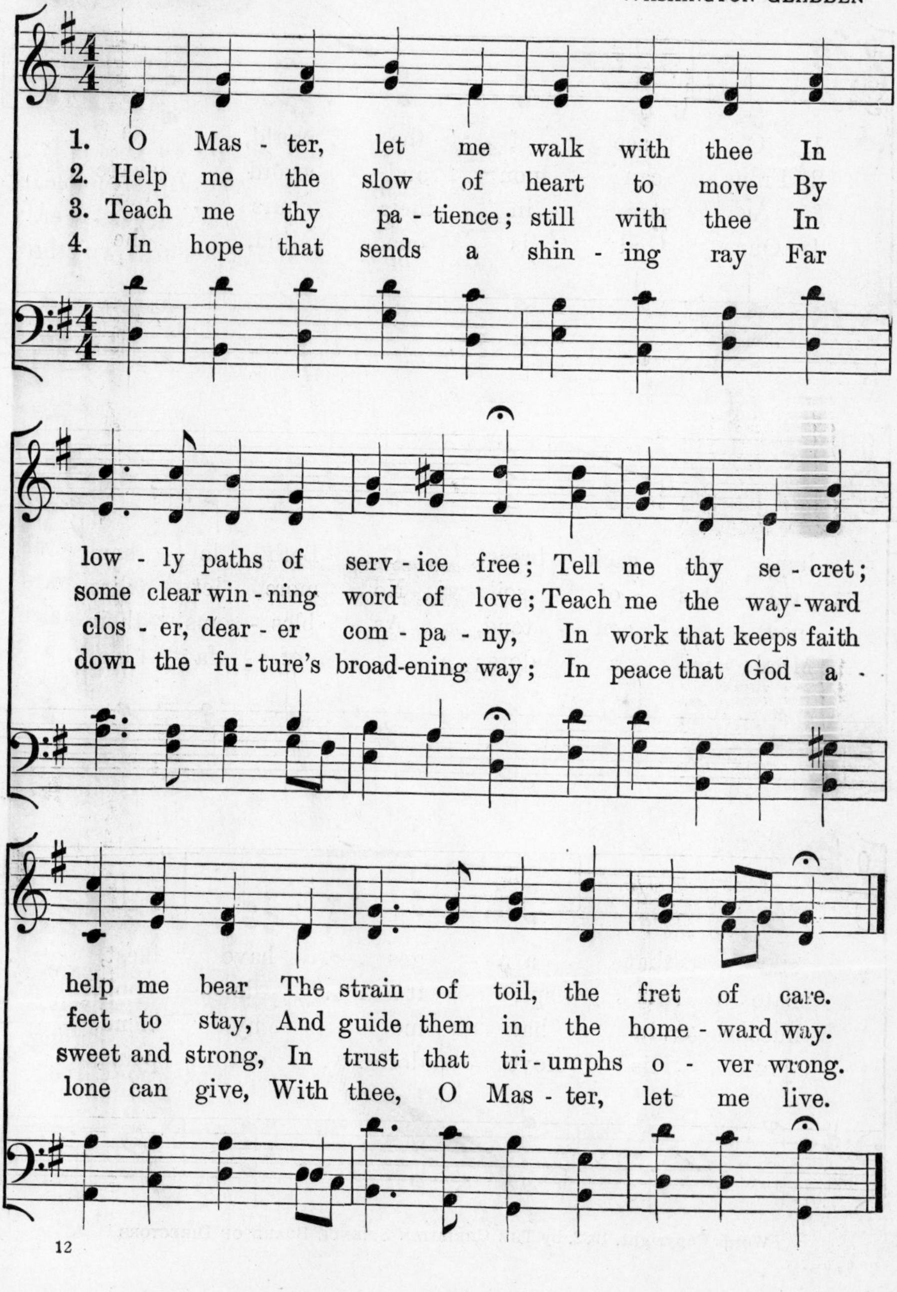

1. O Mas - ter, let me walk with thee In
2. Help me the slow of heart to move By
3. Teach me thy pa - tience; still with thee In
4. In hope that sends a shin - ing ray Far

low - ly paths of serv - ice free; Tell me thy se - cret;
some clear win - ning word of love; Teach me the way - ward
clos - er, dear - er com - pa - ny, In work that keeps faith
down the fu - ture's broad-ening way; In peace that God a -

help me bear The strain of toil, the fret of care.
feet to stay, And guide them in the home - ward way.
sweet and strong, In trust that tri - umphs o - ver wrong.
lone can give, With thee, O Mas - ter, let me live.

236

HANOVER 10. 10. 11. 11.

WILLIAM CROFT — IRVING C. TOMLINSON

1. O peace of the world, O hope in each breast, O Beth - le - hem star that a - ges . . have blest,
2. From can - non and sword shape till - ers of soil, No more let dire hate man's spir - it . . de - spoil,
3. As stars in their cours - es nev - er con - tend, As blos - soms their hues in har - mo - ny blend,
4. Our God is one Mind, the Mind we a - dore; In - ef - fa - ble joy His love doth . . out - pour;

A day of fresh prom - ise breaks
Let Truth be pro - claimed, let God's
As bird - voi - ces min - gle in
Let na - tions be one in a
o - ver the land, Gaunt war - fare is
love be re - told, That men of good
joy - ful re - frain, So God's lov - ing
un - ion of love, God's boun - ti - ful
doomed, and God's king - dom at hand
will may their breth - ren up - hold.
chil - dren in con - cord re - main.
peace, all earth's treas - ures a - bove.

237

## CAROL MELODY 8. 7. 8. 7.

14th Century Carol

F. L.

1. O may we be still and seek Him, Seek with
2. He hath prom - ised we . . shall find Him, Love di -
3. If we pray to Him in se - cret, Lift to
4. Then up - on the pre - cious met - al God's own
con - se - cra - tion whole, Lis - tening thus to
vine its prom - ise keeps; God is watch - ing
Him the heart's de - sire, . . We shall find our
im - age will ap - pear, Faith - ful - ly to
hear the mes - sage, Far from sense and hid in Soul.
with the watch - ful, God is Life that nev - er sleeps.
earth - ly long - ings All made pure by Love's pure fire.
Him re - flect - ed, One with Him for - ev - er near.

# 238†

**GERMANY (Fulda) L. M.**

Gardiner's Sacred Melodies, 1812

Attributed to LUDWIG VAN BEETHOVEN — JOHN GREENLEAF WHITTIER*

1. O, sometimes gleams up - on.. our sight, Through pres - ent
2. For all of good the past hath had Re - mains to
3. Through the harsh nois - es of.. our day, A low sweet
4. Hence-forth my heart shall sigh no more For old - en
wrong, th'e - ter - nal right; And step by step, since
make our own time glad, Our com - mon, dai - ly
prel - ude finds its way; Through clouds of doubt and
time and ho - lier shore: God's love and bless - ing,
time be - gan, We see the stead - y gain of man.
life di - vine, And ev - ery land a Pal - es - tine.
creeds of fear A light is break-ing, calm and clear.
then and there, Are now and here and ev - ery - where.

# 239†

## ST. GREGORY L. M.

Harmonischer Liederschatz, 1755
Harmonized by W. H. MONK

JOHN GREENLEAF WHITTIER*

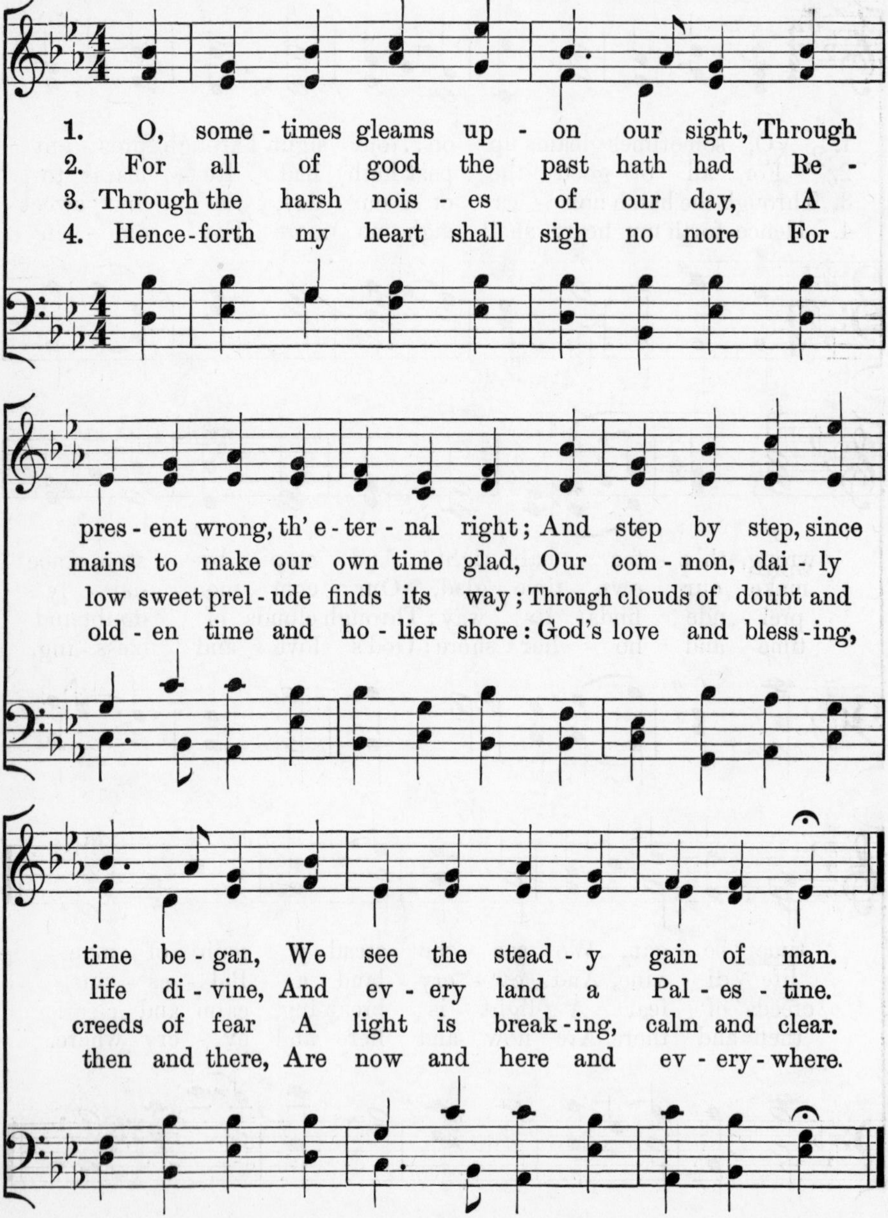

1. O, some - times gleams up - on our sight, Through
2. For all of good the past hath had Re -
3. Through the harsh nois - es of our day, A
4. Hence-forth my heart shall sigh no more For

pres - ent wrong, th' e - ter - nal right; And step by step, since
mains to make our own time glad, Our com - mon, dai - ly
low sweet prel - ude finds its way; Through clouds of doubt and
old - en time and ho - lier shore: God's love and bless - ing,

time be - gan, We see the stead - y gain of man.
life di - vine, And ev - ery land a Pal - es - tine.
creeds of fear A light is break - ing, calm and clear.
then and there, Are now and here and ev - ery - where.

# 240†

**THATCHER** S.M.

Arranged from GEORG FRIEDRICH HÄNDEL

BENJAMIN BEDDOME
Adapted

1. O Spir - it, source of light, Thy grace is
2. Now to .. our eyes dis - play The truth Thy
3. Thy teach - ings make us know The mys - teries
un - con - fined; Dis - pel . . the gloom - y
words re - veal; Cause us . . to . . run . . the
of Thy love; The van - i - ty . . . of
shades of . . night, Re - veal the light of Mind.
heaven - ly . . way, De - light - ing in Thy will.
things be - low, The joy . . of things a - bove.

241†

**ST. EDMUND** S.M.

EDMUND GILDING

BENJAMIN BEDDOME
Adapted

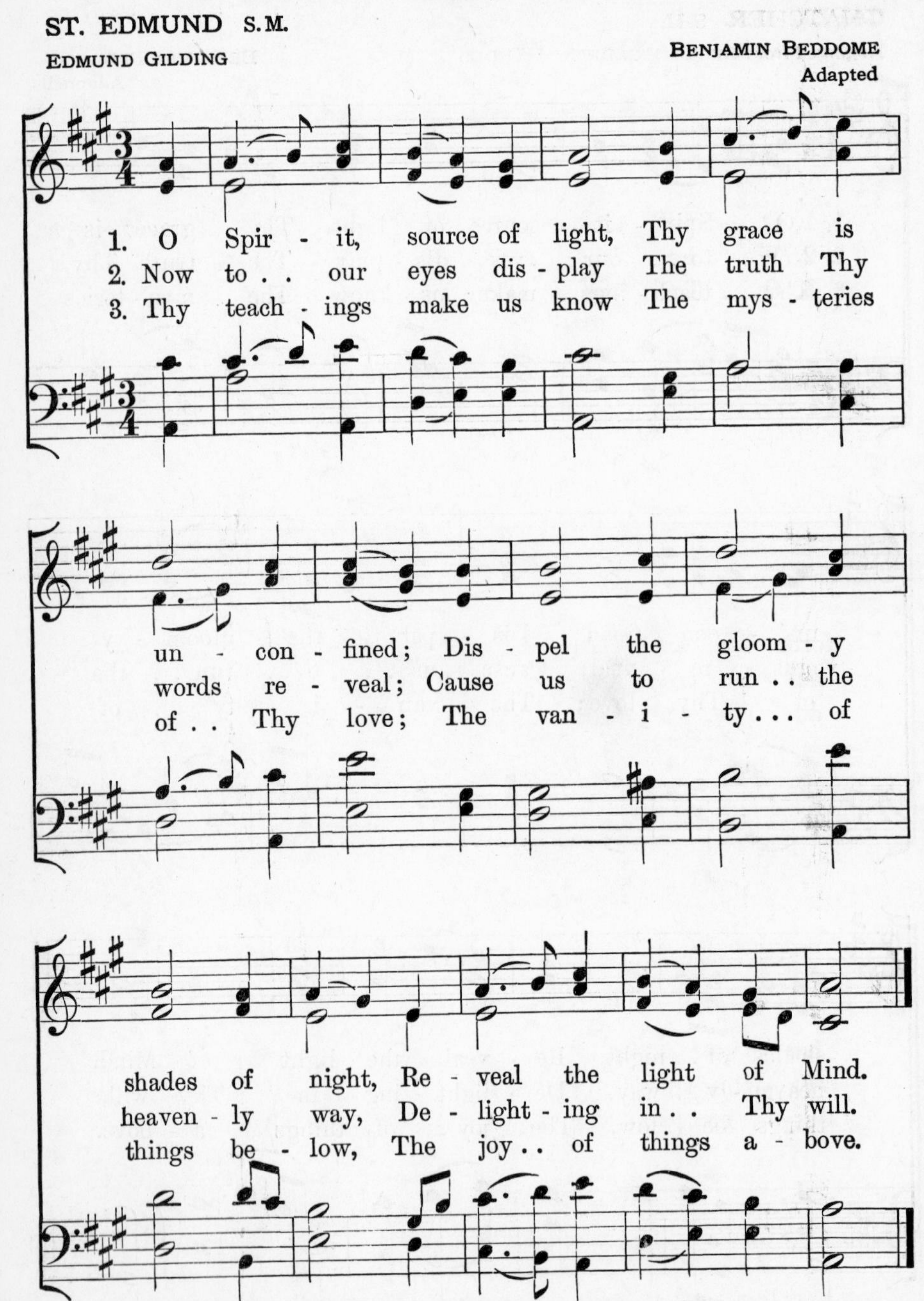
1. O Spir - it, source of light, Thy grace is un - con - fined; Dis - pel the gloom - y shades of night, Re - veal the light of Mind.
2. Now to . . our eyes dis - play The truth Thy words re - veal; Cause us to run . . the heaven - ly way, De - light - ing in . . Thy will.
3. Thy teach - ings make us know The mys - teries of . . Thy love; The van - i - ty . . . of things be - low, The joy . . of things a - bove.

**CAPEL** C. M.

English Traditional Carol Melody — SAMUEL LONGFELLOW

1. O, .. still in .. ac - cents sweet and strong Sounds
2. We hear the call; no .. more in dreams And
3. O .. Thou whose call our hearts hath stirred, To
forth the an - cient word: More reap - ers for .. white
self - ish ease we .. lie, But gird - ed for .. our ..
do Thy will we .. come, Thrust in our sick - les ..
har - vest fields, More la - borers for the Lord.
Fa - ther's work, Go forth be - neath His sky.
at Thy word, And bear our har - vest home.

Music from SONGS OF PRAISE: By permission of the OXFORD UNIVERSITY PRESS

## 243†

**OMBERSLEY** L. M.

WILLIAM H. GLADSTONE — ELLA A. STONE

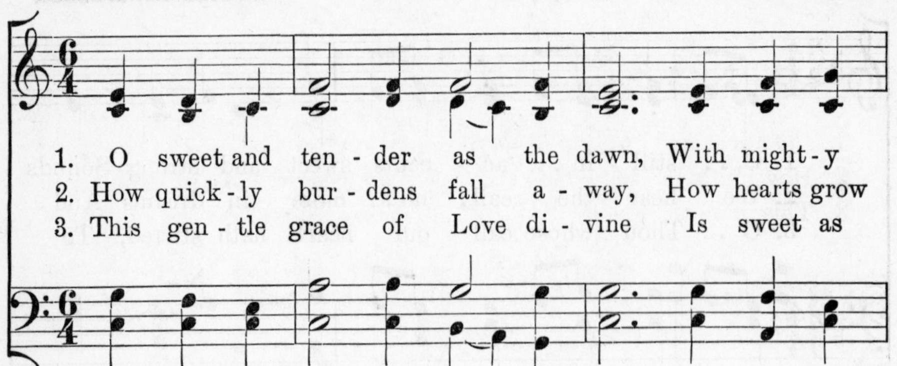
1. O sweet and tender as the dawn, With might-y
2. How quick-ly burdens fall a-way, How hearts grow
3. This gen-tle grace of Love di-vine Is sweet as

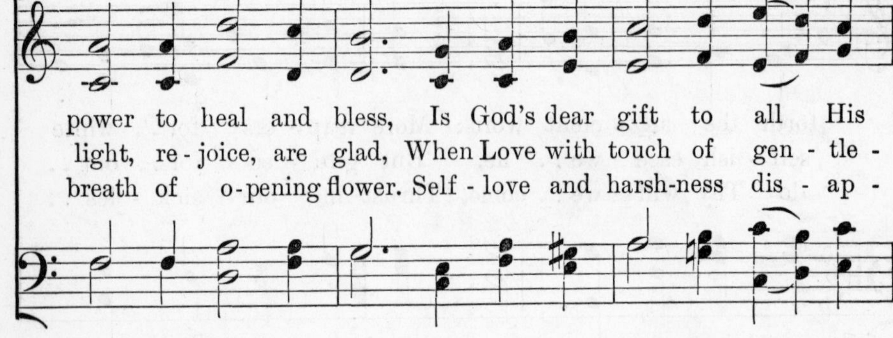
power to heal and bless, Is God's dear gift to all His
light, re-joice, are glad, When Love with touch of gen-tle-
breath of o-pening flower. Self-love and harsh-ness dis-ap-

own: The hap-py grace of gen-tle-ness.
ness Up-lifts the sin-ning and the sad.
pear Be-neath its ten-der, heal-ing power.

## 244†

**HESPERUS** L.M.

HENRY BAKER — ELLA A. STONE

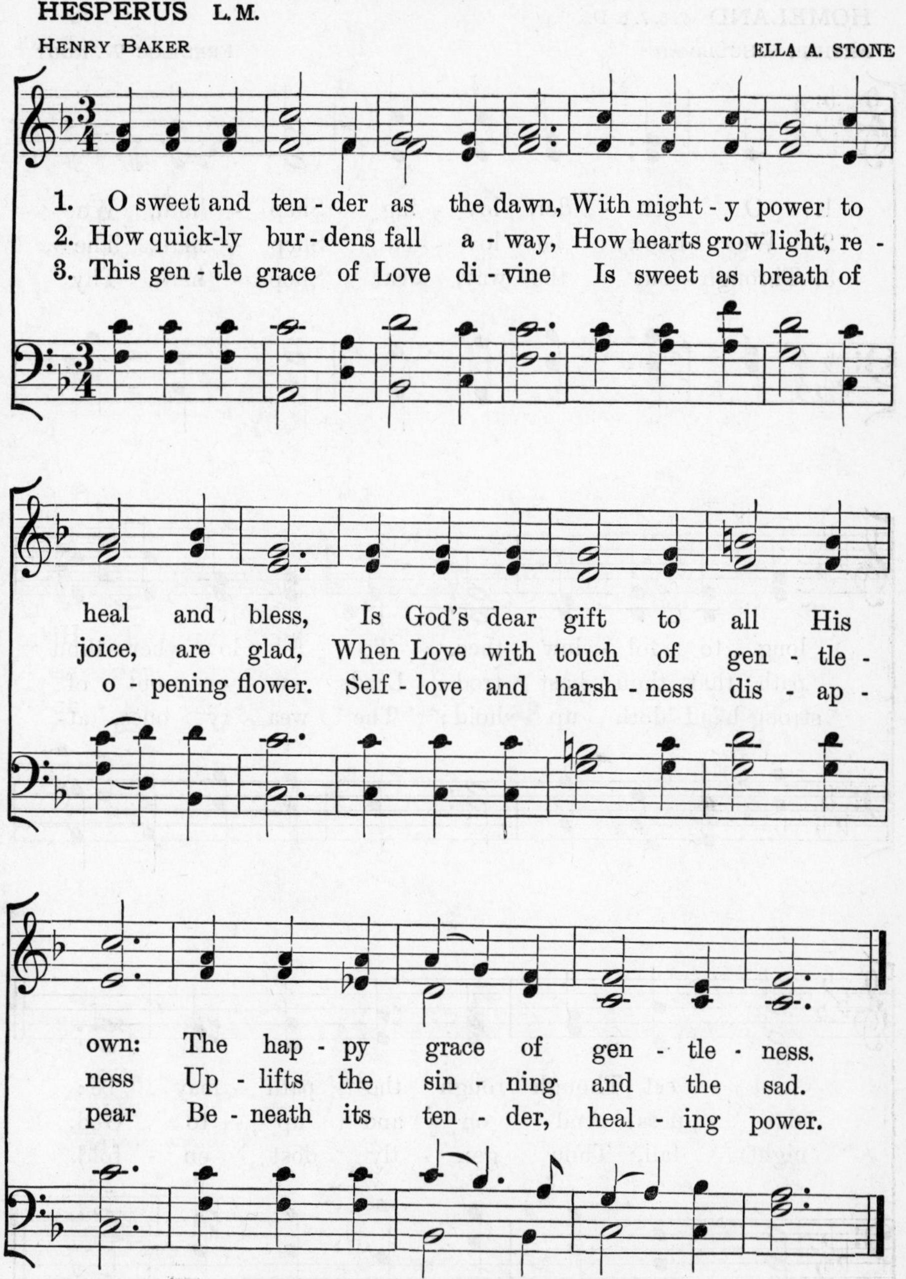
1. O sweet and ten - der as the dawn, With might - y power to
2. How quick-ly bur - dens fall a - way, How hearts grow light, re -
3. This gen - tle grace of Love di - vine Is sweet as breath of
heal and bless, Is God's dear gift to all His
joice, are glad, When Love with touch of gen - tle -
o - pening flower. Self - love and harsh - ness dis - ap -
own: The hap - py grace of gen - tle - ness.
ness Up - lifts the sin - ning and the sad.
pear Be - neath its ten - der, heal - ing power.

Music by permission of the Misses HORDER

# 245

**HOMELAND** 7. 6. 7. 6. D.

ARTHUR S. SULLIVAN — FREDERIC W. ROOT

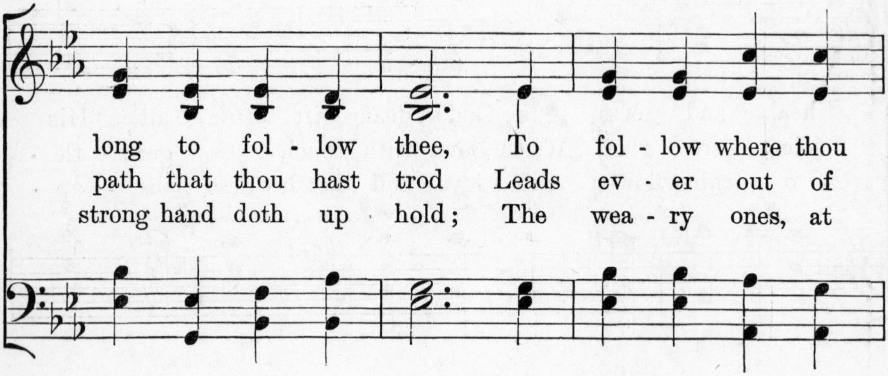

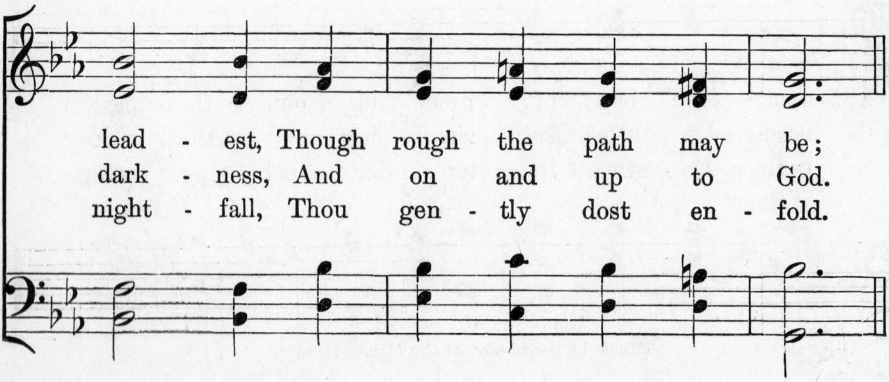

1. O tender, loving Shepherd, We long to follow thee, To follow where thou leadest, Though rough the path may be;

2. We know, beloved Shepherd, The path that thou hast trod Leads ever out of darkness, And on and up to God.

3. Throughout the way, dear Shepherd, Thy strong hand doth uphold; The weary ones, at nightfall, Thou gently dost enfold.

Though dark and heav - y shad - ows En -
If from that path we wan - der, And
And when to Truth's green pas - tures With
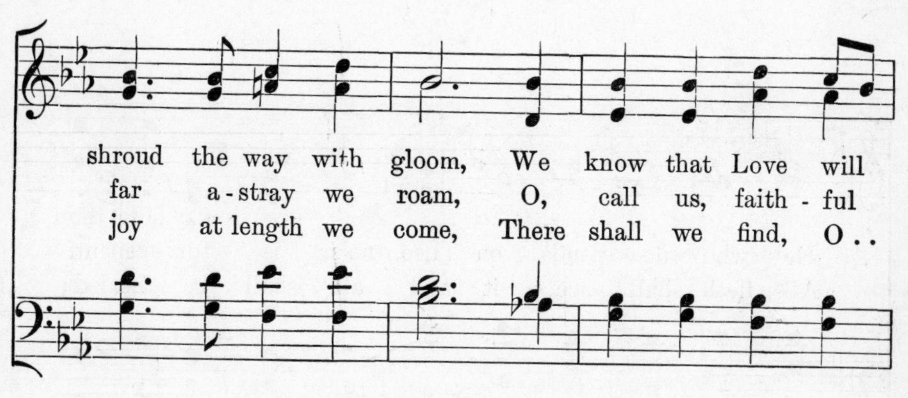
shroud the way with gloom, We know that Love will
far a - stray we roam, O, call us, faith - ful
joy at length we come, There shall we find, O ..

guide us, And safe - ly lead us home.
Shep - herd, And bring us safe - ly home.
Shep - herd, Our blest, e - ter - nal home.

# 246

**VALERIUS** 10. 10. 11. 11. and Refrain

Old Dutch Hymn

ISAIAH 40

From Dutch Version

1. O Thou who spread - est the heaven like a tent,
2. So shall the glo - ry of God be re - vealed,
He who de - pends on Thee, ne'er is for - spent,
All flesh shall see it and all shall be healed;
Still for his might on Thee he ev - er count-eth,
In word and deed de - clare Him and a - dore Him.

On wings of ea - gles he, un - wea - ried,
God's will is done, and all is plain be -
REFRAIN
mount - eth. Have ye not heard, have ye . . . not known The
fore Him.
ev - er - last - ing God . . Cre - a - tor is . . of
heaven and earth, And He . . a - lone is Lord.

# 247†

**ST. LEONARD** C.M.

HENRY SMART | THOMAS H. GILL*

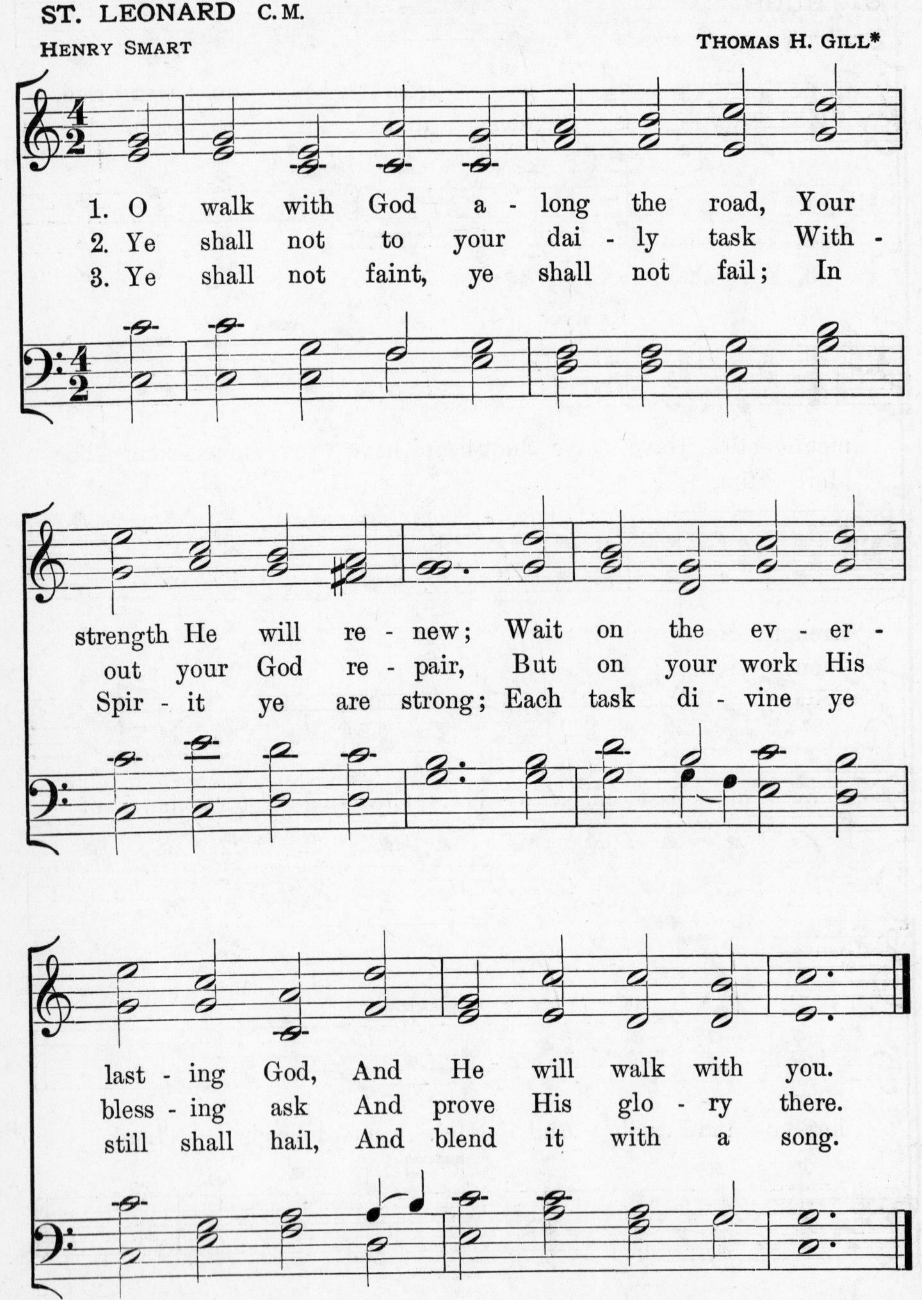
1. O walk with God a - long the road, Your
2. Ye shall not to your dai - ly task With -
3. Ye shall not faint, ye shall not fail; In
strength He will re - new; Wait on the ev - er -
out your God re - pair, But on your work His
Spir - it ye are strong; Each task di - vine ye
last - ing God, And He will walk with you.
bless - ing ask And prove His glo - ry there.
still shall hail, And blend it with a song.

## 248†

ST. HUGH C.M.

English Traditional Melody

THOMAS H. GILL*

1. O walk with God a - long the road, Your strength He will re - new; Wait on the ev - er - last - ing God, And He will walk with you.
2. Ye shall not to your dai - ly task With - out your God re - pair, But on your work His bless - ing ask And prove His glo - ry there.
3. Ye shall not faint, ye shall not fail; In Spir - it ye are strong; Each task di - vine ye still shall hail, And blend it with a song.

## 249†

**BERNO** 7. 6. 7. 6. D.

ARTHUR H. MANN

VIVIAN BURNETT

1. O, when we see God's mer - cy Wide - spread in ev - ery place And know how flows the foun - tain Of His un - bound - ed grace,
2. Our grat - i - tude is rich - es, Com - plaint is pov - er - ty, . . Our tri - als bloom in bless - ings, They test our con - stan - cy.

Music by permission of A. GOODLIFFE

Can we with - hold a trib - ute, For -
O, life from joy is mint - ed, An
bear a psalm to raise, Or leave un - sung one
ev - er - last - ing gold, True glad - ness is the
bless - ing, In this our hymn of praise?
treas - ure That grate - ful hearts will hold.

# 250†

**WOLVERCOTE** 7. 6. 7. 6. D.

W. HAROLD FERGUSON | VIVIAN BURNETT

To be sung in unison
1. O, when we see God's mer - cy Wide-spread in ev - ery place And know how flows the.. foun - tain Of.. His un - bound-ed grace,
2. Our grat - i - tude is.. rich - es, Com-plaint is pov - er - ty, Our tri - als bloom in.. bless - ings, They test our con - stan - cy.

Music by permission of W. HAROLD FERGUSON

Can we with - hold a . . . trib - ute, For -
O, life from joy is . . mint - ed, An . .
bear a psalm to raise, Or leave un - sung one
ev - er - last - ing gold, True glad - ness is the
bless - ing, In . . this our hymn of praise?
treas - ure That grate - ful hearts will hold.

# 251†

**BENTLEY** 7. 6. 7. 6. D.

JOHN P. HULLAH

WILLIAM W. HOW
Adapted

1. O Word of God, most ho - ly, O wis - dom from on high, O Truth, un - changed, un - chang - ing, O light of earth's dark sky,
2. O Word of God the Fa - ther, Thou art the gift di - vine, And still thy light is lift - ed, O'er all the lands to shine.

We bless Thee for the ra - diance That
It is the chart and com - pass To

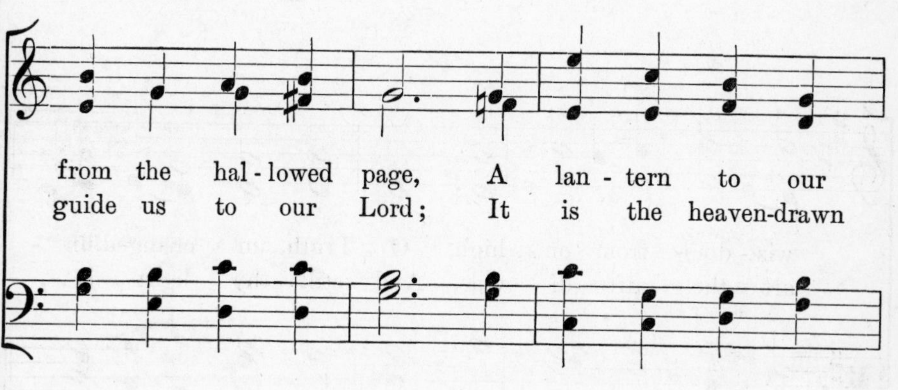
from the hal - lowed page, A lan - tern to our
guide us to our Lord; It is the heaven-drawn

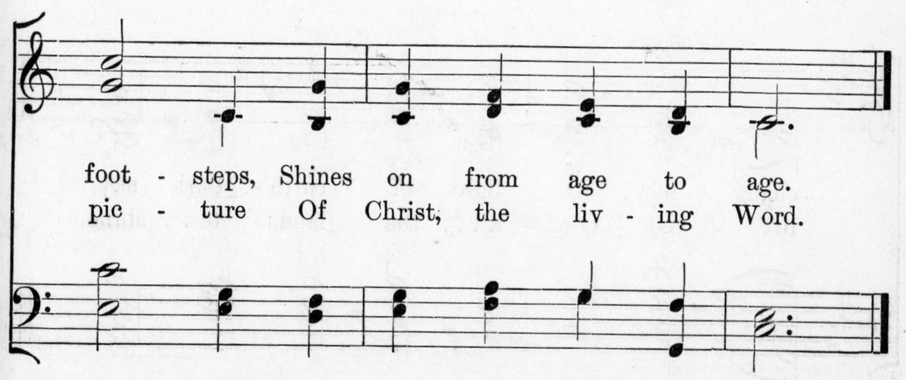
foot - steps, Shines on from age to age.
pic - ture Of Christ, the liv - ing Word.

## 252†

HERZLICH THUT MICH VERLANGEN 7.6.7.6.D.
HANS L. HASSLER
Harmonized by J. S. BACH
WILLIAM W. HOW
Adapted
1. O Word of God, most ho - ly, O wis - dom from on . . high, O Truth, un - changed, un - chang - ing, O light of earth's dark sky,
2. O Word of God the . . Fa - ther, Thou art the gift di - vine, And still thy light is . . lift - ed, O'er all . . the lands to . . shine.

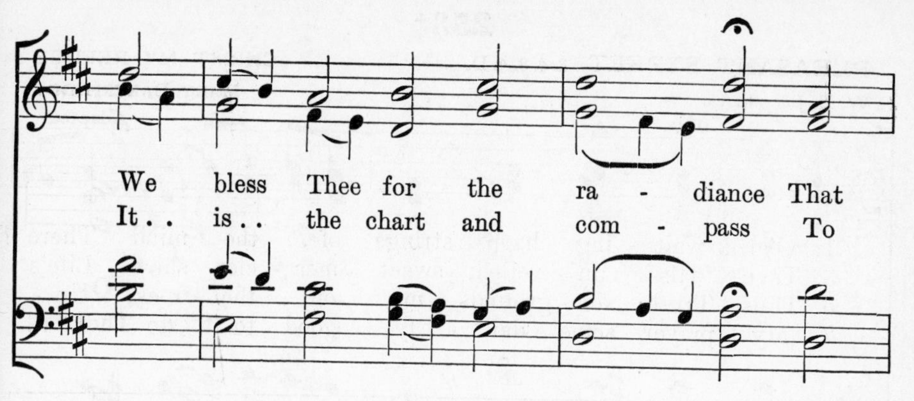
We bless Thee for the ra - diance That
It.. is.. the chart and com - pass To

from the hal-lowed page, A lan-tern to our
guide us to our Lord; It is.. the heaven-drawn

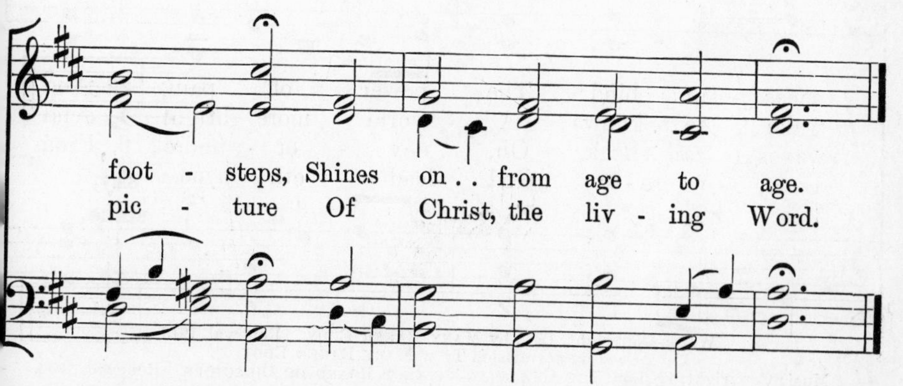
foot - steps, Shines on.. from age to age.
pic - ture Of Christ, the liv - ing Word.

PLEASANT STREET 8. 4. 8. 4. D.
CHRIST MY REFUGE
MARY BAKER EDDY
W. L. J.
1. O'er wait - ing harp - strings of . . the mind There
3. Then His un - veiled, sweet mer - cies show Life's
5. Thus Truth en - grounds me on . . the rock, Up -
7. My prayer, some dai - ly good to . . do To . .
sweeps a strain, Low, sad, and sweet, whose
bur - dens light. I kiss the cross, and
on . . Life's shore, 'Gainst which the winds and
Thine, for Thee; An of - fering pure of
FINE
meas - ures bind The power of pain, 2. And
wake to . . know A world more bright. 4. And
waves can shock, Oh, nev - er - more! 6. From
Love, where - to God lead - eth me.

wake a white - winged an - gel . . throng
o'er earth's trou - bled, an - gry . . sea
tir - ed joy and grief . . a - far,
Of thoughts, il - lumed By faith, and . . breathed in
I see Christ walk, And come to . . . me, and
And near - er Thee,— . . Fa - ther, where Thine own
D.C.
rap - tured song, With love per - fumed.
ten - der - ly, Di - vine - ly talk.
chil - dren are, I love to be.

# 254†

**NORTON** 8. 4. 8. 4. — **CHRIST MY REFUGE**

LYMAN BRACKETT — MARY BAKER EDDY

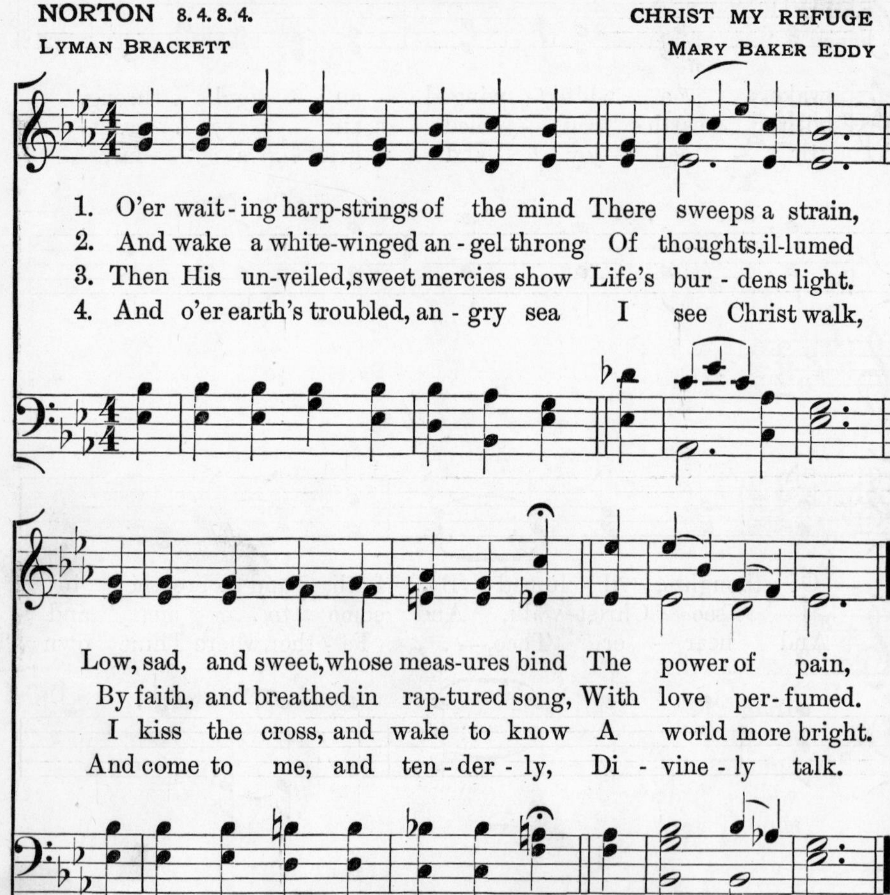
1. O'er wait - ing harp-strings of the mind There sweeps a strain,
2. And wake a white-winged an - gel throng Of thoughts, il-lumed
3. Then His un-veiled, sweet mercies show Life's bur - dens light.
4. And o'er earth's troubled, an - gry sea I see Christ walk,
Low, sad, and sweet, whose meas-ures bind The power of pain,
By faith, and breathed in rap-tured song, With love per- fumed.
I kiss the cross, and wake to know A world more bright.
And come to me, and ten - der - ly, Di - vine - ly talk.

5. Thus Truth engrounds me on the rock,
Upon Life's shore,
'Gainst which the winds and waves can shock,
Oh, nevermore!

6. From tired joy and grief afar,
And nearer Thee,—
Father, where Thine own children are,
I love to be.

7. My prayer, some daily good to do
To Thine, for Thee;
An offering pure of Love, whereto
God leadeth me.

# 255†

**REFUGE** 8. 4. 8. 4. **CHRIST MY REFUGE**

PERCY C. BUCK MARY BAKER EDDY

*To be sung in unison. With free rhythm*

1. O'er wait-ing harp-strings of the mind There sweeps a
2. And wake a white-winged an-gel throng Of thoughts, il-
3. Then His un-veiled, sweet mer-cies show Life's bur-dens
4. And o'er earth's troubled, an-gry sea I see Christ
5. Thus Truth en-grounds me on the rock, Up-on Life's

strain, Low, sad, and sweet, whose measures bind The power of pain,
lumed By faith, and breathed in raptured song, With love perfumed.
light. I kiss the cross, and wake to know A world more bright.
walk, And come to me, and ten-der-ly, . . . Di-vine-ly talk.
shore, 'Gainst which the winds and waves can shock, Oh, nev-er-more!

6. From tired joy and grief afar,
And nearer Thee,— [are,
Father, where Thine own children
I love to be.

7. My prayer, some daily good to do
To Thine, for Thee;
An offering pure of Love, whereto
God leadeth me.

**OLDOWN** 8. 4. 8. 4. D.

**CHRIST MY REFUGE**

MARY BAKER EDDY

BASIL HARWOOD

*Not slow. To be sung in unison*

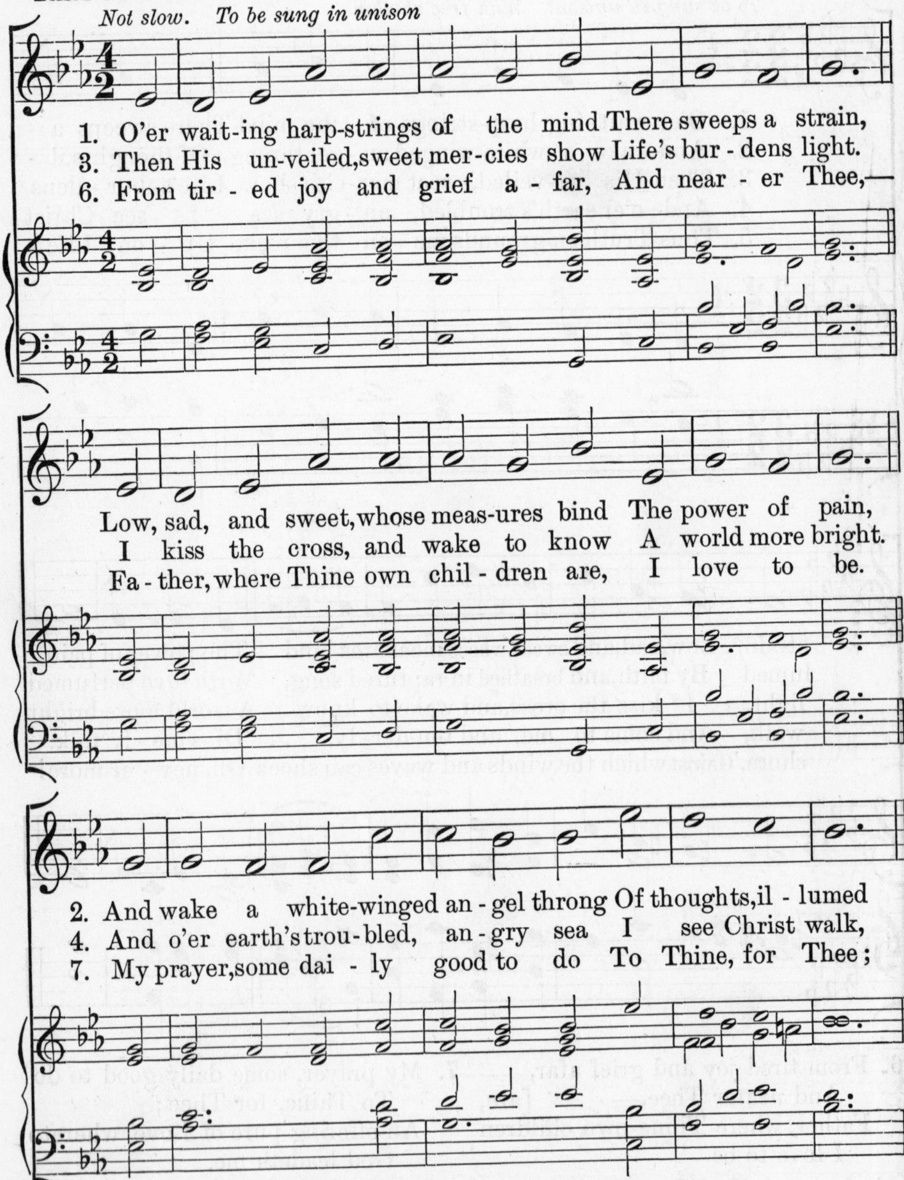

1. O'er wait-ing harp-strings of the mind There sweeps a strain,
3. Then His un-veiled, sweet mer-cies show Life's bur - dens light.
6. From tir - ed joy and grief a - far, And near - er Thee,—

Low, sad, and sweet, whose meas-ures bind The power of pain,
I kiss the cross, and wake to know A world more bright.
Fa - ther, where Thine own chil - dren are, I love to be.

2. And wake a white-winged an - gel throng Of thoughts, il - lumed
4. And o'er earth's trou - bled, an - gry sea I see Christ walk,
7. My prayer, some dai - ly good to do To Thine, for Thee;

D.C. for 3rd verse
By faith, and breathed in rap - tured song, With love per - fumed.
And come to me, and ten - der - ly, Di - vine - ly talk.
An of - fering pure of Love, where - to God lead - eth me.
Fine
5th verse only
5. Thus Truth en - grounds me on the rock, Up - on Life's shore,
D.C. for 6th verse
'Gainst which the winds and waves can shock, Oh, nev - er - more!

# 257†

**OBLATION** 8.4.8.4.

PERCY WHITLOCK

**CHRIST MY REFUGE**

MARY BAKER EDDY

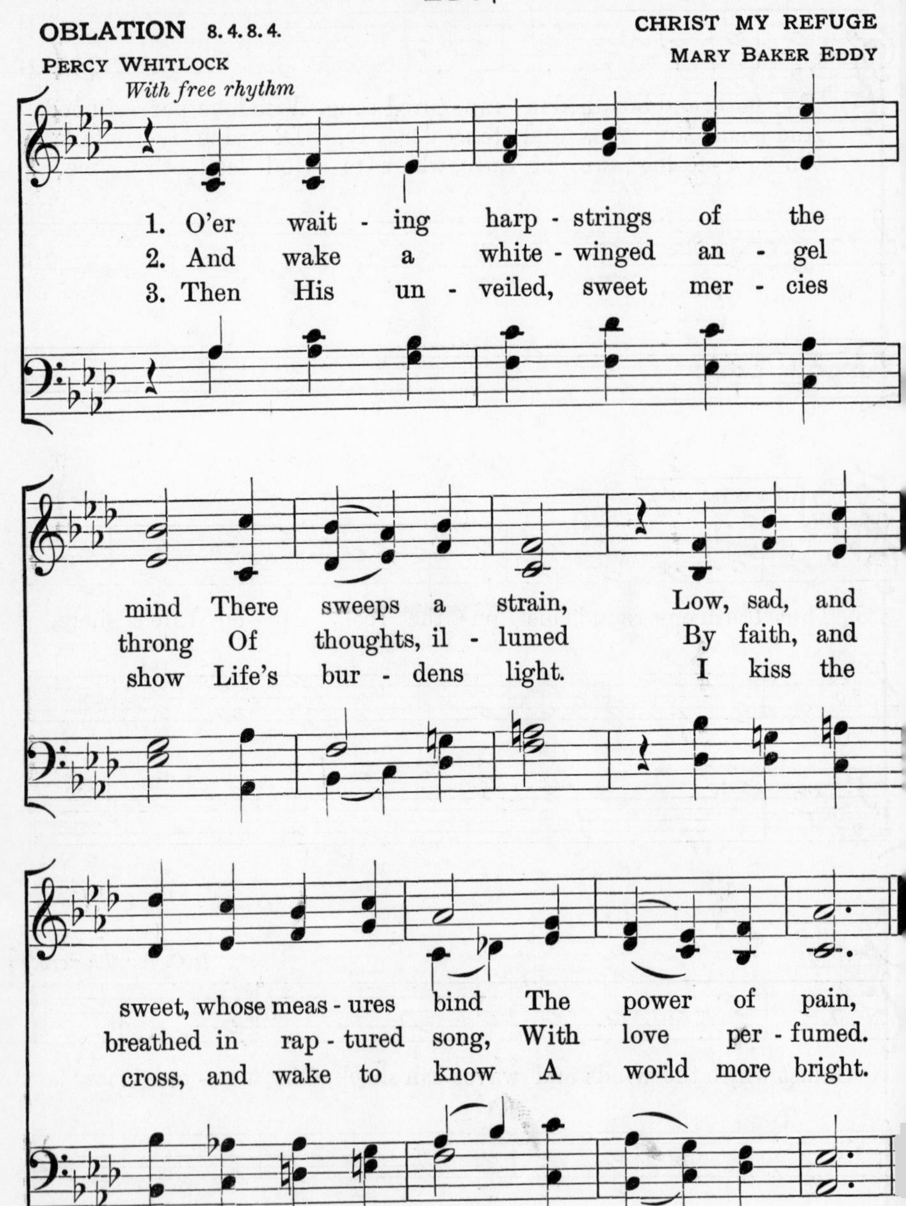
With free rhythm
1. O'er waiting harp-strings of the mind There sweeps a strain, Low, sad, and sweet, whose measures bind The power of pain,
2. And wake a white-winged angel throng Of thoughts, illumed By faith, and breathed in raptured song, With love perfumed.
3. Then His unveiled, sweet mercies show Life's burdens light. I kiss the cross, and wake to know A world more bright.

## 257†

**Stanzas Four to Seven**

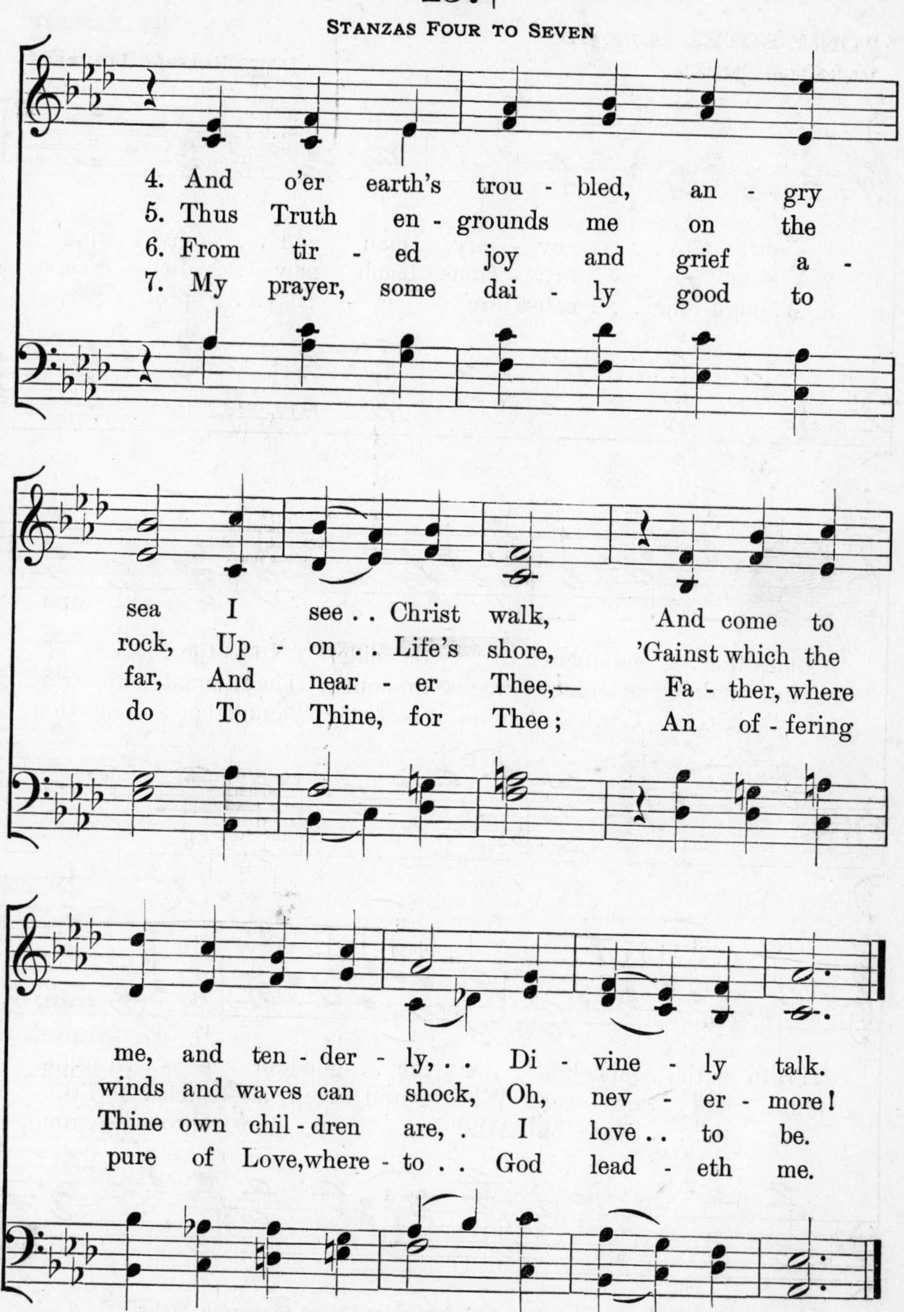
4. And o'er earth's trou - bled, an - gry
5. Thus Truth en - grounds me on the
6. From tir - ed joy and grief a -
7. My prayer, some dai - ly good to
sea I see . . Christ walk, And come to
rock, Up - on . . Life's shore, 'Gainst which the
far, And near - er Thee,— Fa - ther, where
do To Thine, for Thee; An of - fering
me, and ten - der - ly, . . Di - vine - ly talk.
winds and waves can shock, Oh, nev - er - more!
Thine own chil - dren are, . I love . . to be.
pure of Love, where - to . . God lead - eth me.

TON-Y-BOTEL 8.7.8.7. D.

Welsh Hymn Melody

JAMES RUSSELL LOWELL
Adapted

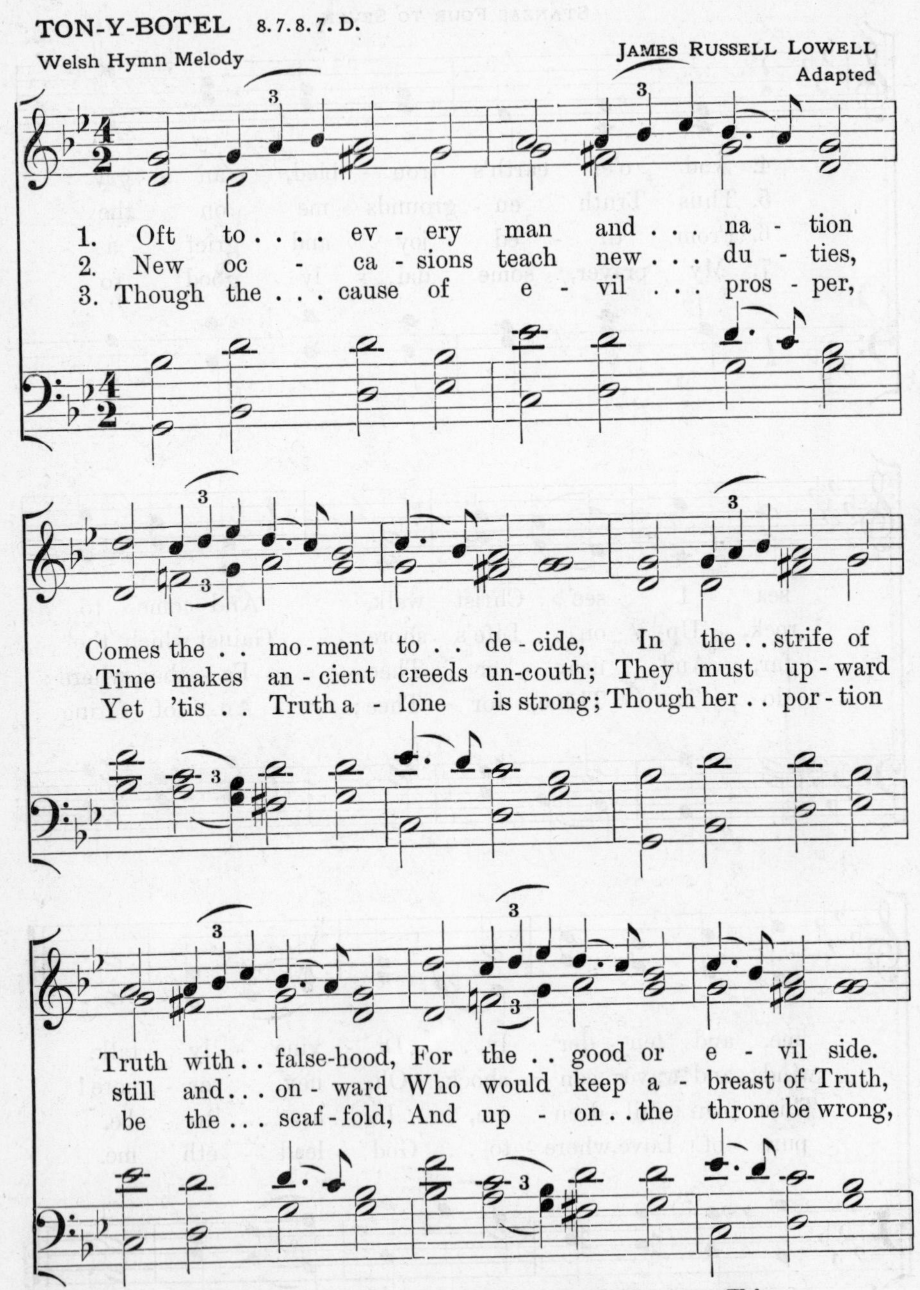
1. Oft to . . . ev - ery man and . . . na - tion
2. New oc - ca - sions teach new . . . du - ties,
3. Though the . . . cause of e - vil . . . pros - per,
Comes the . . mo - ment to . . de - cide, In the . . strife of
Time makes an - cient creeds un-couth; They must up - ward
Yet 'tis . . Truth a - lone is strong; Though her . . por - tion
Truth with . . false-hood, For the . . good or e - vil side.
still and . . . on - ward Who would keep a - breast of Truth,
be the . . . scaf - fold, And up - on . . the throne be wrong,

Music used by permission of W. GWENLYN EVANS, Carnarvon, Wales

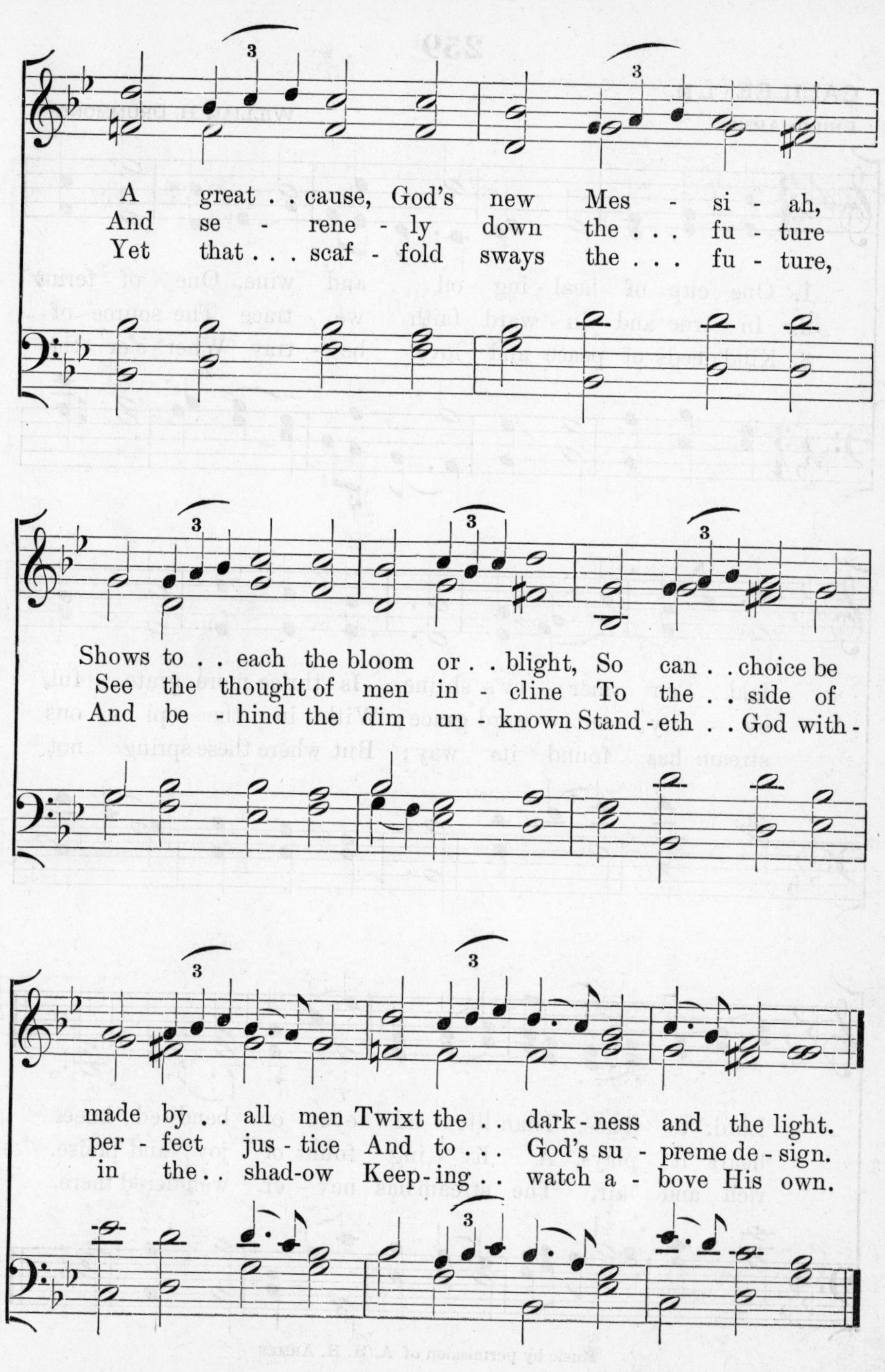
3
A great . . cause, God's new Mes - si - ah,
And se - rene - ly down the . . fu - ture
Yet that . . . scaf - fold sways the . . . fu - ture,
3
3
3
Shows to . . each the bloom or . . blight, So can . . choice be
See the thought of men in - cline To the . . side of
And be - hind the dim un - known Stand - eth . . God with -
3
3
made by . . all men Twixt the . . dark - ness and the light.
per - fect jus - tice And to . . . God's su - preme de - sign.
in the . . shad - ow Keep - ing . . watch a - bove His own.
3

# 259

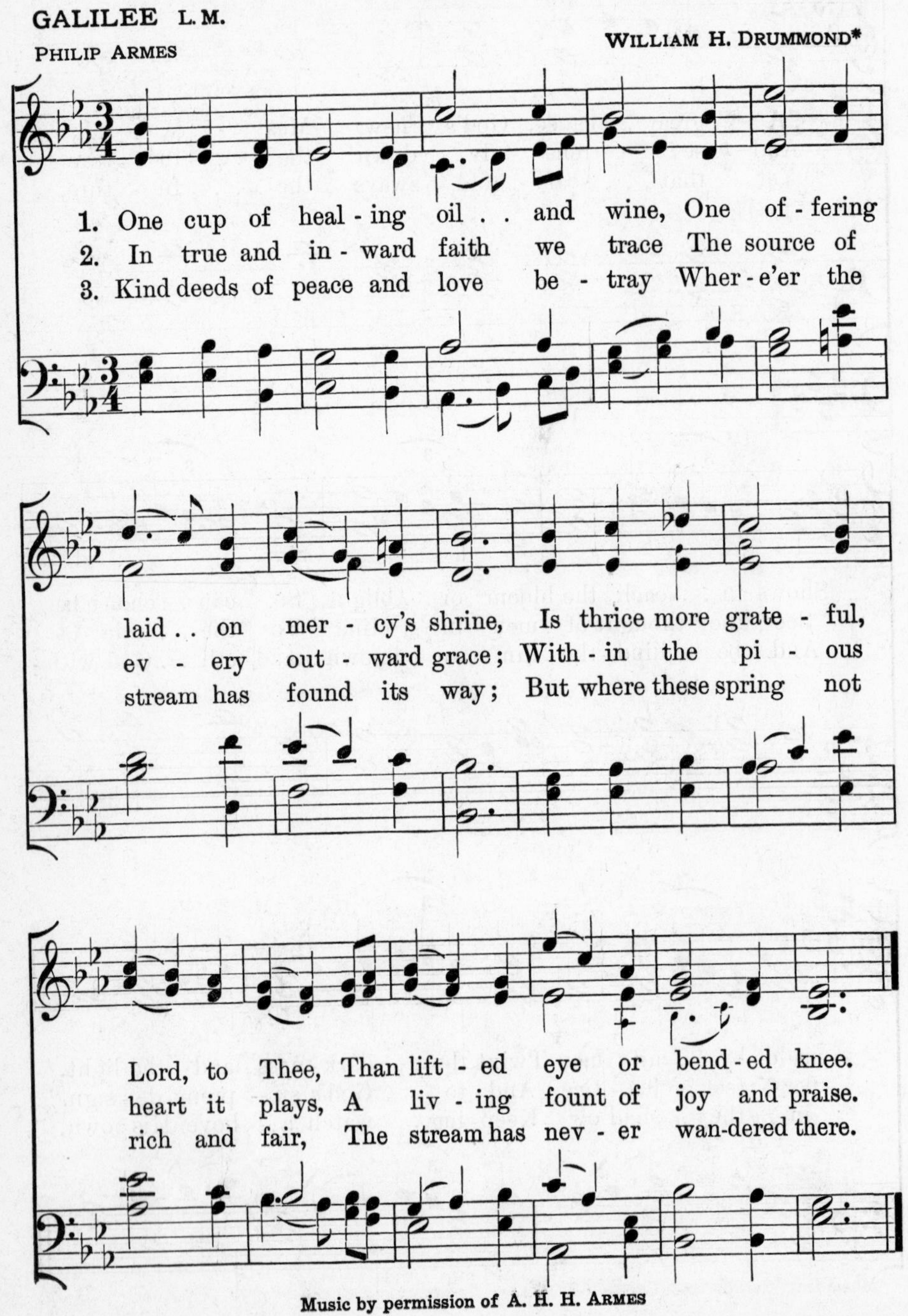
GALILEE L. M.
PHILIP ARMES
WILLIAM H. DRUMMOND*
1. One cup of heal - ing oil . . and wine, One of - fering
2. In true and in - ward faith we trace The source of
3. Kind deeds of peace and love be - tray Wher - e'er the
laid . . on mer - cy's shrine, Is thrice more grate - ful,
ev - ery out - ward grace; With - in the pi - ous
stream has found its way; But where these spring not
Lord, to Thee, Than lift - ed eye or bend - ed knee.
heart it plays, A liv - ing fount of joy and praise.
rich and fair, The stream has nev - er wan-dered there.

Music by permission of A. H. H. ARMES

# 260

**FINGAL** C. M.

JAMES S. ANDERSON

FREDERICK L. HOSMER
Adapted

1. One thought I have, my am - ple creed, So
2. Each morn un - folds His bless - ings new, I
3. To this their se - cret strength they owed, The
4. Be still the light up - on my way, My
deep it is and broad, And e - qual to my
take in trust my road; And ris - ing fresh - ly
mar - tyr's path who trod; The foun - tains of their
pil - grim staff and rod, My rest by night, my
ev - ery need,— It is the thought of God.
to my view, Shines forth the thought of God.
pa - tience flowed From out their thought of God.
strength by day, O bless - ed thought of God.

Music from the Revised Church Hymnary: By permission of the Oxford University Press

## 261†

**NOX PRAECESSIT** C. M.

JOHN B. CALKIN — SAMUEL LONGFELLOW

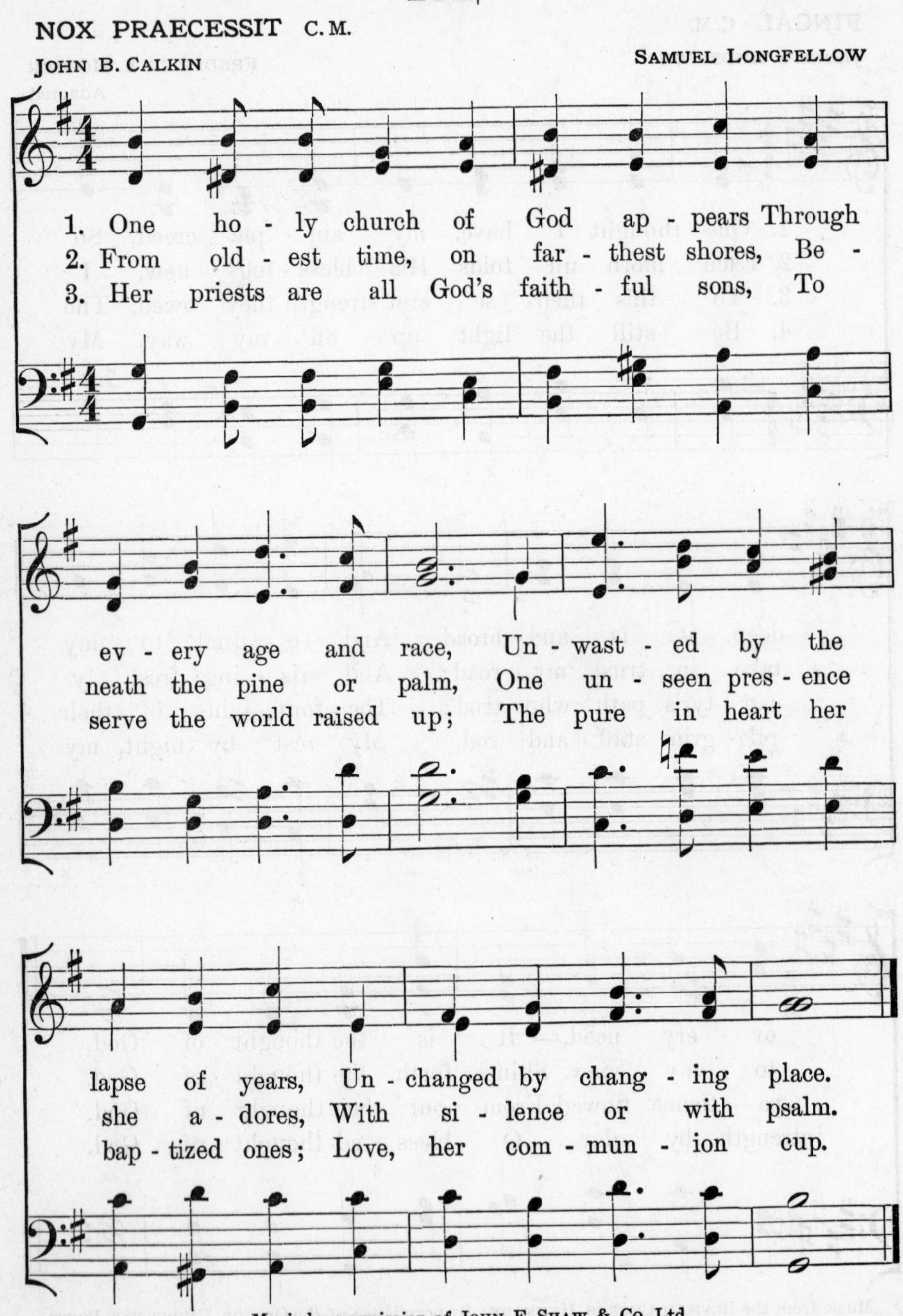
1. One holy church of God appears Through every age and race, Unwasted by the lapse of years, Unchanged by changing place.
2. From oldest time, on farthest shores, Beneath the pine or palm, One unseen presence she adores, With silence or with psalm.
3. Her priests are all God's faithful sons, To serve the world raised up; The pure in heart her baptized ones; Love, her communion cup.

Music by permission of JOHN F. SHAW & Co. Ltd.

## 262†

**SONG** 67 C. M.

ORLANDO GIBBONS — SAMUEL LONGFELLOW

1. One ho - ly church of God ap - pears Through ev - ery age and race, Un - wast - ed by the lapse of years, Un - changed by chang - ing place.
2. From old - est time, on far - thest shores, Be - neath the pine or palm, One un - seen pres - ence she a - dores, With si - lence or with psalm.
3. Her priests are all God's faith - ful sons, To serve the world raised up; The pure in heart her bap - tized ones; Love, her com - mun - ion cup.

# 263

**GLADNESS** 8.7.8.7.D.

Glädje utan Gud ej finnes

GUSTAF DÜBEN

From the Swedish of

J. O. WALLIN

1. On - ly God can bring us . . glad - ness,
2. As the stars in or - der go - ing,
3. So we find the true a - tone - ment,
On - ly God can give us peace; Joys are vain that
All - har - mo - nious, He doth move; Heaven - ly calm and
Know in God the per - fect Friend; For in Love is
end in . . sad - ness, Joy di - vine shall nev - er cease.
com - fort show - ing, Comes the heal - ing word of Love.
our at - one - ment, Where all hearts in Him may blend.

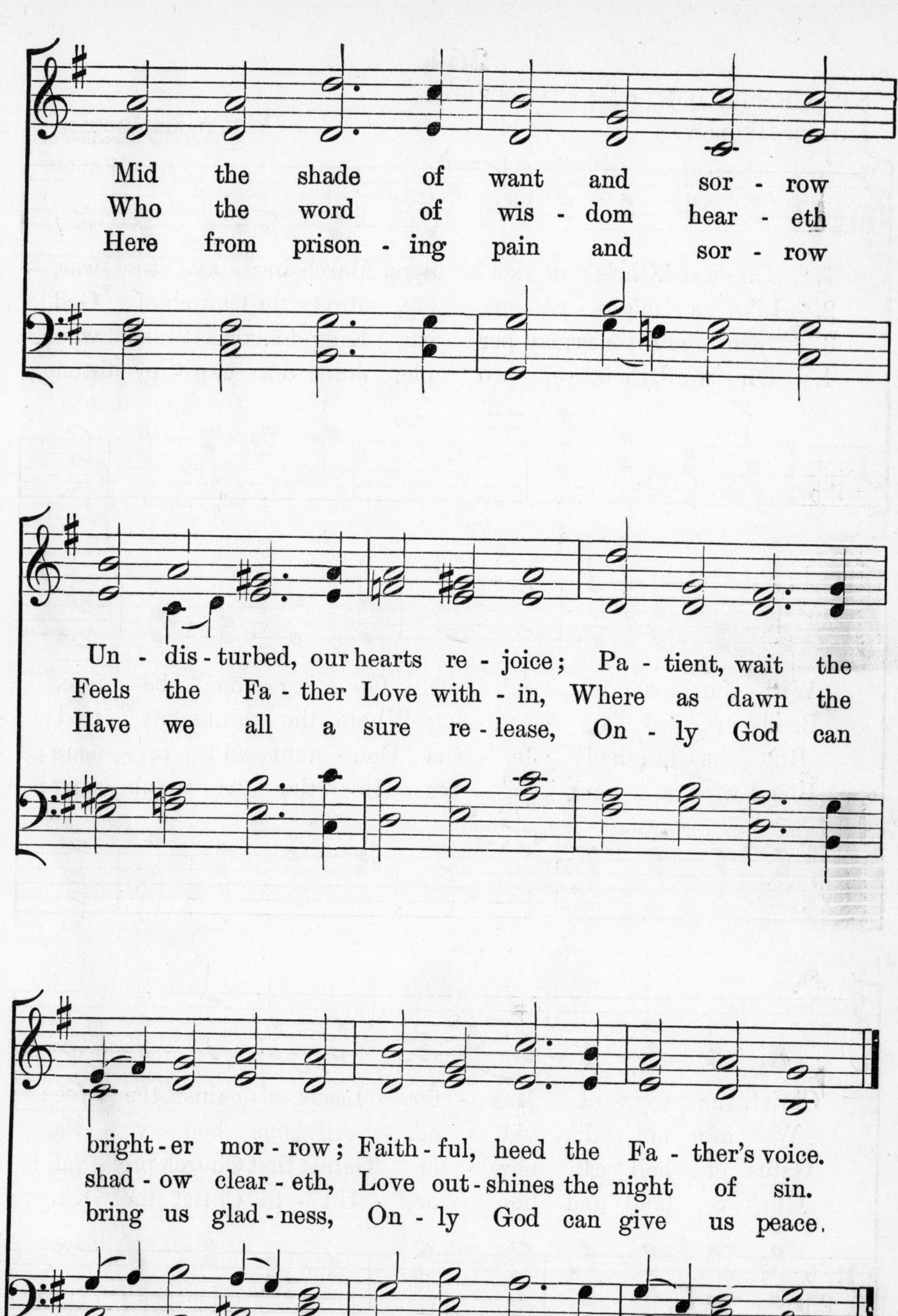
Mid the shade of want and sor - row
Who the word of wis - dom hear - eth
Here from prison - ing pain and sor - row
Un - dis - turbed, our hearts re - joice; Pa - tient, wait the
Feels the Fa - ther Love with - in, Where as dawn the
Have we all a sure re - lease, On - ly God can
bright - er mor - row; Faith - ful, heed the Fa - ther's voice.
shad - ow clear - eth, Love out - shines the night of sin.
bring us glad - ness, On - ly God can give us peace.

# 264

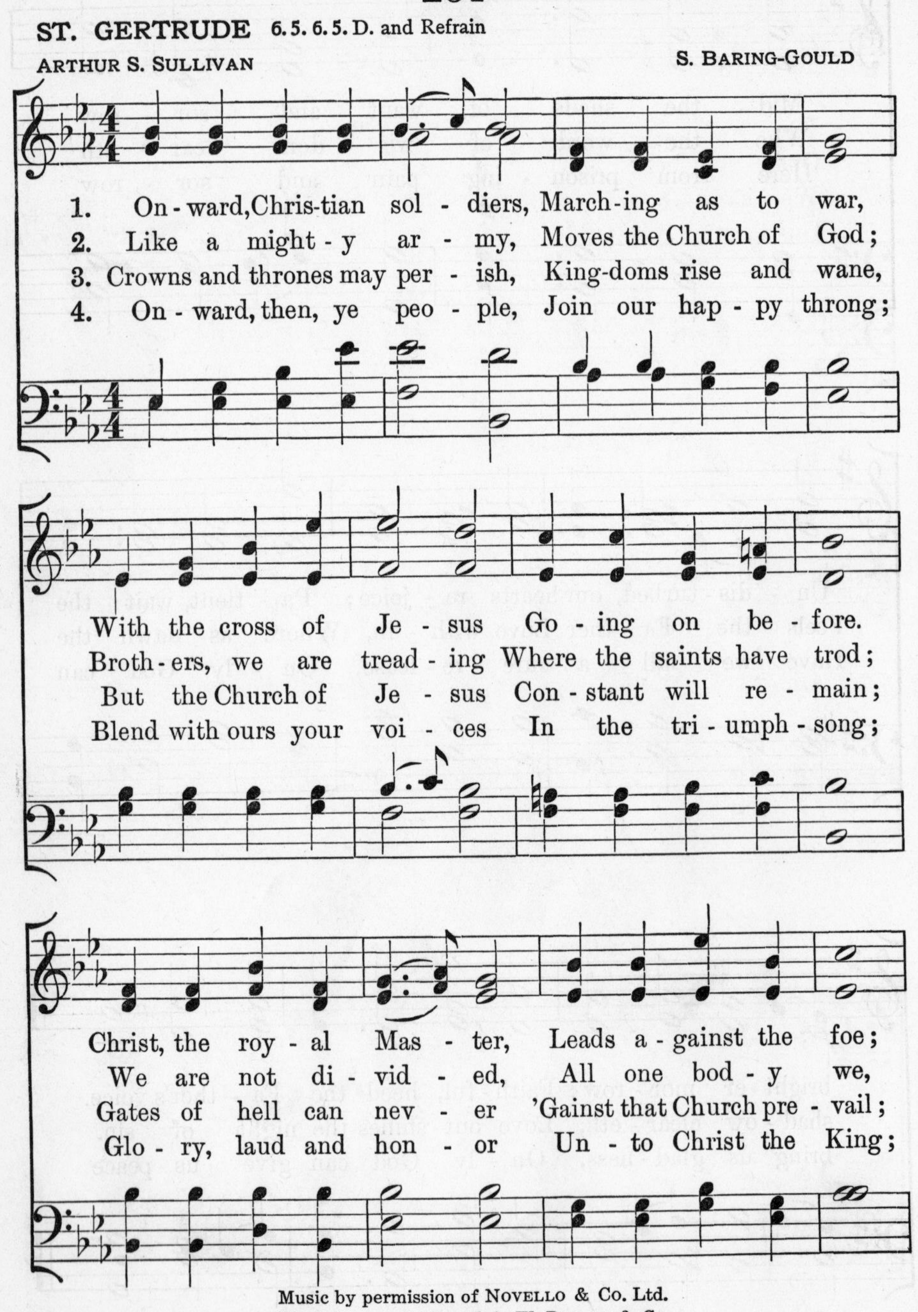
ST. GERTRUDE 6. 5. 6. 5. D. and Refrain
ARTHUR S. SULLIVAN
S. BARING-GOULD
1. On-ward, Chris-tian sol - diers, March-ing as to war,
2. Like a might - y ar - my, Moves the Church of God;
3. Crowns and thrones may per - ish, King-doms rise and wane,
4. On - ward, then, ye peo - ple, Join our hap - py throng;
With the cross of Je - sus Go - ing on be - fore.
Broth - ers, we are tread - ing Where the saints have trod;
But the Church of Je - sus Con - stant will re - main;
Blend with ours your voi - ces In the tri - umph - song;
Christ, the roy - al Mas - ter, Leads a - gainst the foe;
We are not di - vid - ed, All one bod - y we,
Gates of hell can nev - er 'Gainst that Church pre - vail;
Glo - ry, laud and hon - or Un - to Christ the King;

Music by permission of NOVELLO & Co. Ltd.
Words by permission of A. W. RIDLEY & Co.

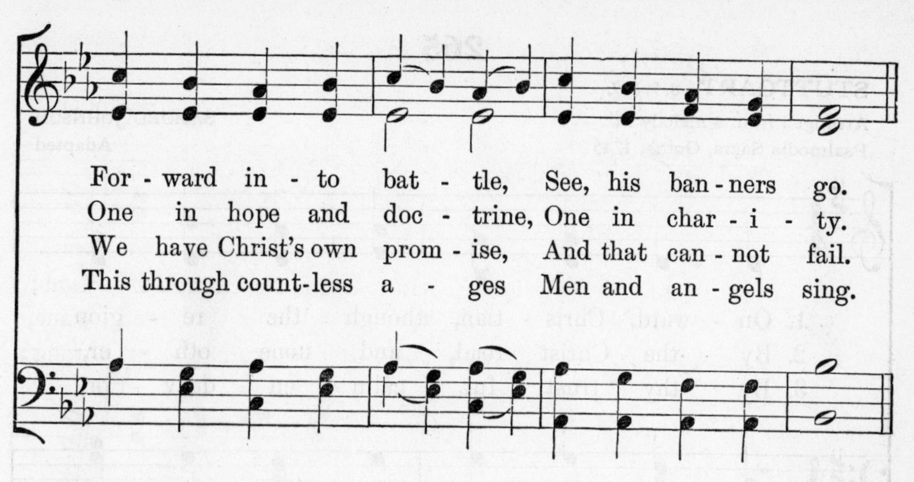
For - ward in - to bat - tle, See, his ban - ners go.
One in hope and doc - trine, One in char - i - ty.
We have Christ's own prom - ise, And that can - not fail.
This through count-less a - ges Men and an - gels sing.

Refrain
On - ward, Chris-tian sol - - diers, March-ing as to war,

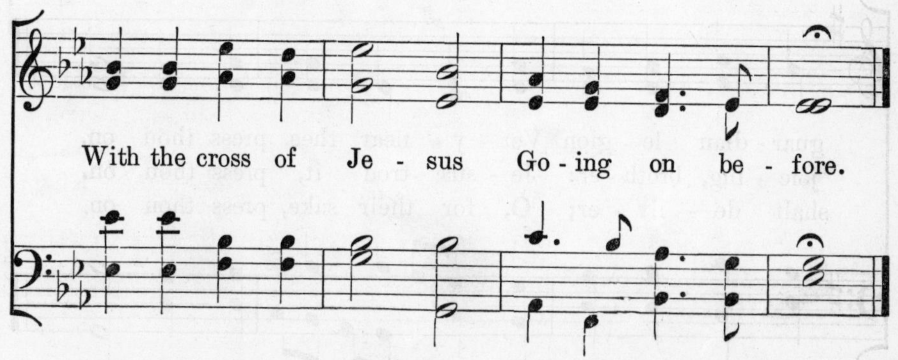
With the cross of Je - sus Go - ing on be - fore.

# 265

**STUTTGART** 8.7.8.7.

Arranged from a melody in Psalmodia Sacra, Gotha, 1715

SAMUEL JOHNSON
Adapted

1. Onward, Christian, though the region
Where thou art seem drear and lone;
God hath set a guardian legion
Very near thee, press thou on.

2. By the Christ road, and none other,
Is the mount of vision won;
Tread it with rejoicing, brother:
Jesus trod it, press thou on.

3. By thy trustful, calm endeavor,
Guiding, cheering, like the sun,
Earth-bound hearts thou shalt deliver;
O, for their sake, press thou on.

## 266

**MARTYRDOM** (AVON) C. M.

HUGH WILSON — Attributed to THOMAS COTTERILL, Adapted

1. Our God is Love, and all His sons His image bear, we know; The heart with love to God inspired, With love to man will glow.
2. Teach us to love each other, Lord, As we are loved by Thee; None who are truly born of God Can live in enmity.
3. Heirs of the same immortal bliss, Our hopes and aims the same, In bonds of love our hearts unite, To praise His holy name.
4. So may we all with one accord Learn how true Christians love; And glorify our Father's grace, And seek that grace to prove.

# 267†

**MOSELEY** 6. 6. 6. 6.

HENRY SMART — EMILY F. SEAL

1. Our God is All - in - all, His
2. Our God is All; in space No
3. We see cre - a - tive Mind, The
4. O, Per - fect and Di - vine, We
chil - dren can - not fear; See base - less e - vil
sub - tle er - ror creeps; We see Truth's glow - ing
Prin - ci - ple, the Life; And Soul and sub - stance
hear Thy lov - ing call, And seek no earth - ly
fall, And know that God is here.
face, And Love that nev - er sleeps.
find, But nev - er dis - cord, strife.
shrine But crown Thee Lord of all.

# 268†

QUAM DILECTA 6. 6. 6. 6.

HENRY L. JENNER — EMILY F. SEAL

1. Our God is All-in-all,
His children cannot fear;
See baseless evil fall,
And know that God is here.

2. Our God is All; in space
No subtle error creeps;
We see Truth's glowing face,
And Love that never sleeps.

3. We see creative Mind,
The Principle, the Life;
And Soul and substance find,
But never discord, strife.

4. O, Perfect and Divine,
We hear Thy loving call,
And seek no earthly shrine
But crown Thee Lord of all.

HAYDN C. M. D.

FRANZ JOSEPH HAYDN

FREDERIC W. ROOT

1. Our God is Love, un - chang - ing Love, And can we ask for more? Our prayer for Love's in - crease is vain; 'Twas in - fi - nite be - fore. Ask
2. Our God is Mind, the per - fect Mind, In - tel - li - gence di - vine; Shall mor - tal man ask Him to change His in - fi - nite de - sign? The
3. O lov - ing Fa - ther, well we know That words a - lone are vain, That those who seek Thy will to do, The true com - mun - ion gain. Then

not the Lord with breath of praise For
heart that yearns for right - eous - ness, With
may our deeds our pure de - sire For

more than we ac - cept; .. The o - pen fount is . .
long - ing un - al - loyed, .. In such de - sire sends
growth in grace ex - press, .. That we may know how

free to all, God's prom - is - es are kept.
up a prayer That ne'er re - turn - eth void.
Love di - vine For - ev - er waits to bless.

270†
KINGSFOLD C. M. D.
English Traditional Melody
FREDERIC W. ROOT
1. Our God is Love, un - chang - ing Love, And
2. Our God is Mind, the per - fect Mind, In -
3. O . . lov - ing Fa - ther, well we know That
can we ask for more? Our prayer for Love's in -
tel - li - gence di - vine; Shall mor - tal man ask
words a - lone are vain, That those who seek Thy
crease is vain; 'Twas in - fi - nite be - fore.
Him to change His in - fi - nite de - sign?
will to do, The true com - mun - ion gain.

Music from the ENGLISH HYMNAL: By permission of the OXFORD UNIVERSITY PRESS

Ask not the Lord with breath of praise For
The heart that yearns for right - eous - ness, With
Then may our deeds our pure de - sire For
more than we ac - cept; The o - pen fount is . .
long - ing un - al - loyed, In such de - sire . . sends
growth in grace ex - press, That we may know how
free to . . all, God's prom - is - es . . are kept.
up a . . prayer That ne'er re - turn - eth void.
Love di - vine For - ev - er waits to bless.

# 271†

**GONFALON ROYAL** L. M.

PERCY C. BUCK

ISAAC WATTS
Adapted

Not slow. To be sung in unison
1. Our God shall reign wher - e'er the sun . . .
2. All peo - ple shall with joy - ful tongue . .
3. For bless - ings flow wher - e'er He reigns; . .
4. Let ev - ery crea - ture rise, and bring . . .

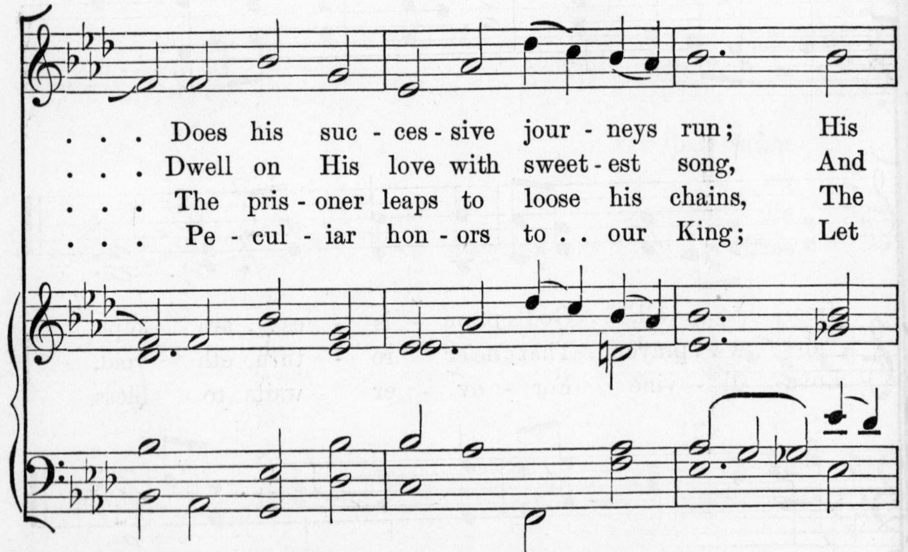

. . . Does his suc - ces - sive jour - neys run; His
. . . Dwell on His love with sweet - est song, And
. . . The pris - oner leaps to loose his chains, The
. . . Pe - cul - iar hon - ors to . . our King; Let

Music by permission of PERCY C. BUCK

king - dom stretch from shore to shore, Till
in - fant voi - ces shall pro - claim Their
wea - ry find e - ter - nal rest, And
an - gel songs be heard a - gain And
Last verse only
moons shall wax and wane no more.
ear - ly . . bless-ings on His name.
all the sons of want are blest.
earth re - peat the long A - men, the long A - men.

## 272†

**TALLIS' CANON** L.M.

THOMAS TALLIS

ISAAC WATTS
Adapted

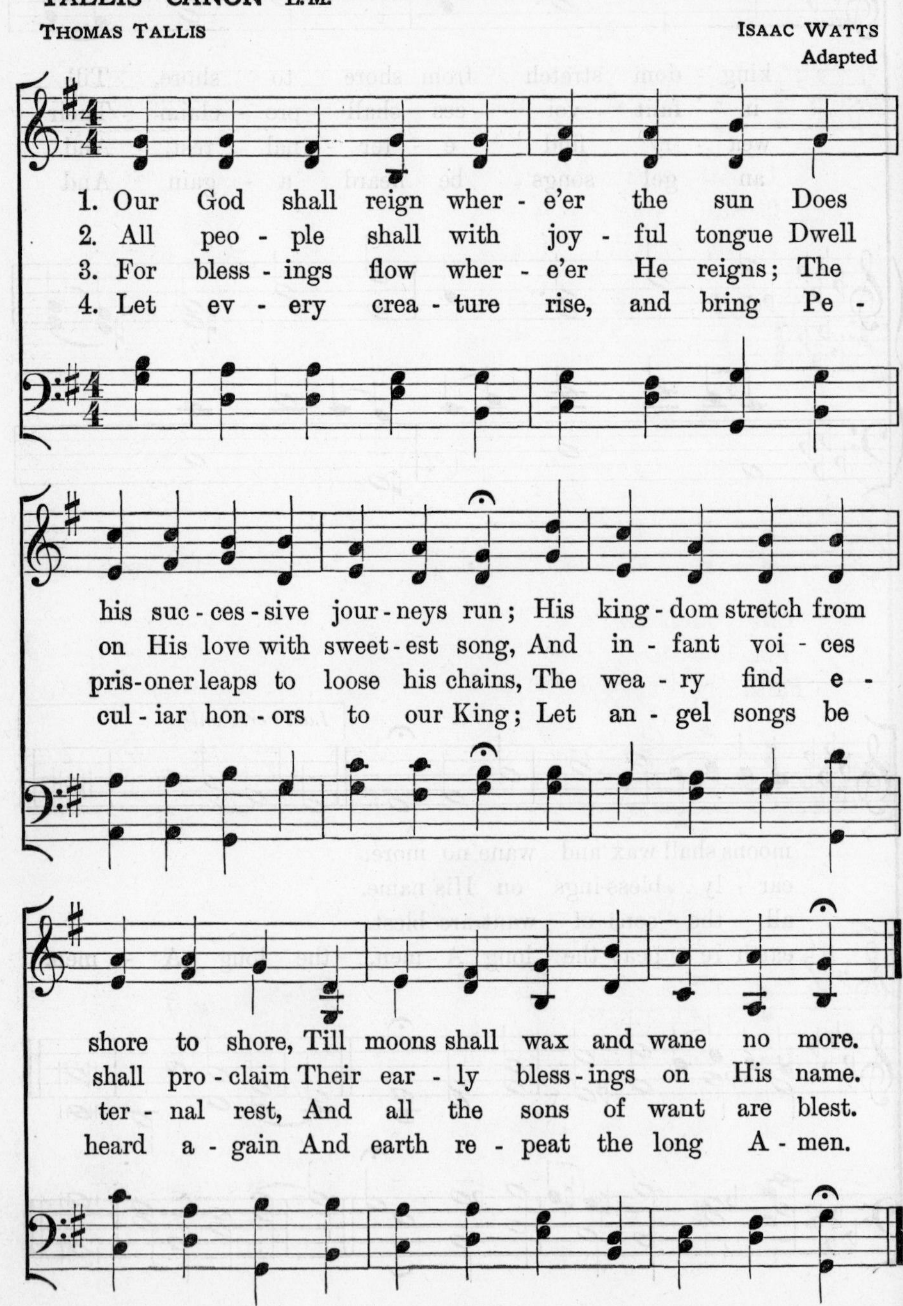
1. Our God shall reign wher - e'er the sun Does his suc - ces - sive jour - neys run; His king - dom stretch from shore to shore, Till moons shall wax and wane no more.
2. All peo - ple shall with joy - ful tongue Dwell on His love with sweet - est song, And in - fant voi - ces shall pro - claim Their ear - ly bless - ings on His name.
3. For bless - ings flow wher - e'er He reigns; The pris - oner leaps to loose his chains, The wea - ry find e - ter - nal rest, And all the sons of want are blest.
4. Let ev - ery crea - ture rise, and bring Pe - cul - iar hon - ors to our King; Let an - gel songs be heard a - gain And earth re - peat the long A - men.

# 273†

**ST. BEES** 7.7.7.7.

JOHN B. DYKES — CHARLES WESLEY*

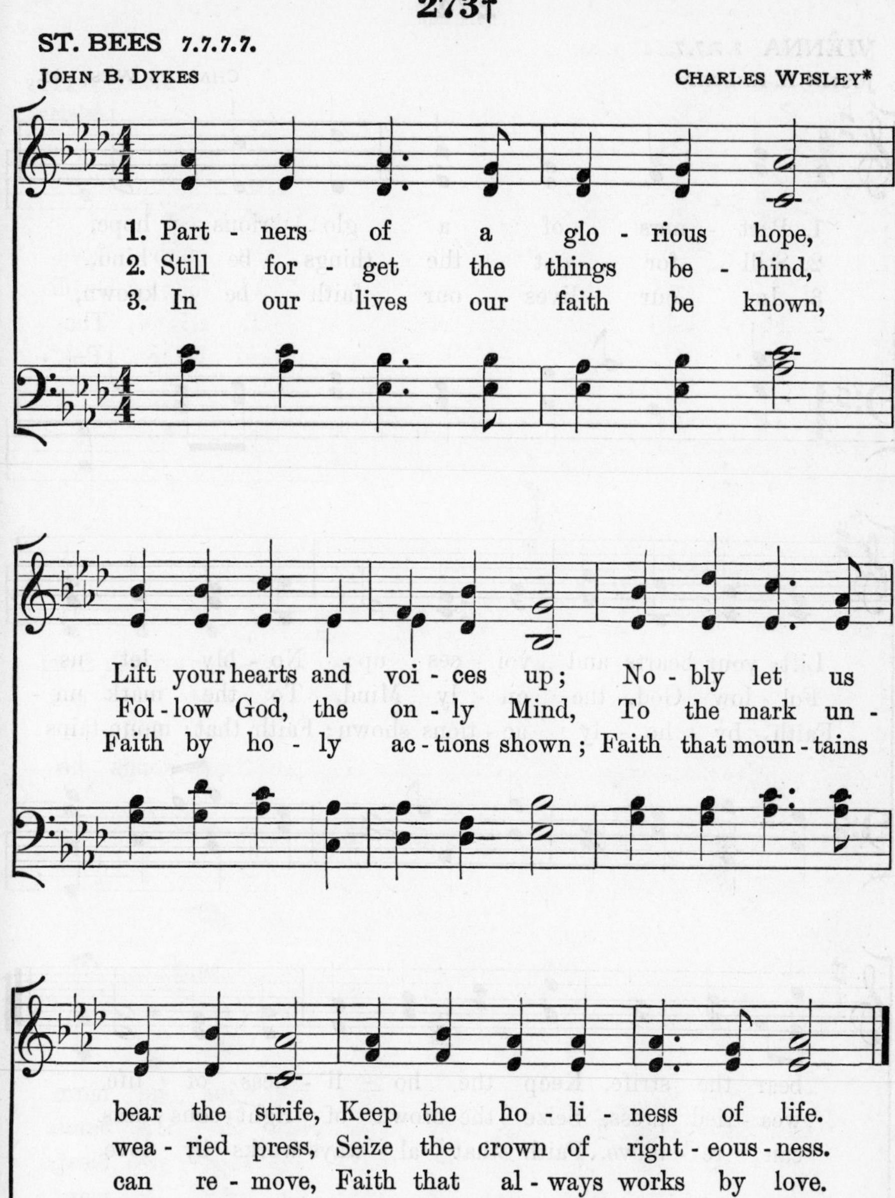
1. Part - ners of a glo - rious hope,
2. Still for - get the things be - hind,
3. In our lives our faith be known,
Lift your hearts and voi - ces up; No - bly let us
Fol - low God, the on - ly Mind, To the mark un -
Faith by ho - ly ac - tions shown; Faith that moun - tains
bear the strife, Keep the ho - li - ness of life.
wea - ried press, Seize the crown of right - eous - ness.
can re - move, Faith that al - ways works by love.

## 274†

VIENNA 7.7.7.7.
JUSTIN H. KNECHT
CHARLES WESLEY*
1. Partners of a glorious hope, Lift your hearts and voices up; Nobly let us bear the strife, Keep the holiness of life.
2. Still forget the things behind, Follow God, the only Mind, To the mark unwearied press, Seize the crown of righteousness.
3. In our lives our faith be known, Faith by holy actions shown; Faith that mountains can remove, Faith that always works by love.

# 275

**CRUSADER'S HYMN** 668. 668.

Silesian Melody
Arranged by R. S. WILLIS

WILLIAM P. MCKENZIE

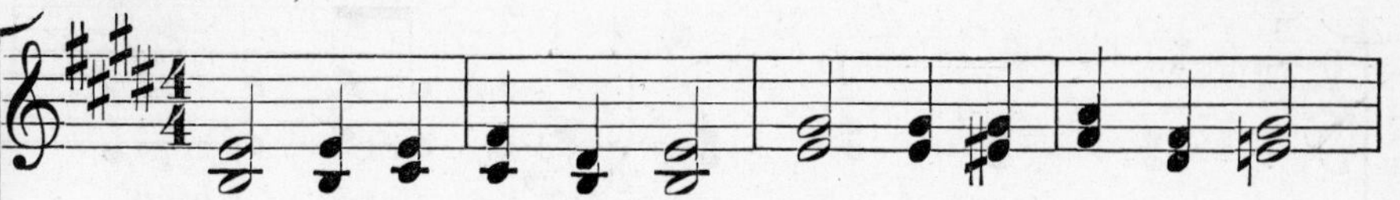

1. Praise now cre - a - tive Mind, Mak - er of earth and heaven;
2. A - ges have seen His might, Fa - ther we call His name;
3. Sav - iour from death is He; Life is our her - i - tage;

Glo - ry and power to . . Him be - long, Joy of the sun and skies,
Nights of our mourning and sor - row end, Light bless-es o-pened eyes,
Mer - cy and good-ness for-ev - er guide; Ours is the ris-en Christ,

Strength where the hills a - rise, So let us praise with joy and song.
Joys like the dawns a - rise As we see Him our God and Friend.
Dai - ly we keep our tryst, And ev - er-more in Love con - fide.

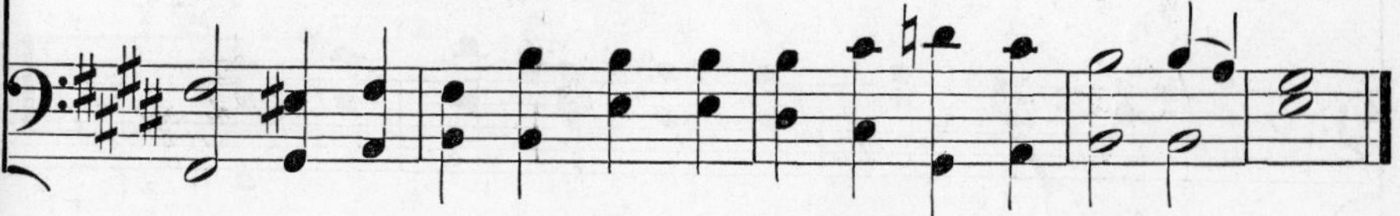

# 276†

**BEECHER** 8.7.8.7.D.

JOHN ZUNDEL

CHARLES WESLEY
Adapted

1. Peace be to this con - gre - ga - tion;
2. O Thou God of peace, be . . near us,
Peace to ev - ery heart there - in; Peace, the ear - nest
Fix with - in our hearts Thy home; With Thy bright ap -
of sal - va - tion; Peace, the fruit of con - quered sin;
pear - ing cheer us, In Thy bless - ed free - dom come.

Peace, that speaks the heaven - ly . . Giv - er;
Come with all Thy rev - e - la - tions,
Peace, to world - ly minds un - known; Peace, that flow - eth
Truth which we so long have sought; Come with Thy deep
as a . . riv - er From th' e - ter - nal source a - lone.
con - so - la - tions, Peace of God which pass - eth thought.

277†

BETHANY 8.7.8.7.D.

HENRY SMART

CHARLES WESLEY
Adapted

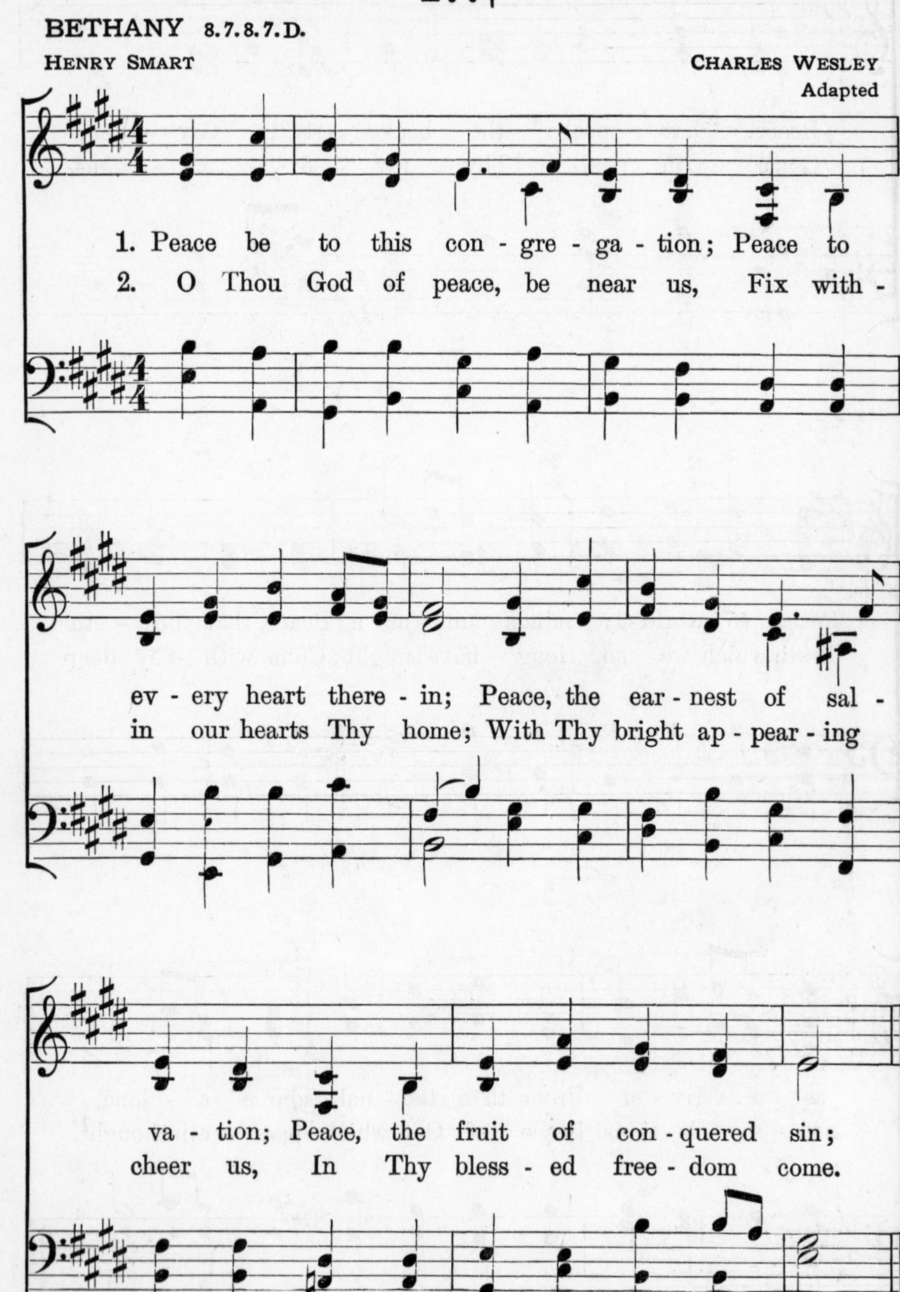
1. Peace be to this con - gre - ga - tion; Peace to ev - ery heart there - in; Peace, the ear - nest of sal - va - tion; Peace, the fruit of con - quered sin;
2. O Thou God of peace, be near us, Fix with - in our hearts Thy home; With Thy bright ap - pear - ing cheer us, In Thy bless - ed free - dom come.

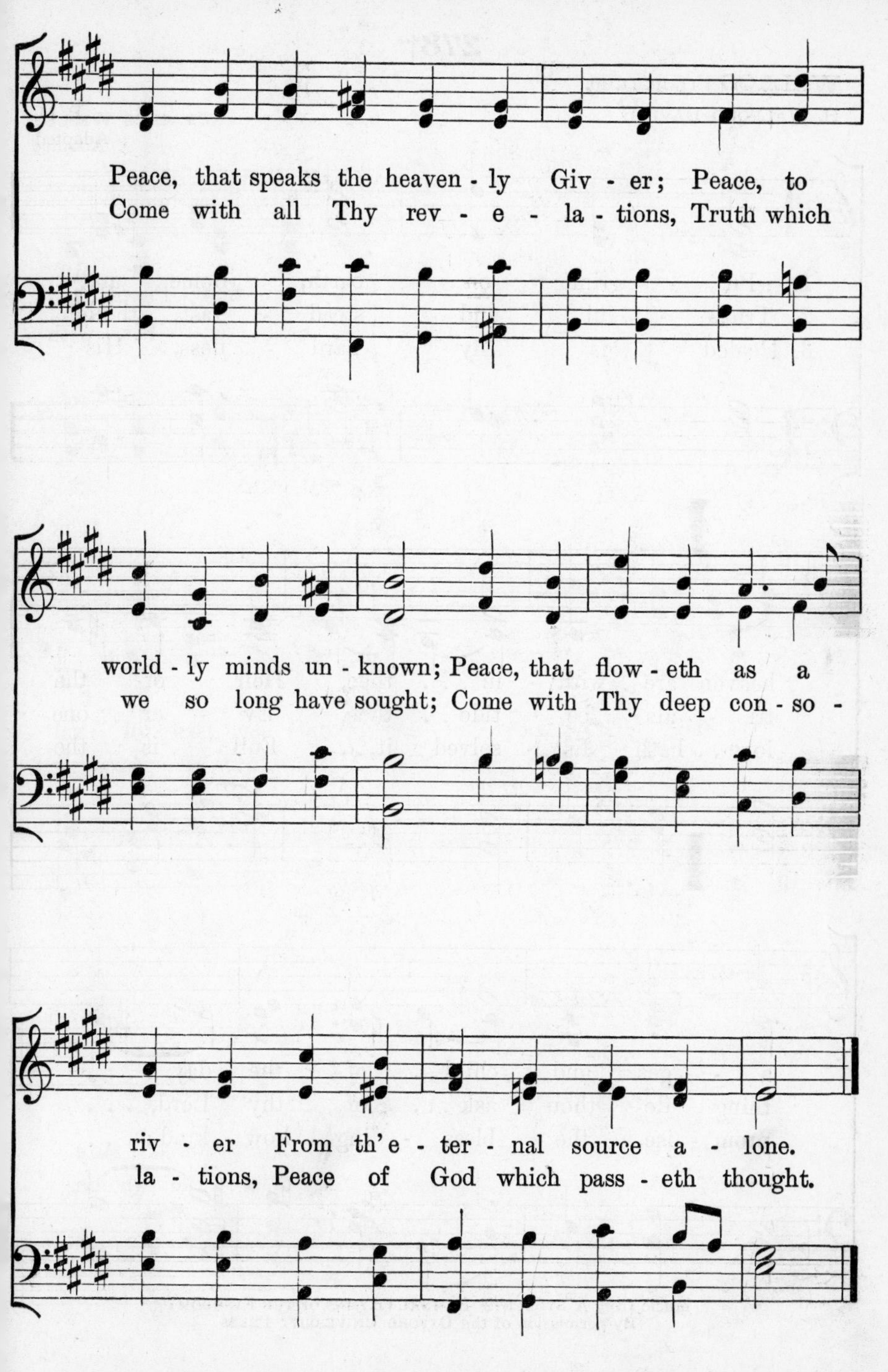
Peace, that speaks the heaven - ly Giv - er; Peace, to
Come with all Thy rev - e - la - tions, Truth which
world - ly minds un - known; Peace, that flow - eth as a
we so long have sought; Come with Thy deep con - so -
riv - er From th'e - ter - nal source a - lone.
la - tions, Peace of God which pass - eth thought.

# 278†

WALLOG 11. 10. 11. 10.

H. WALFORD DAVIES

P. M.
Adapted

1. Pil - grim on earth, home and heaven are with - in . . . thee, Heir of the a - ges and child . . of the day. . . .
2. Truth - ful and stead - fast though tri - als be - tide . . thee, Ev - er one thing do thou ask . . . of thy Lord, . . .
3. Healed is thy hard - ness, His love . . hath dis - solved it, . . . Full is the prom - ise, the bless - ing how kind; . . .

Music from A STUDENTS' HYMNAL (HYMNS OF THE KINGDOM)
By permission of the OXFORD UNIVERSITY PRESS

Cared . . for, watched o - - ver, be -
Grace . . to go for - ward, wher -
So . . . . shall His ten - der - ness . . . . . .
loved and pro - tect - ed, Walk thou with
ev - er He guide thee, Glad - ly o -
teach thee com - pas - sion, So . . all the
cour - age each step . . of the way.
bey - ing the call . . of His word.
mer - ci - ful, mer - cy shall find.

**LIME STREET** 11. 10. 11. 10.

GEOFFREY SHAW

P. M.
Adapted

*To be sung in unison*

1. Pil - grim on earth, home and heaven are with - in thee,
2. Truth - ful and stead - fast though tri - als be - tide thee,
3. Healed is thy hard - ness, His love hath dis - solved it,

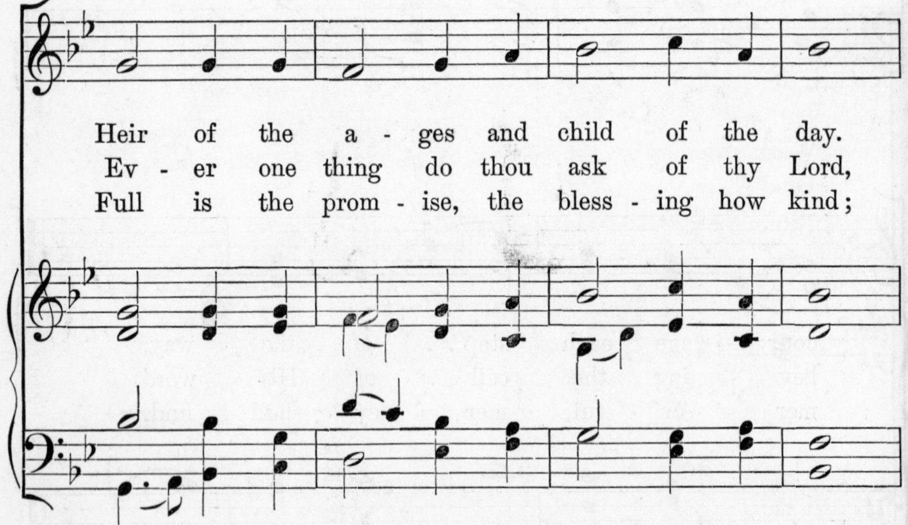
Heir of the a - ges and child of the day.
Ev - er one thing do thou ask of thy Lord,
Full is the prom - ise, the bless - ing how kind;

Music by permission, from CURWEN EDITION No. 6300, published by J. CURWEN & SONS Ltd., 24 Berners Street, London, W. 1.

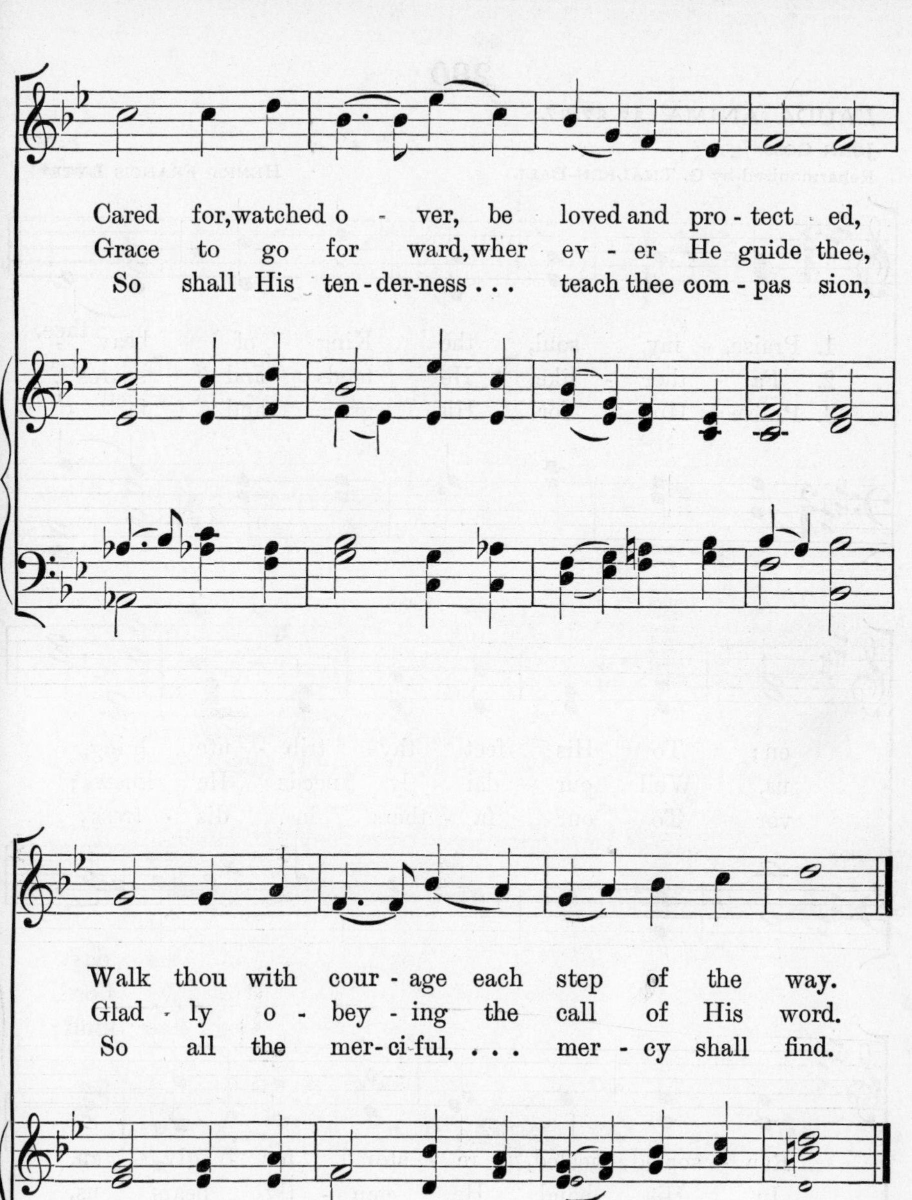
Cared for, watched o - ver, be loved and pro - tect - ed,
Grace to go for ward, wher ev - er He guide thee,
So shall His ten-der-ness . . . teach thee com - pas sion,
Walk thou with cour - age each step of the way.
Glad - ly o - bey - ing the call of His word.
So all the mer-ci-ful, . . . mer - cy shall find.

# 280

**LAUDA ANIMA** 87. 87. 87.

JOHN GOSS
Reharmonized by G. THALBEN-BALL

HENRY FRANCIS LYTE*

1. Praise, my soul, the King of heav - en; To His feet thy trib - ute bring.
2. Fa - ther - like, He tends and spares us, Well our dai - ly needs He knows;
3. Praise Him for His grace and fa - vor To our fa - thers in dis - tress;
Ran - somed, healed, re - stored, for - giv - en,
In His hand He gen - tly bears us,
Praise Him still the same for - ev - er,

Music by permission of G. THALBEN-BALL

Who like us His praise should sing?
Res - cues us from all our foes.
Slow to chide, and swift to bless.
Praise Him, praise Him, praise Him, praise Him,
Praise Him, praise Him, praise Him, praise Him,
Praise Him, praise Him, praise Him, praise Him,
Praise the.. ev - er - last - ing King.
Wide - ly .. as His mer - cy flows.
Glo - rious in His faith - ful - ness.

## 281

MOOZ ZUR 77.77.67.67.
Old Hebrew Melody
HARRIET AUBER
Adapted
1. Praise our great and gracious Lord, Call up-on His holy name; Strains of joy tune every chord, All His might-y acts pro-claim.
2. He has given the cloud by day, Given the mov-ing fire by night; Guides His Is-rael on their way From the dark-ness in-to light.

How He leads His chos - en Un - to Ca - naan's
He it is who grants us Sure re - treat and

prom - ised land, . . How the Word . . we have
ref - uge nigh. . . Light of dawn . . leads us

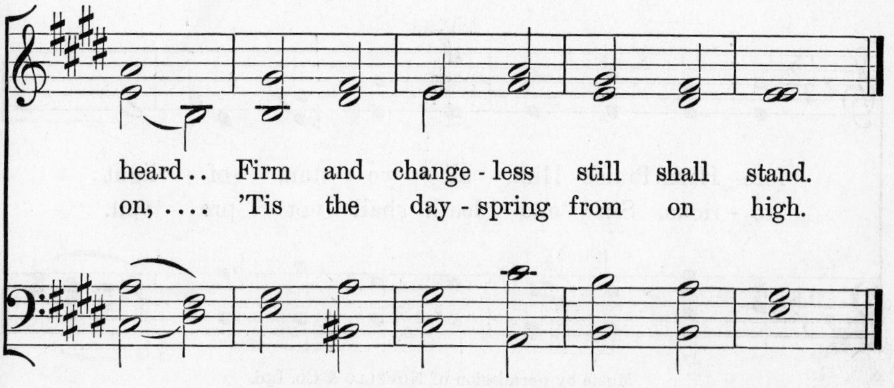
heard . . Firm and change - less still shall stand.
on, . . . . 'Tis the day - spring from on high.

282

**SURSUM VOCES** 8.7.8.7.D.

H. ELLIOT BUTTON — HENRY FRANCIS LYTE

1. Praise the Lord, ye heavens, a - dore Him; Praise Him,
2. Praise the Lord, for He is glo - rious; Nev - er

an - gels, in the height; Sun and moon, re - joice be -
shall His prom - ise fail; God hath made His saints vic -

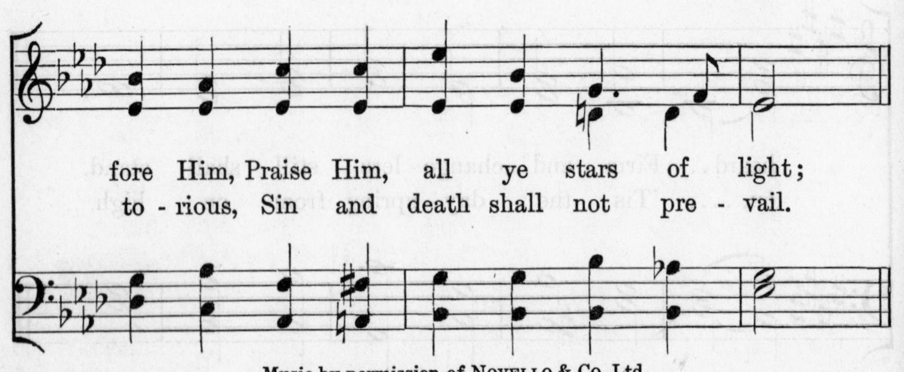
fore Him, Praise Him, all ye stars of light;
to - rious, Sin and death shall not pre - vail.

Music by permission of NOVELLO & Co. Ltd.

Praise the Lord, for He hath spo - ken, Worlds His
Praise the God of our sal - va - tion; Hosts on
might - y voice o - beyed; Laws that nev - er shall be
high, His power pro - claim; Heaven and earth, and all cre -
bro - ken For their guid - ance hath He made.
a - tion, Laud and mag - ni - fy His name.

# 283

**PRAISE** 14. 14. 4 7. 8.

Lobe den Herren
Stralsund Gesangbuch, 1665

From German of
JOACHIM NEANDER

1. Praise we the Lord, for His mer - cy en -
2. Praise we the Lord, who our foot - steps still
3. Praise we the Lord with a joy - ous and
dur - eth for - ev - - er. Let us ex -
hold - eth from slid - - ing; Dai - ly He
glad ad - o - ra - - tion; Lo, un - to
tol Him with joy - ous and lov - ing en -
camp - eth a - bout us, pro - tect - ing and
them that be - lieve there is no con - dem -

deav - - or; Come let us sing,
guid - - ing; E'en while we sleep
na - - tion; Now will we raise

Prais - ing our God and our King, Should we be
Watch doth He ten - der - ly keep; Ev - er new
Songs of thanks - giv - ing and praise, Christ is be -

si - lent? Ah, nev - - er.
mer - cies pro - vid - - - ing.
come our sal - va - - - tion.

284†

BEATITUDO C. M.
JOHN B. DYKES
JAMES MONTGOMERY*
1. Prayer is the heart's sin - cere . . de - sire,
2. Prayer is the sim - plest form of speech
3. Prayer is the Chris - tian's vi - tal breath,
Ut - tered or un - ex - pressed; The mo - tion of a
That in - fant lips can try; And prayer's sub - lim - est
The Chris - tian's na - tive air: His watch - word, o - ver -
hid - den fire That trem - bles in the breast.
strain doth reach The Maj - es - ty on high.
com - ing death: He en - ters heaven with prayer.

# 285†

**PRAYER** C. M.

E. N. G. JAMES MONTGOMERY*

1. Prayer is the heart's sin - cere de - sire,
2. Prayer is the sim - plest form of speech That
3. Prayer is the Chris - tian's vi - tal breath, The
Ut - tered or un - ex - pressed; The mo - tion of a
in - fant lips can try; And prayer's sub - lim - est
Chris - tian's na - tive air: His watch - word, o - ver -
hid - den fire That trem - bles in the breast.
strain doth reach The Maj - es - ty on high.
com - ing death: He en - ters heaven with prayer.
*

* This chord omitted in verse 1

# 286†

**CHESHIRE** C. M.

Este's Psalter, 1592
Arranged by CHARLES WOOD

JAMES MONTGOMERY*

1. Prayer is the heart's sin - cere de -
2. Prayer is the sim - plest form of
3. Prayer is the Chris - tian's vi - tal
sire, Ut - tered or un - ex - pressed; The mo - tion
speech That in - fant lips can try; And prayer's sub -
breath, The Chris - tian's na - tive air: His watch-word,
of a hid - den fire That trem-bles in the breast.
lim - est strain doth reach The Maj - es - ty on high.
o - ver - com - ing death: He en - ters heaven with prayer.

* This chord omitted in verse 1.

# 287

## NUN DANKET ALL C. M.

JOHANN CRÜGER — EDITH GADDIS BREWER

1. Prayer with our wak - ing thought as - cends, Great God of
2. Lo, to our wid - ening vi - sion dawns The realm of
3. Thus in Thy ra - diance van - ish - es Death's drear and
light, to Thee; Dark - ness is ban - ished
Soul su - preme, Faith - light - ed peaks of
gloom - y night; Thus all cre - a - tion
in the glow Of Thy re - al - i - ty.
Spir - it stand Re - vealed in morn - ing's beam.
hears a - new Truth's call, Let there be light.

*These words have another setting in the* SUPPLEMENT, No. 408

# 288†

**VALETE** 88. 88. 88.

ARTHUR S. SULLIVAN — M. BETTIE BELL

1. Press on, dear trav - eler, press thou on, I
2. Press on, and know that God is all; He

am the Way, the Truth, the Life. It
is the Life, the Truth, the Love. It

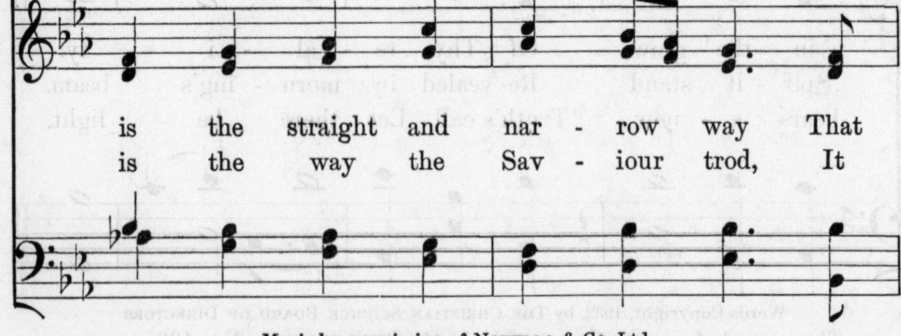
is the straight and nar - row way That
is the way the Sav - iour trod, It

Music by permission of NOVELLO & Co. Ltd.

leads to that e - ter - nal day, That
is the way that leads to God. Think

turns the dark - ness in - to light, That
of the words: No cross, no crown; Though

bur - ies wrong and hon - ors right.
tasks are sore, be not cast down.

# 289†

**YATTENDON 12.** 88.88.88.

Old English Melody

Harmonized by H. E. WOOLDRIDGE

M. BETTIE BELL

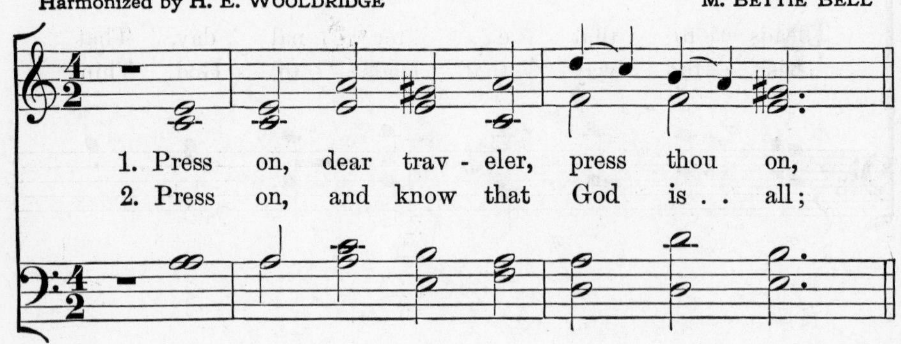

1. Press on, dear trav - eler, press thou on,
2. Press on, and know that God is . . all;

I am the . . Way, the Truth, the Life.
He is the . . Life, the Truth, the Love.

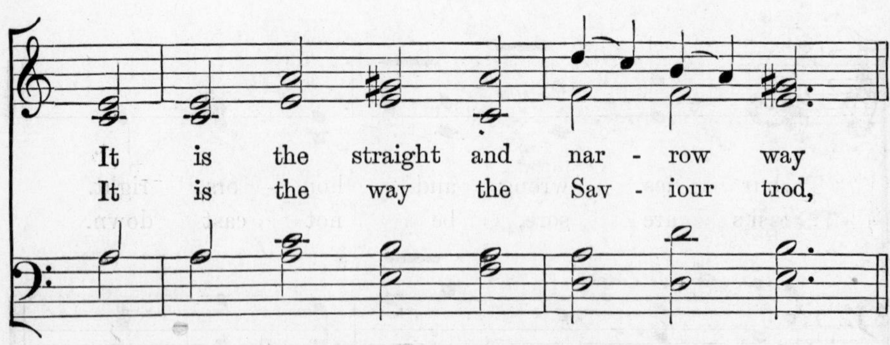

It is the straight and nar - row way
It is the way the Sav - iour trod,

That leads to that e - ter - nal day,
It is the way that leads to God.

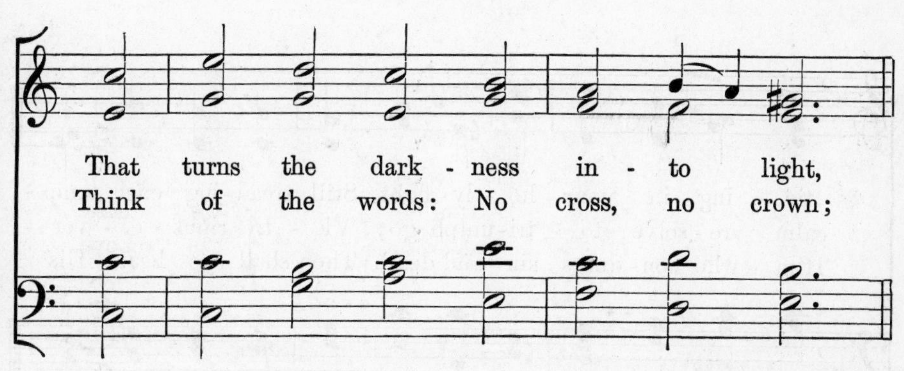
That turns the dark - ness in - to light,
Think of the words: No cross, no crown;

That bur - ies . . wrong and hon - ors right.
Though tasks are . . sore, be not cast down.

# 290

CHURCH TRIUMPHANT L. M.
JAMES W. ELLIOTT
WILLIAM GASKELL
Adapted
1. Press on, press on, ye sons of light, Un -
2. Press on, press on, and fear no foe, With
3. Press on, press on, still look in faith To
tir - ing in your ho - ly fight, Still tread-ing each temp -
calm re - solve to tri - umph go; Vic - to - rious o - ver
Him who con - quers sin and death; Then shall ye hear His
ta - tion down, And bat - tling for a bright - er crown.
ev - ery ill, Press on to high - er glo - ry still.
word, Well done! True to the last, press on, press on.

Music by permission of NOVELLO & Co. Ltd.

# 291

**PASCHAL** 77.77.77.

**Påskemorgen slukker sorgen**

LUDVIG M. LINDEMAN — JOHN NEWTON*

1. Qui - et, Lord, my fro-ward heart, Make me gen - tle, pure, and mild,
2. What Thou shalt to - day pro - vide Let me as a . . child re - ceive,
3. As a lit - tle child re - lies On a care be - yond its own,

Up - right, sim - ple, free from art; Make me as a . . lit - tle child,
What to - mor - row may be - tide Calm - ly . . to Thy wis - dom leave;
Be - ing nei - ther strong nor wise, Will not take a . . step a - lone,

From dis - trust and en - vy free, Pleased with all that pleas - eth Thee.
'Tis e - nough that Thou wilt care, Why should I the bur - den bear?
Let me thus with Thee a - bide, As my Fa - ther, Friend, and Guide.

# 292

PROTECTION 12. 11. 13. 11.
Dutch Folk Song
MARIA LOUISE BAUM
May be sung in unison
1. Put on the whole ar - mor of pure con - se - cra - tion, The breast - plate of right - eous - ness val - iant - ly gird,
2. For His is the great - ness, the power and the glo - ry, The vic - to - ry His, when for suc - cor we call;

With shield of true faith, and the
His maj - es - ty shines in cre -
hel - met of sal - va - tion— The
a - tion's won - drous sto - ry, And
sword of the Spir - it is God's might - y Word!
He. . is ex - alt - ed as head o - ver all!

## 293†

**TOPLADY** 77.77.77.

THOMAS HASTINGS

FREDERIC W. ROOT
Based on hymn by A. M. TOPLADY

1. Rock of A - ges, Truth di - vine, Be Thy strength forev - er mine;
2. Rock of Truth, our for-tress strong, Thou our ref - uge from all wrong,
3. Christ, the Truth, foun - da - tion sure, On this rock we are se - cure;

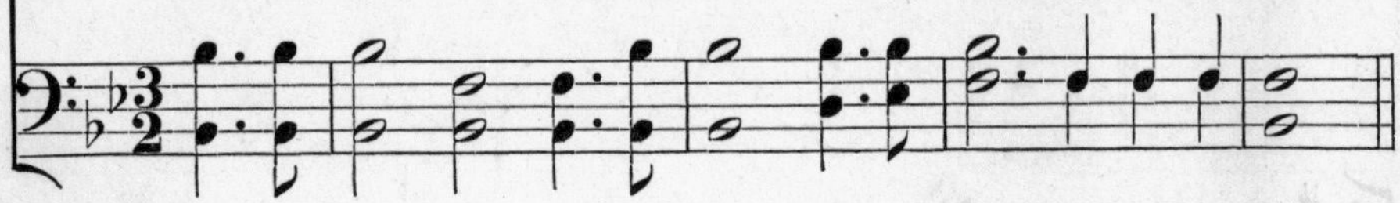

Let me rest se - cure on Thee, Safe a - bove life's rag - ing sea.
When from mor - tal sense I flee, Let me hide my - self in Thee.
Peace is there our life to fill, Cure is there for ev - ery ill.

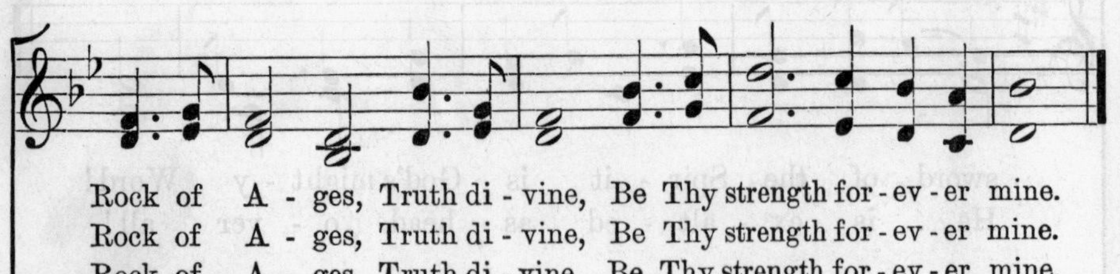

Rock of A - ges, Truth di - vine, Be Thy strength for - ev - er mine.
Rock of A - ges, Truth di - vine, Be Thy strength for - ev - er mine.
Rock of A - ges, Truth di - vine, Be Thy strength for - ev - er mine.

## 294†

**HOUGHTON** 77.77.77.

SAMUEL S. WESLEY

FREDERIC W. ROOT
Based on hymn by A. M. TOPLADY

1. Rock of A - ges, Truth di - vine, Be Thy strength for - ev - er mine;
2. Rock of Truth, our for-tress strong, Thou our ref - uge from all wrong,
3. Christ, the Truth, foun - da - tion sure, On this rock we are se - cure;

Let me rest se - cure on Thee, Safe a - bove life's rag - ing sea. .
When from mor - tal sense I flee, Let me hide my - self in Thee.
Peace is there our life to fill, Cure is there for ev - ery ill. .

Rock of A - ges, Truth di - vine, Be Thy strength for - ev - er mine.
Rock of A - ges, Truth di - vine, Be Thy strength for - ev - er mine.
Rock of A - ges, Truth di - vine, Be Thy strength for - ev - er mine.

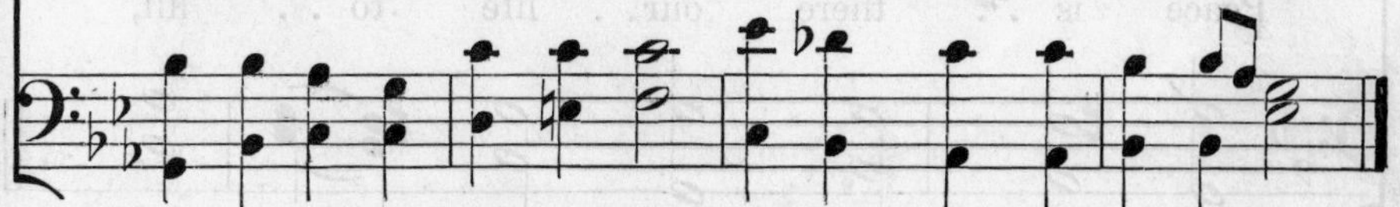

# 295†

**NICHT SO TRAURIG** 77. 77. 77.

Attributed to
JOHANN SEBASTIAN BACH

FREDERIC W. ROOT
Based on a hymn by A. M. TOPLADY

1. Rock of . . . A - ges, . . Truth di - vine,
2. Rock of . . . Truth, our . . for - tress . . strong,
3. Christ, the . . Truth, foun - da - tion . . sure,

Be . . Thy strength for - ev - er mine;
Thou our ref - uge from all wrong,
On . . this rock . . we are se - cure;

Let me . . rest . . se - cure on . . Thee,
When from mor - tal . . sense I . . . flee,
Peace is . . there our . . life to . . fill,

Safe a - bove life's rag - ing sea.
Let . . me hide my - self in Thee.
Cure is there for ev - ery ill.

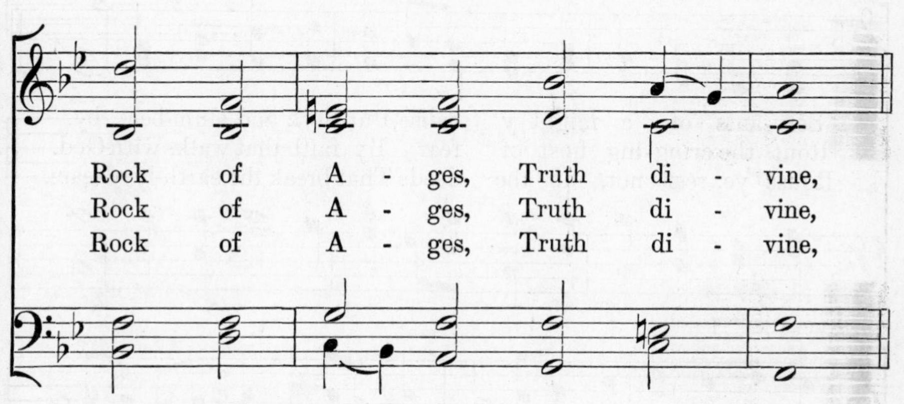
Rock of A - ges, Truth di - vine,
Rock of A - ges, Truth di - vine,
Rock of A - ges, Truth di - vine,

Be Thy strength for - ev - er . . . mine.
Be Thy strength for - ev - er . . . mine.
Be Thy strength for - ev - er . . . mine.

**AMSTERDAM** 7. 6. 7. 6. and Refrain

JAMES NARES

MARIA LOUISE BAUM
Based on hymn by M. H. TIPTON

1. Rouse ye, sol-diers of the cross, And lift your ban-ner high;
Serv-ants of a might-y cause, Put sloth and slum-ber by.

2. Wak-en, hear your Cap-tain's call, And fol-low where he trod;
Rout the cring-ing host of fear By faith that walks with God.

3. Rouse ye: long the con-quest waits For val-or's act su-preme;
Rouse ye, rest not, do the deeds That break the earth-ly dream.

REFRAIN

Rouse ye, rouse ye, face the foe, Rise to con-quer death and sin;
On with Christ to vic-tory go, O side with God, and win!

## 297

**DALKEITH** 10. 10. 10. 10.

THOMAS HEWLETT — R. B. L.

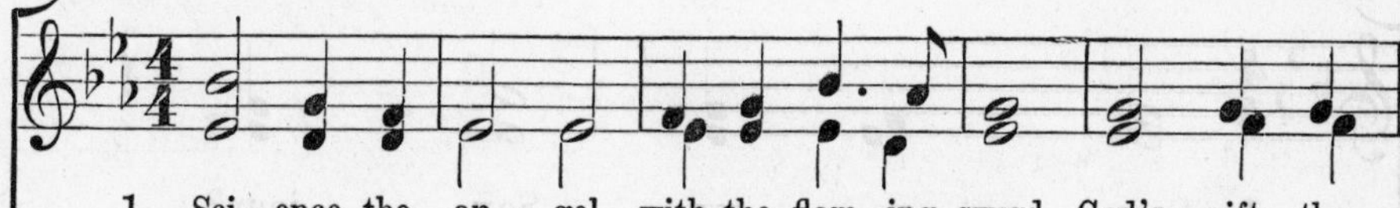

1. Sci - ence, the an - gel with the flam - ing sword, God's gift, the
2. Calm of She - ki - nah where hope an - chors fast, Har - bor of
3. Place of com - mun - ion with the Lamb of God, Fold where the
4. Loos - ener of pris - on bands at mid-night hour, Of self-forged

glo - ry of the ris - en Lord; Light of the world, in
ref - uge till the storm be past; Sweet, se - cret place where
sheep must pass be - neath His rod; Ark where the dove may
chains that fall through Love's all - power; Christ's morn - ing meal by

whose light we shall see Fa - ther and per-fect Son, blest u - ni - ty;
God and men do meet, Ho - reb where-on we walk with un - shod feet;
close her fal-tering wings, Love's law di - vine that makes us priests and kings;
joy - ous Gal - i - lee: Sci - ence, thou dost ful - fill all proph - e - cy.

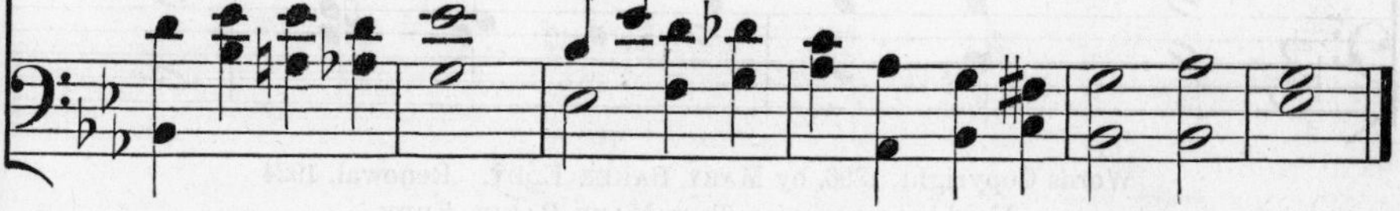

COMMUNION 10 7. 7 7 9.
LYMAN BRACKETT

COMMUNION HYMN
MARY BAKER EDDY

1. Saw ye my Sav - iour? Heard .. ye the glad sound? Felt ye the power of the Word?
2. Mourn - er, it calls you,— "Come to my bos - om, Love wipes your tears all a - way,
3. Sin - ner, it calls you,— "Come to this foun - tain, Cleanse the foul sens - es with - in;
4. Strong - est de - liv - erer, friend of the friend - less, Life of all be - ing di - vine:

'Twas the Truth that made us free,
And will lift the shade of gloom,
'Tis the Spir - it that makes pure,
Thou the Christ, and not the creed;
And was found by you and me
And for you make ra - diant room
That ex - alts thee, and will cure
Thou the Truth in thought and deed;
In the life and the love of our Lord.
Midst the glo - ries of one end - less day."
All thy sor - row and sick - ness and sin."
Thou the wa - ter, the bread, and the wine.

# 299†

SAVIOUR 10 7. 7 7 9.
WALTER E. YOUNG
COMMUNION HYMN
MARY BAKER EDDY
1. Saw ye my Sav - iour? Heard .. ye the glad sound? Felt ye the power of the Word?
2. Mourn - er, it calls . . . you,— "Come to my bos - om, Love wipes your tears all a - way,
3. Sin - ner, it calls . . . you,— "Come to this foun - tain, Cleanse the foul sens - es with - in;
4. Strong - est de - liv - erer, friend .. of the friend - less, Life of all be - ing di - vine:

'Twas the Truth that made us free, And was
And will lift the shade of gloom, And for
'Tis the Spir - it that makes pure, That ex -
Thou the Christ, and not the creed; Thou the
found by you.. and me In the
you make ra - diant room Midst the
alts thee, and.. will cure All thy
Truth in thought and deed; Thou the
life.. and the love.. of our Lord.
glo - ries of one.. end - less day."
sor - row and sick - ness and sin."
wa - ter, the bread, and the wine.

# 300†

LAUNDON 10 7.7 7 9.

G. THALBEN-BALL

COMMUNION HYMN

MARY BAKER EDDY

1. Saw ye my Sav - iour?
2. Mourn - er, it calls you,—
3. Sin - ner, it calls you,—
4. Strong - est de - liv - erer,
Heard ye the glad sound?
"Come to my bos - om,
"Come to this foun - tain,
friend of the friend - less,
Felt ye the power of the Word?
Love wipes your tears . . all a - way,
Cleanse the foul sens - es with - in;
Life of all be - ing di - vine:

'Twas the Truth that made us free, And was
And will lift the shade of gloom, And for
'Tis the Spir - it that makes pure, That ex -
Thou the Christ, and not the creed; Thou the
found by you and me In the
you make ra - diant room Midst the
alts thee, and will cure All thy
Truth in thought and deed; Thou the
life and the love of our Lord.
glo - ries of one end - less day."
sor - row and sick - ness and sin."
wa - ter, the bread, and the wine.

# 301†

FAITH 10 7. 7 7 9.
G. O'CONNOR-MORRIS

COMMUNION HYMN
MARY BAKER EDDY

1. Saw ye my Sav - iour? Heard . . . ye the glad sound? . . Felt ye the power . . of the Word?
2. Mourn - er, it calls you,— "Come . . . . to my bos - om, . . . Love wipes your tears . . all a - way,
3. Sin - ner, it calls you,— "Come . . . . to this foun - tain, . . . Cleanse the foul sens - es with - in;
4. Strong - est de - liv - erer, friend . . . . . of the friend - less, . . . Life of all be - ing di - vine:

'Twas the Truth that made us free, And was
And will lift the shade of gloom, And for
'Tis the Spir - it that makes pure, That ex -
Thou the Christ, and not the creed; Thou the
found by you and me In the
you make ra - diant room Midst the
alts thee, and will cure All thy
Truth in thought and deed; Thou the
life . . . and the love of our Lord.
glo - - ries of one end - less day."
sor - - row and sick - ness and sin."
wa - - ter, the bread, and the wine.

# 302†

**FREEDOM** 10 7. 7 7 9. — **COMMUNION HYMN**

E. N. G. — MARY BAKER EDDY

*May be sung in unison*
1. Saw ye my Sav - iour? Heard ye the glad sound? Felt ye the power of the Word? 'Twas the Truth that made us free, And was found by you and me In the life and the love of our Lord.
2. Mourn - er, it calls you,—"Come to my bos - om, Love wipes your tears all a - way, And will lift the shade of gloom, And for you make ra - diant room Midst the glo - ries of one end - less day."
3. Sin - ner, it calls you,—"Come to this foun - tain, Cleanse the foul sens - es with - in; 'Tis the Spir - it that makes pure, That ex - alts thee, and will cure All thy sor - row and sick - ness and sin."
4. Strong - est de - liv - erer, friend of the friend - less, Life of all be - ing di - vine: Thou the Christ, and not the creed; Thou the Truth in thought and deed; Thou the wa - ter, the bread, and the wine.

# 303

**ST. HUGH** C. M.

EDWARD J. HOPKINS — Anonymous

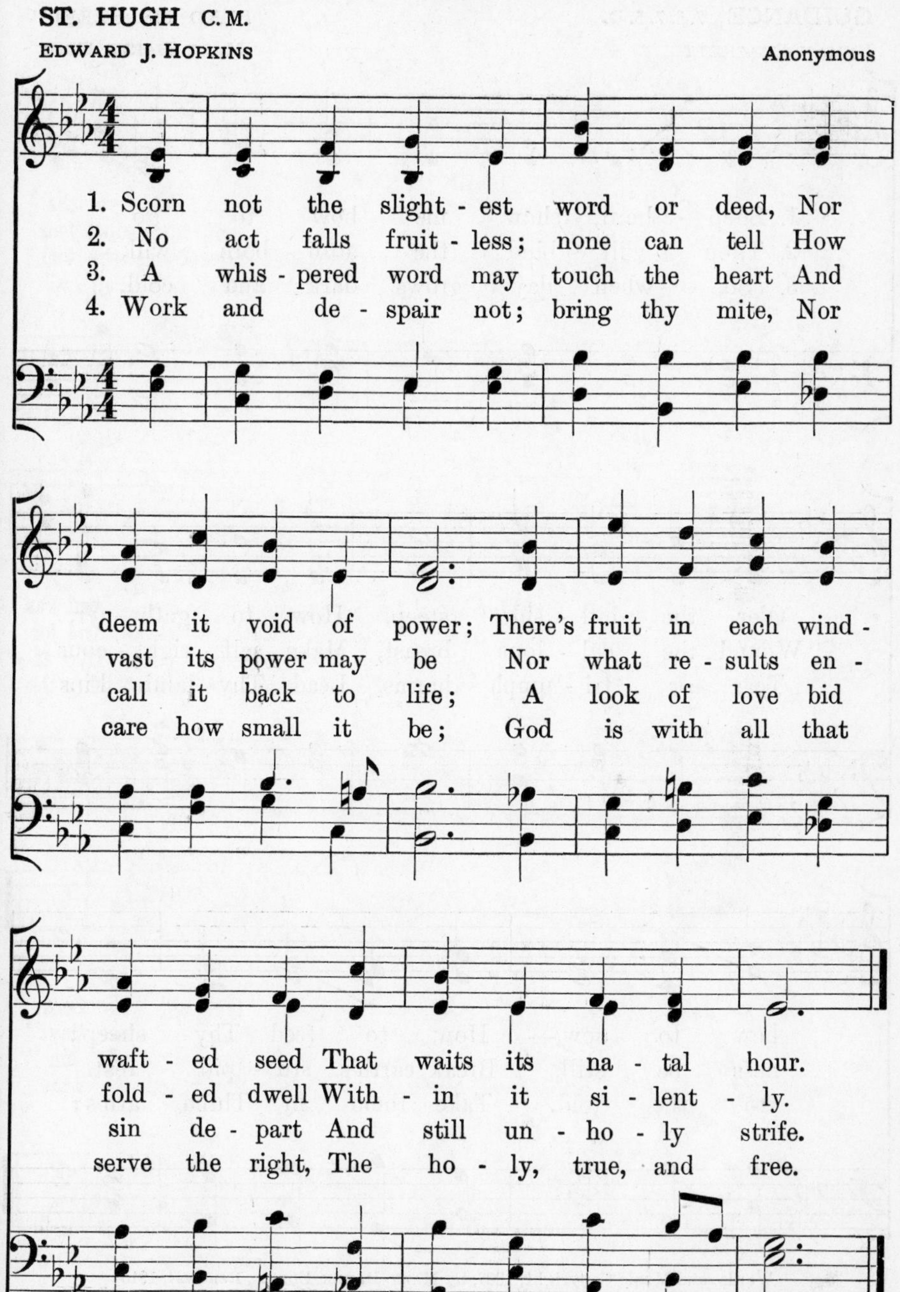
1. Scorn not the slight - est word or deed, Nor deem it void of power; There's fruit in each wind - waft - ed seed That waits its na - tal hour.
2. No act falls fruit - less; none can tell How vast its power may be Nor what re - sults en - fold - ed dwell With - in it si - lent - ly.
3. A whis - pered word may touch the heart And call it back to life; A look of love bid sin de - part And still un - ho - ly strife.
4. Work and de - spair not; bring thy mite, Nor care how small it be; God is with all that serve the right, The ho - ly, true, and free.

# 304†

**GUIDANCE** 7.5.7.5.D. "FEED MY SHEEP"

LYMAN BRACKETT MARY BAKER EDDY

1. Shep - herd, show me how to go
2. Thou wilt bind the stub - born will,
3. So, when day grows dark and cold,
O'er the hill - side steep, How to gath - er,
Wound the cal - lous breast, Make self - right - eous -
Tear or tri - umph harms, Lead Thy lamb - kins
how to sow,— How to feed Thy sheep;
ness be still, Break earth's stu - pid rest.
to the fold, Take them in Thine arms;

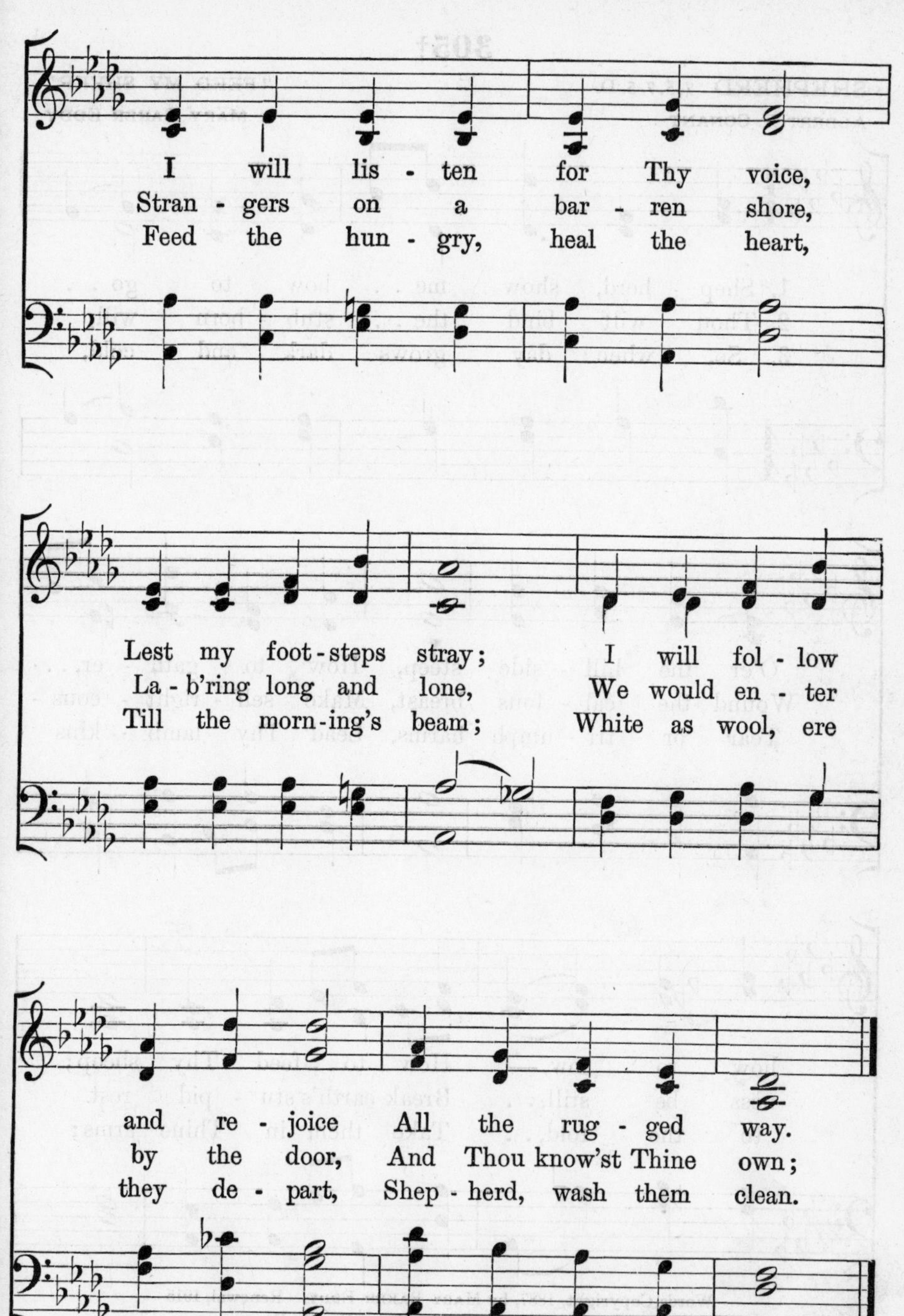
I will lis - ten for Thy voice,
Stran - gers on a bar - ren shore,
Feed the hun - gry, heal the heart,
Lest my foot - steps stray; I will fol - low
La - b'ring long and lone, We would en - ter
Till the morn - ing's beam; White as wool, ere
and re - joice All the rug - ged way.
by the door, And Thou know'st Thine own;
they de - part, Shep - herd, wash them clean.

305†
SHEPHERD 7.5.7.5.D.
"FEED MY SHEEP"
ALBERT F. CONANT
MARY BAKER EDDY
1. Shep - herd, show me . . how to go . .
2. Thou wilt bind the . . stub - born will,
3. So, when day grows dark and cold,
O'er the hill - side steep, How to gath - er, . .
Wound the cal - lous breast, Make self - right - eous -
Tear or tri - umph harms, Lead Thy lamb - kins
how to sow, — How to . . feed Thy sheep;
ness be still, . . Break earth's stu - pid rest.
to the fold, . . Take them in Thine arms;

I will lis - ten for Thy voice, . .
Stran - gers on a bar - ren shore, . .
Feed the hun - gry, heal the heart, . .
Lest my foot - steps stray; I will fol - low
La - b'ring long and lone, We would en - ter
Till the morn - ing's beam; White as . . wool, ere
and re - joice . . All . . the rug - ged way.
by the . . door, . . And Thou know'st Thine own;
they de - part, . . Shep - herd, wash them clean.

306†

CONCORD 7.5.7.5.D.
W. L. J.
"FEED MY SHEEP"
MARY BAKER EDDY
1. Shep - herd, show me how to go
2. Thou wilt bind the stub - born will,
3. So, when day grows dark and cold,
O'er the hill - side steep, How to gath - er,
Wound the cal - lous breast, Make self - right - eous -
Tear or tri - umph harms, Lead Thy lamb - kins
how to sow,— How to feed Thy sheep;
ness be still, Break earth's stu - pid rest.
to the fold, Take them in Thine arms;

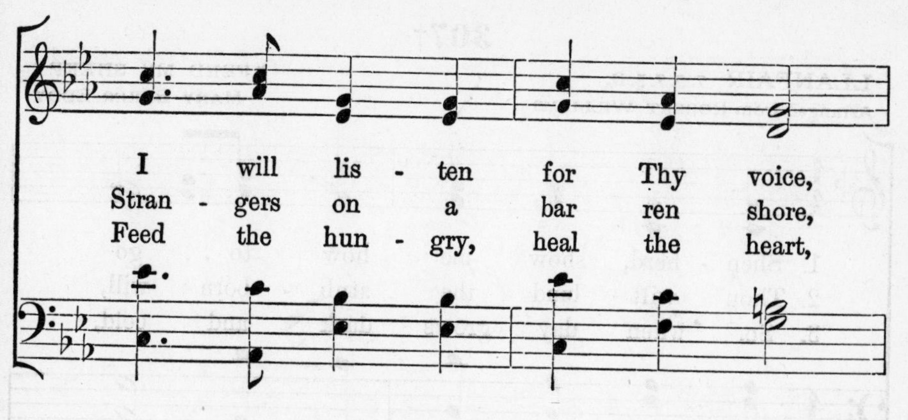
I will lis - ten for Thy voice,
Stran - gers on a bar ren shore,
Feed the hun - gry, heal the heart,

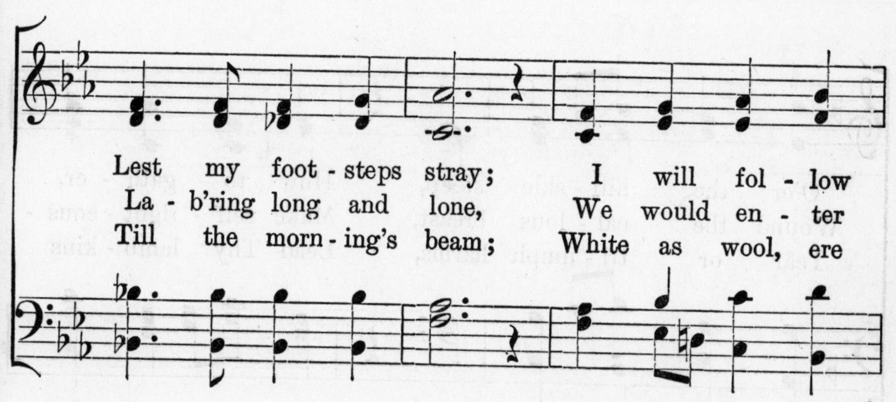
Lest my foot - steps stray; I will fol - low
La - b'ring long and lone, We would en - ter
Till the morn - ing's beam; White as wool, ere

and re - joice All the rug - ged way.
by the door, And Thou know'st Thine own;
they de - part, Shep - herd, wash them clean.

# 307†

**LLANFAIR** 7. 5. 7. 5. D.
Arranged from ROBERT WILLIAMS

"FEED MY SHEEP"
MARY BAKER EDDY

1. Shep - herd, show me how to . . go
2. Thou wilt bind the stub - born will,
3. So, when day grows dark and cold,
O'er the hill - side steep, How to gath - er,
Wound the cal - lous breast, Make self - right - eous -
Tear or tri - umph harms, Lead Thy lamb - kins
how to . . sow,— How to feed Thy sheep;
ness be . . still, Break earth's stu - pid rest.
to the fold, Take them in . . Thine arms;

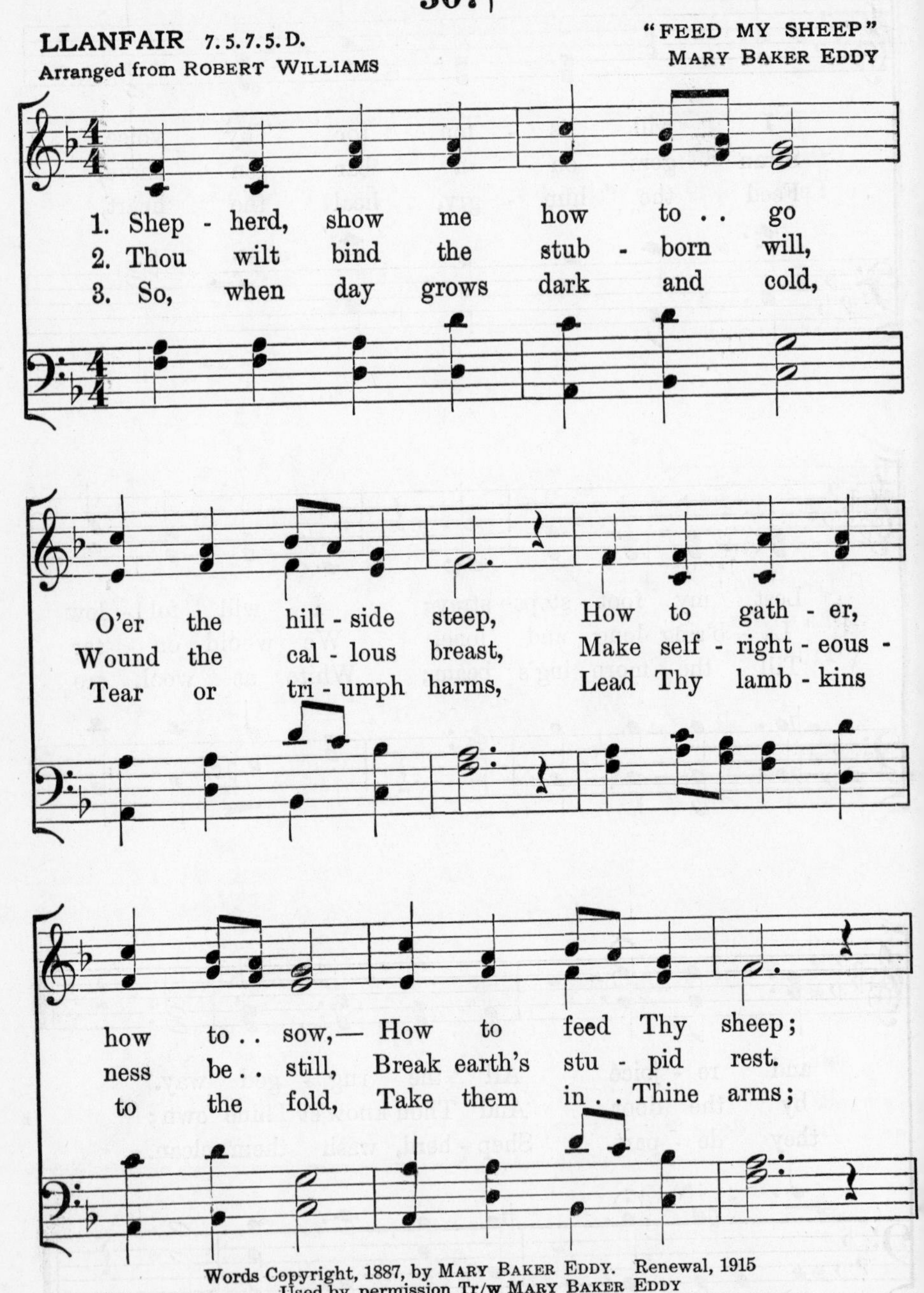

I will lis - ten for . . Thy . . voice,
Stran - gers on a bar - ren . . shore,
Feed the hun - gry, heal the . . heart,
Lest my foot - steps stray; . . I will fol - low
La - b'ring long and lone, . . . We would en - ter
Till the morn - ing's beam; . . White as wool, ere
and re - joice All the rug - ged way.
by the door, And Thou know'st Thine own;
they de - part, Shep - herd, wash them clean.

## 308†

**EGERTON** 7.5.7.5.D. — "FEED MY SHEEP"

G. THALBEN-BALL — MARY BAKER EDDY

1. Shep - herd, show me how to go
2. Thou wilt bind the stub - born will,
3. So, when day grows dark and cold,
O'er the hill - side steep, . . . How to gath - er,
Wound the cal - lous breast, . . . Make self - right - eous -
Tear or tri - umph harms, . . . Lead Thy lamb - kins
how to sow,— How to feed Thy sheep; . . .
ness be still, . . Break earth's stu - pid rest. . . . . .
to the fold, . . Take them in Thine arms; . . .

I will lis - ten for Thy voice,
Stran - gers on a bar - ren shore,
Feed the hun - gry, heal the heart,
Lest my foot-steps stray; . . . . . . I will fol - low
La - b'ring long and lone, . . . . . . . We would en - ter
Till the morn-ing's beam; . . . . . . White as wool, ere
and re - joice All the rug - ged way.
by the door, And Thou know'st Thine own;
they de - part, Shep - herd, wash them clean.

BENEVOLENCE 7.5.7.5.D. "FEED MY SHEEP"

E. N. G. MARY BAKER EDDY

1. Shep - herd, show me how to go
2. Thou wilt bind the stub - born will,
3. So, when day grows dark and cold,
O'er the hill - side steep, How to gath - er,
Wound the cal - lous breast, Make self - right - eous -
Tear or tri - umph harms, Lead Thy lamb - kins
how to sow,— How to feed Thy sheep;
ness be still, Break earth's stu - pid rest.
to the fold, Take them in Thine arms;

I will lis - ten . . for Thy voice,
Stran - gers on a . . . bar - ren shore,
Feed the hun - gry, . . heal the heart,
Lest my foot - steps stray; I will fol - low
La - b'ring long and lone, We would en - ter
Till the morn - ing's beam; White as wool, ere
and re - joice All the rug - ged way.
by the door, And Thou know'st Thine own;
they de - part, Shep - herd, wash them clean.

**BETHLEHEM** 7.7.7.7. D. and Refrain

MENDELSSOHN — CUMMINGS | JOHN RANDALL DUNN

1. Sing, ye joy - ous chil-dren, sing, Glo-rious is the Christ, our
2. When the stars to-geth - er sang, Then the Truth tri - um-phant
king, Truth has come a - gain to earth, Through the
rang: Be there light; And there was light. Gone are
low - ly Sav-iour's birth. Men and an - gels, an-thems raise; Hymns of
cha - os, fear and night; Truth hath rolled the mists a - way; Dawns on

Music by permission of NOVELLO & Co. Ltd.

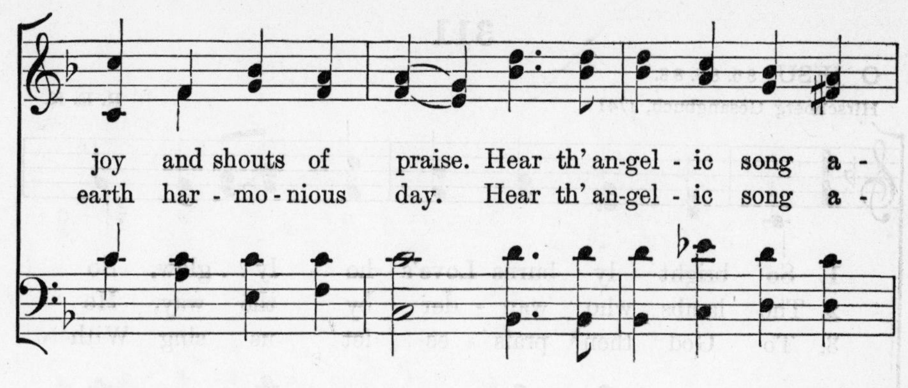
joy and shouts of praise. Hear th' an-gel - ic song a -
earth har - mo - nious day. Hear th' an-gel - ic song a -

Refrain
gain: Peace on earth, good will to men. Sing, ye
gain: Peace on earth, good will to men. Sing, ye

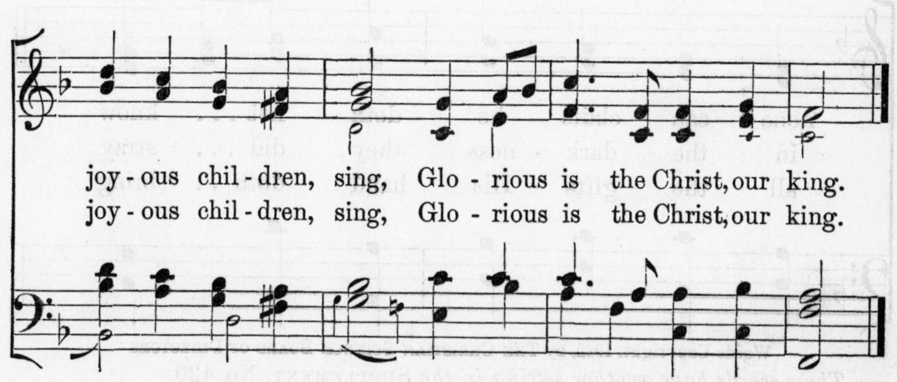
joy - ous chil - dren, sing, Glo - rious is the Christ, our king.
joy - ous chil - dren, sing, Glo - rious is the Christ, our king.

O JESU 86. 86. 88.
Hirschberg Gesangbuch, 1741
R. E. K.
1. So bright - ly burns Love's ho - ly . . glow, So con - stant . . shines its light, That none can claim he doth not . . . know
2. The lambs who wan - der by the way, He tak - eth . . . in His arm; For in the dark - ness they did . . . stray
3. To God then prais - es let us sing With glad . . and . . . will - ing mind For all the gifts His hand doth . . bring

*These words have another setting in the* SUPPLEMENT, No. 420

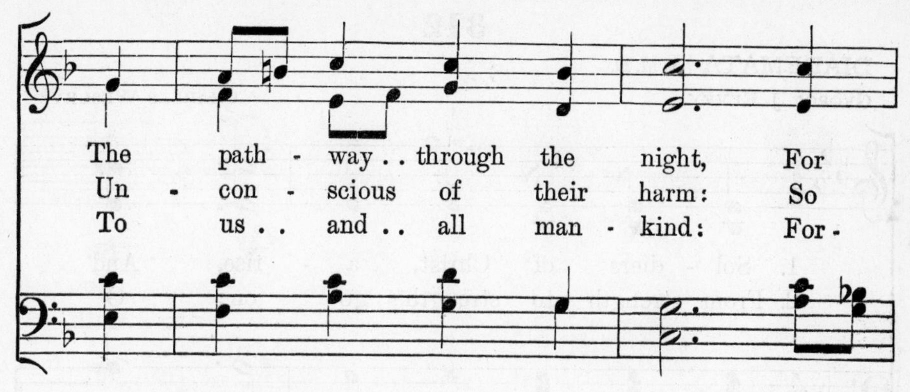
The path - way . . through the night, For
Un - con - scious of their harm: So
To us . . and . . all man - kind: For -

see, 'tis lit by Love di - vine To
com - eth He to all who roam, To
ev - er doth His gift of love Pour

trace for us His wise de - sign.
lead them safe - ly, sure - ly . . . home.
warmth and ra - diance from a - bove.

DIADEMATA S. M. D.

GEORGE J. ELVEY

CHARLES WESLEY*

1. Sol - diers of Christ, a - rise, And
2. From strength to strength go on; O
put your ar - mor on, Strong in the strength which
wres - tle, fight, and pray; Tread all the powers of
God sup - plies Through His e - ter - nal Son.
dark - ness down, And win the well - fought day.

Stand then in His great might, With
That, hav - ing all things done, And

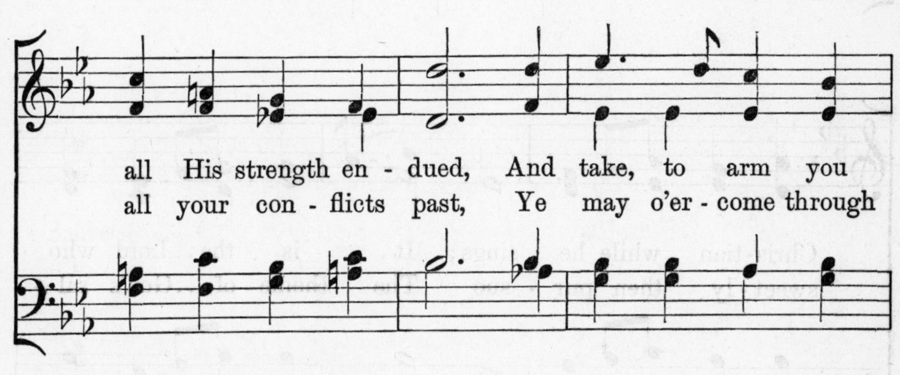
all His strength en - dued, And take, to arm you
all your con - flicts past, Ye may o'er - come through

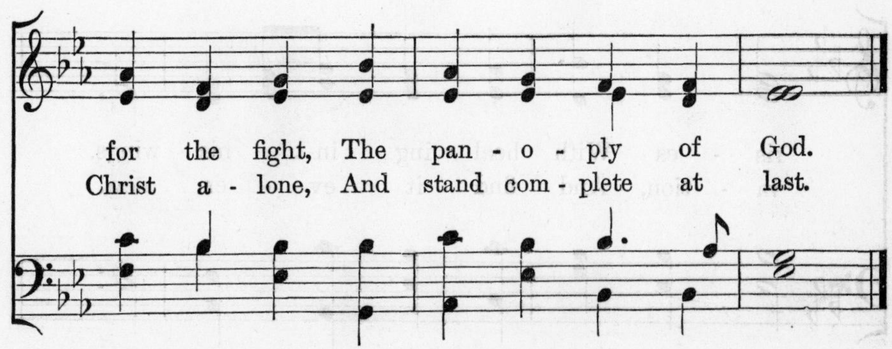
for the fight, The pan - o - ply of God.
Christ a - lone, And stand com - plete at last.

# 313

MEIRIONYDD 7.6.7.6.D.
Welsh Hymn Melody
WILLIAM LLOYD
WILLIAM COWPER
Adapted
1. Some - times a . . light sur - pris - es The
2. In . . ho - ly . . con - tem - pla - tion We
Chris - tian while he sings; It . . is the . . Lord who
sweet - ly then pur - sue The theme of . . . God's sal -
ris - es With heal - ing in . . his wings.
va - tion, And find it ev - er new.

When com - fort seems de - clin - ing, There
To God, in light a - bid - ing, True

comes to us a - gain A .. sea - son.. of clear
praise shall tune my voice, For.. while in .. Him con -

shin - ing, To cheer us aft - er rain.
fid - ing, I can - not but.. re - joice.

**SELMA** S. M.

Traditional Melody, Isle of Arran
Arranged by R. A. SMITH

JAMES MONTGOMERY
Adapted

1. Sow in the morn thy . . . seed, At eve hold not thy hand; To doubt and fear give thou no heed; Broad - cast it o'er the land.
2. It du - ly shall ap - pear In ver - dure, beau - ty, . . strength, The ten - der blade, the stalk, the ear; The full corn comes at length.
3. The har - vest now is . . . . white; Lift up thine eyes, be - hold, Il - lumed by Love's trans- form - ing light, God's bless-ings man - i - fold.

315†

SAWLEY C.M.

JAMES WALCH
Arranged

DAVID BATES

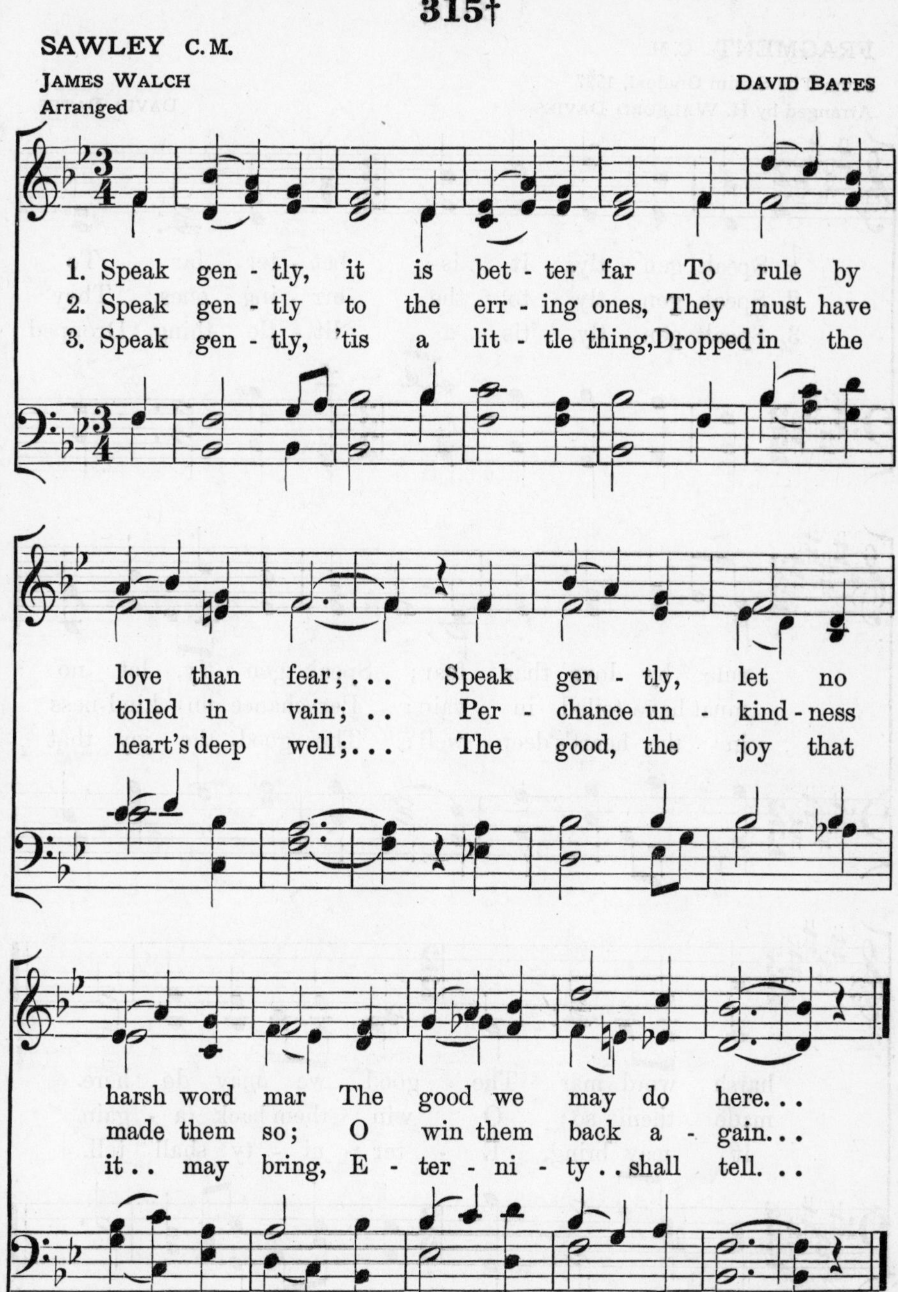
1. Speak gen - tly, it is bet - ter far To rule by love than fear; . . . Speak gen - tly, let no harsh word mar The good we may do here. . .
2. Speak gen - tly to the err - ing ones, They must have toiled in vain; . . Per - chance un - kind - ness made them so; O win them back a - gain. . .
3. Speak gen - tly, 'tis a lit - tle thing, Dropped in the heart's deep well; . . . The good, the joy that it . . may bring, E - ter - ni - ty . . shall tell. . .

Music by permission of Mrs. M. WALCH

# 316†

**FRAGMENT** C. M.

From The Sarum Gradual, 1527
Arranged by H. WALFORD DAVIES

DAVID BATES

1. Speak gen - tly, it is bet - ter far To rule by love than fear; Speak gen - tly, let no harsh word mar The good we may do here.
2. Speak gen - tly to the err - ing ones, They must have toiled in vain; Per-chance un - kind-ness made them so; O win them back a - gain.
3. Speak gen - tly, 'tis a lit - tle thing, Dropped in the heart's deep well; The good, the joy that it may bring, E - ter - ni - ty shall tell.

Music from A STUDENTS' HYMNAL ( HYMNS OF THE KINGDOM )
By permission of the OXFORD UNIVERSITY PRESS

# 317

## STRENGTH AND STAY 11. 10. 11. 10.

JOHN B. DYKES — HARRIET BEECHER STOWE, Adapted

1. Still, still with Thee when pur - ple morn - ing break - eth, When the bird
2. A - lone with Thee, a - mid the chang-ing shad - ows, Sol - emn the
3. So shall it ev - er be in the bright morn - ing, When hearts a -
wak - eth, and the shad-ows flee, Fair - er than morn - ing, .
hush of na - ture, new - ly born; A - lone with Thee, in . .
wak - ing see the shad-ows flee, O, in that hour, and
love-lier than the day - light, Dawns the sweet consciousness, I am with Thee.
breath-less ad - o - ra - tion, In the calm dew and freshness of the morn.
fair - er than the dawn-ing, Ris - es the glorious thought, I am with Thee.

## 318

**BAIRN** 98.884.

Lille Guds Barn
Danish Folk Melody

Based on the Danish of
NIKOLAJ F. S. GRUNDTVIG

To be sung in unison
1. Suf - fer the chil - dren to come to
2. He who re - ceiv - eth the Word as
3. See ye the lil - ies, how fair . . they
me, This was the Mas - ter's ten - der
they, Teach - a - ble, read - y to choose my
grow, Clothed in a glo - ry kings ne'er
plea; Gen - tle and lov - ing,
way, He shall have peace . . of
know; They, like the spar - rows,

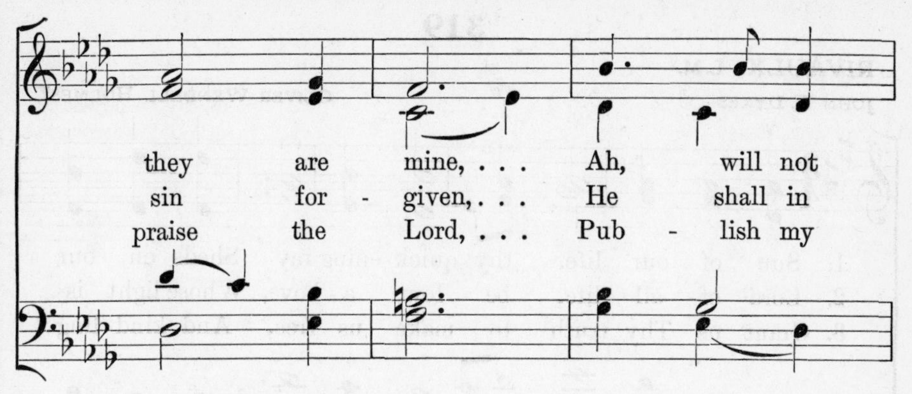
they are mine, . . . Ah, will not
sin for - given, . . . He shall in
praise the Lord, . . . Pub - lish my

ye . . . who see this sign
this . . wise en - ter heaven;
call . . with clear ac - cord,

Come . . . . un - to me? . . . .
Come . . . . un - to me. . . . .
Come . . . . un - to me. . . . .

## 319

**RIVAULX** L. M.

JOHN B. DYKES — OLIVER WENDELL HOLMES*

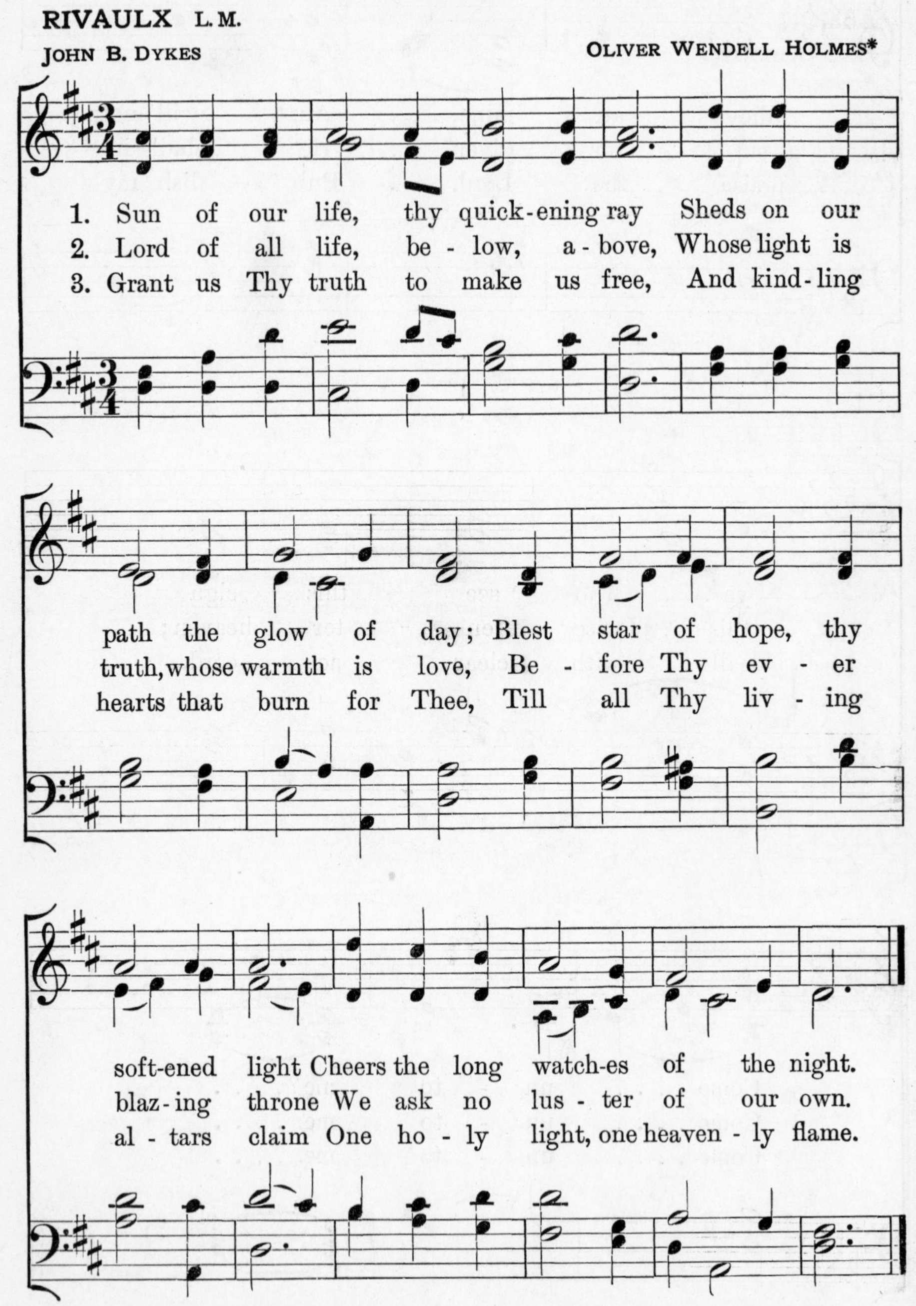
1. Sun of our life, thy quick-ening ray Sheds on our
2. Lord of all life, be - low, a - bove, Whose light is
3. Grant us Thy truth to make us free, And kind-ling
path the glow of day; Blest star of hope, thy
truth, whose warmth is love, Be - fore Thy ev - er
hearts that burn for Thee, Till all Thy liv - ing
soft-ened light Cheers the long watch-es of the night.
blaz-ing throne We ask no lus - ter of our own.
al - tars claim One ho - ly light, one heaven - ly flame.

# 320†

**AZMON** C. M.

CARL G. GLÄSER
Arranged

ISAAC WATTS
Arr. by WILLIAM CAMERON
Adapted

1. Su - preme in wis - dom as in power, The
2. He gives the con - quest to the meek, Sup -
3. Mere hu - man en - er - gy shall faint, And
4. They, with un - wea - ried step, shall tread The

Rock of A - ges stands; Canst thou not search His
ports the faint - ing heart; And cour - age in the
youth - ful vig - or cease; But those who wait up -
path of life di - vine; With grow - ing ar - dor

word, and trace The work - ing of His hands?
e - vil hour His heaven - ly aids im - part.
on the Lord In .. strength shall still in - crease.
on - ward move, With grow - ing bright - ness shine.

*Another version of this music will be found in the* SUPPLEMENT, No. 409

# 321†

**BURFORD** C. M.

Chetham's Psalmody, 1718

ISAAC WATTS

Arr. by WILLIAM CAMERON

Adapted

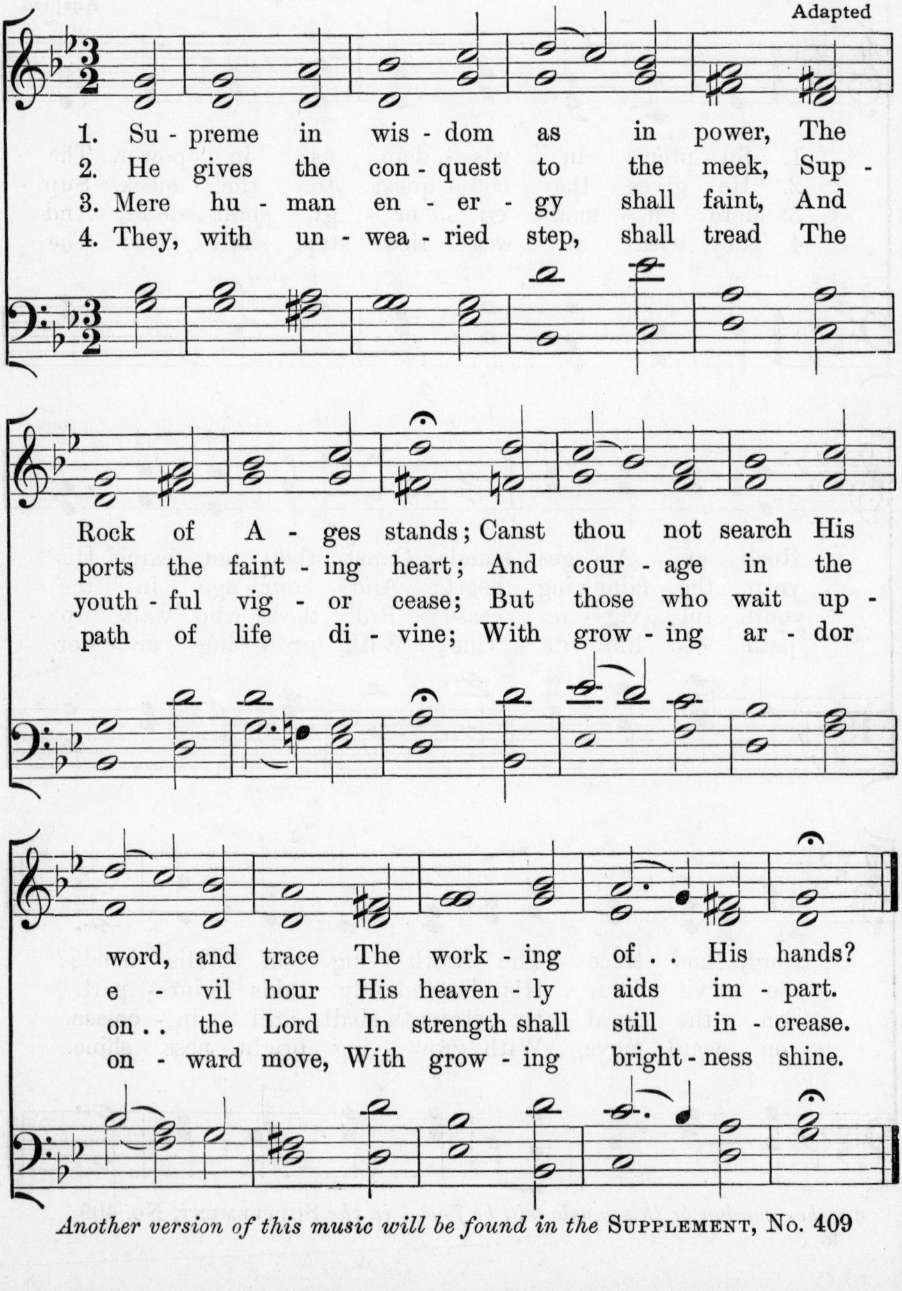

1. Su - preme in wis - dom as in power, The
2. He gives the con - quest to the meek, Sup -
3. Mere hu - man en - er - gy shall faint, And
4. They, with un - wea - ried step, shall tread The

Rock of A - ges stands; Canst thou not search His
ports the faint - ing heart; And cour - age in the
youth - ful vig - or cease; But those who wait up -
path of life di - vine; With grow - ing ar - dor

word, and trace The work - ing of . . His hands?
e - vil hour His heaven - ly aids im - part.
on . . the Lord In strength shall still in - crease.
on - ward move, With grow - ing bright - ness shine.

*Another version of this music will be found in the* SUPPLEMENT, No. 409

# 322†

## CANONBURY L. M.

ROBERT SCHUMANN
Arranged

CAROLINE GILMAN
Adapted

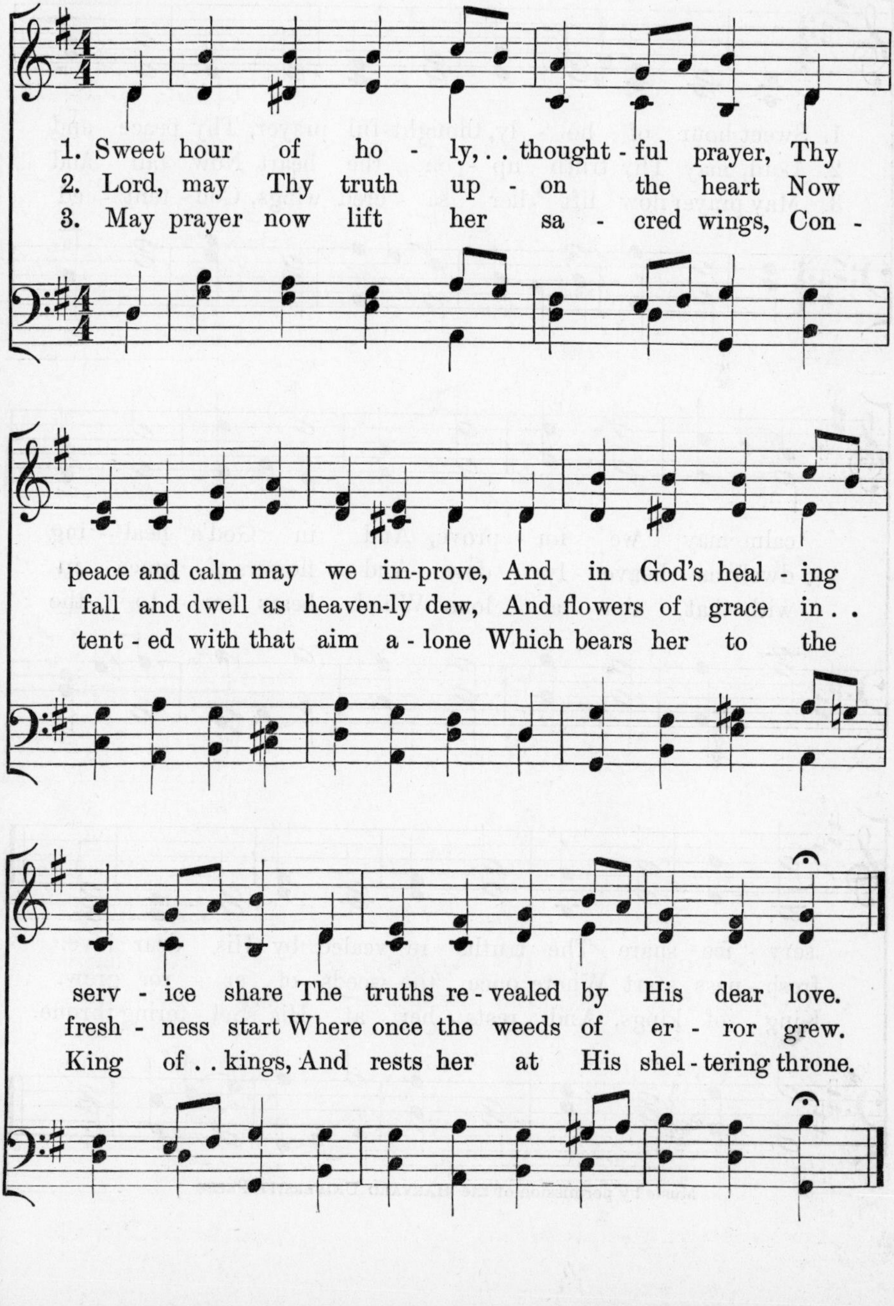

1. Sweet hour of ho - ly, . . thought - ful prayer, Thy
2. Lord, may Thy truth up - on the heart Now
3. May prayer now lift her sa - cred wings, Con -

peace and calm may we im-prove, And in God's heal - ing
fall and dwell as heaven-ly dew, And flowers of grace in . .
tent - ed with that aim a - lone Which bears her to the

serv - ice share The truths re - vealed by His dear love.
fresh - ness start Where once the weeds of er - ror grew.
King of . . kings, And rests her at His shel - tering throne.

## 323†

**PUER NOBIS NASCITUR** L. M.

MICHAEL PRAETORIUS | CAROLINE GILMAN
Adapted

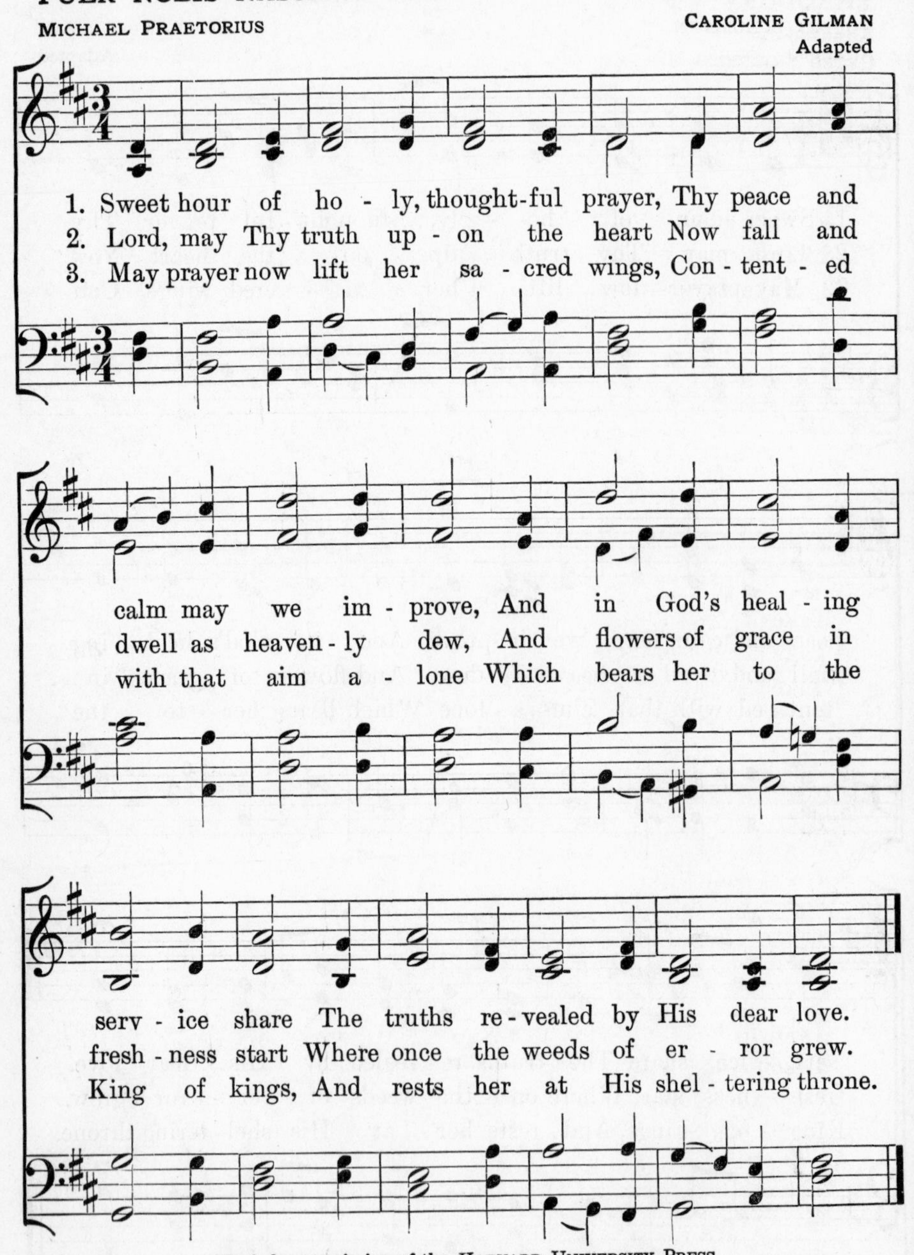
1. Sweet hour of ho - ly, thought-ful prayer, Thy peace and
2. Lord, may Thy truth up - on the heart Now fall and
3. May prayer now lift her sa - cred wings, Con - tent - ed
calm may we im - prove, And in God's heal - ing
dwell as heaven - ly dew, And flowers of grace in
with that aim a - lone Which bears her to the
serv - ice share The truths re - vealed by His dear love.
fresh - ness start Where once the weeds of er - ror grew.
King of kings, And rests her at His shel - tering throne.

Music by permission of the HARVARD UNIVERSITY PRESS

# 324

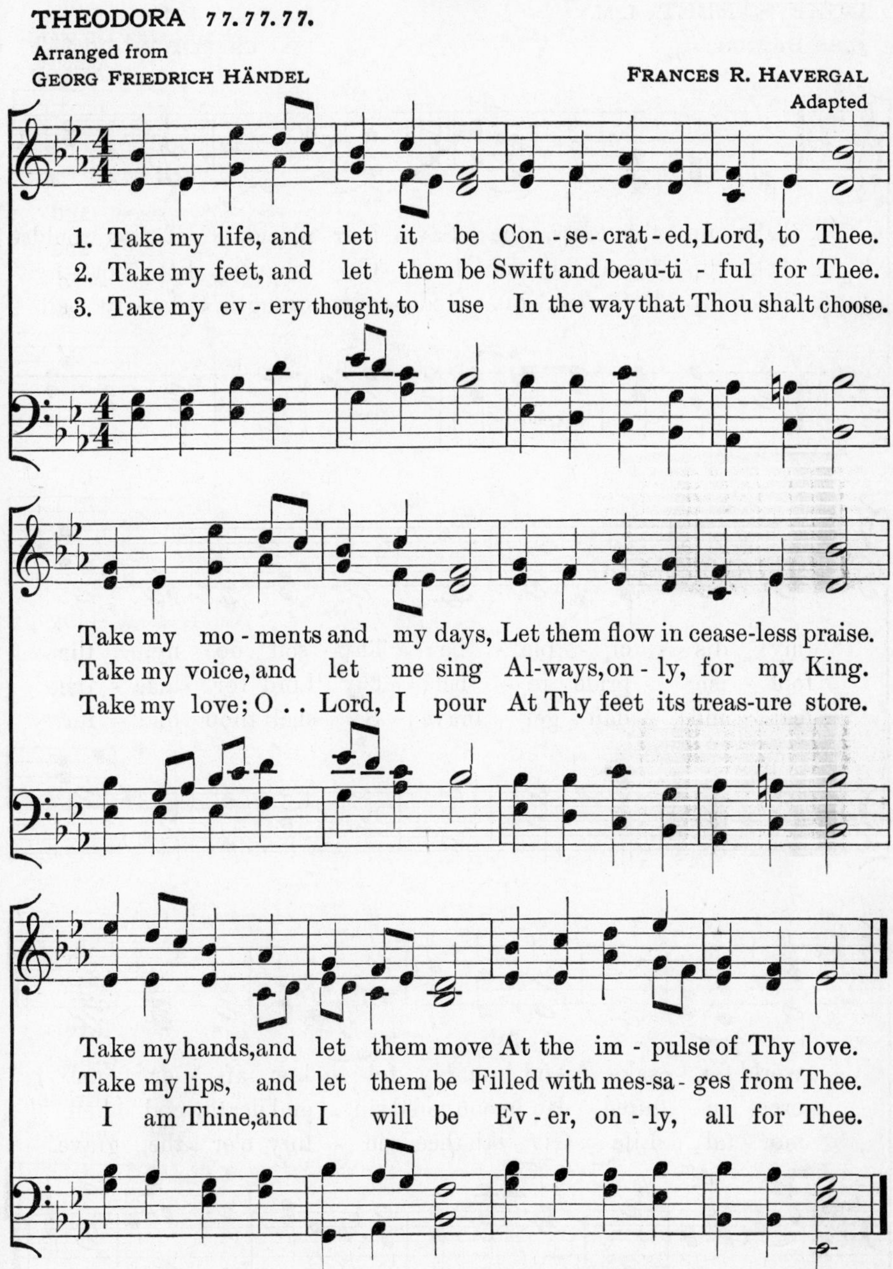
THEODORA 77.77.77.
Arranged from
GEORG FRIEDRICH HÄNDEL
FRANCES R. HAVERGAL
Adapted
1. Take my life, and let it be Con - se - crat - ed, Lord, to Thee.
2. Take my feet, and let them be Swift and beau - ti - ful for Thee.
3. Take my ev - ery thought, to use In the way that Thou shalt choose.
Take my mo - ments and my days, Let them flow in cease - less praise.
Take my voice, and let me sing Al - ways, on - ly, for my King.
Take my love; O . . Lord, I pour At Thy feet its treas - ure store.
Take my hands, and let them move At the im - pulse of Thy love.
Take my lips, and let them be Filled with mes - sa - ges from Thee.
I am Thine, and I will be Ev - er, on - ly, all for Thee.

# 325

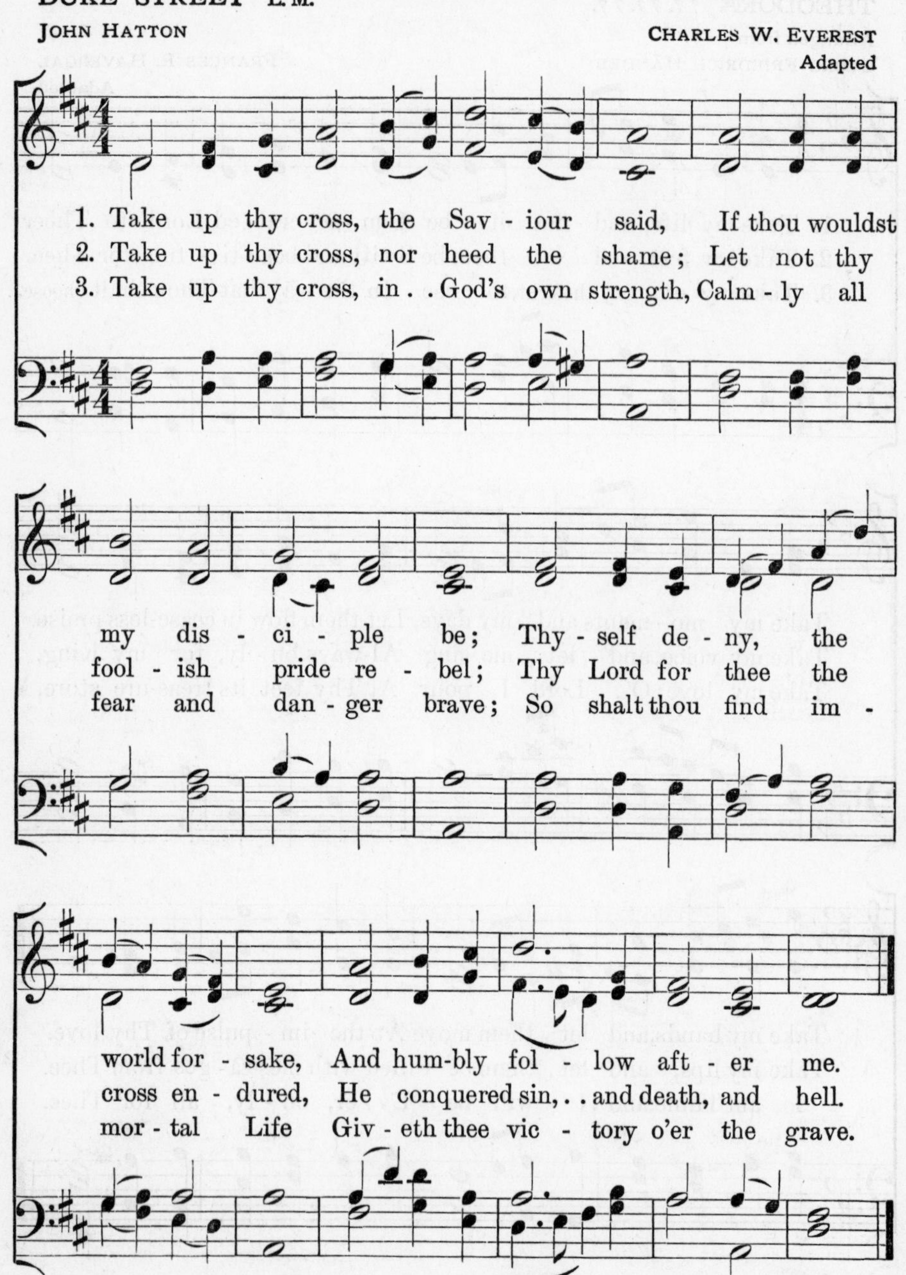
DUKE STREET L. M.
JOHN HATTON
CHARLES W. EVEREST
Adapted
1. Take up thy cross, the Sav - iour said, If thou wouldst
2. Take up thy cross, nor heed the shame; Let not thy
3. Take up thy cross, in . . God's own strength, Calm - ly all
my dis - ci - ple be; Thy - self de - ny, the
fool - ish pride re - bel; Thy Lord for thee the
fear and dan - ger brave; So shalt thou find im -
world for - sake, And hum-bly fol - low aft - er me.
cross en - dured, He conquered sin, . . and death, and hell.
mor - tal Life Giv - eth thee vic - tory o'er the grave.

**TRURO** L. M.

Psalmodia Evangelica, 1790 — JAMES MONTGOMERY*

1. The Chris - tian war - rior, see him stand In
2. In pan - o - ply of truth com - plete, Sal -
3. With this om - nip - o - tence he moves; From
4. Thus strong in his Re - deem - er's strength, Sin,

all the ar - mor of his God; The Spir - it's sword is
va - tion's hel - met on his head, With right-eous-ness, a
this the al - ien ar - mies flee; Un - til he more than
death and hell he tram - ples down, Fights his good fight and

in . . his hand; His feet are with the gos - pel shod:
breast-plate meet, And faith's broad shield be - fore him spread.
con-queror proves, Through Christ, who gives him vic - to - ry.
wins at length, Through mer - cy, an im - mor - tal crown.

327†

**COVENTRY** C. M.

English Melody
Arranged by FREDERIC W. ROOT

Author Unknown

1. The God who made both heaven and earth And
2. The poor and all . . op - pressed by wrong Are
3. By Him the blind re - ceive their sight, By
all . . that they con - tain Will nev - er quit His
saved by His de - cree; He gives the hun - gry
Him the fall - en rise; With con - stant care, His
stead - fast truth Nor make His prom - ise vain.
need - ful food And sets the cap - tive free.
ten - der love All hu - man need sup - plies.

## ST. MAGNUS C.M.

JEREMIAH CLARK

Author Unknown

1. The God who made both heaven and .. earth And all that they con - tain Will nev - er quit His stead - fast truth Nor make His prom - ise vain.
2. The poor and all op - pressed by .. wrong Are saved by His de - cree; He gives the hun - gry need - ful food And sets the cap - tive free.
3. By Him the blind re - ceive their sight, By Him the fall - en rise; With con - stant care, His ten - der love All hu - man need sup - plies.

# 329

**ST. ANSELM** 7.6.7.6.D.

JOSEPH BARNBY — FREDERIC W. ROOT

1. The heavens de - clare the glo - ry Of
2. His law man's path - way bright - ens, His
3. In dai - ly con - tem - pla - tion Of
Him who made all things; Each day re - peats the
judg - ments all are pure, His Word the thought en -
Thee, I take de - light; O, let my med - i -
sto - ry, Each night its trib - ute brings.
light - ens, And ev - er shall en - dure.
ta - tion Lay hold of Thee a - right.

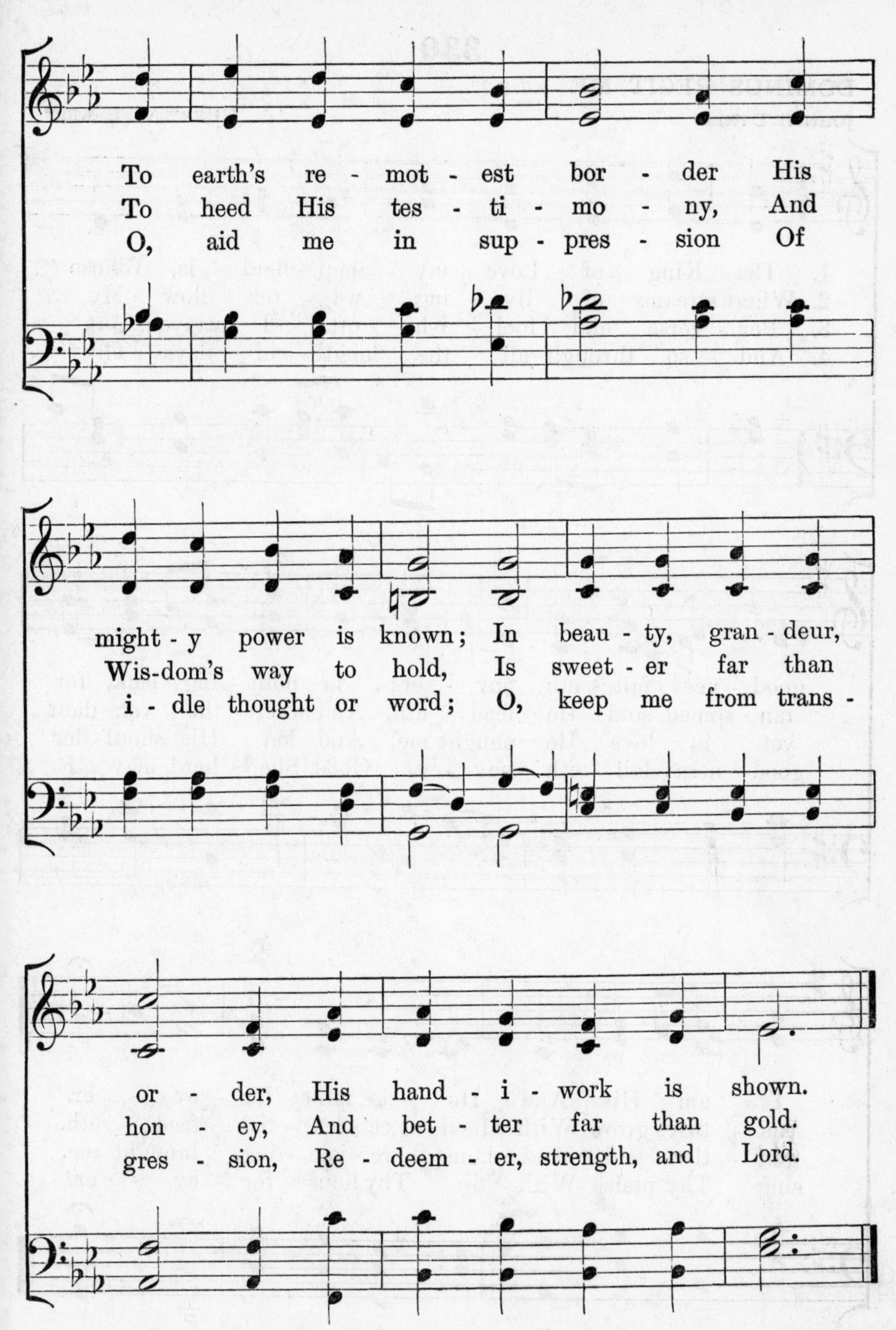
To earth's re - mot - est bor - der His
To heed His tes - ti - mo - ny, And
O, aid me in sup - pres - sion Of
might - y power is known; In beau - ty, gran - deur,
Wis - dom's way to hold, Is sweet - er far than
i - dle thought or word; O, keep me from trans -
or - der, His hand - i - work is shown.
hon - ey, And bet - ter far than gold.
gres - sion, Re - deem - er, strength, and Lord.

# 330

**DOMINUS REGIT ME** 8.7.8.7.

JOHN B. DYKES — HENRY W. BAKER*

1. The King of Love my Shep - herd is, Whose good - ness fail - eth nev - er; I noth - ing lack, for I am His And He is mine for - ev - er.
2. Where streams of liv - ing wa - ter flow My ran - somed soul He lead - eth, And where the ver - dant pas - tures grow, With food ce - les - tial feed - eth.
3. Per - verse and fool - ish oft I strayed, But yet in love He sought me, And on His shoul - der gen - tly laid, And home, re - joic - ing, brought me.
4. And so through all the length of days Thy good - ness fail - eth nev - er; Good Shep - herd, may I sing Thy praise With - in Thy house for - ev - er.

## ST. SEPULCHRE L.M.

GEORGE COOPER — THOMAS SCOTT*

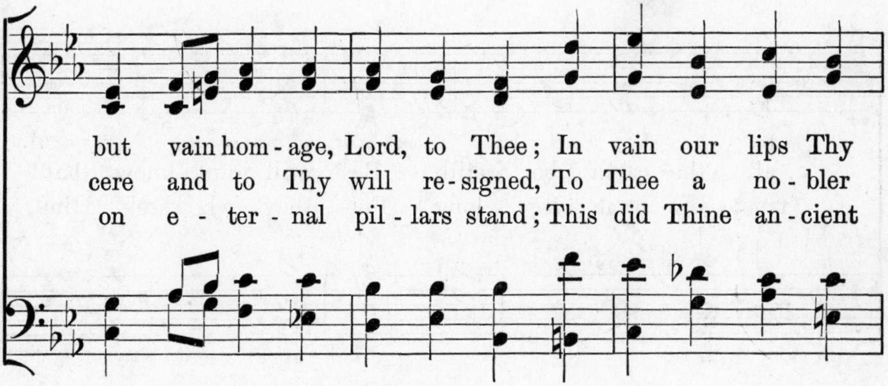

1. The lifted eye and bended knee
Are but vain homage, Lord, to Thee;
In vain our lips Thy praise prolong,
The heart a stranger to the song.

2. The pure, the humble, contrite mind,
Sincere and to Thy will resigned,
To Thee a nobler offering yields
Than Sheba's groves or Sharon's fields.

3. Love God and man: this great command
Doth on eternal pillars stand;
This did Thine ancient prophets teach,
And this Thy Well-Belovèd preach.

# 332

NESTLING 86.86.888.
Som Hønen klukker mindelig
AUGUST H. WINDING
Based on the Danish of
NIKOLAJ F. S. GRUNDTVIG
To be sung in unison
1. The Lord is in His ho - ly place, Let
2. So hear and heed His faith - ful Word, And
all the earth be still, Be still and know that
trust His prom - ise long, For they who seek Him
He is God, And wait to do His will.
Life shall find, And shall in Him be strong;

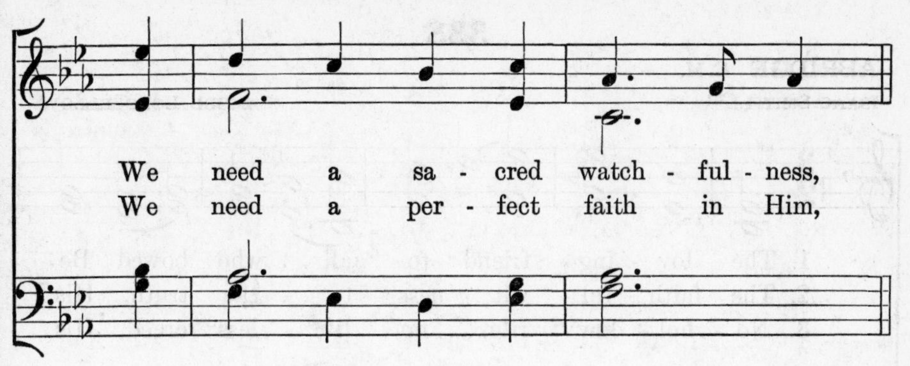
We need a sa - cred watch - ful - ness,
We need a per - fect faith in Him,

An ear - nest deep de - sire for grace, Our
With un - der - stand - ing nev - er dim, To . .

lives with true con - tent to fill.
fill our dai - ly lives with song.

# 333

**ABRIDGE** C.M.

ISAAC SMITH — SAMUEL LONGFELLOW

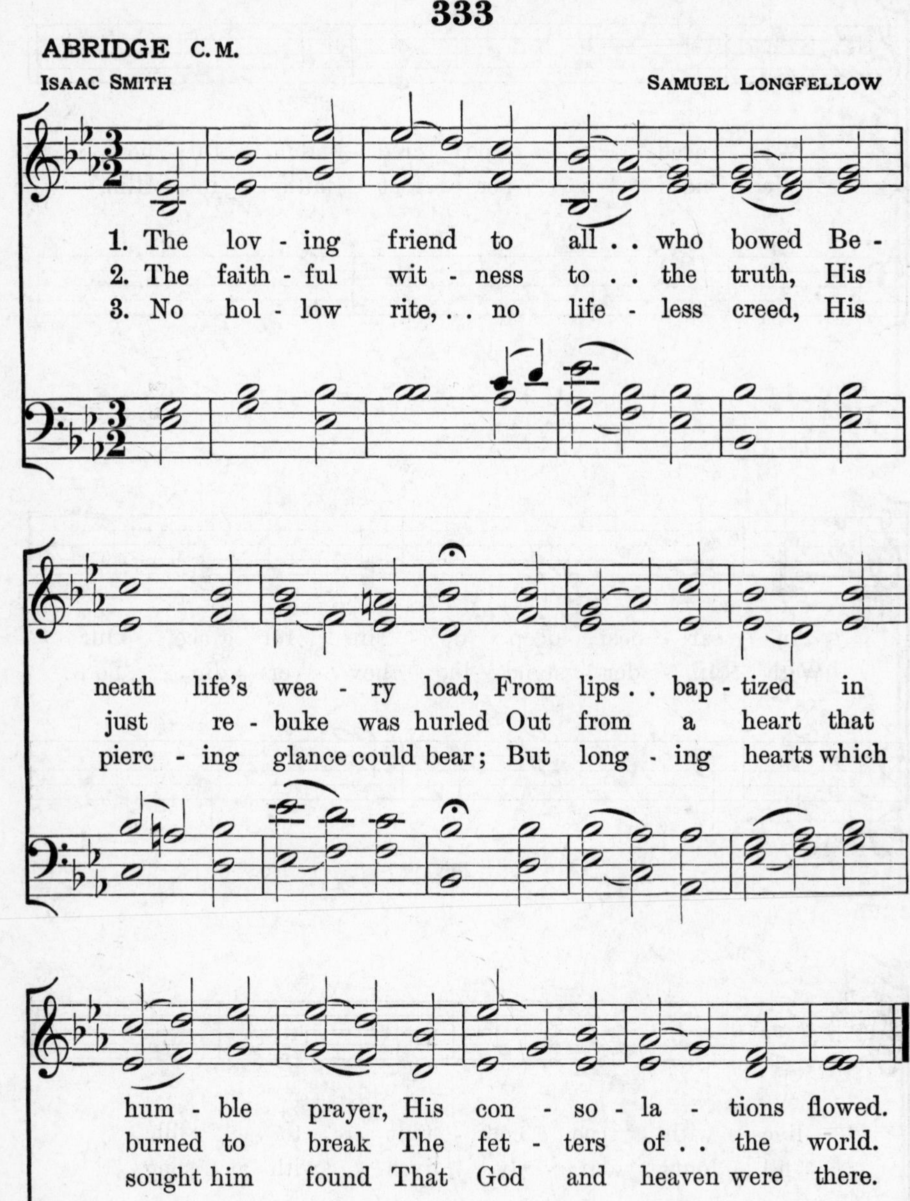
1. The lov - ing friend to all . . who bowed Be - neath life's wea - ry load, From lips . . bap - tized in hum - ble prayer, His con - so - la - tions flowed.
2. The faith - ful wit - ness to . . the truth, His just re - buke was hurled Out from a heart that burned to break The fet - ters of . . the world.
3. No hol - low rite, . . no life - less creed, His pierc - ing glance could bear; But long - ing hearts which sought him found That God and heaven were there.

# 334

**ST. STEPHEN** C. M.

WILLIAM JONES — WILLIAM COWPER*

1. The spir - it breathes up - on the Word And brings the truth to sight; Pre - cept and prom - ise still af - ford A sanc - ti - fy - ing light.
2. A glo - ry gilds the sa - cred page, Ma- jes - tic like the sun; It gives a light to ev - ery age, It gives but bor - rows none.
3. Let ev - er - last - ing thanks be Thine For such a bright dis - play As makes a world of dark - ness shine With beams of heaven - ly day.

# 335

## MORNING LIGHT 7. 6. 7. 6. D.

GEORGE J. WEBB — SAMUEL F. SMITH

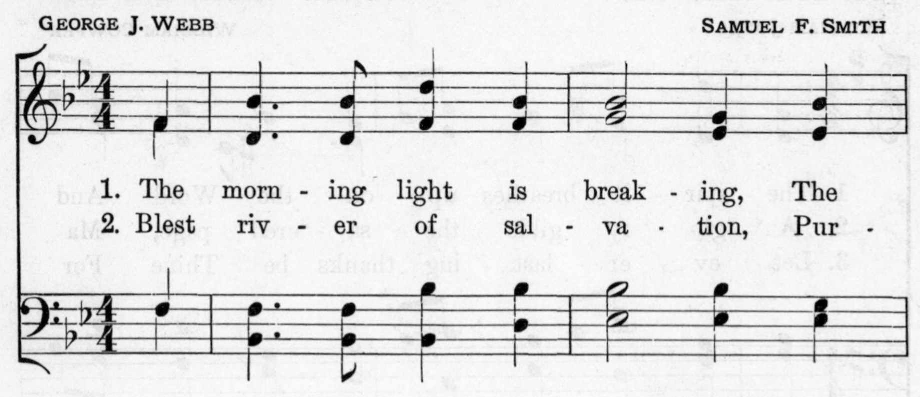
1. The morn - ing light is break - ing, The
2. Blest riv - er of sal - va - tion, Pur -

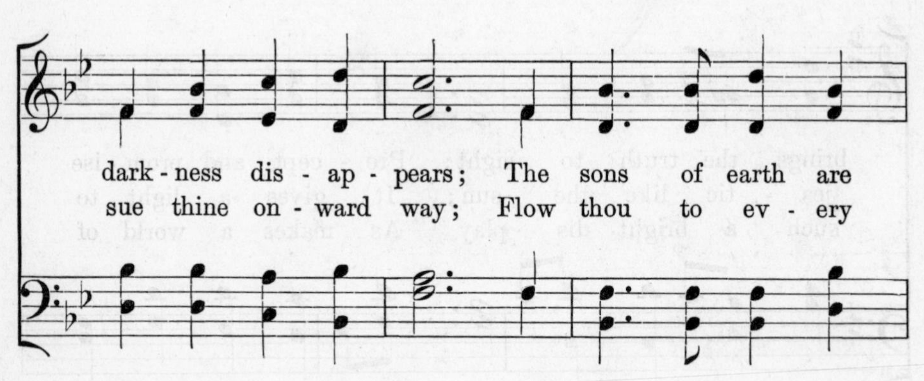
dark - ness dis - ap - pears; The sons of earth are
sue thine on - ward way; Flow thou to ev - ery

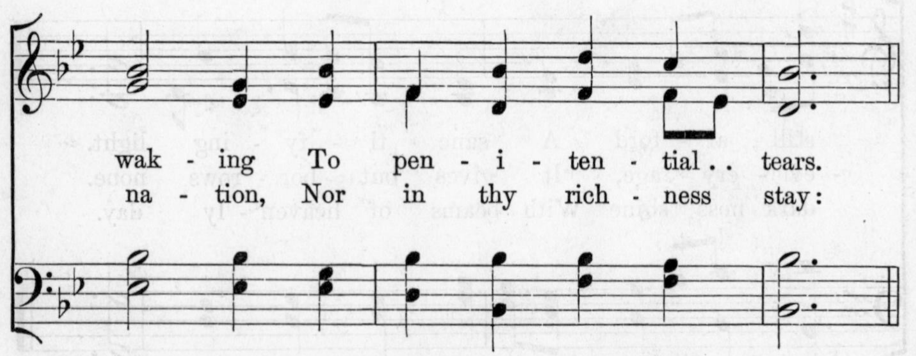
wak - ing To pen - i - ten - tial . . tears.
na - tion, Nor in thy rich - ness stay:

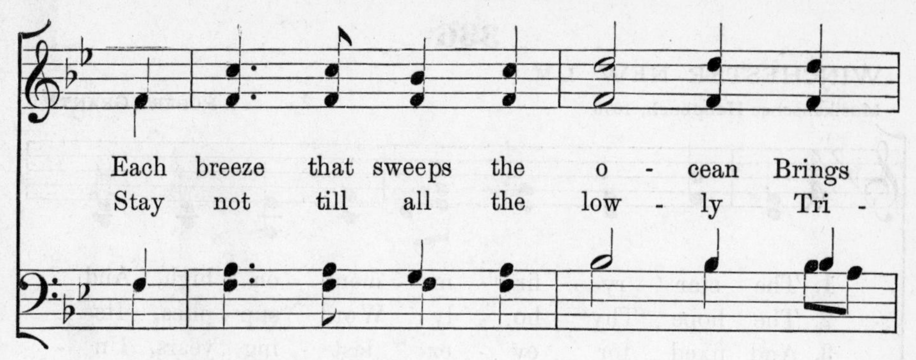
Each breeze that sweeps the o - cean Brings
Stay not till all the low - ly Tri -

ti - dings from a - far, . . Of na - tions in com -
um - phant reach their home: Stay not till all the

mo - tion, Pre - pared for Zi - on's war.
ho - ly Pro - claim, The Lord is come.

# 336

## WINCHESTER NEW L. M.

Musikalisches Handbuch, 1690 ROBERT GRANT*

1. The star - ry fir - ma - ment on . . high, And
2. The hope Thy ho - ly Word sup - plies, Its
3. And fixed for ev - er - last - ing years, Un -
all the glo - ries of the sky, These shine not to Thy
truth di - vine and pre - cepts wise, In each a heaven - ly
moved, a - mid dis - solv - ing spheres, Thy Word shall shine in
praise, O Lord, So bright - ly as Thy sa - cred Word.
beam I see, And ev - ery beam con - ducts to Thee.
cloud - less day, When heaven and earth have past a - way.

## 337†

**ST. MABYN** 8.7.8.7.

ARTHUR H. BROWN — ROBERT C. WATERSTON

1. The - o - ries, which thou - sands cher - ish,
2. World - lings blind - ly may re - fuse Her,
3. Thrones may tot - ter, em - pires crum - ble,
Pass like clouds that sweep the sky; Creeds and dog - mas
Close their eyes and call it night; Learn - ed scoff - ers
All their glo - ries cease to be; While She, Christ-like,
all may per - ish; Truth Her - self can nev - er die.
may a - buse Her, But they can - not quench Her light.
crowns the hum - ble, And from bond - age sets them free.

Music from the REVISED CHURCH HYMNARY: By permission of the OXFORD UNIVERSITY PRESS

## 338†

**SUSSEX** 8.7.8.7.

English Traditional Melody
Arranged

ROBERT C. WATERSTON

1. The - o - ries, which thou - sands cher - ish,
2. World - lings blind - ly may re - fuse Her,
3. Thrones may tot - ter, em - pires crum - ble,

Pass like clouds that sweep the sky; Creeds and dog - mas
Close their eyes and call it night; Learn - ed scoff - ers
All their glo - ries cease to be; While She, Christ-like,

all may per - ish; Truth Her - self can nev - er die.
may a - buse Her, But they can - not quench Her light.
crowns the hum - ble, And from bond - age sets them free.

Music from the ENGLISH HYMNAL: By permission of the OXFORD UNIVERSITY PRESS

## 339

**ST. COLUMBA (ERIN) C. M.**

Old Irish Hymn Melody — WILLIAM P. McKENZIE

1. There are none friend - less, none a - fraid, The sav - ing Truth who know, . . . Their shin - ing path leads from the shade, And up to light they go. . . . .
2. It set - teth free from thought of sin, It heal - eth sor - row's blight, . . . Im - mor - tal joy is found there - in, And there shall be no night. . . .
3. And O, may we, God's chil - dren true, His heal - ing love make known, . . And see by faith all things made new When ruled by Love a - lone. . . .

# 340

SLINGSBY 8.7.8.7.

EDMUND S. CARTER | FREDERICK W. FABER*

1. There's a wide - ness in God's mer - cy,
2. For the love of . . God is broad - er
3. If our love were but more sim - ple,
Like the wide - ness of the sea; There's a . . kind - ness
Than is seen by hu - man mind, And the heart of
We should take Him at His word; And our lives would
in His jus - tice, Which is more than lib - er - ty.
the E - ter - nal Is most won - der - ful - ly kind.
be all sun - shine In the sweet - ness of our Lord.

# 341

**PEACEFIELD** 7.7.7.7.

Ancient Irish Melody
Harmonized by D. F. R. WILSON

OLIVER HOLDEN

1. They who seek the throne of grace, Find that throne in ev - ery place: If we live a life of prayer, God is pres - ent ev - ery - where.
2. In our sick - ness, in our health, In our want, or in our wealth, If we look to God in prayer, God is pres - ent ev - ery - where.
3. Then, my heart, in ev - ery strait, To thy Fa - ther come, and wait; He will an - swer ev - ery prayer, God is pres - ent ev - ery - where.

Music by permission of DAVID F. R. WILSON

## ANGELS' SONG C. M. D.

FELIX MENDELSSOHN-BARTHOLDY
Arranged by E. J. HOPKINS

L. L. R.

1. This is the day the Lord hath made; Be glad, give thanks, re - joice; Stand in His pres - ence, un - a - fraid, In praise lift up your voice.
2. The Lord will hear be - fore we call, And ev - ery need sup - ply; Good things are free - ly given to all Who on His word re - ly.
3. For sin de - stroyed, for sor - row healed, For health and peace re - stored; For Life and Love by Truth re - vealed, We thank and bless the Lord.

All per - fect gifts are from a - bove, And
We come to - day to bring Him praise Not
This is the day the Lord hath made, In
all our bless - ings show . . The am - pli - tude of
for such gifts a - lone, . . But for the high - er,
praise lift up your voice. . . In shin - ing robes of
God's dear love Which ev - ery heart may know.
deep - er ways In which His love is shown.
joy ar - rayed, Be glad, give thanks, re - joice.

## 343†

**STRACATHRO** C.M.

Scottish Hymn Melody — GEORGE W. DOANE, Adapted

1. Thou art the Way: to thee.. a - lone From
2. Thou art the Truth: thy word a - lone True
3. Thou art the Life: the rend - ing tomb Pro -
4. Thou art the Way, the Truth, the Life: Grant
sin.. and death we flee; And he.. who would the
wis - dom doth im - part; Thou on - ly canst un -
claims thy con - quering arm; And those who put their
us.. that Way to know, That Truth to trust, that
Fa - ther seek, Must seek Him, Lord, by thee.
fold that Truth, And pu - ri - fy the heart.
trust in thee Nor death nor hell shall harm.
Life to learn, Whose joys e - ter - nal flow.

*These words have another setting in the* SUPPLEMENT, No. 429

# 344†

**ST. ANDRÉ** C. M.

H. WALFORD DAVIES | GEORGE W. DOANE, Adapted

1. Thou art the Way: to thee a - lone From
2. Thou art the Truth: thy word a - lone True
3. Thou art the Life: the rend - ing tomb Pro -
4. Thou art the Way, the Truth, the Life: Grant
sin and death we flee; And he who would the
wis - dom doth im - part; Thou on - ly canst un -
claims thy con - quering arm; And those who put their
us that Way to . . know, That Truth to trust, that
Fa - ther seek, Must seek Him, Lord, by thee.
fold that Truth, And pu - ri - fy the heart.
trust in thee Nor death nor hell shall harm.
Life to learn, Whose joys e - ter - nal flow.

Music by permission of H. WALFORD DAVIES

*These words have another setting in the* SUPPLEMENT, No. 429

CHARTERHOUSE 11. 10. 11. 10.
DAVID EVANS
L. M. G.
To be sung in unison
1. Thou liv - ing light of pen - te - cos - tal glo - ry, . .
2. Per - fect and pure, in - ef - fa - ble in beau - ty, . .
3. So all shall see where Thine ef - ful - gence glow - eth, . .
. . Lo, wide we fling the sun - less pris - on doors; . . .
. . Thy stain - less ra - diance e'en to us im - part, . . . .
. Through pur - er lives of men, a count - less host, . . . .

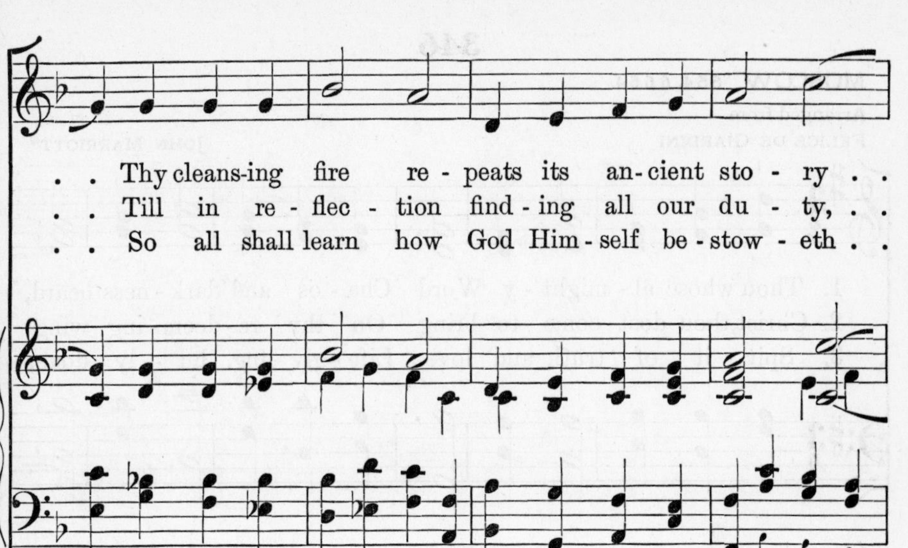

. . Thy cleans-ing fire re - peats its an-cient sto - ry . .
. . Till in re - flec - tion find - ing all our du - ty, . .
. . So all shall learn how God Him - self be - stow - eth . .


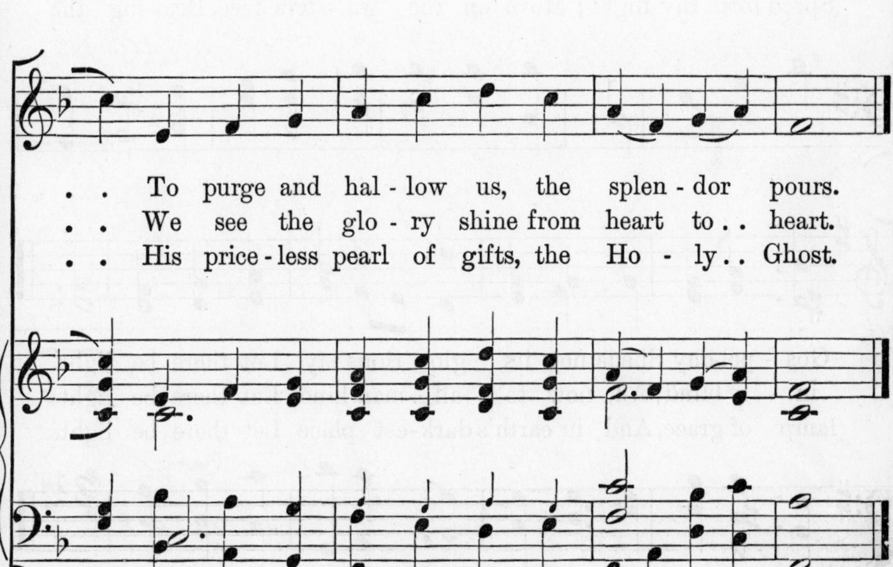

. . To purge and hal - low us, the splen - dor pours.
. . We see the glo - ry shine from heart to . . heart.
. . His price - less pearl of gifts, the Ho - ly . . Ghost.

# 346

**MOSCOW** 664. 6664.

Arranged from
FELICE DE GIARDINI

JOHN MARRIOTT*

1. Thou whose al - might - y Word Cha - os and dark - ness heard,
2. Christ, thou dost come to bring On thy re - deem - ing wing
3. Spir - it of truth and love, Life - giv - ing, ho - ly dove,

And took their flight; Hear us, we hum - bly pray, And where the
Heal-ing and sight, Health to the sick in mind, Sight to the
Speed forth thy flight; Move on the wa - ters' face, Bear-ing the

Gos - pel-day Sheds not its glo - rious ray, Let there be light.
in - ly blind; Ah, now to all man-kind Let there be light.
lamp of grace, And in earth's dark-est place Let there be light.

*Another version of this music will be found in the* SUPPLEMENT, No. 401

347†
BRISTOL C. M.
EDWARD HODGES
U. R. L.
1. Though moun - tains may de - part from thee, And
2. O thou af - flict - ed, tossed with doubt, God
3. Es - tab - lished in His right - eous - ness, He
4. All tongues that rise con - demn - ing thee Are
hills be far re - moved, His kind - ness shall re -
bids the storm to cease; His chil - dren shall be . .
holds thee free from fear; No wea - pon formed a -
si - lenced by His word; This is thy . . pre - cious
main with thee, His cov - e - nant be proved.
taught of . . Him And great shall be their peace.
gainst His own Shall pros - per nor come near.
her - i - tage, Thou serv - ant of the Lord.

# 348†

BANGOR C. M.

WILLIAM TANS'UR — U. R. L.

1. Though mountains may depart from thee,
And hills be far removed,
His kindness shall remain with thee,
His covenant be proved.

2. O thou afflicted, tossed with doubt,
God bids the storm to cease;
His children shall be taught of Him
And great shall be their peace.

3. Established in His righteousness,
He holds thee free from fear;
No weapon formed against His own
Shall prosper nor come near.

4. All tongues that rise condemning thee
Are silenced by His word;
This is thy precious heritage,
Thou servant of the Lord.

# 349

**REMEMBRANCE** L. M.

SAMUEL S. WESLEY
Reharmonized

1. Thy will, al - might - y Fa - ther, Thine, And
2. Re - flect - ing tru - ly all Thou art And
3. We walk in free - dom and in peace Thy
Thine a - lone be ev - er done; For Thou art Life and
all the sun-shine of Thy love, No life we know from
ho - ly pur - pose to ful - fill, And Thou dost ev - er
Truth and Love, The great, e - ter - nal, Ho - ly One.
Thee a - part, But peace on earth from heaven a - bove.
point the path
lov - ing serv - ants of Thy will.

## 350

**AR HYD Y NOS** 84.84.88.84.

Welsh Melody

MARY PETERS
Adapted

1. Through the love of God our Sav - iour
2. Though we pass through trib - u - la - tion,
3. We ex - pect a bright to - mor - row,
All will be well; Free and change - less
All will be well; Ours is such a
All will be well; Faith can sing through
is His fa - vor; All must be well;
full sal - va - tion, All must be well;
days of sor - row, All must be well;

Pre - cious is the Love that healed us,
Hap - py still, in God con - fid - ing,
While His truth we are ap - ply - ing,

Per - fect is the grace that sealed us, Strong the hand stretched
Fruit - ful, when in Christ a - bid - ing, Ho - ly, through the
And up - on His love re - ly - ing, God is ev - ery

forth to shield us; All, all is well.
Spir - it's guid - ing; All, all is well.
need sup - ply - ing, All, all is well.

# 351

**ST. ASAPH** 8.7.8.7.D.

WILLIAM S. BAMBRIDGE

BERNHARD S. INGEMANN
S. BARING-GOULD, Tr.

1. Through the night of doubt and sor - row
2. One, the light of God's own pres - ence,
3. One, the strain the lips of thou - sands

On - ward goes the pil - grim band, Sing - ing songs of
O'er His ran - somed peo - ple shed, Chas - ing far the
Lift as from the heart of one; One the con - flict,

ex - pec - ta - tion, March - ing to the prom - ised land.
gloom and ter - ror, Bright-ening all the path we tread:
one the per - il, One, the march in God be - gun:

Words by permission of A. W. RIDLEY & Co.

Clear be - fore us through the dark - ness
One, the ob - ject of our jour - ney,
One, the glad - ness of re - joic - ing
Gleams and burns the guid - ing light; Broth - er clasps the
One, the faith which nev - er tires, One, the ear - nest
On the far e - ter - nal shore Where the One Al -
hand of broth - er, Step - ping fear - less through the night.
look - ing for - ward, One, the hope our God in - spires;
might - y Fa - ther Reigns in love for - ev - er - more.

# 352†

**FEDERAL STREET** L. M.

HENRY K. OLIVER — ARTHUR C. COXE, Adapted

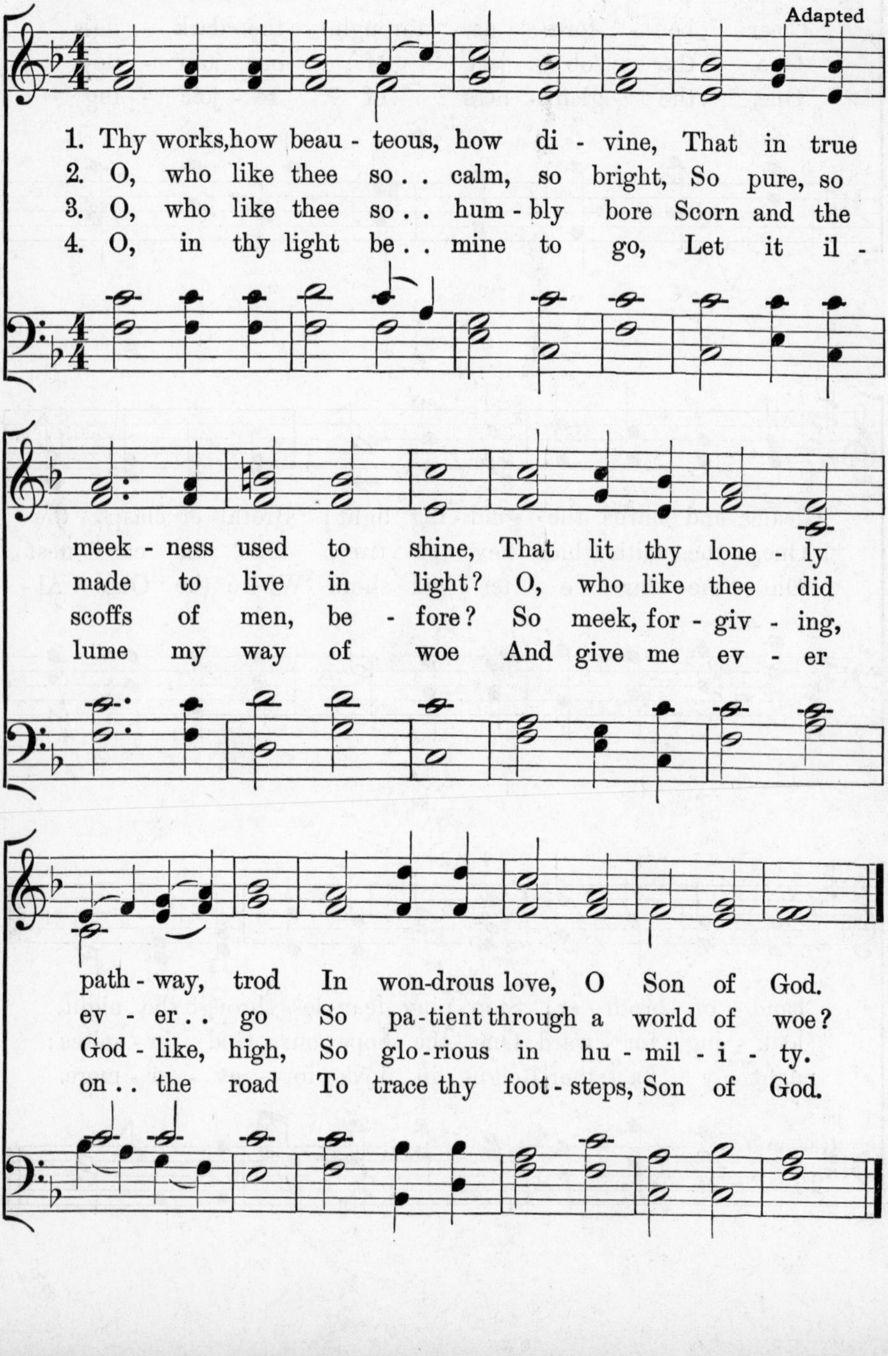

1. Thy works, how beau - teous, how di - vine, That in true
2. O, who like thee so . . calm, so bright, So pure, so
3. O, who like thee so . . hum - bly bore Scorn and the
4. O, in thy light be . . mine to go, Let it il -

meek - ness used to shine, That lit thy lone - ly
made to live in light? O, who like thee did
scoffs of men, be - fore? So meek, for - giv - ing,
lume my way of woe And give me ev - er

path - way, trod In won-drous love, O Son of God.
ev - er . . go So pa - tient through a world of woe?
God - like, high, So glo - rious in hu - mil - i - ty.
on . . the road To trace thy foot - steps, Son of God.

## 353†

**BABYLON'S STREAMS** L. M.

THOMAS CAMPION

ARTHUR C. COXE
Adapted

Not slow
1. Thy works, how beau - teous, how di - vine, That
2. O, who like thee . . so calm, so bright, So
3. O, who like thee . . so hum - bly bore Scorn
4. O, in thy light . . be mine to go, Let
in true meek-ness used to shine, That lit thy
pure, so made to live in light? O, who like
and the scoffs of men, be - fore? So meek, for-
it il - lume my way of woe And give me
lone - ly path-way, trod In won-drous love, O . . Son of God.
thee did ev - er go So pa - tient through a . . world of woe?
giv - ing, God-like, high, So glo - rious in hu - mil - i - ty.
ev - er on the road To trace thy foot - steps, Son of God.

# 354

**ST. THOMAS** S. M.

Williams' Psalmody, 1770

BENJAMIN BEDDOME
Adapted

1. 'Tis God the Spir - it . . leads In . . paths be - fore un - known; The work to be per - formed is . . . ours, The strength is . . all His own.
2. Sup - port - ed by His . . grace, We . . still pur - sue our way; As - sured that we shall reach the . . prize, Se - cure in end - less day.
3. God works in us to . . will, He . . works in . . us to do; His is the power by which we . . act, His be . . the glo - ry too.

# 355

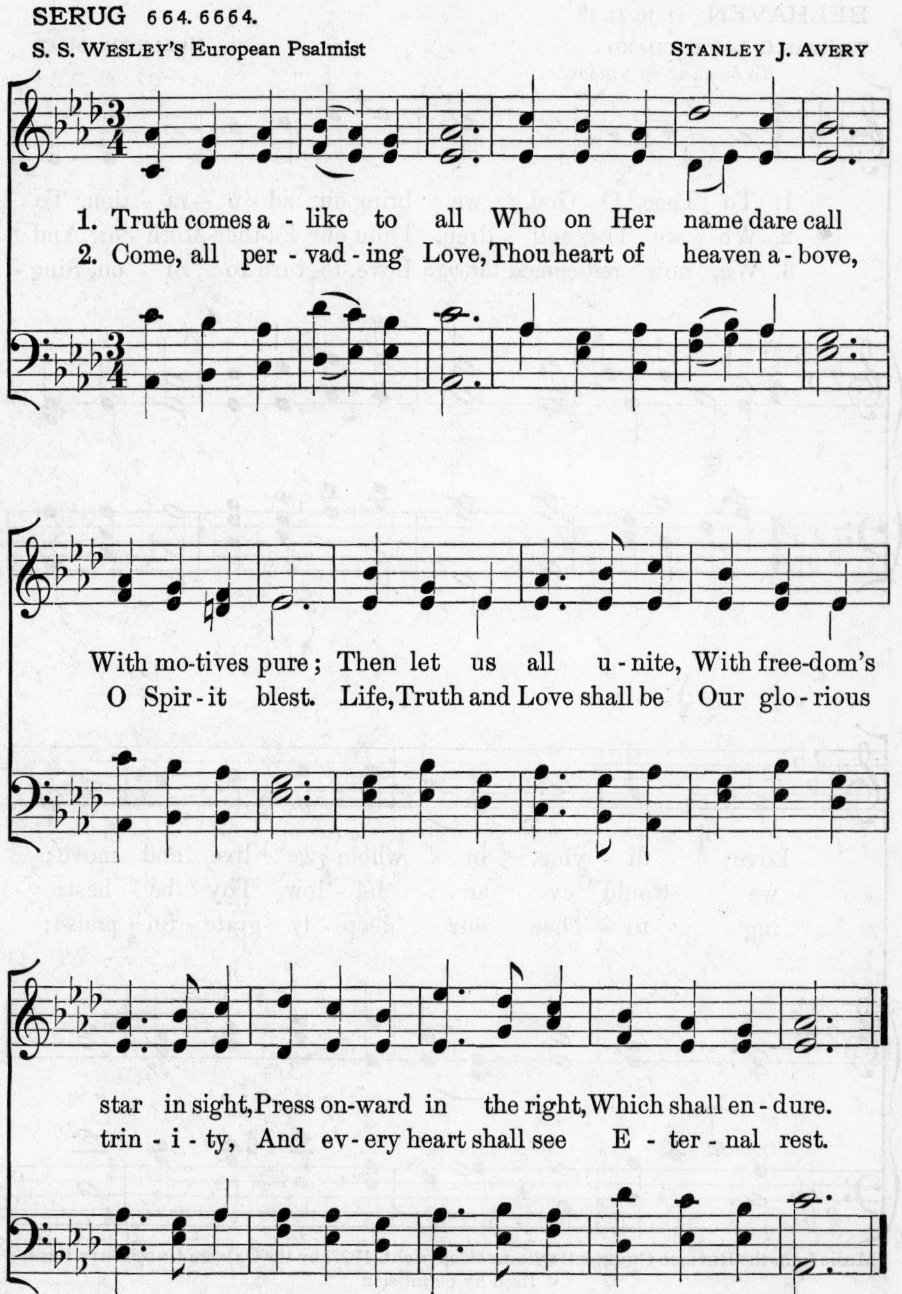
SERUG 664. 6664.
S. S. WESLEY'S European Psalmist
STANLEY J. AVERY
1. Truth comes a - like to all Who on Her name dare call
2. Come, all per - vad - ing Love, Thou heart of heaven a - bove,
With mo-tives pure; Then let us all u - nite, With free-dom's
O Spir - it blest. Life, Truth and Love shall be Our glo - rious
star in sight, Press on-ward in the right, Which shall en - dure.
trin - i - ty, And ev - ery heart shall see E - ter - nal rest.

# 356

**BELHAVEN** 11. 10. 11. 10.

THOMAS C. L. PRITCHARD — NELLIE B. MACE

*To be sung in unison*

1. To Thee, O God, we bring our ad - o - ra - tion, To
2. We are Thy chil - dren, Thou our Fa-ther-Moth - er, And
3. We, now re-deemed through Love, re- turn to Zi - on, Sing -

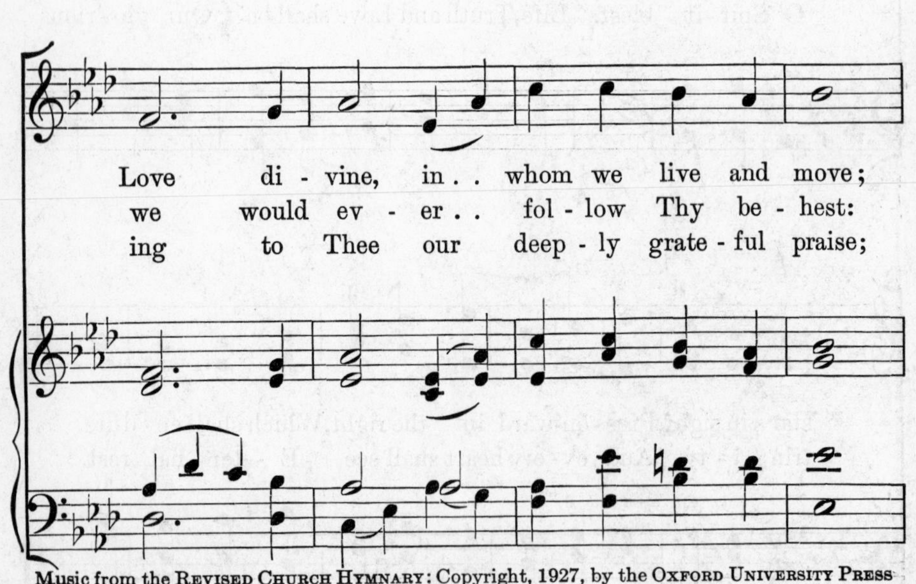

Love di - vine, in . . whom we live and move;
we would ev - er . . fol - low Thy be - hest:
ing to Thee our deep - ly grate - ful praise;

For Thou hast shown to us our per - fect self - hood
Help us to un - der - stand Thy ho - ly coun - sel,
For we are Christ's, and Christ is Thine, O Fa - ther:
In Thy loved Son, . . whom Je - sus came to prove.
For in o - be - dience lies our ac - tive rest.
His joy re - mains in us through end - less days.

# 357†

**EVAN** C. M.

WILLIAM H. HAVERGAL — Author Unknown*

1. To Thee, our lov - ing Fa - ther, God, A glad-some song be - gin, Whose smile is on the world a - broad, Whose joy our hearts with - in.
2. We need not, Lord, our glad - ness leave, To wor - ship Thee a - right; Our joy - ful - ness for praise re - ceive, Thou mak'st our lives so bright.
3. The pure in heart are al - ways glad; The smile of God they feel; He doth the se - cret of His joy To blame - less hearts re - veal.

*Another version of this music will be found in the* SUPPLEMENT, No. 407

## 358†

**ST. BERNARD** C. M.

From Tochter Sion, 1741 — Author Unknown*

1. To Thee, our lov - ing .. Fa - ther, God, A glad - some song be - gin, Whose smile is on the world a - broad, Whose joy our hearts with - in.
2. We need not, Lord, our .. glad - ness leave, To wor - ship Thee a - right; Our joy - ful - ness for praise re - ceive, Thou mak'st our lives so bright.
3. The pure in heart are .. al - ways glad; The smile of God they feel; He doth the se - cret of His joy To blame - less hearts re - veal.

*Another version of this music will be found in the* SUPPLEMENT, No. 407

## WILLINGHAM 11. 10. 11. 10.

FRANZ ABT — WILLIAM P. MCKENZIE

1. Trust the Eternal when the shadows gather, When joys of daylight seem so like a dream;
2. Trust the Eternal, for the clouds that vanish No more can move the . . mountains from their base
3. Trust the Eternal, and repent in meekness Of that heart's pride which frowns and will not yield,

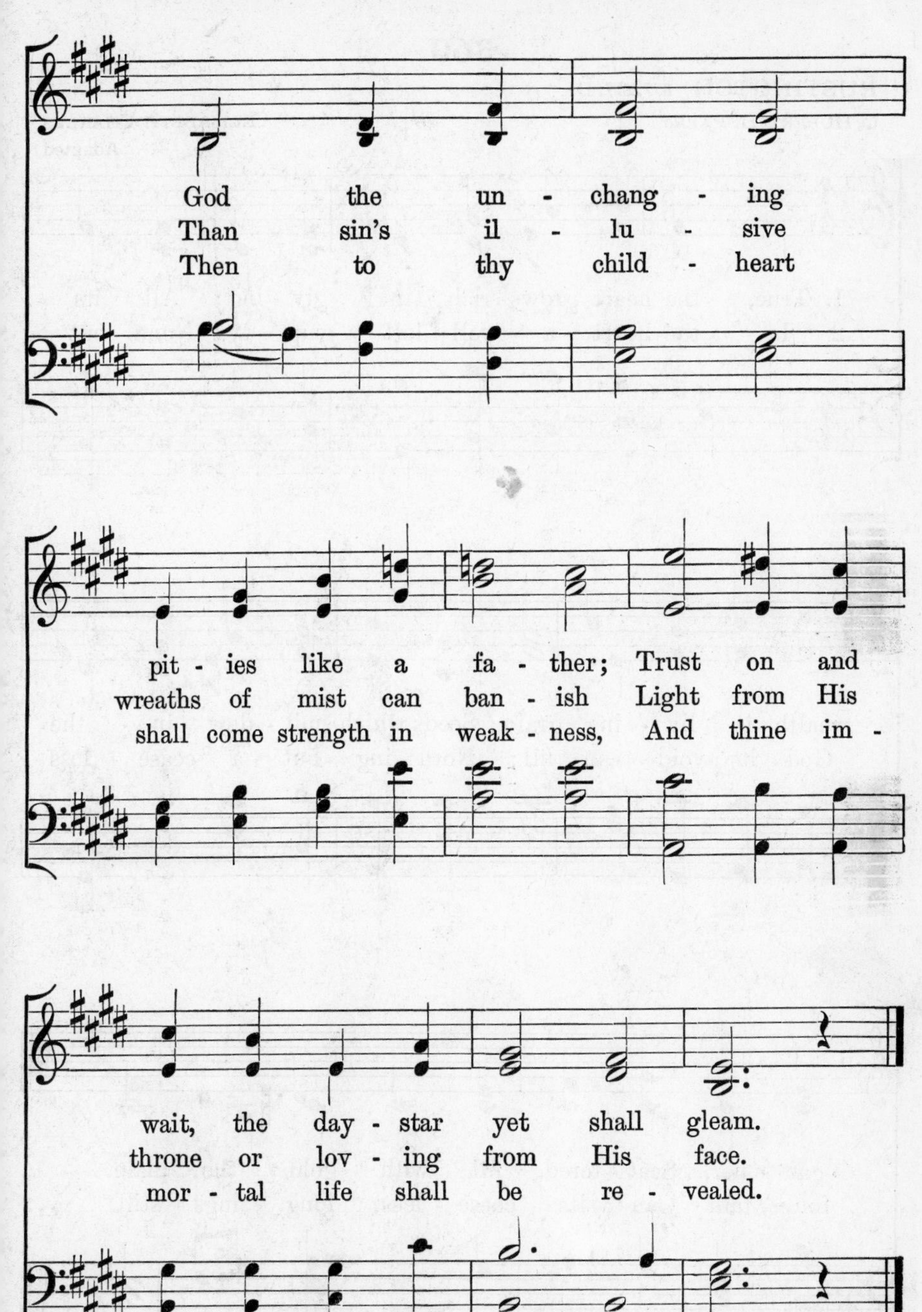
God the un - chang - ing
Than sin's il - lu - sive
Then to thy child - heart
pit - ies like a fa - ther; Trust on and
wreaths of mist can ban - ish Light from His
shall come strength in weak - ness, And thine im -
wait, the day - star yet shall gleam.
throne or lov - ing from His face.
mor - tal life shall be re - vealed.

# 360

RUSTINGTON 8. 7. 8. 7. D.

C. HUBERT H. PARRY

ELIZABETH CHARLES
Adapted

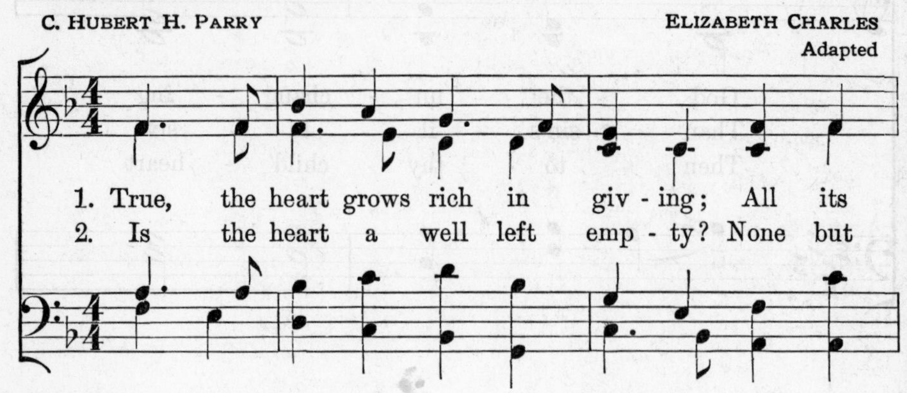
1. True, the heart grows rich in giv - ing; All its
2. Is the heart a well left emp - ty? None but

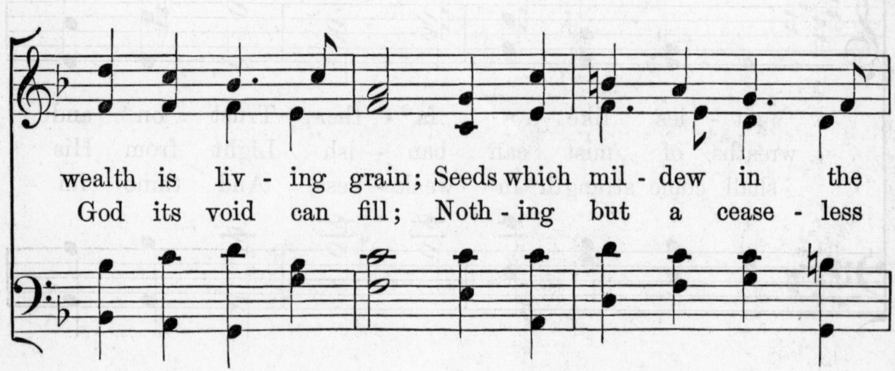
wealth is liv - ing grain; Seeds which mil - dew in the
God its void can fill; Noth - ing but a cease - less

gar - ner, Scat - tered, fill with gold the plain.
foun - tain Can its cease - less long - ings still.

Is thy bur - den hard and heav - y? Do thy
Is the heart a liv - ing pow - er? Self - en -
steps drag wea - ri - ly? Help to bear thy broth - er's
twined its strength sinks low; It can on - ly live in
bur - den, God will bear both it and thee.
lov - ing, And, by serv - ing, love will grow.

## INNSBRUCK 776.778.

Nun ruhen alle Wälder
HEINRICH ISAAC
Harmonized by J. S. BACH

PAUL GERHARDT
Based on Danish translation of
STENER J. STENERSEN

*To be sung in unison*

1. Trust all to God, the Fa - ther, Con - fide thou in none
2. Be - hold His works of won - der, Yea, all His do - ings
3. God lights the way of du - ty, And gives, for ash - es,

oth - er, He is thy sole de - fense;
pon - der, Else is thy toil in vain;
beau - ty, And naught His hand de - lays;

He cares for thee past meas - ure, Seek Him who has thy
Thy car - ing and con - triv - ing, Thy tak - ing thought and
Who trusts in His pro - vid - ing, All glad in this con -
treas - ure, Thy help - er is om - nip - o - tence.
striv - ing Are naught un - less the Lord or - dain.
fid - ing, Is he who with - out ceas - ing prays.

## 362

CHRISTMAS C. M.

GEORG FRIEDRICH HÄNDEL | JOHN MORISON, Adapted

1. To.. us a Child of Hope is.. born, To.. us a Son is.. given; Him shall the tribes of earth o - bey, And all the hosts of heaven, And all the hosts of heaven.
2. His name shall be.. the Prince of.. Peace, For - ev - er-more a - dored; The Won-der - ful, the Coun-sel - lor, The great and might - y Lord, The great and might - y Lord.
3. His power, in - creas - ing, still shall spread; His reign shall nev - er.. cease; For jus-tice ev - er guards his throne, And all his paths are peace, And all his paths are peace.

# 363

## PHILIPPINE L. M.

R. E. ROBERTS — JOHN BOWRING, Adapted

1. Up - on .. the Gos - pel's sa - cred page The gath - ered
2. On might - ier wing, in loft - ier flight, From year to
3. More glo - rious still, as cen - turies roll, New re - gions
4. Shall flow to bless but not de - stroy; As when the
beams of a - ges shine; And, as it has - tens,
year does knowl - edge soar; And, as it soars, the
blest, new powers un - furled, So Truth re - veals the
cloud - less lamp of day Pours out its floods of
ev - ery age But makes its bright - ness more di - vine.
Gos - pel light Be - comes ef - ful - gent more and more.
per - fect whole, Its ra - diance shall o'er - flow the world,—
light and joy, And sweeps the lin - gering mist a - way.
*
*

*Tenors may sing the melody between these two points.

**MARCHING** 8.7.8.7.

MARTIN SHAW — HARRIET AUBER, Adapted

1. Vain - ly, through night's wea - ry hours, . .
2. Vain were all our toil and la - bor,
3. Vain - er still the hope of heav - en
Keep we watch, lest foes a - larm; Vain our bul - warks
Did not God that la - bor bless; Vain, with - out His
That on hu - man strength re - lies; But to him all
and our tow - ers, But for God's pro - tect - ing arm.
grace and fa - vor, Ev - ery tal - ent we pos - sess.
good is giv - en Who in faith to God ap - plies.

## 365†

**SEYMOUR** 7.7.7.7.

Arranged from
CARL MARIA VON WEBER

WILLIAM F. LLOYD

1. Wait, my soul, up - on the .. Lord,
2. If the sor - rows of thy .. case
3. Rock of A - ges, I'm se - cure
To His gra - cious prom - ise flee, Lay - ing hold up -
Seem pe - cul - iar still to thee, God has prom - ised
With Thy prom - ise full and free, Faith - ful, pos - i -
on His Word: As thy days thy strength shall be.
need - ful grace: As thy days thy strength shall be.
tive, and sure: As thy days thy strength shall be.

# 366†

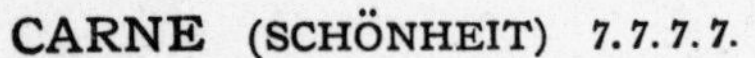

**CARNE** (SCHÖNHEIT) 7.7.7.7.

From MICHAEL PRAETORIUS (?) — WILLIAM F. LLOYD

1. Wait, my soul, upon the Lord,
To His gracious promise flee,
Laying hold upon His Word:
As thy days thy strength shall be.

2. If the sorrows of thy case
Seem peculiar still to thee,
God has promised needful grace:
As thy days thy strength shall be.

3. Rock of Ages, I'm secure
With Thy promise full and free,
Faithful, positive, and sure:
As thy days thy strength shall be.

# 367

**METZLER** C. M.

RICHARD REDHEAD | BERNARD BARTON*

1. Walk in the light, so thou shalt know That
2. Walk in the light, and thou shalt find Thy
3. Walk in the light, and thou shalt own Thy
4. Walk in the light, and thou shalt see Thy
fel - low - ship of love His spir - it on - ly . .
heart made tru - ly His, Who dwells in cloud - less
dark - ness past a - way, Be - cause that light on . .
path, though thorn - y, bright; For God by grace shall
can be - stow Who reigns in light a - bove.
light en - shrined, In whom no dark - ness is.
thee hath shone In which is per - fect day.
dwell with thee, And God Him - self is Light.

## 368†

**WATCHMAN** 7.7.7.7. D.

LOWELL MASON — JOHN BOWRING

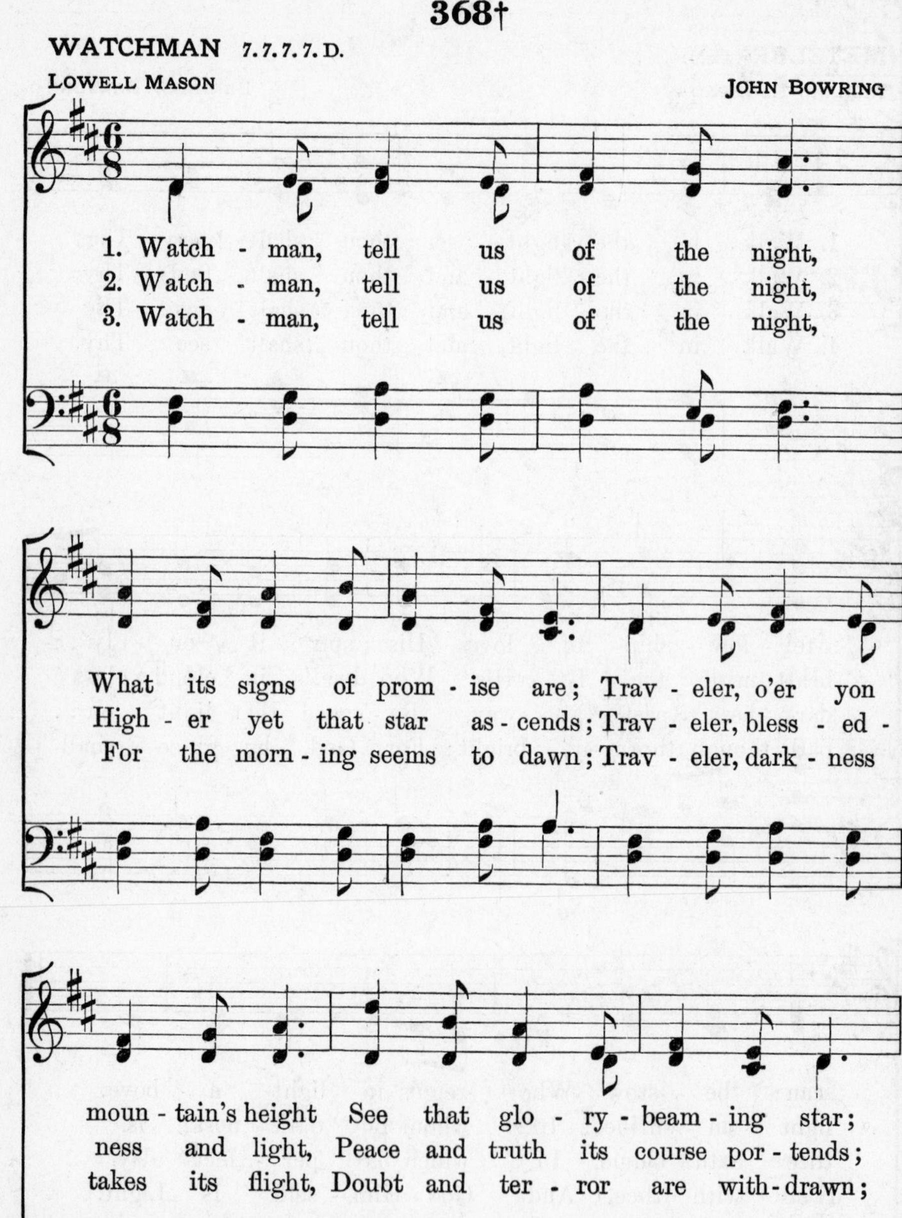
1. Watch - man, tell us of the night,
2. Watch - man, tell us of the night,
3. Watch - man, tell us of the night,
What its signs of prom - ise are; Trav - eler, o'er yon
High - er yet that star as - cends; Trav - eler, bless - ed -
For the morn - ing seems to dawn; Trav - eler, dark - ness
moun - tain's height See that glo - ry - beam - ing star;
ness and light, Peace and truth its course por - tends;
takes its flight, Doubt and ter - ror are with - drawn;

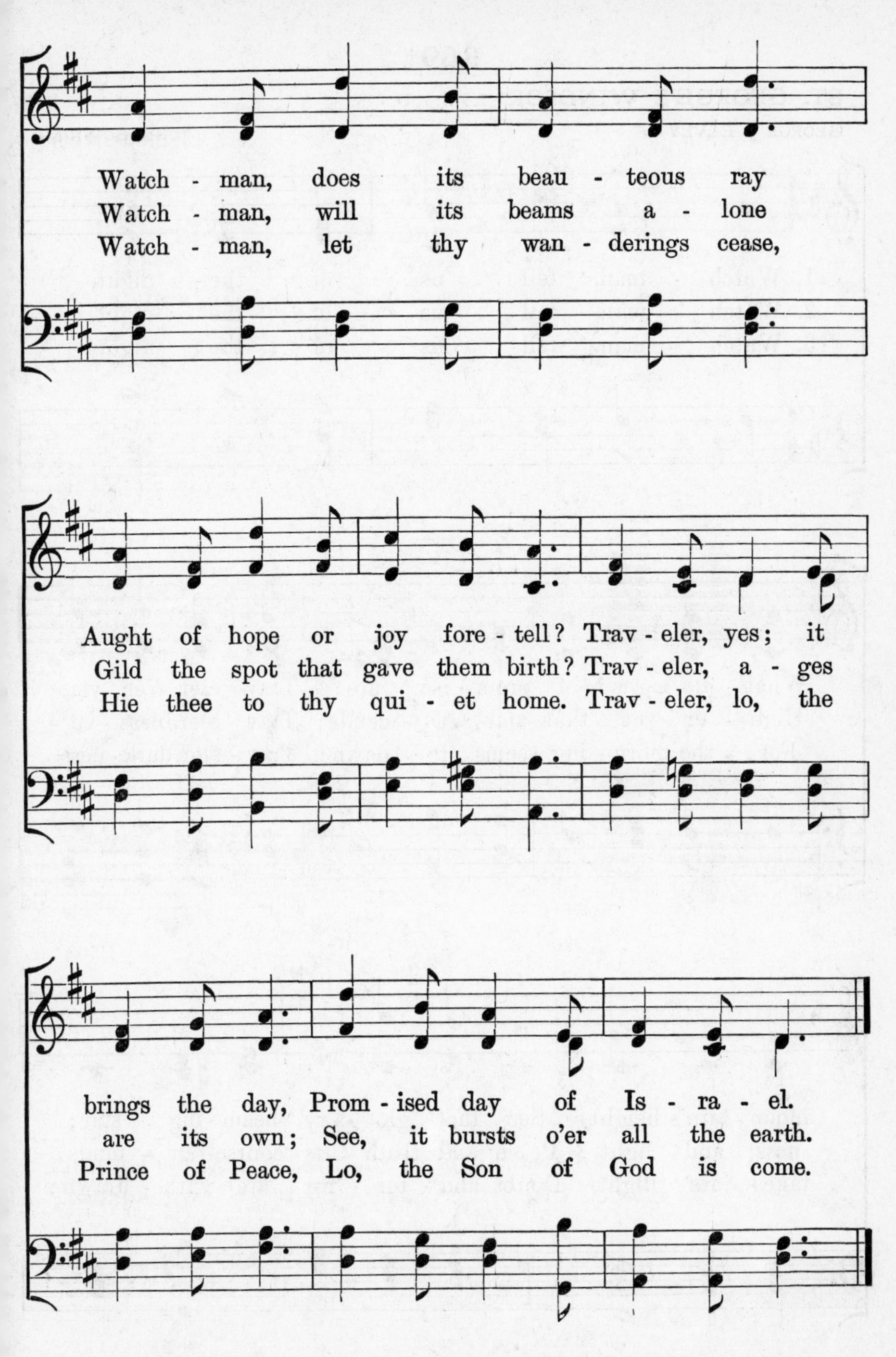
Watch - man, does its beau - teous ray
Watch - man, will its beams a - lone
Watch - man, let thy wan - derings cease,
Aught of hope or joy fore - tell? Trav - eler, yes; it
Gild the spot that gave them birth? Trav - eler, a - ges
Hie thee to thy qui - et home. Trav - eler, lo, the
brings the day, Prom - ised day of Is - ra - el.
are its own; See, it bursts o'er all the earth.
Prince of Peace, Lo, the Son of God is come.

## ST. GEORGE'S WINDSOR 7.7.7.7.D.

GEORGE J. ELVEY JOHN BOWRING

1. Watch - man, tell us of the night,
2. Watch - man, tell us of the night,
3. Watch - man, tell us of the night,
What its signs of prom - ise are; Trav - eler, o'er yon
High - er yet that star as - cends; Trav - eler, bless - ed -
For the morn - ing seems to dawn; Trav - eler, dark - ness
moun - tain's height See that glo - ry - beam - ing star;
ness and light, Peace and truth its course por - tends;
takes its flight, Doubt and ter - ror are with - drawn;

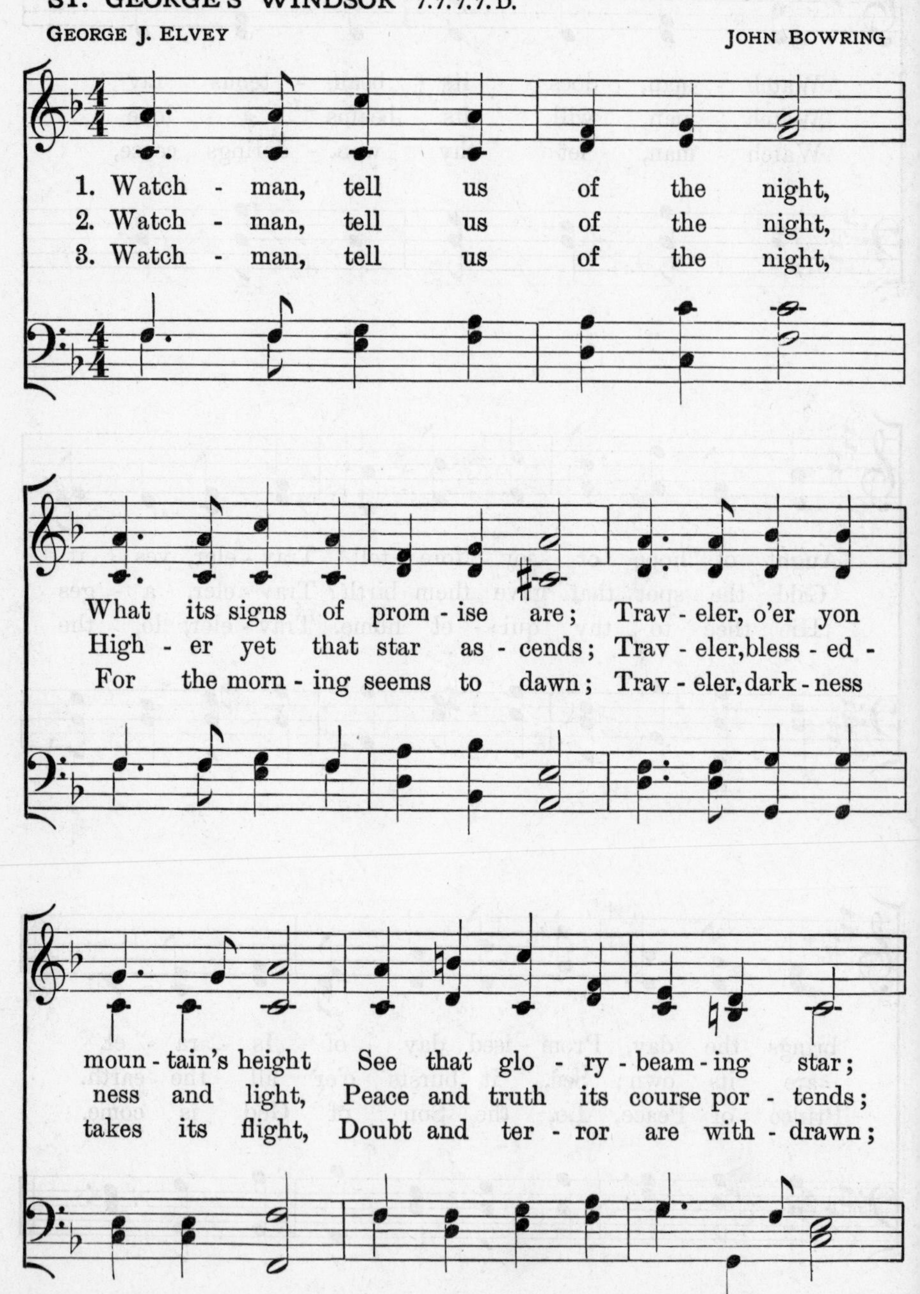

Watch - man, does its beau - teous ray
Watch - man, will its beams a - lone
Watch - man, let thy wan - derings cease,
Aught of hope or joy fore - tell? Trav - eler, yes; it
Gild the spot that gave them birth? Trav - eler, a - ges
Hie thee to thy qui - et home. Trav - eler, lo, the
brings the day, Prom - ised day of Is - ra - el.
are its own; See, it bursts o'er all the earth.
Prince of Peace, Lo, the Son of God is come.

# 370

**DEERHURST** 8.7.8.7.D.

JAMES LANGRAN NELLIE B. MACE

1. We are hid with Christ for - ev - er
2. Hid with Christ in God, O glad - ness:

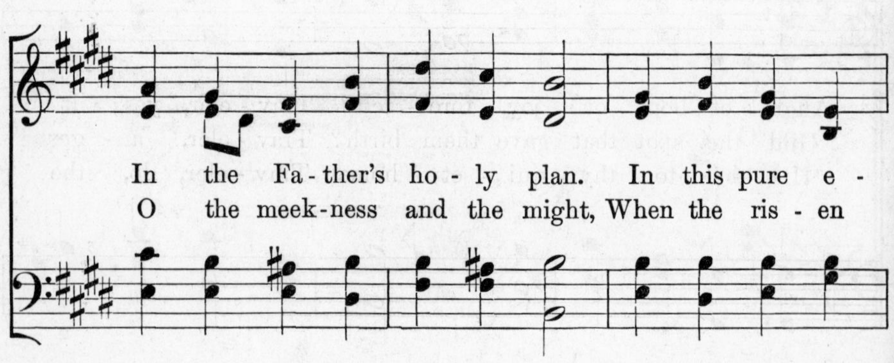
In the Fa - ther's ho - ly plan. In this pure e -
O the meek - ness and the might, When the ris - en

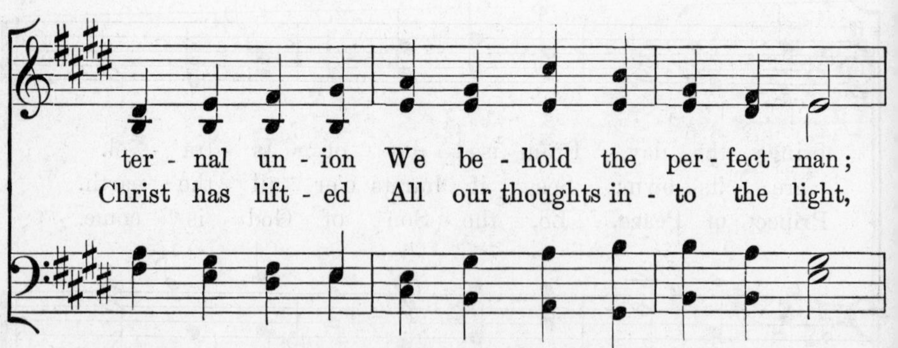
ter - nal un - ion We be - hold the per - fect man;
Christ has lift - ed All our thoughts in - to the light,

Music by permission of NOVELLO & Co. Ltd.

And we know that sin can nev - er
Light of Truth where - in no sad - ness

O - ver - throw the sa - cred rod Of do - min - ion
Dims the ra - diant peace we find, As we set our

o - ver e - vil: We are hid with Christ in God.
whole af - fec - tion On the beau-teous things of Mind.

LEONI 6. 6. 8. 4. D.
Hebrew Melody
M. M.
1. We lift our hearts in praise, O God of Life, to Thee, And would re - flect in all our ways Thy pu - ri - ty.
2. We lift our hearts in praise, O God of Truth, to Thee, And find with - in Thy per - fect law Our lib - er - ty.
3. We lift our hearts in praise, O God of Love, to Thee, With joy to find through dark - ened days Thy har - mo - ny.

Thy thoughts our lives en - fold, And
We bless Thy might - y name In . .
O Fa - ther - Moth - er Love, We
free us . . from all fear; . . All strife is stilled, all
this ex - alt - ed hour, . . And to the world in
tri - umph 'neath Thy rod, . . We glo - ry in Thy
grief con - soled, For Thou art here.
faith pro - claim Thy heal - ing power.
light, and prove That Thou art God.

# 372†

THOMAS A. ARNE — JOHN GREENLEAF WHITTIER

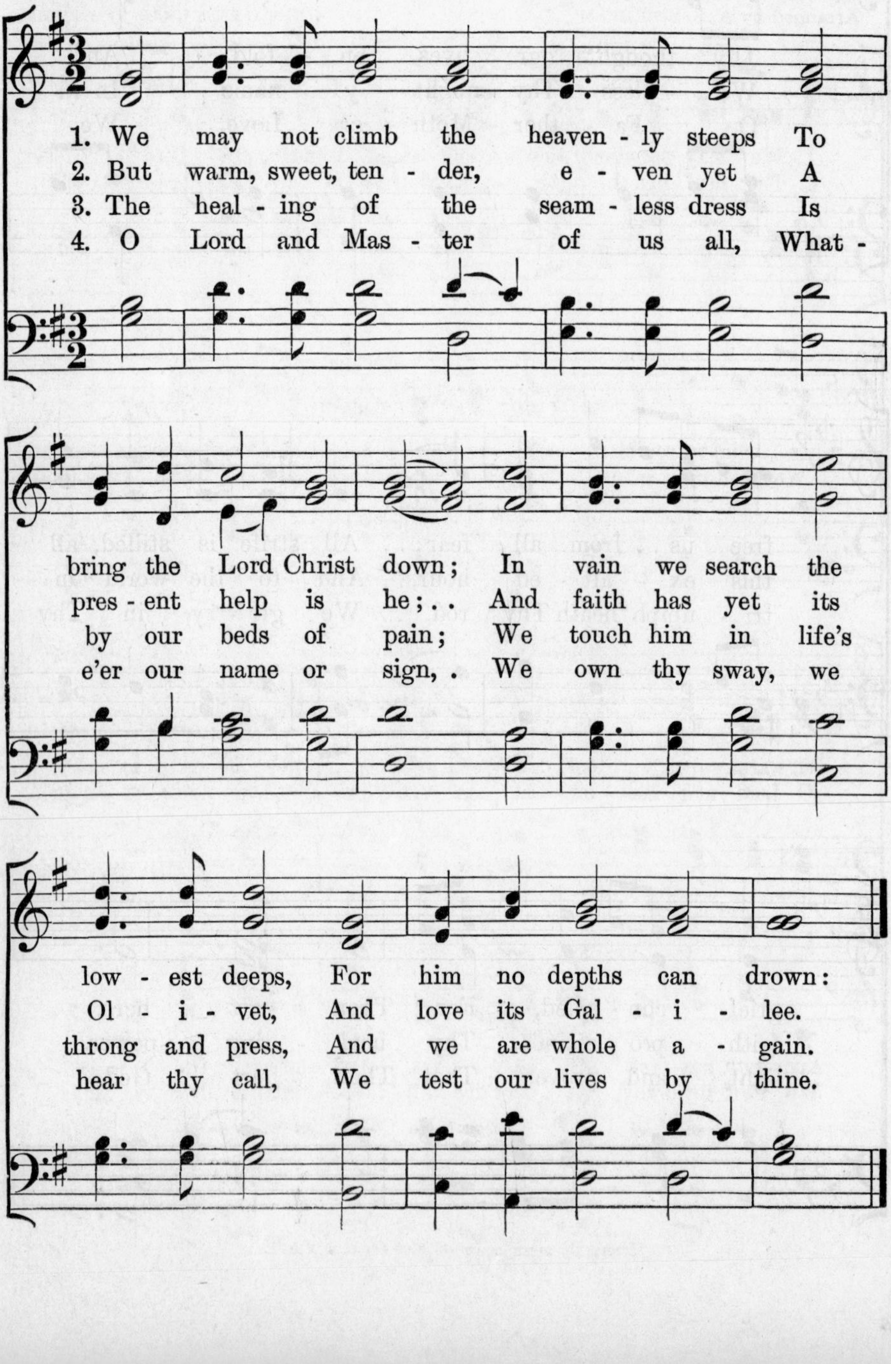

1. We may not climb the heaven - ly steeps To
2. But warm, sweet, ten - der, e - ven yet A
3. The heal - ing of the seam - less dress Is
4. O Lord and Mas - ter of us all, What -

bring the Lord Christ down; In vain we search the
pres - ent help is he; . And faith has yet its
by our beds of pain; We touch him in life's
e'er our name or sign, . We own thy sway, we

low - est deeps, For him no depths can drown:
Ol - i - vet, And love its Gal - i - lee.
throng and press, And we are whole a - gain.
hear thy call, We test our lives by thine.

## 373†

**NOEL** C. M. D.

Traditional Melody
Arranged by A. S. SULLIVAN
JOHN GREENLEAF WHITTIER
1. We may not climb the heaven-ly steeps To bring the Lord Christ down;
2. The heal - ing of the seam-less dress Is by our beds of pain;
In vain we search the low - est deeps, For him no depths can drown:
We touch him in life's throng and press, And we are whole a - gain.
But warm, sweet, ten - der, e - ven yet A pres - ent help is he;
O Lord and Mas - ter of us all, What - e'er our name or sign,
And faith has yet its Ol - i - vet, And love its Gal - i - lee.
We own thy sway, we hear thy call, We test our lives by thine.

Music by permission of NOVELLO & Co. Ltd.

374†

**ALL SAINTS NEW** 7.6.7.6.D.

HENRY S. CUTLER — JOHN RANDALL DUNN

1. We thank Thee and we bless Thee, O
2. We thank Thee and we bless Thee, O
3. We thank Thee, Fa - ther - Moth - er, For
Fa - ther of us all, . . That e'en be - fore we
Lord of all a - bove, That now Thy chil - dren
bless - ings, light and grace Which bid man - kind to
ask Thee Thou hear'st Thy chil - dren's call.
know Thee As ev - er - last - ing Love.
wak - en And see Thee face to face.

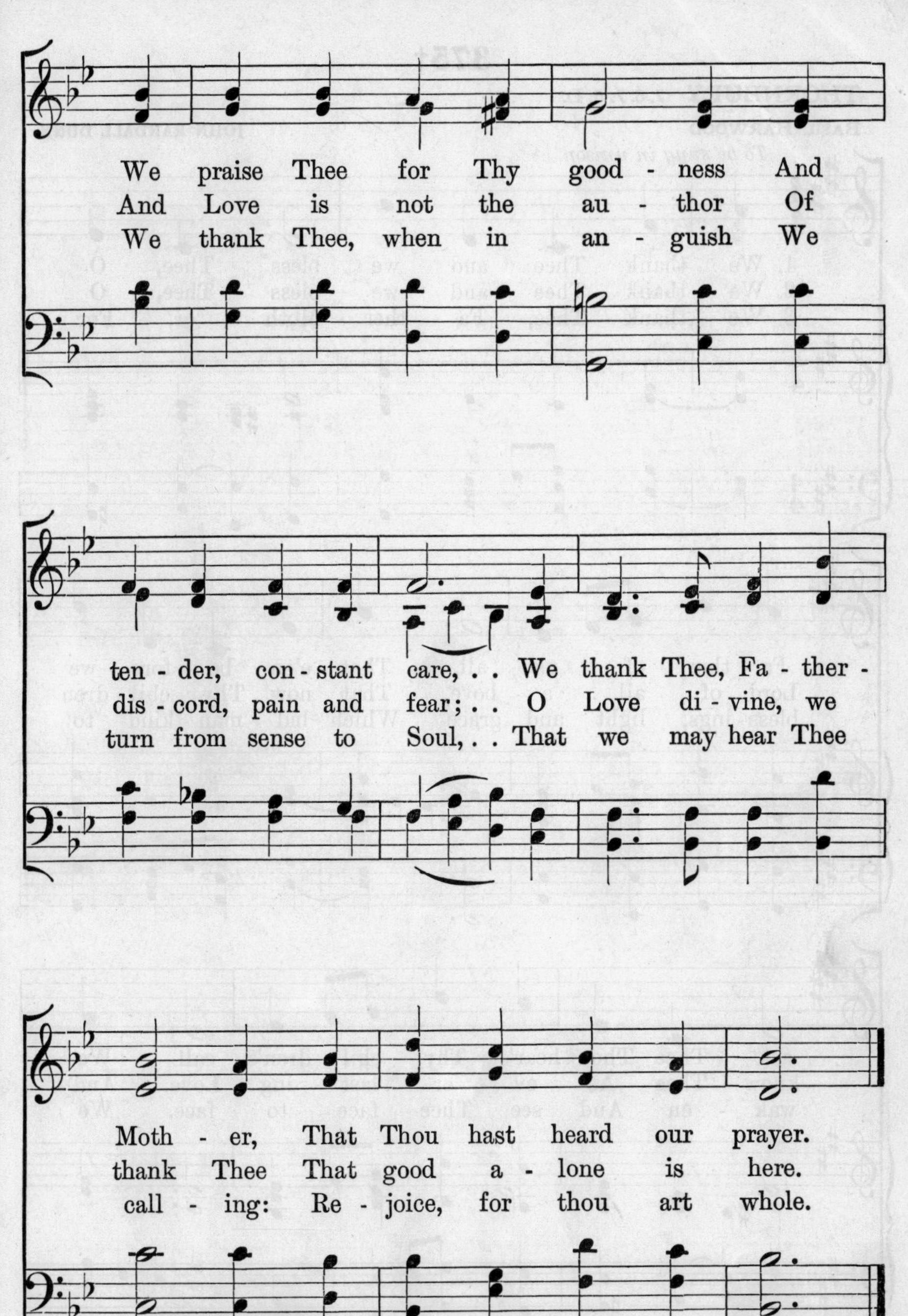

We praise Thee for Thy good - ness And
And Love is not the au - thor Of
We thank Thee, when in an - guish We
ten - der, con - stant care, . . We thank Thee, Fa - ther -
dis - cord, pain and fear; . . O Love di - vine, we
turn from sense to Soul, . . That we may hear Thee
Moth - er, That Thou hast heard our prayer.
thank Thee That good a - lone is here.
call - ing: Re - joice, for thou art whole.

# 375†

**THORNBURY** 7. 6. 7. 6. D.

BASIL HARWOOD | JOHN RANDALL DUNN

*To be sung in unison*

1. We thank Thee and we bless Thee, O
2. We thank Thee and we bless Thee, O
3. We thank Thee, Fa - ther - Moth - er, For

Fa - ther of . . us all, That e'en be - fore we
Lord of all . a - bove, That now Thy chil - dren
bless - ings, light and grace Which bid man - kind to

ask Thee Thou hear'st Thy chil - dren's call. We
know Thee As ev - er - last - ing Love. And
wak - en And see Thee face to face. We

Music by permission of BASIL HARWOOD

praise Thee for Thy good - ness And ten - der, con - stant
Love is not the au - thor Of dis - cord, pain and
thank Thee, when in an - guish We turn from sense to
care, We thank Thee, Fa - ther - Moth - er, That
fear; O Love di - vine, we thank Thee That
Soul, That we may hear Thee call - ing: Re -
Thou hast heard our prayer. . . . .
good a - lone is here. . . . . .
joice, for thou art whole. . . . .

# 376†

**RELIANCE** 7.6.7.6.D.

Arranged from
FELIX MENDELSSOHN-BARTHOLDY

M. FANNIE WHITNEY

1. We thank Thee, heavenly Fa - ther, For Thy cor - rect - ing rod,
2. O may we tread the path - way, Nor ev - er turn a - side,
Which guides us in our jour - ney And leads us home to God.
Al - lured by ways of er - ror, Whose paths are broad and wide.
It tells us not of an - ger, The weap - on mor - tals sway,
Toward Thee, while pressing on - ward, The way will brighter grow,
But Love di - vine, that helps us To keep the bet - ter way.
For Thou throughout the jour - ney Thy lov - ing care wilt show.

# 377†

**GOSTERWOOD** 7.6.7.6.D.

English Traditional Melody — M. Fannie Whitney

1. We thank Thee, heavenly Fa - ther, For Thy cor - rect-ing rod,
Which guides us in our jour - ney And leads us home to God.
It tells us not of an - ger, The weap - on mor - tals sway,
But Love di - vine, that helps us To keep the bet - ter way.

2. O may we tread the path-way, Nor ev - er turn a - side,
Al - lured by ways of er - ror, Whose paths are broad and wide.
Toward Thee, while pressing on - ward, The way will bright - er grow,
For Thou throughout the jour - ney Thy lov - ing care wilt show.

Music from the English Hymnal: By permission of the Oxford University Press

## HUSSITE HYMN 6 6. 6 6. 3.

Traditional | F. T. H.

1. We turn to Thee, O Lord, And sing in
2. Our hearts re - deemed from strife, And com - fort -
3. O God, we bless Thy name, Thy won - drous

sweet ac - cord; We would Thy beau - ty see,
ed in grief, Heal - ing and joy are ours,
power ac - claim, Lord, Thy sal - va - tion strong,

Lift - ing our lives to Thee, Thou art . . God.
Bless - ings of peace - ful hours, Thou art . . Life.
Now is be - come our song, Great I . . . AM.

# 379†

**RATHBUN** 8.7.8.7.

ITHAMAR CONKEY

CATHERINE WINKWORTH, Tr.*
From the German

1. Well for him who, all . . things los - ing,
2. Well for him who noth - ing know - eth
3. Well for him who, all . for - sak - ing,
4. O that we our hearts might sev - er

E'en him - self doth count as naught, Still the one thing
But his God, whose boundless love Makes the heart where -
Walk - eth not in shad - ows vain, But the path of
From earth's tempt - ing van - i - ties, Fix - ing them on

need - ful choos-ing That with all true bliss is fraught.
in . . it . . glow-eth Calm and pure and faith - ful prove.
peace is . . tak - ing Through the vale of tears and pain.
Him for - ev - er In whom all our full - ness lies.

# 380†

COURAGE 8.7.8.7.

University of Wales
Arranged by H. WALFORD DAVIES

CATHERINE WINKWORTH, Tr.*
From the German

1. Well for him who, all things los - ing,
2. Well for him who noth - ing . . know - eth
3. Well for him who, all for - sak - ing,
4. O that we our hearts might sev - er
E'en him - self doth count as naught, Still the one thing
But his God, whose bound-less love Makes the heart where -
Walk - eth not in shad - ows vain, But the path of . .
From earth's tempt-ing van - i - ties, Fix - ing them on . .
need - ful choos - ing That with all true bliss is fraught.
in it glow - eth Calm and pure and faith - ful prove.
peace is tak - ing Through the vale of tears and pain.
Him for - ev - er In whom all our full - ness lies.

Music from A STUDENTS' HYMNAL (HYMNS OF THE KINGDOM)
By permission of the OXFORD UNIVERSITY PRESS
Rhythm altered in last line by permission

## 381

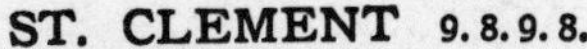

**ST. CLEMENT** 9. 8. 9. 8.

CLEMENT C. SCHOLEFIELD — WILLIAM P. MCKENZIE

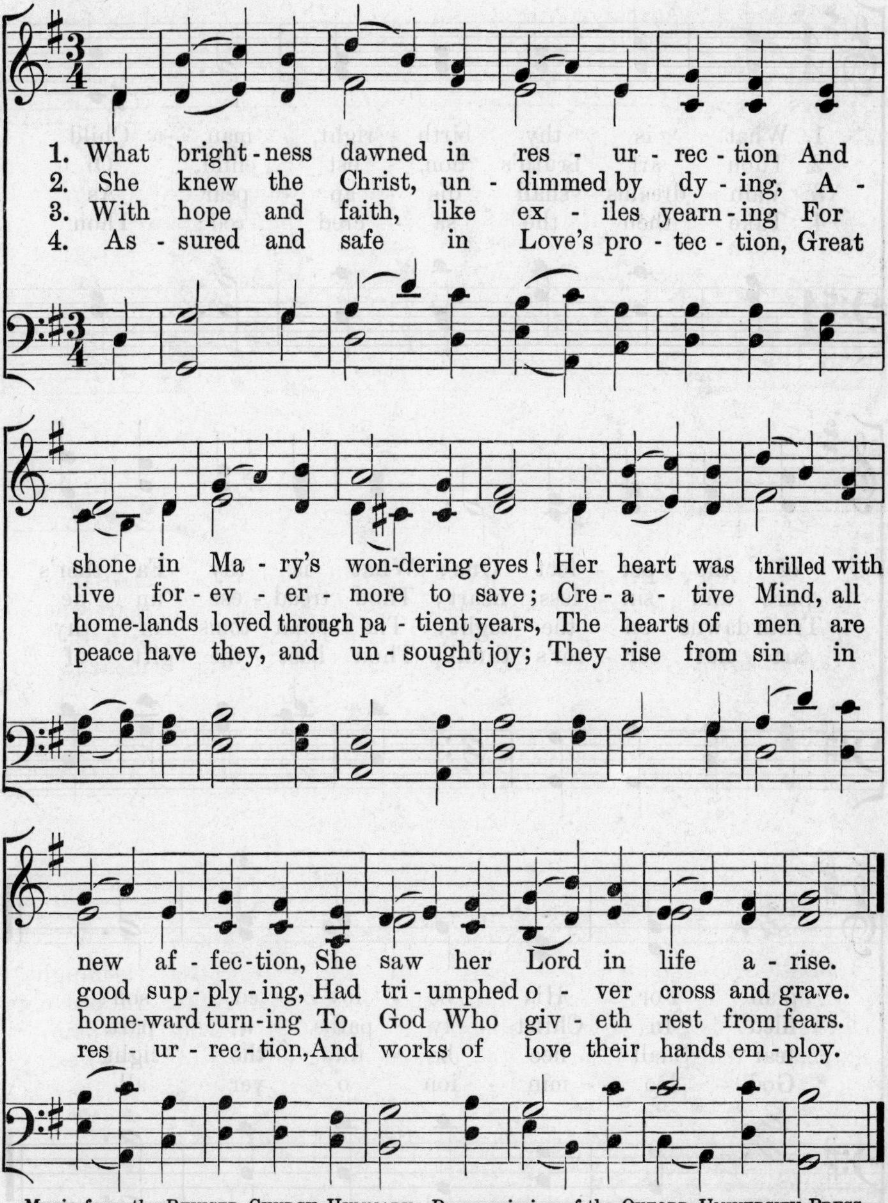
1. What bright-ness dawned in res - ur - rec - tion And
2. She knew the Christ, un - dimmed by dy - ing, A -
3. With hope and faith, like ex - iles yearn - ing For
4. As - sured and safe in Love's pro - tec - tion, Great
shone in Ma - ry's won-dering eyes! Her heart was thrilled with
live for - ev - er - more to save; Cre - a - tive Mind, all
home-lands loved through pa - tient years, The hearts of men are
peace have they, and un - sought joy; They rise from sin in
new af - fec - tion, She saw her Lord in life a - rise.
good sup - ply - ing, Had tri - umphed o - ver cross and grave.
home-ward turn - ing To God Who giv - eth rest from fears.
res - ur - rec - tion, And works of love their hands em - ploy.

Music from the REVISED CHURCH HYMNARY: By permission of the OXFORD UNIVERSITY PRESS

## 382

**ST. CECILIA** 6. 6. 6. 6.

LEIGHTON G. HAYNE — EMILY F. SEAL

1. What is thy birth - right, man, Child
2. Thou art Truth's hon - est child, Of
3. Vain dreams shall dis - ap - pear As
4. Take then the sa - cred rod; Thou
of the per - fect One; What is thy Fa - ther's
pure and sin - less heart; Thou tread - est un - de -
Truth dawns on the sight; The phan - toms of thy
art not er - ror's thrall; Thou hast the gift of
plan For His be - lov - ed son?
filed In Christ - ly paths a - part.
fear Shall flee be - fore the light.
God— Do - min - ion o - ver all.

# 383

**HORSLEY** C. M.

WILLIAM HORSLEY — MARY W. HALE*

1. What - ev - er dims thy sense of . . truth Or
2. Pre - serve the tab - let of thy thoughts From
3. And pray of God, that grace be given To
stains thy pu - ri - ty, Though light as breath of
ev - ery blem - ish free, For our Re - deem - er's
tread the nar - row way: How dark so - ev - er
sum - mer air, O count it sin to thee.
ho - ly faith Its tem - ple makes with thee.
it may seem, It leads to cloud - less day.

# 384

**MORNING HYMN** L. M.

FRANÇOIS H. BARTHÉLÉMON | HOSEA BALLOU, Adapted

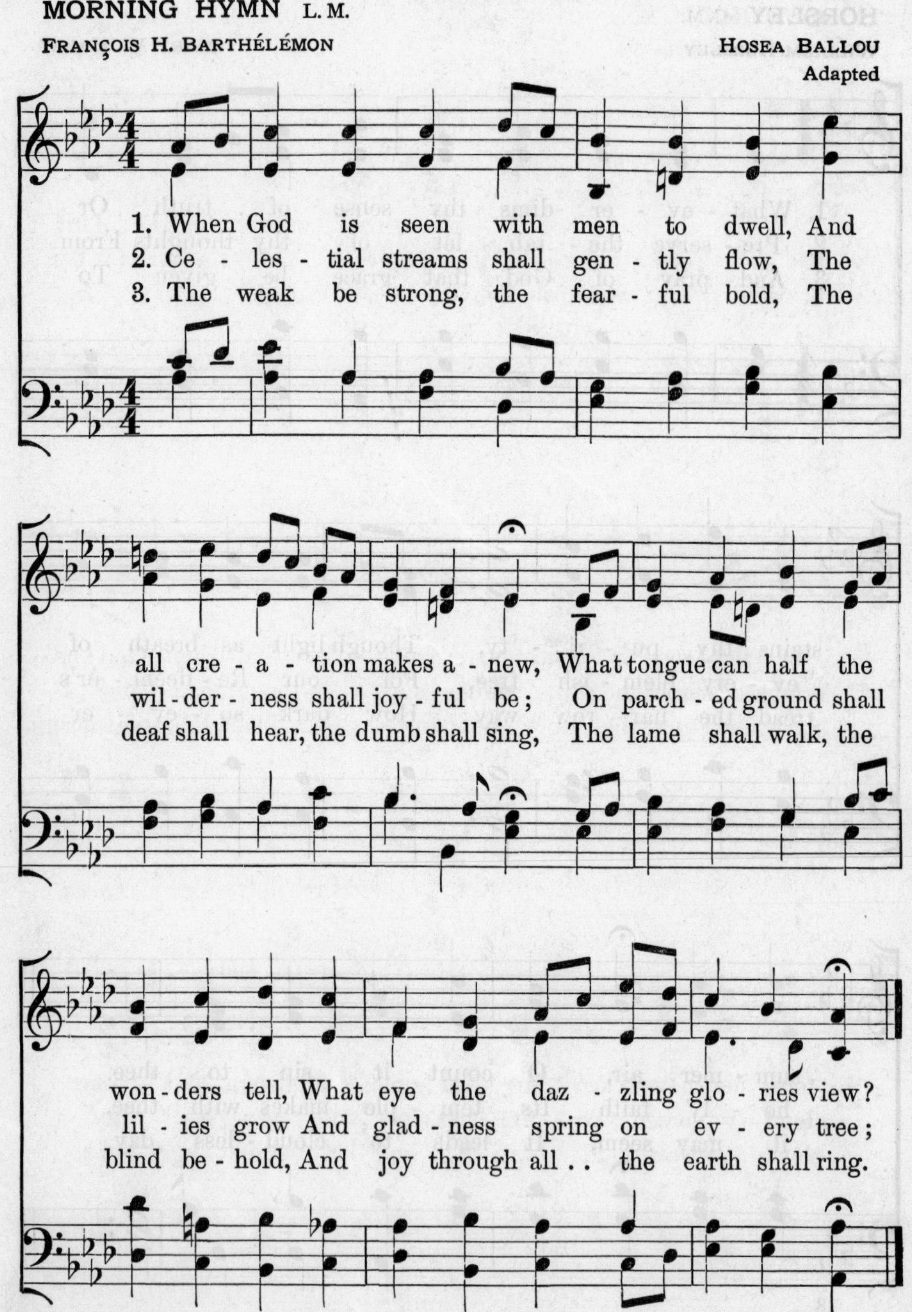
1. When God is seen with men to dwell, And
2. Ce - les - tial streams shall gen - tly flow, The
3. The weak be strong, the fear - ful bold, The
all cre - a - tion makes a - new, What tongue can half the
wil - der - ness shall joy - ful be; On parch - ed ground shall
deaf shall hear, the dumb shall sing, The lame shall walk, the
won - ders tell, What eye the daz - zling glo - ries view?
lil - ies grow And glad - ness spring on ev - ery tree;
blind be - hold, And joy through all . . the earth shall ring.

**SOLOTHURN** L. M.

Swiss Traditional Melody — WALTER SCOTT*

*To be sung in unison*

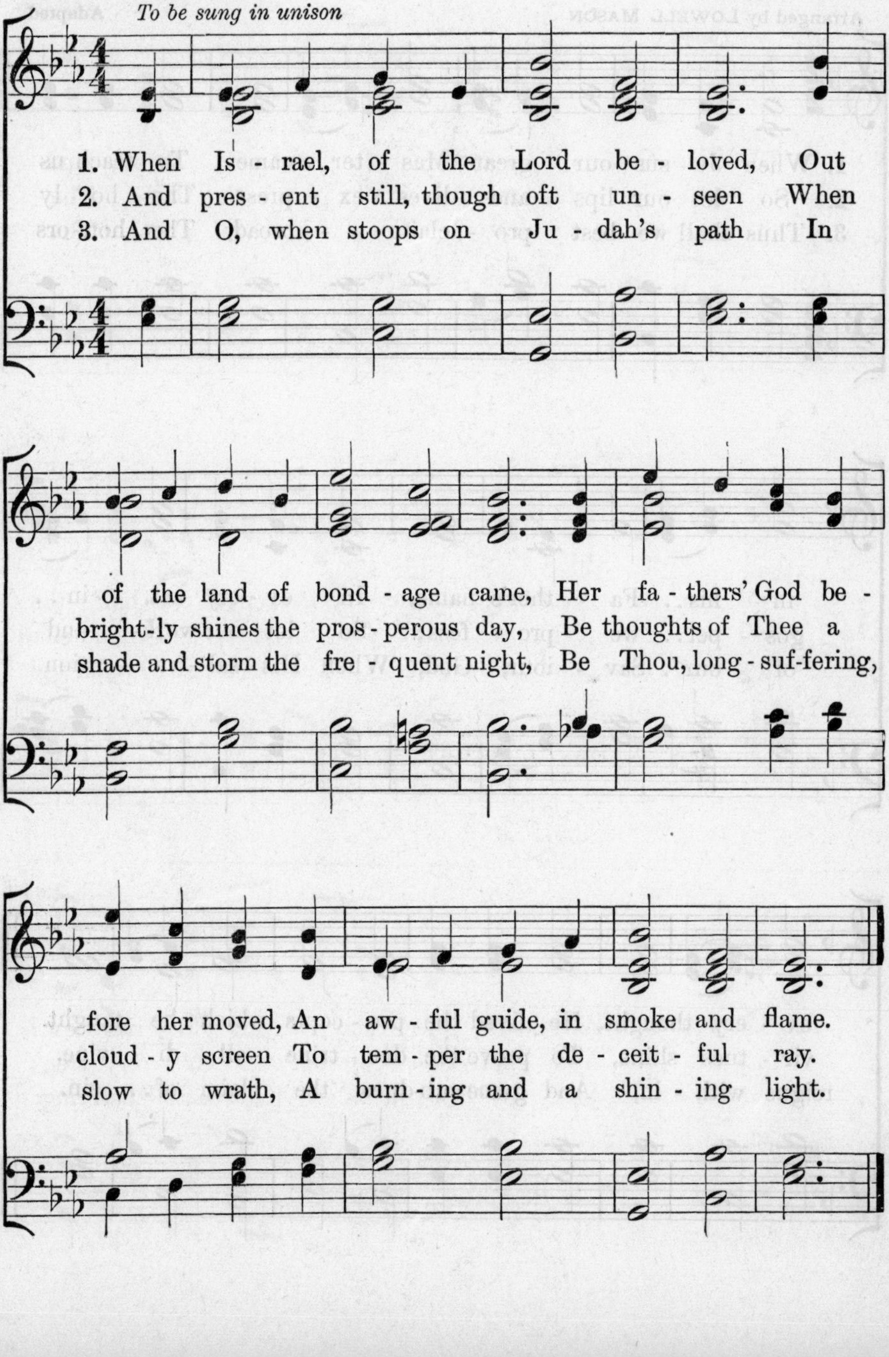

1. When Is - rael, of the Lord be - loved, Out
2. And pres - ent still, though oft un - seen When
3. And O, when stoops on Ju - dah's path In

of the land of bond - age came, Her fa - thers' God be -
bright-ly shines the pros - perous day, Be thoughts of Thee a
shade and storm the fre - quent night, Be Thou, long - suf-fering,

fore her moved, An aw - ful guide, in smoke and flame.
cloud - y screen To tem - per the de - ceit - ful ray.
slow to wrath, A burn - ing and a shin - ing light.

# 386†

**HAMBURG** L. M.

From a Gregorian Chant
Arranged by LOWELL MASON

ISAAC WATTS
Adapted

1. When Je - sus our great Mas - ter.. came To teach us
2. So let our lips and lives ex - press The ho - ly
3. Thus shall we best pro - claim a - broad, The hon - ors
in his.. Fa - ther's name, In ev - ery act, in..
gos - pel.. we pro - fess; So let our works and
of our . Sav - iour, God, When His sal - va - tion
ev - ery thought, He lived the pre - cepts which he taught.
vir - tues shine, To prove the doc - trine all di - vine.
reigns with - in, And grace sub-dues the claim of.. sin.

# 387†

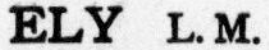

**ELY** L. M.

THOMAS TURTON | ISAAC WATTS
Adapted

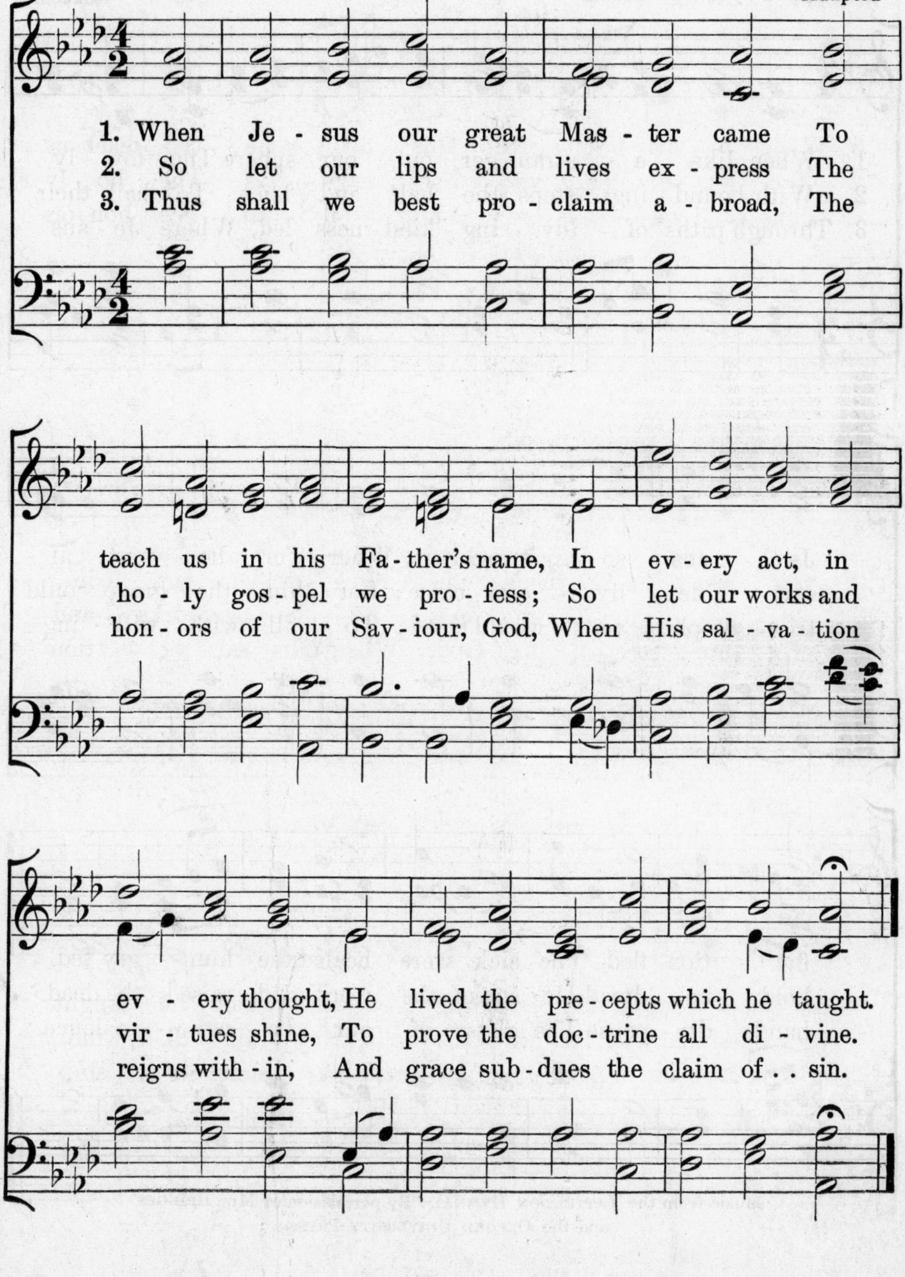

1. When Je - sus our great Mas - ter came To
2. So let our lips and lives ex - press The
3. Thus shall we best pro - claim a - broad, The

teach us in his Fa - ther's name, In ev - ery act, in
ho - ly gos - pel we pro - fess; So let our works and
hon - ors of our Sav - iour, God, When His sal - va - tion

ev - ery thought, He lived the pre - cepts which he taught.
vir - tues shine, To prove the doc - trine all di - vine.
reigns with - in, And grace sub - dues the claim of . . sin.

## 388

**BROMLEY** L. M.

JEREMIAH CLARK
Harmonized by M. M. BRIDGES

JAMES MONTGOMERY
Adapted

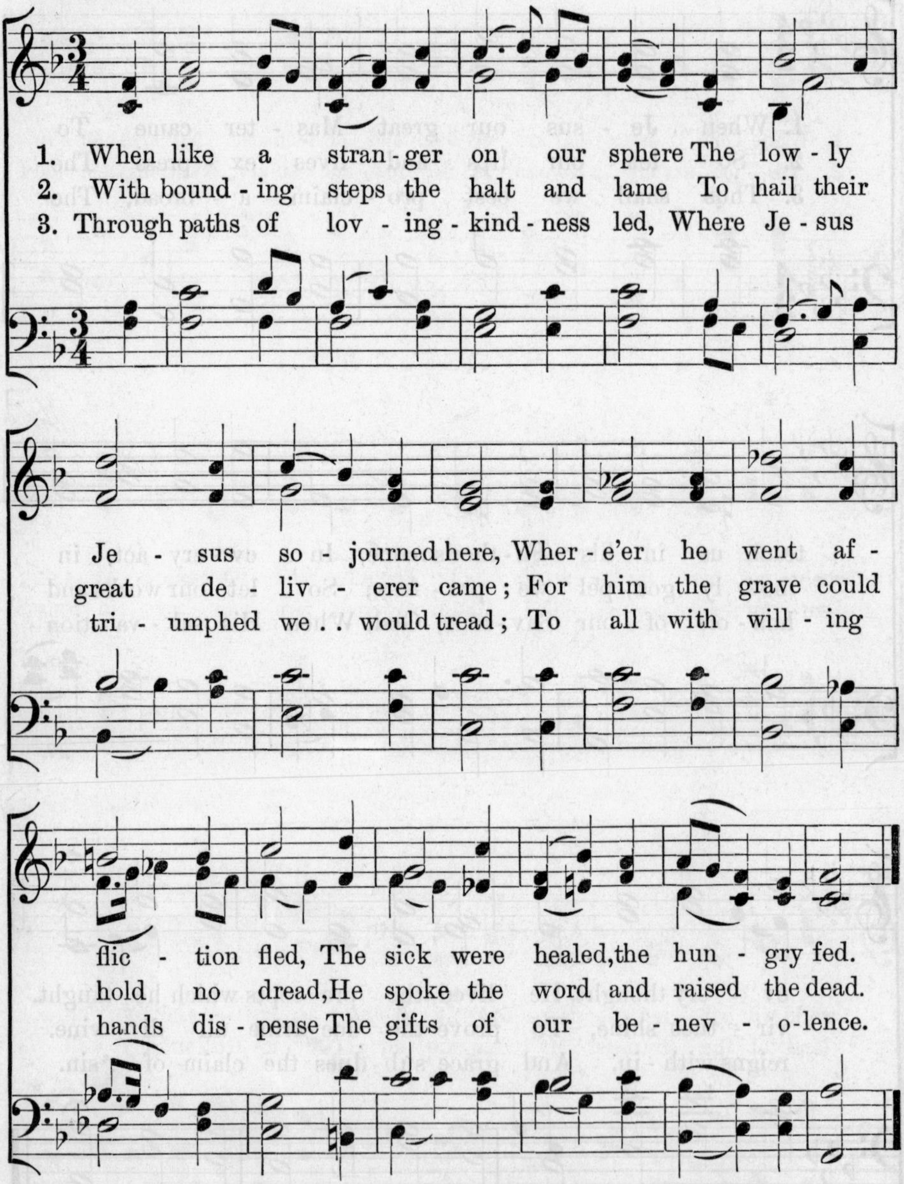

1. When like a stran - ger on our sphere The low - ly
2. With bound - ing steps the halt and lame To hail their
3. Through paths of lov - ing - kind - ness led, Where Je - sus

Je - sus so - journed here, Wher - e'er he went af -
great de - liv - erer came; For him the grave could
tri - umphed we . . would tread; To all with will - ing

flic - tion fled, The sick were healed, the hun - gry fed.
hold no dread, He spoke the word and raised the dead.
hands dis - pense The gifts of our be - nev - o - lence.

Music from the YATTENDON HYMNAL: By permission of MRS. BRIDGES and the OXFORD UNIVERSITY PRESS

# 389

## O CHRISTLICHE HERZEN 12. 11. 12. 11.

Portnersches Gesangbuch, 1831 WILLIAM YOUNG

1. While Thou, O my God, art my help and de-fend - er, No cares can o'er -
2. Yes, Thou art my ref - uge in sor - row and dan-ger; My strength, should I
whelm me, no ter - rors ap - pall; The wiles and the snares of this
suf - fer; my hope, should I fall; My com - fort and joy in this
world will but ren - der More live - ly my hope in my God and my all.
land of the stran-ger; My treas-ure, my glo - ry, my God, and my all.

# 390

**LANGRAN** 10. 10. 10. 10.

JAMES LANGRAN — WILLIAM F. SHERWIN, Adapted

1. Why is thy faith in God's great love so small?
2. O blest as - sur - ance from our ris - en Lord;
3. Ask what thou wilt, but O, re - mem - ber this,
Why doth thy heart shrink back at du - ty's call?
O pre - cious com - fort breath - ing from the Word.
We ask and have not when we ask a - miss.
Art thou o - bey - ing this: A - bide in me;
How great the prom - ise, could there great - er be?
If weak in faith, we on - ly half be - lieve
And doth the Mas - ter's word a - bide in thee?
Ask what thou wilt, it shall be done for thee.
That what we ask we real - ly shall re - ceive.

Music by permission of NOVELLO & Co. Ltd.

## WAREHAM L. M.

WILLIAM KNAPP — CHARLES H. BARLOW

1. Why search the future and the past? Why do ye look with tearful eyes And seek far off for paradise? Before your feet Life's pearl is cast.

2. As deathless as His spirit free, The Perfect lives and works to-day As in the ancient prophets' lay, Where there's an open eye to see.

3. Of all that was and is to come The present holds the Mind and Cause; For God lives in eternal laws, And here to-day upholds His throne.

4. Then rise and greet the signs that prove Unreal the ages' long lament; The "one far-off divine event" Is now, and that event is Love.

## 392†

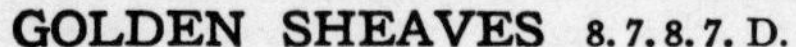

**GOLDEN SHEAVES** 8.7.8.7. D.

ARTHUR S. SULLIVAN — LAURA C. NOURSE

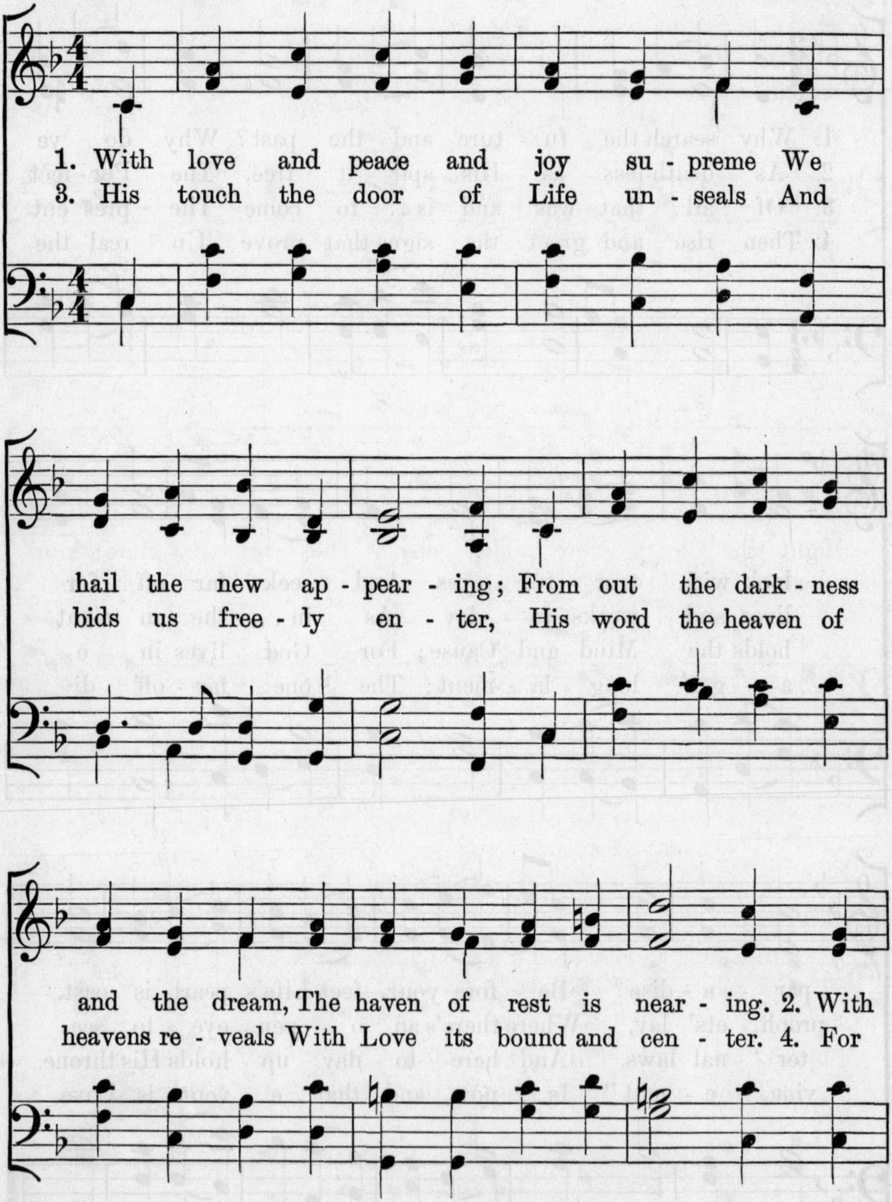
1. With love and peace and joy su - preme We
3. His touch the door of Life un - seals And
hail the new ap - pear - ing; From out the dark - ness
bids us free - ly en - ter, His word the heaven of
and the dream, The haven of rest is near - ing. 2. With
heavens re - veals With Love its bound and cen - ter. 4. For

Music by permission of NOVELLO & Co. Ltd.

gifts of heal - ing in his wings To
God is all, and Christ the way; Our

light the Christ now guides us, The heart that knows him
meek and bold de - fend - er Has cleft the night and

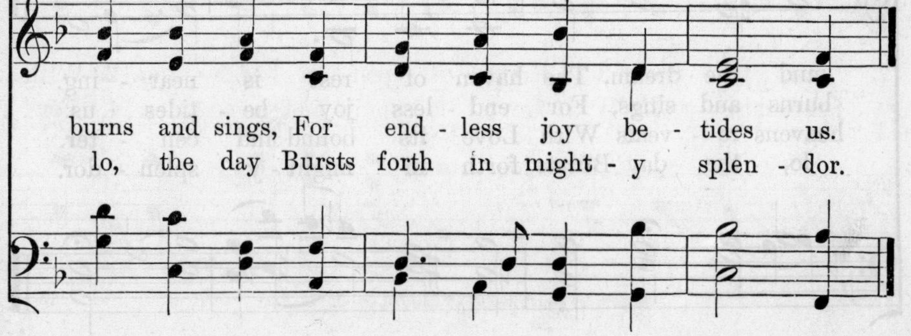
burns and sings, For end - less joy be - tides us.
lo, the day Bursts forth in might - y splen - dor.

# 393†

**ACH GOTT UND HERR** 8.7.8.7.

Melody by C. PETER
Harmonized by J. S. BACH

LAURA C. NOURSE

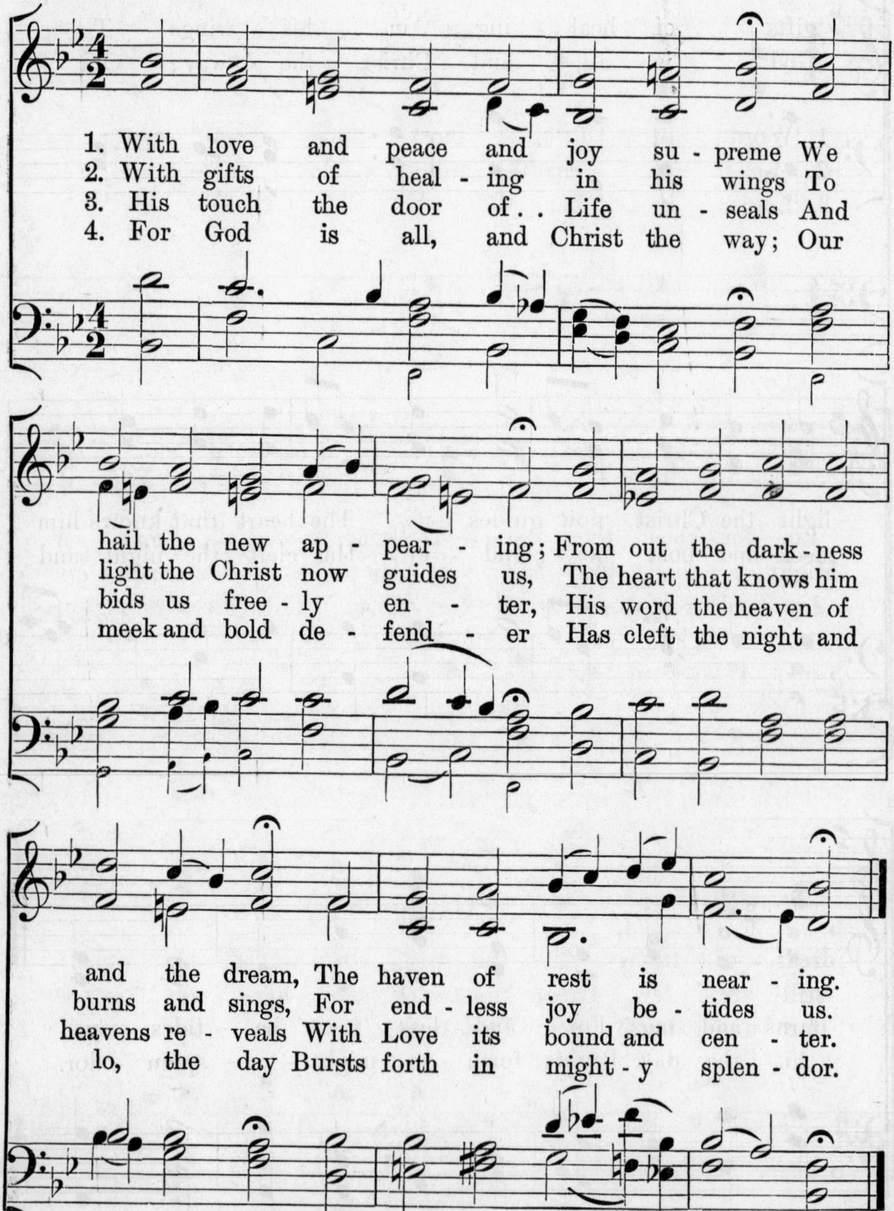

1. With love and peace and joy su - preme We
2. With gifts of heal - ing in his wings To
3. His touch the door of . . Life un - seals And
4. For God is all, and Christ the way; Our

hail the new ap - pear - ing; From out the dark - ness
light the Christ now guides us, The heart that knows him
bids us free - ly en - ter, His word the heaven of
meek and bold de - fend - er Has cleft the night and

and the dream, The haven of rest is near - ing.
burns and sings, For end - less joy be - tides us.
heavens re - veals With Love its bound and cen - ter.
lo, the day Bursts forth in might - y splen - dor.

## 394†

**PLEYEL'S HYMN** 7.7.7.7.

IGNACE J. PLEYEL

JONATHAN F. BAHNMAIER
Tr. CATHERINE WINKWORTH

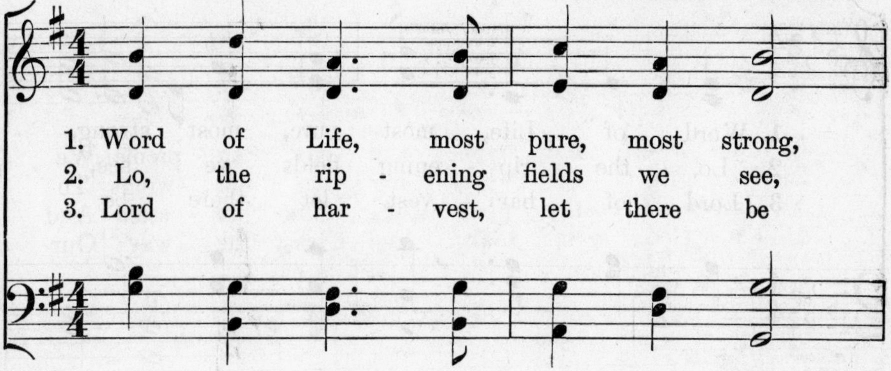

1. Word of Life, most pure, most strong,
Lo, for thee the na - tions long; Spread, till from its
drear - y night All the world a - wakes to light.

2. Lo, the rip - ening fields we see,
Might - y shall the har - vest be; But the reap - ers
still are few, Great the work they have to do.

3. Lord of har - vest, let there be
Joy and strength to work for Thee, Till the na - tions
far and near See Thy light, Thy law re - vere.

## 395†

**PALMS OF GLORY** 7.7.7.7.

WILLIAM D. MACLAGAN

JONATHAN F. BAHNMAIER
Tr. CATHERINE WINKWORTH

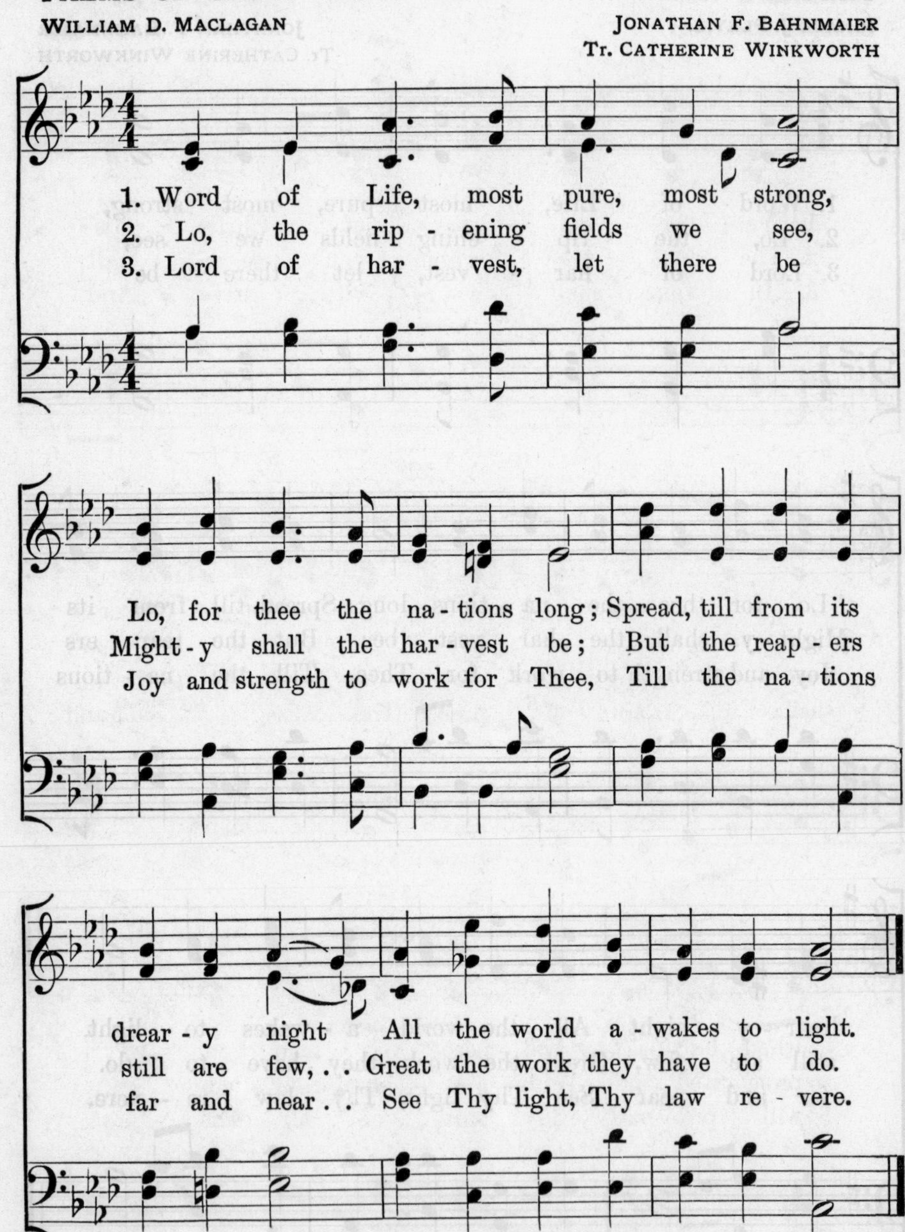
1. Word of Life, most pure, most strong,
2. Lo, the rip - ening fields we see,
3. Lord of har - vest, let there be
Lo, for thee the na - tions long; Spread, till from its
Might - y shall the har - vest be; But the reap - ers
Joy and strength to work for Thee, Till the na - tions
drear - y night All the world a - wakes to light.
still are few, . . Great the work they have to do.
far and near . . See Thy light, Thy law re - vere.

Music by permission of ERIC MACLAGAN

# 396†

**CARLISLE** S. M.

CHARLES LOCKHART

MRS. VOKES
Adapted

1. Ye mes - sen - gers .. of ... Christ, His sov - ereign voice o - bey; A - rise, and fol - low where he .. leads, And peace at - tend your way.
2. The Mas - ter whom you .. serve Will need - ful strength be - stow; De - pend - ing on .. his prom - ised aid, With sa - cred cour - age go.
3. In vain shall e - vil ... strive, And hell in .. vain op - pose; The cause is .. God's and will pre - vail, In spite of .. all His foes.

# 397†

SONG 20 S.M.
ORLANDO GIBBONS
MRS. VOKES
Adapted
1. Ye mes - sen - gers of Christ, His sov - ereign voice o - bey; A - rise, and fol - low where he leads, And peace at - tend your way.
2. The Mas - ter whom you serve Will need - ful strength be - stow; De - pend - ing on his prom - ised aid, With sa - cred cour - age go.
3. In vain shall e - vil strive, And hell in vain op - pose; The cause is God's and will pre - vail, In spite of all His foes.

# 398

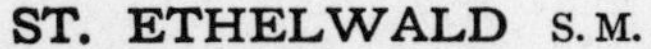

**ST. ETHELWALD** S. M.

WILLIAM H. MONK — PHILIP DODDRIDGE, Adapted

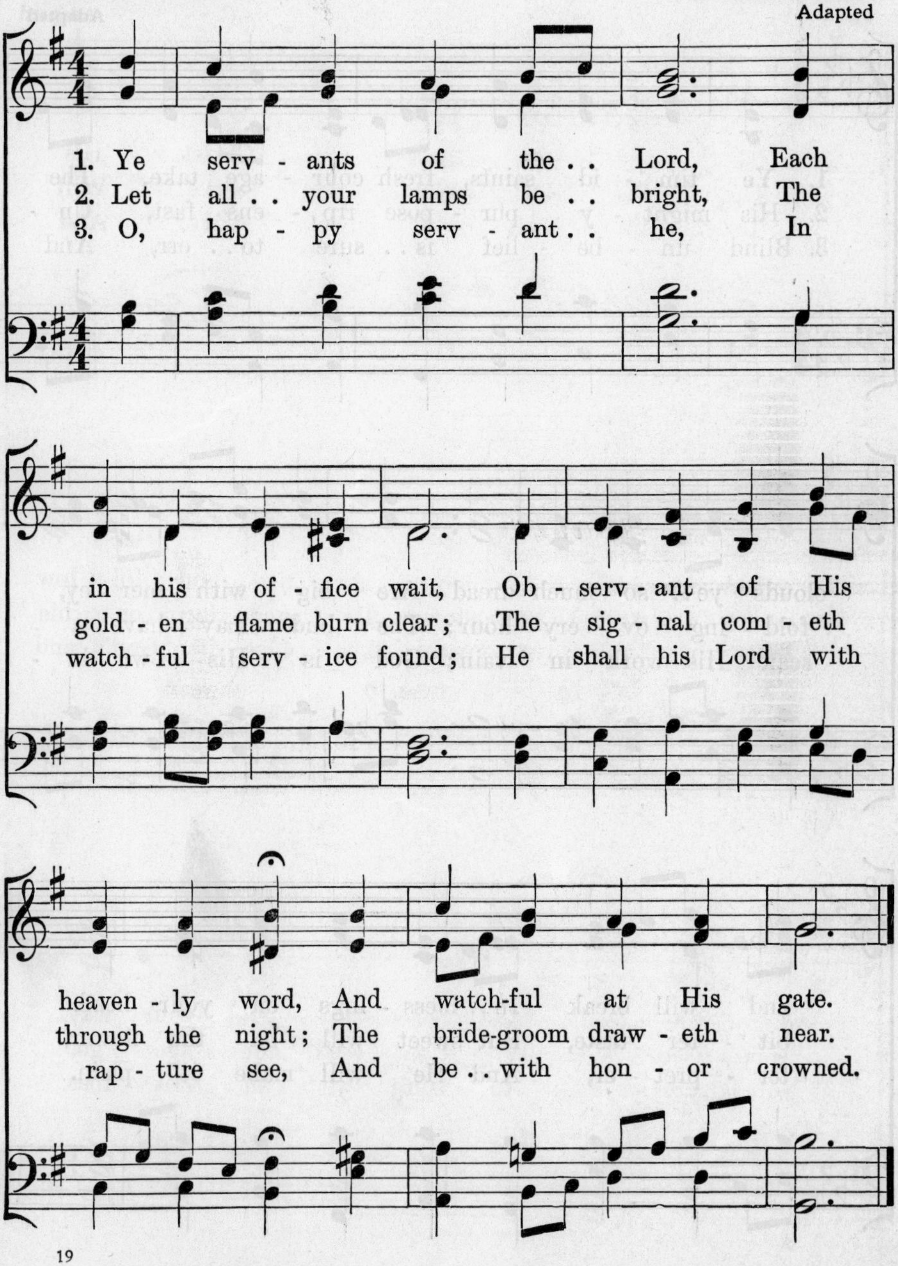

1. Ye serv - ants of the . . Lord, Each in his of - fice wait, Ob - serv - ant of His heaven - ly word, And watch-ful at His gate.

2. Let all . . your lamps be . . bright, The gold - en flame burn clear; The sig - nal com - eth through the night; The bride-groom draw - eth near.

3. O, hap - py serv - ant . . he, In watch - ful serv - ice found; He shall his Lord with rap - ture see, And be . . with hon - or crowned.

# 399†

**SOUTHWELL** C.M.

HERBERT S. IRONS | WILLIAM COWPER
Adapted

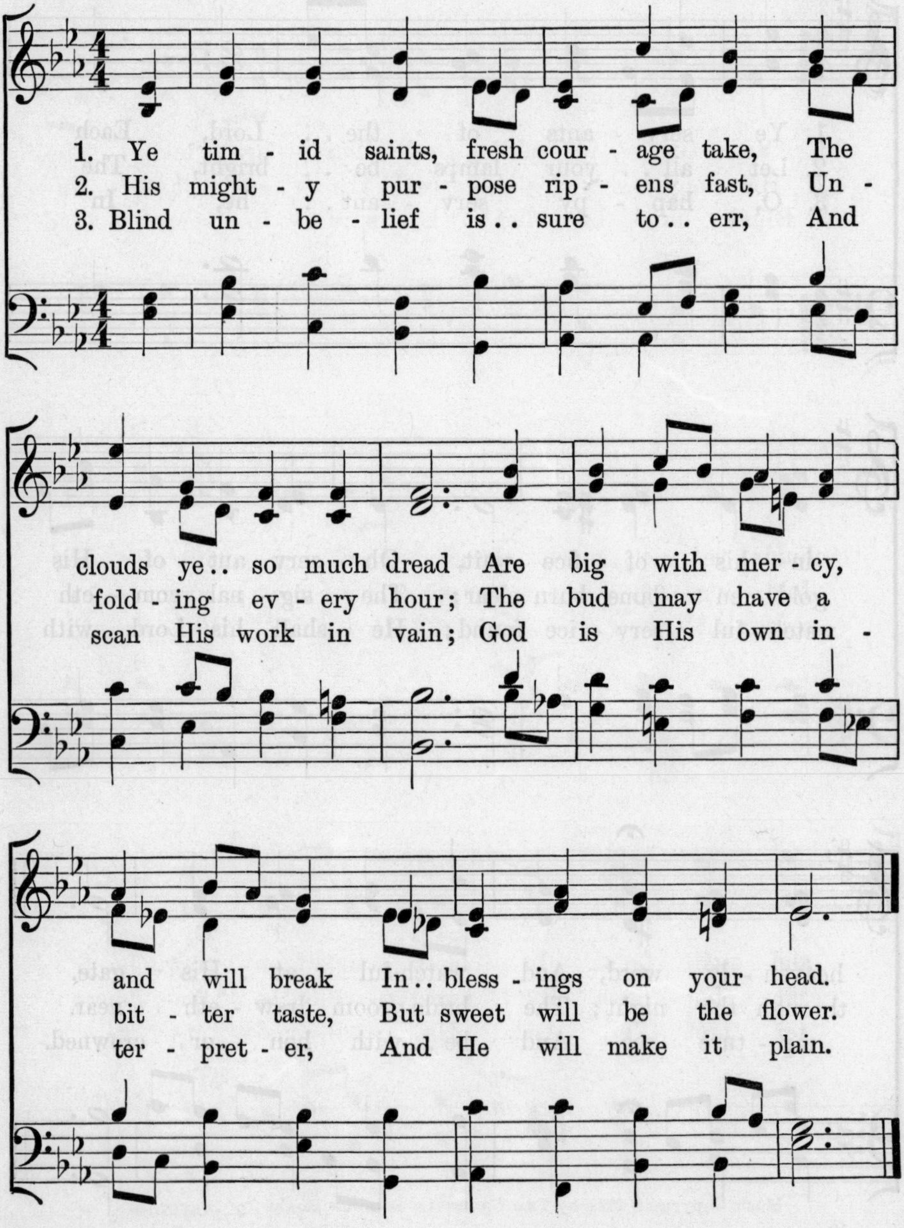

1. Ye tim - id saints, fresh cour - age take, The
2. His might - y pur - pose rip - ens fast, Un -
3. Blind un - be - lief is.. sure to.. err, And

clouds ye.. so much dread Are big with mer - cy,
fold - ing ev - ery hour; The bud may have a
scan His work in vain; God is His own in -

and will break In.. bless - ings on your head.
bit - ter taste, But sweet will be the flower.
ter - pret - er, And He will make it plain.

400†

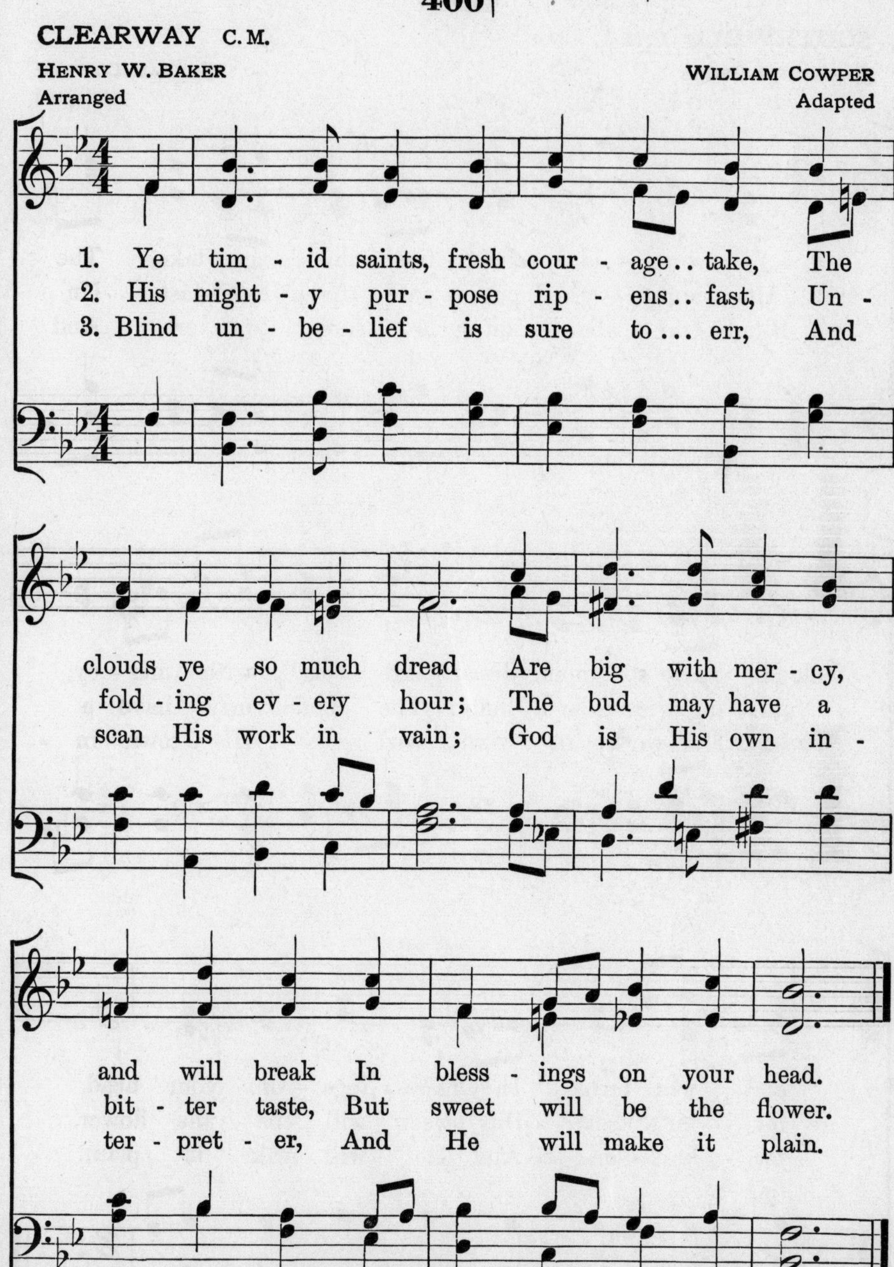
CLEARWAY C. M.
HENRY W. BAKER
Arranged
WILLIAM COWPER
Adapted
1. Ye tim - id saints, fresh cour - age.. take, The clouds ye so much dread Are big with mer - cy, and will break In bless - ings on your head.
2. His might - y pur - pose rip - ens.. fast, Un - fold - ing ev - ery hour; The bud may have a bit - ter taste, But sweet will be the flower.
3. Blind un - be - lief is sure to... err, And scan His work in vain; God is His own in - ter - pret - er, And He will make it plain.

# SUPPLEMENT

# 401

**ITALIAN HYMN** 664. 66 64.

Arranged from
FELICE DE GIARDINI | JOHN MARRIOTT*

1. Thou whose al - might - y Word Cha - os and dark - ness heard,
2. Christ, thou dost come to bring On thy re - deem - ing wing
3. Spir - it of truth and love, Life - giv - ing, ho - ly dove,
And took their flight; Hear us, we hum - bly pray, And where the
Heal - ing and sight, Health to the sick in mind, Sight to the
Speed forth thy flight; Move on the wa - ters' face, Bear - ing the
Gos - pel - day Sheds not its glo - rious ray, Let there be light.
in - ly blind; Ah, now to all man-kind Let there be light.
lamp of grace, And in earth's dark - est place Let there be light.

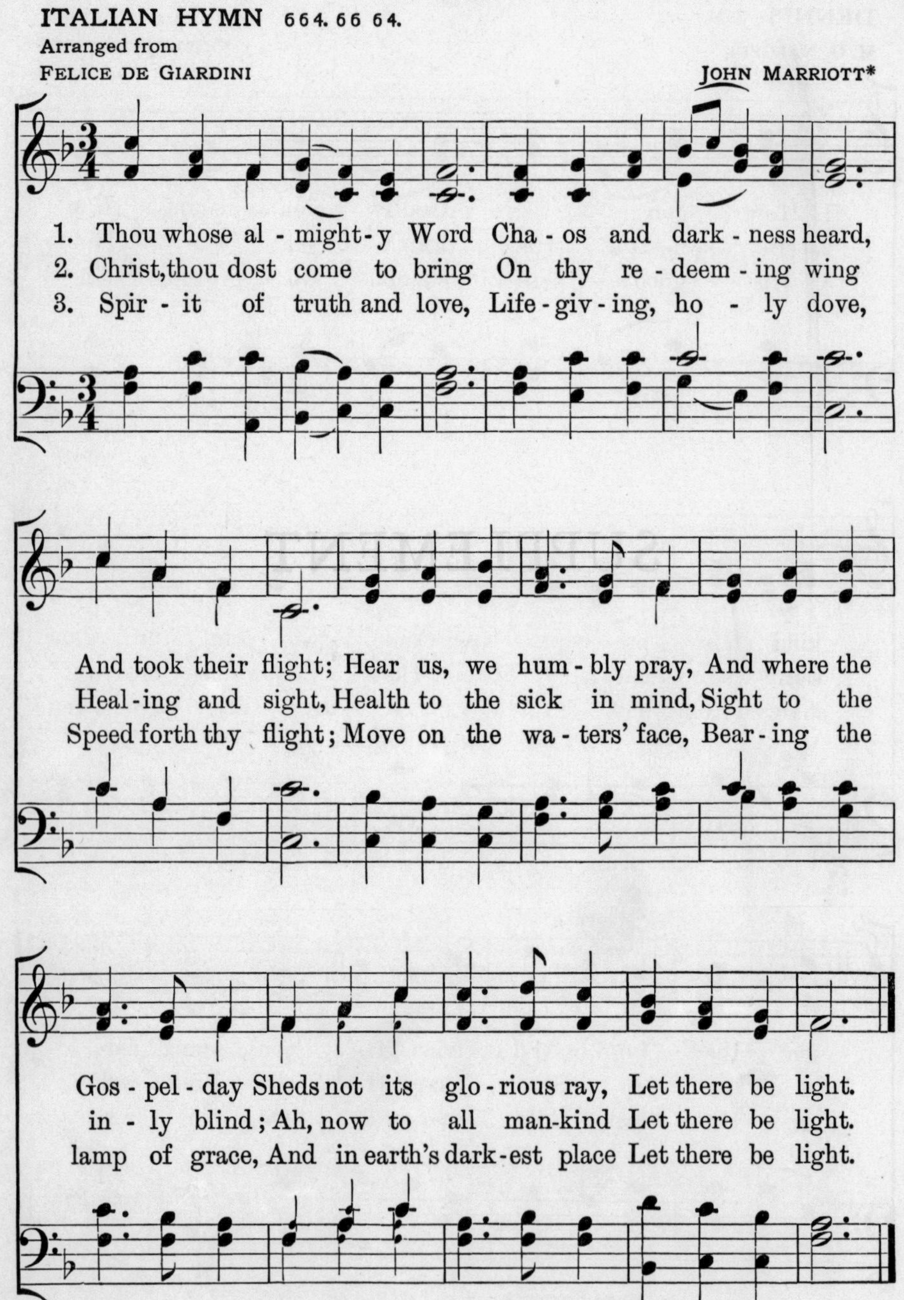

# 402

DENNIS S. M.
H. G. NAEGELI
PHILIP DODDRIDGE
Adapted
1. How gen - tle God's com - mands, How
2. Be - neath .. His watch - ful eye His
3. His good - ness stands ap - proved, Un -
kind His pre - cepts are; Come, cast your bur - dens
saints se - cure - ly dwell; That hand which bears cre -
changed from day to day: I drop my bur - den
on the Lord, And trust His con - stant care.
a - tion up Shall guard His chil - dren well.
at His feet, And bear a song a - way.

Music by permission of THE PARISH CHOIR

## 403

### BALERMA C. M.

Spanish Melody
JOSEPH SWAIN
Adapted
1. How sweet, how heaven - ly is the sight,
2. When, free from en - vy, scorn, and pride,
3. Let love, in one de - light - ful stream,
4. Love is the gold - en chain that binds
When those who love the Lord In one an -
Our wish - es all a - bove, Each can his
Through ev - ery bos - om flow; And un - ion
The hearts that faith - ful prove; And he's an
oth - er's peace de - light, And so ful - fill His word;
broth - er's fail - ings hide, And show a broth - er's love.
sweet, and dear es - teem In ev - ery ac - tion glow.
heir of heaven who finds His bos - om glow with love.

# 404

**OLMUTZ** S. M.

Arranged by LOWELL MASON
CHARLES PARSONS
1. O do not bar your mind Against the light of good; But open wide, let in the Word, And Truth will be your food.
2. Truth will from error free Your long enslaved mind, And bring the light of liberty Where it shall be enshrined.
3. Hid treasures it reveals To all who know its power; And all who will may light receive In this most gracious hour.
4. Then open wide your heart To Truth and Light and Love; You then shall know your life is hid With Christ in God above.

# 405

**BENEVENTO** 7.7.7.7.D.

SAMUEL WEBBE
Revised

CHARLES WESLEY and JOHN TAYLOR
Adapted

1. Glo-ry be to God on high, God whose glo-ry fills the sky;
2. Mark the won-ders of His hand: Power no em-pire can with-stand;

Peace on earth to man is given, Man, the well-be-loved of heaven.
Wis-dom, an-gels' glo-rious theme; Good-ness one e-ter-nal stream.

Gra-cious Fa-ther, in Thy love, Send Thy bless-ings from a-bove;
All ye peo-ple, raise the song, End-less thanks to God be-long;

Let Thy light, Thy truth, Thy peace Bid all strife and tu-mult cease.
Hearts o'er-flow-ing with His praise Join the hymns your voi-ces raise.

# 406

**ST. MARGARET** 88. 886.

A. L. PEACE — M. G. M.

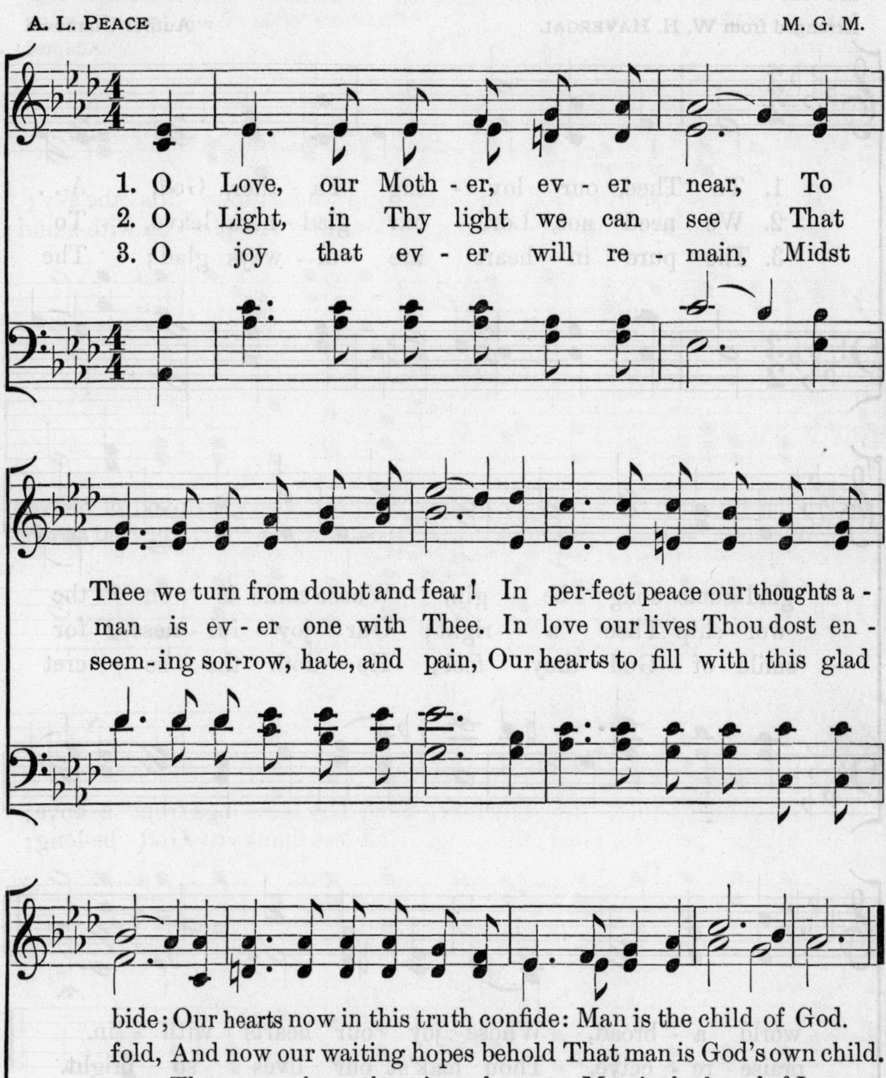

1. O Love, our Moth-er, ev-er near, To Thee we turn from doubt and fear! In per-fect peace our thoughts a-bide; Our hearts now in this truth confide: Man is the child of God.
2. O Light, in Thy light we can see That man is ev-er one with Thee. In love our lives Thou dost en-fold, And now our waiting hopes behold That man is God's own child.
3. O joy that ev-er will re-main, Midst seem-ing sor-row, hate, and pain, Our hearts to fill with this glad song That soars above the mists of wrong: Man is the loved of Love.

Music by permission of NOVELLO & Co. Ltd.

## EVAN NEW C. M.

Arranged from W. H. HAVERGAL — Author Unknown

1. To Thee, our lov - ing Fa - ther, God, A..
2. We need not, Lord, our glad - ness leave, To
3. The pure in heart are al - ways glad; The
glad - some song be - gin, Whose smile is on the
wor - ship Thee a - right; Our joy - ful - ness for
smile of God they feel; He doth the se - cret
world a - broad, Whose joy our hearts with - in.
praise re - ceive, Thou mak'st our lives so bright.
of His joy To blame - less hearts re - veal.

# 408

GERONTIUS C. M.
JOHN B. DYKES
EDITH GADDIS BREWER
1. Prayer with our wak - ing thought as - cends,
2. Lo, to our wid - ening vi - sion dawns
3. Thus in Thy ra - diance van - ish - es
Great God of light, to Thee; Dark-ness is ban - ished
The realm of Soul su - preme, Faith-light - ed peaks of
Death's drear and gloom - y night; Thus all cre - a - tion
in . . the glow Of Thy re - al - i - ty.
Spir - it stand Re - vealed in morn - ing's beam.
hears a - new Truth's call, Let there be light.

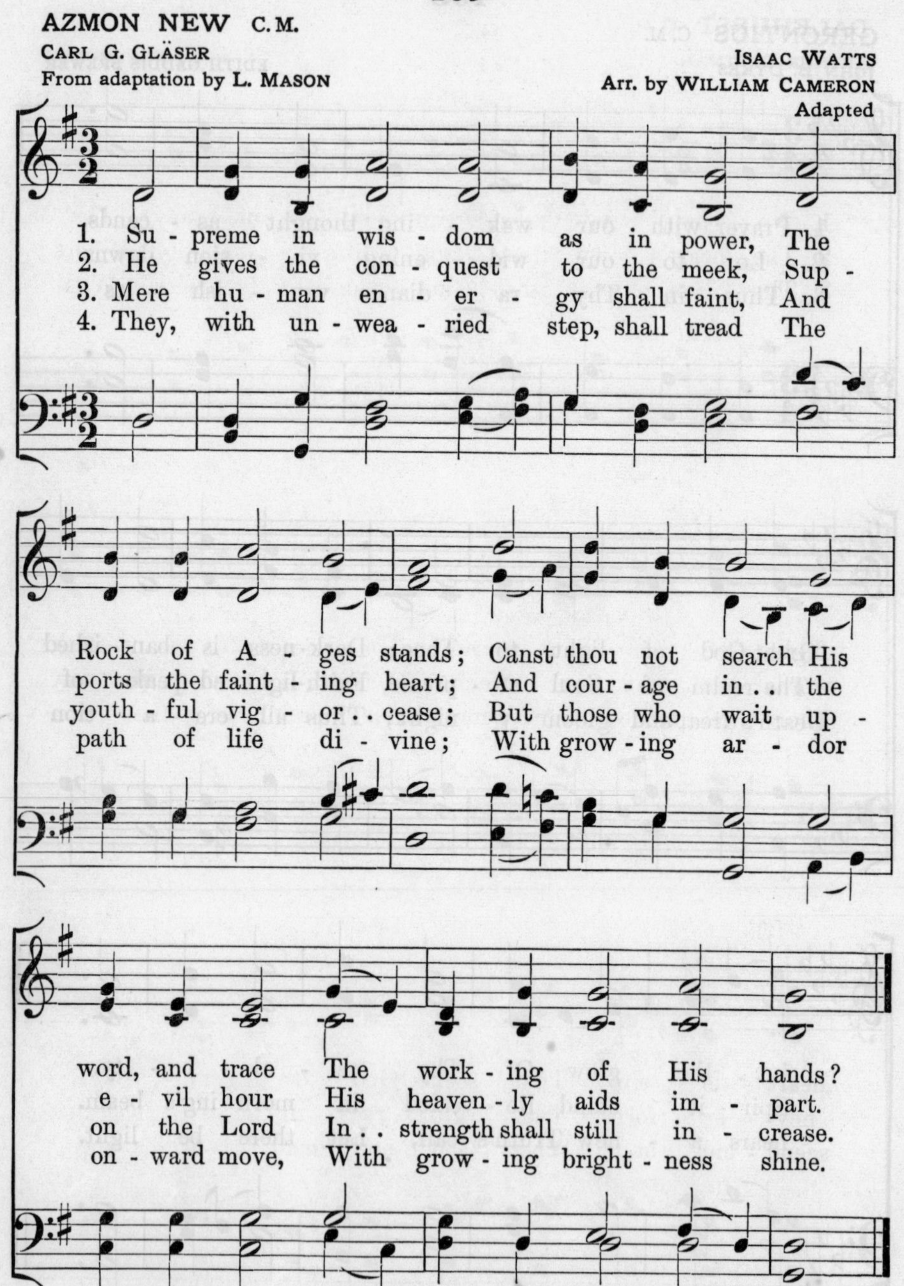
409
AZMON NEW C. M.
CARL G. GLÄSER
From adaptation by L. MASON
ISAAC WATTS
Arr. by WILLIAM CAMERON
Adapted
1. Su - preme in wis - dom as in power, The Rock of A - ges stands; Canst thou not search His word, and trace The work - ing of His hands?
2. He gives the con - quest to the meek, Sup - ports the faint - ing heart; And cour - age in . . the e - vil hour His heaven - ly aids im - part.
3. Mere hu - man en - er - gy shall faint, And youth - ful vig - or . . cease; But those who wait up - on the Lord In . . strength shall still in - crease.
4. They, with un - wea - ried step, shall tread The path of life di - vine; With grow - ing ar - dor on - ward move, With grow - ing bright - ness shine.

## 410

**DALEHURST** C. M.

ARTHUR COTTMAN — SAMUEL GREENWOOD

1. No mor - tal sense can still or stay The
2. The heart's own long - ing lifts it high Where
3. The voi - ces that are world - ly wise, With
flight of si - lent prayer, Un - ceas - ing, voice - less,
words can nev - er reach, Though hu - man lips may
mor - tal modes in tune, Are mute in that tran -
heart - de - sire That seeks God ev - ery - where.
nev - er form That glo - ry in - to speech.
scend - ent hour When God and man com - mune.

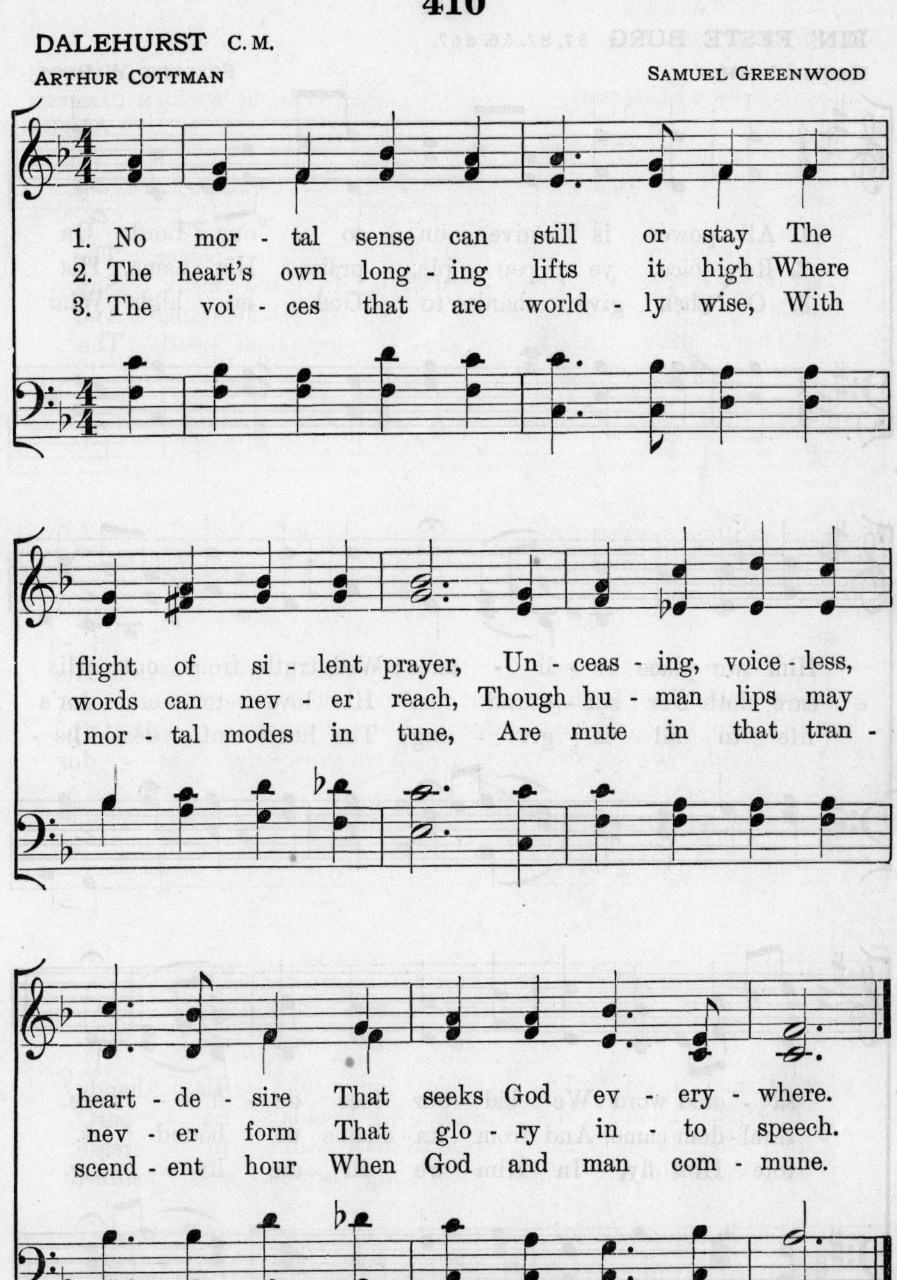

411

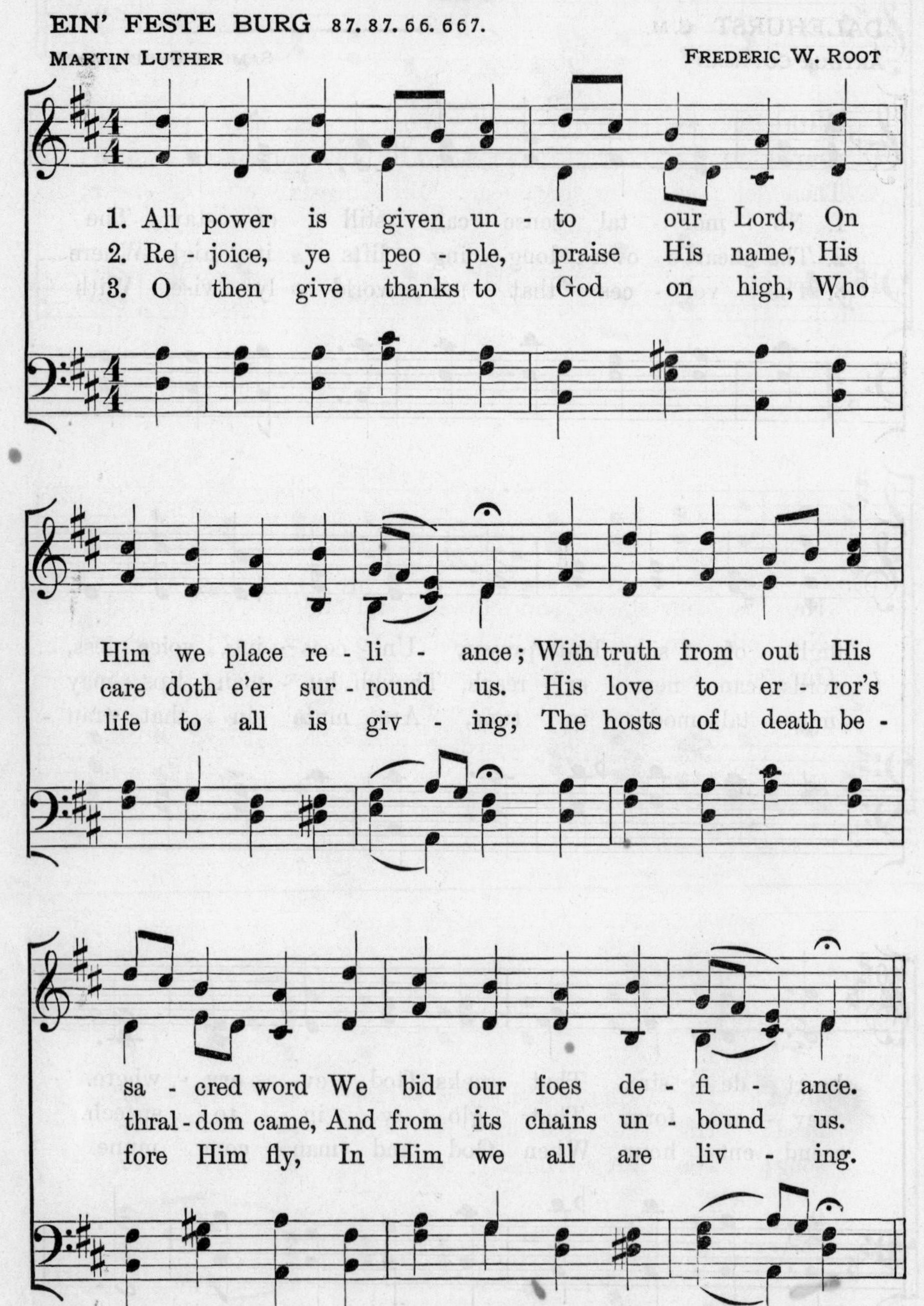
EIN' FESTE BURG 87. 87. 66. 667.
MARTIN LUTHER
FREDERIC W. ROOT
1. All power is given un - to our Lord, On
2. Re - joice, ye peo - ple, praise His name, His
3. O then give thanks to God on high, Who
Him we place re - li - ance; With truth from out His
care doth e'er sur - round us. His love to er - ror's
life to all is giv - ing; The hosts of death be -
sa - cred word We bid our foes de - fi - ance.
thral - dom came, And from its chains un - bound us.
fore Him fly, In Him we all are liv - ing.

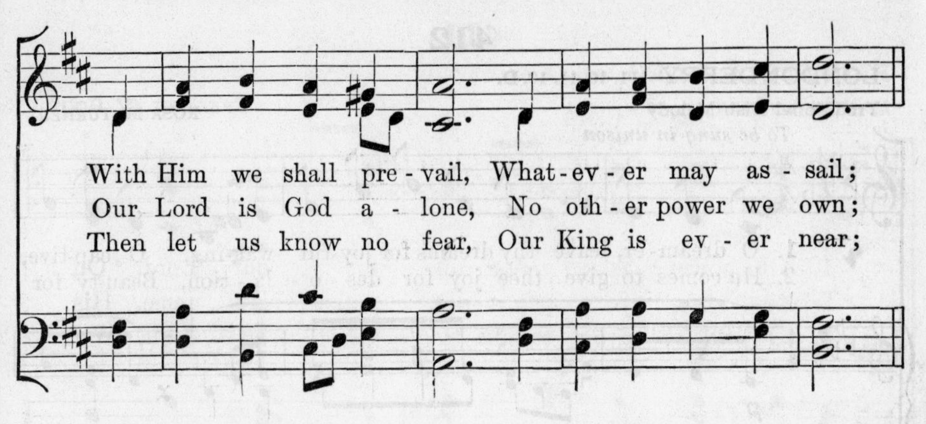
With Him we shall pre - vail, What - ev - er may as - sail;
Our Lord is God a - lone, No oth - er power we own;
Then let us know no fear, Our King is ev - er near;

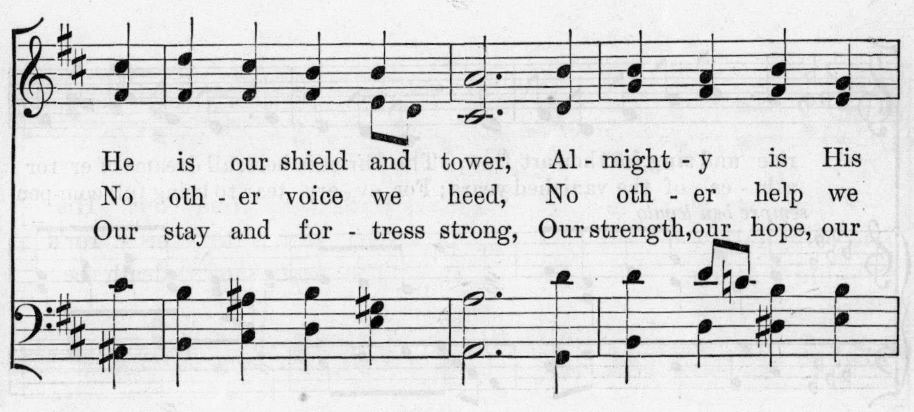
He is our shield and tower, Al - might - y is His
No oth - er voice we heed, No oth - er help we
Our stay and for - tress strong, Our strength, our hope, our

power; His king - dom is for - ev - er.
need; His king - dom is for - ev - er.
song; His king - dom is for - ev - er.

# 412

LONDONDERRY 11. 10. 11. 10. D.
Traditional Irish Melody
ROSA M. TURNER
To be sung in unison
1. O dream-er, leave thy dreams for joy-ful wak-ing, O cap-tive, rise and sing, for thou art free; The Christ is here, all dreams of er-ror break-ing, Un-loos-ing bonds of all cap-tiv-i-ty.
2. He comes to give thee joy for des-o-la-tion, Beau-ty for ash-es of the vanished years; For ev-ery tear to bring full com-pen-sa-tion, To give thee con-fi-dence for all thy fears.
p
sempre ben legato

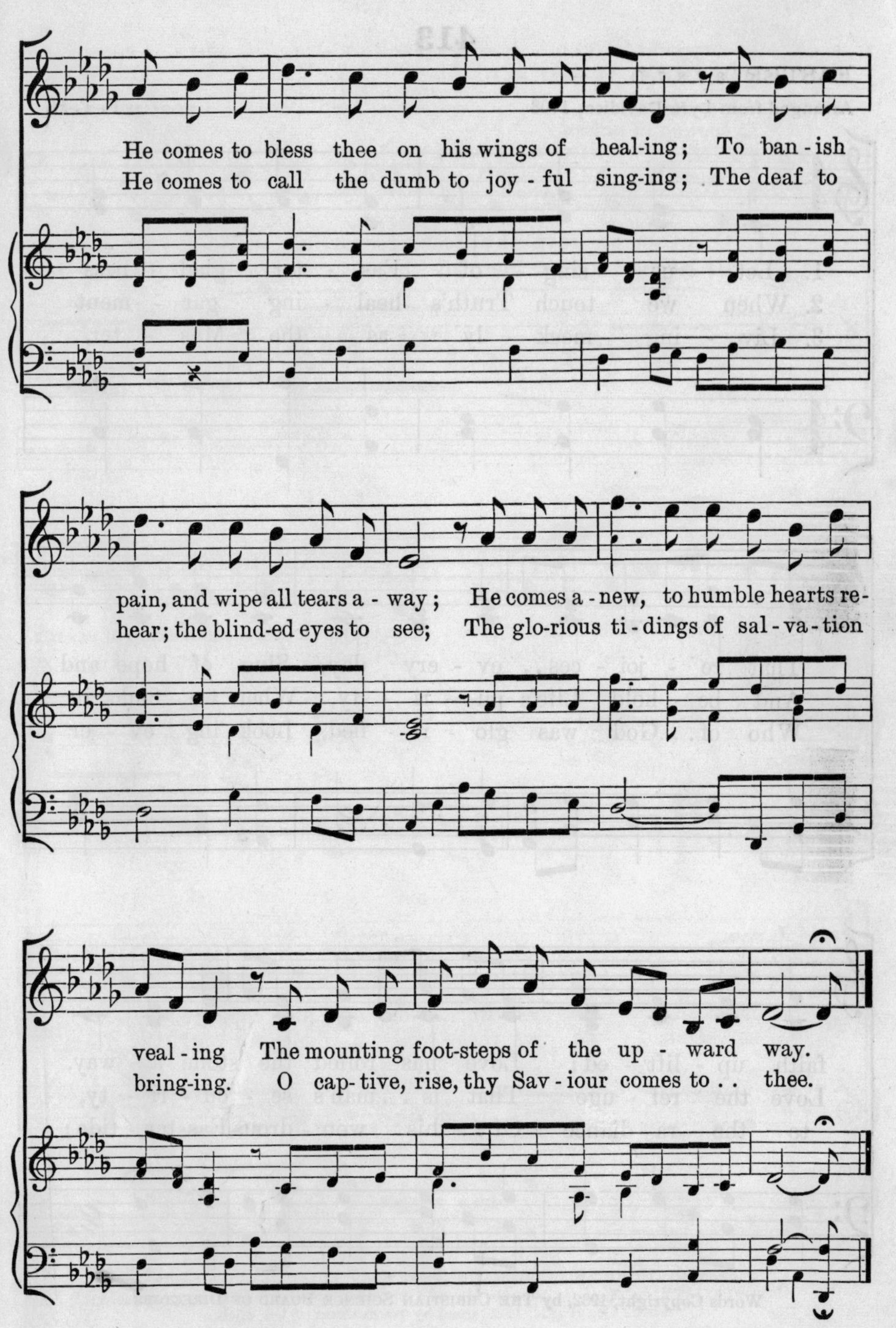
He comes to bless thee on his wings of heal-ing; To ban-ish
He comes to call the dumb to joy-ful sing-ing; The deaf to
pain, and wipe all tears a-way; He comes a-new, to humble hearts re-
hear; the blind-ed eyes to see; The glo-rious ti-dings of sal-va-tion
veal-ing The mounting foot-steps of the up-ward way.
bring-ing. O cap-tive, rise, thy Sav-iour comes to.. thee.

413

EASTER 8.7.8.7.D.
Arranged from Lyra Davidica, 1708
F. T. H.
1. Let us sing of Eas - ter glad - ness
2. When we touch Truth's heal - ing gar - ment
3. Liv - ing meek - ly as the Mas - ter,
That re - joi - ces.. ev - ery day, Sing of hope and
And be - hold Life's pu - ri - ty, When we find in
Who of.. God was glo - ri - fied, Look - ing ev - er
faith up - lift - ed; Love has rolled the stone a - way.
Love the ref - uge That is..man's se - cu - ri - ty,
to the ra - diance Of.. his won - drous Eas - ter - tide;

Lo, the prom - ise and ful - fill - ment,
When we turn from earth to Spir - it,
Freed of fear, of pain, and sor - row,
Lo, the man whom God hath made, Seen in glo - ry
And from self have won re - lease. Then we see the
Giv - ing God the hon - or due, Ev - ery day will
of an Eas - ter Crowned with light that can - not fade.
ris - en Sav - iour: Then we know his prom - ised peace.
be an Eas - ter Filled with ben - e - dic - tions new.

## I LOVE TO TELL THE STORY

7. 6. 7. 6. D. and Refrain

WILLIAM G. FISCHER

KATHERINE HANKEY

1. I love to tell the sto - ry Of un - seen things a - bove,
2. I love to tell the sto - ry, 'Tis pleas - ant to . . re - peat
3. I love to tell the sto - ry, For those who know it best
Of Je - sus and his glo - ry, Of Je - sus and his love,
What seems, each time I tell it, More won - der - ful - ly sweet.
Seem hun - ger - ing and thirst - ing To hear it like the rest.
I love to tell the sto - ry Be - cause I know 'tis true,
I love to tell the sto - ry, For some have nev - er heard
I love to tell the sto - ry, To sing the new, new song

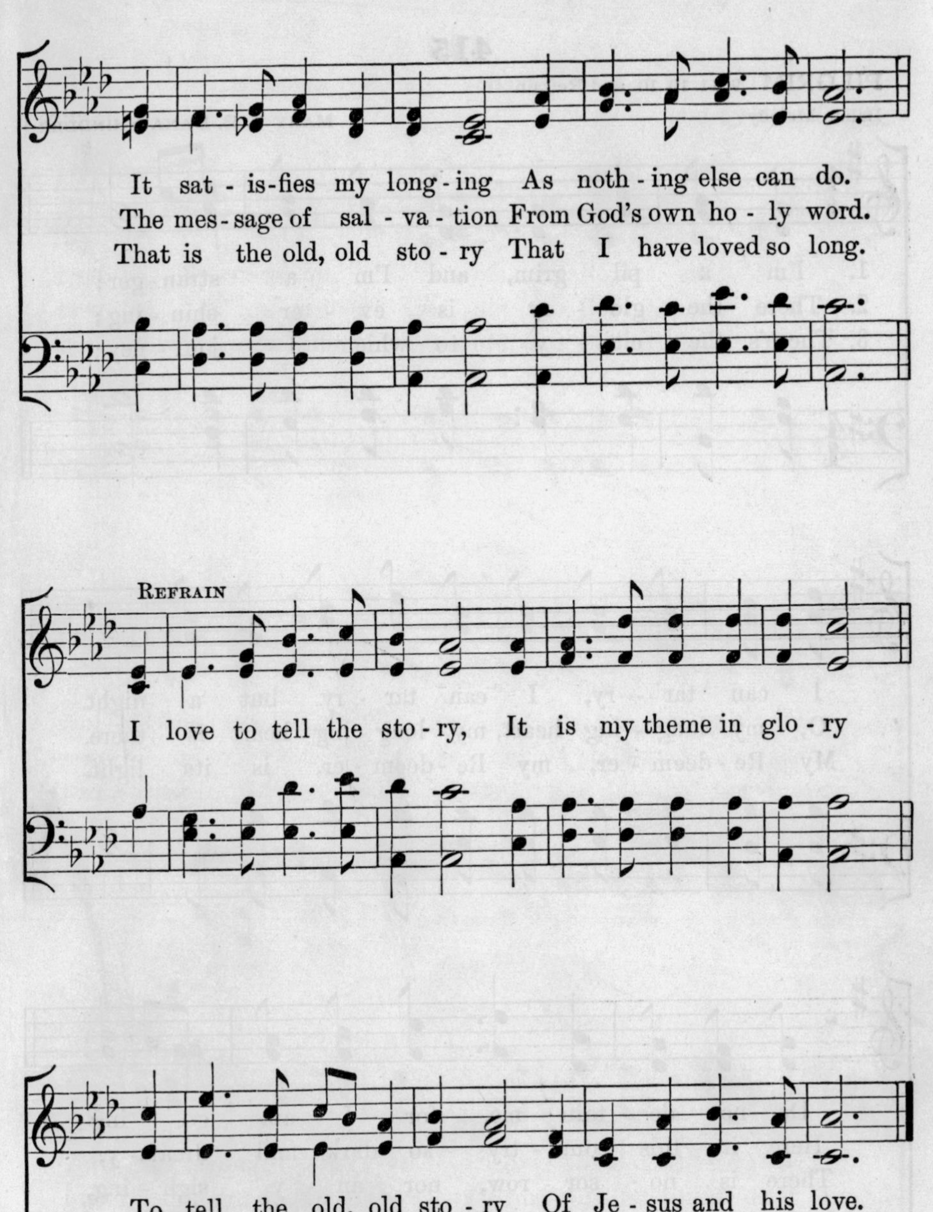
It sat - is-fies my long-ing As noth - ing else can do.
The mes-sage of sal - va - tion From God's own ho - ly word.
That is the old, old sto - ry That I have loved so long.
Refrain
I love to tell the sto - ry, It is my theme in glo - ry
To tell the old, old sto - ry Of Je - sus and his love.

415

**PILGRIM** 9. 11. 10. 10. and Refrain

Italian Melody — MARY S. B. DANA SHINDLER

1. I'm a pil - grim, and I'm a stran - ger;
2. There the glo - ry is ev - er shin - ing;
3. There's the cit - y to which I jour - ney;
I can tar - ry, I can tar - ry but a night.
O, my long - ing heart, my long - ing heart is there.
My Re - deem - er, my Re - deem - er, is its light.
Do not de - tain me, for I am go - ing
Here in this coun - try so dark and drear - y,
There is no sor - row, nor an - y sigh - ing,

By permission of THE CENTURY CO.

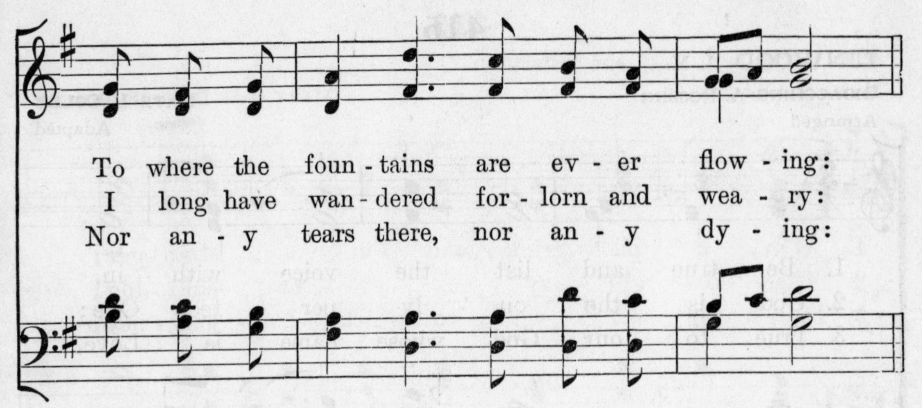
To where the foun - tains are ev - er flow - ing:
I long have wan - dered for - lorn and wea - ry:
Nor an - y tears there, nor an - y dy - ing:

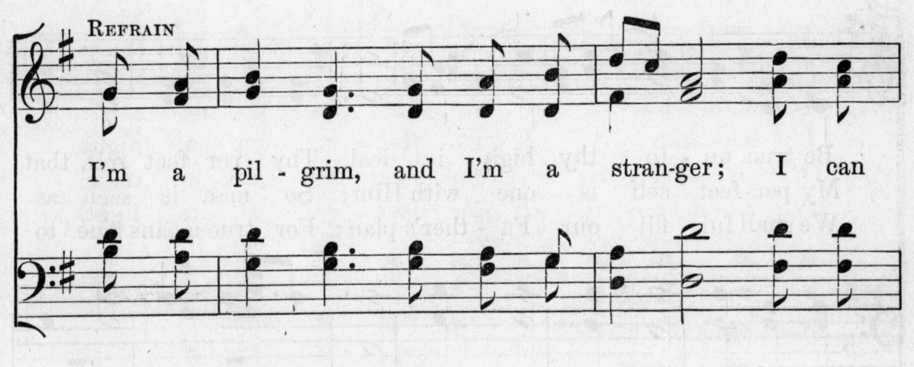
REFRAIN
I'm a pil - grim, and I'm a stran-ger; I can

tar - ry, I can tar - ry but a night.

# 416

LINWOOD L. M.
GIOACCHINO A. ROSSINI
Arranged
KATE L. COLBY
Adapted
1. Be true and list the voice with - in,
2. God is the on - ly per - fect One:
3. True to our God whose name is Love,
Be true un - to thy high i - deal, Thy per - fect self, that
My per - fect self is one with Him; So man is seen as
We shall ful - fill our Fa - ther's plan; For true means true to
knows no sin, That self that is . . the on - ly real.
God's own son, When Truth dis - pels the shad - ows dim.
God a - bove, To self, and to . . our fel - low - man.

Arrangement by permission of Mrs. CHARLES W. ROSAN

# 417

**ANTIOCH** C. M.

GEORG FRIEDRICH HÄNDEL
Arranged by LOWELL MASON

ISAAC WATTS
Adapted

1. Joy to the world, the Lord is come, Let earth re - ceive her King;
Let ev - ery heart pre - pare him room, And heaven and nature sing, And
And heaven and nature
heaven and na-ture sing, And heaven, and heaven and na - ture sing.
sing, And heaven and na-ture sing,

2. No more let sin and sorrow grow,
Nor thorns infest the ground;
Where'er he comes, his blessings flow,
And hope and joy abound.

3. He rules the world with truth and grace,
And makes the nations prove
The glories of his righteousness
And wonders of his love.

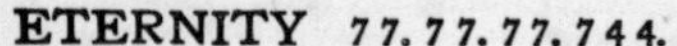

**ETERNITY** 77.77.77.744.

P. P. BLISS — ELLEN M. H. GATES

1. O, the clang - ing bells of time, Night and
2. O, the clang - ing bells of time, How their
3. O, the clang - ing bells of time, To their

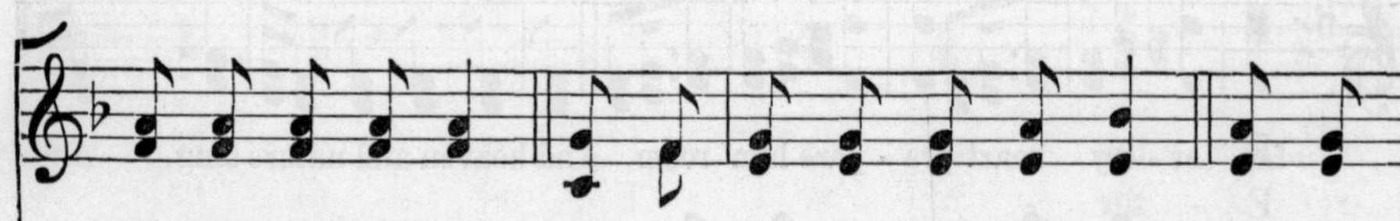

day they nev - er cease; We are wea - ried with their chime, For they
chan - ges rise and fall, But in un - der - tone sub - lime, Sound - ing
voi - ces, loud and low, In a long, un - rest - ing line We are

do not bring us peace; And we hush our breath to hear, And we
clear - ly through them all, Is a voice that must be heard, As our
march - ing to and fro; And we yearn for sight or sound Of the

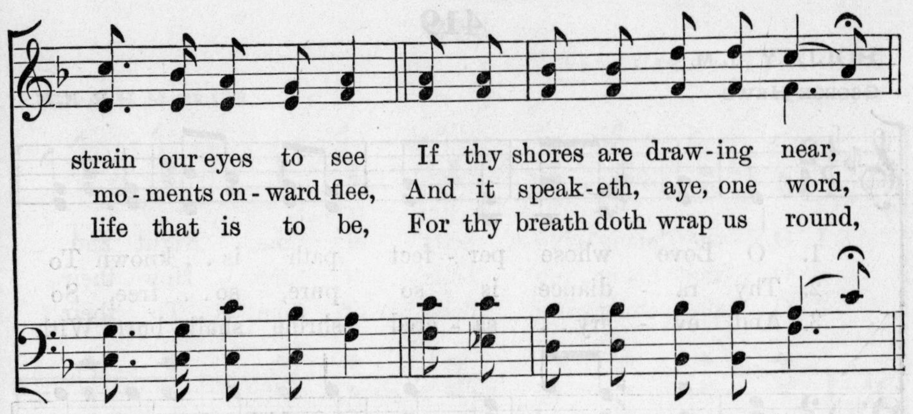
strain our eyes to see If thy shores are draw-ing near,
mo-ments on-ward flee, And it speak-eth, aye, one word,
life that is to be, For thy breath doth wrap us round,

Ritard.
E - ter - ni - ty! E - ter - ni - ty!
E - ter - ni - ty! E - ter - ni - ty!
E - ter - ni - ty! E - ter - ni - ty!

4. O, the clanging bells of time,
Soon their notes will all be dumb,
And in joy and peace sublime,
We shall feel the silence come;
And our souls their thirst will slake,
And our eyes the King will see,
When thy glorious morn shall break,
Eternity! Eternity!

## 419

**HOLLEY** L. M.

GEORGE HEWS

R. E. K.

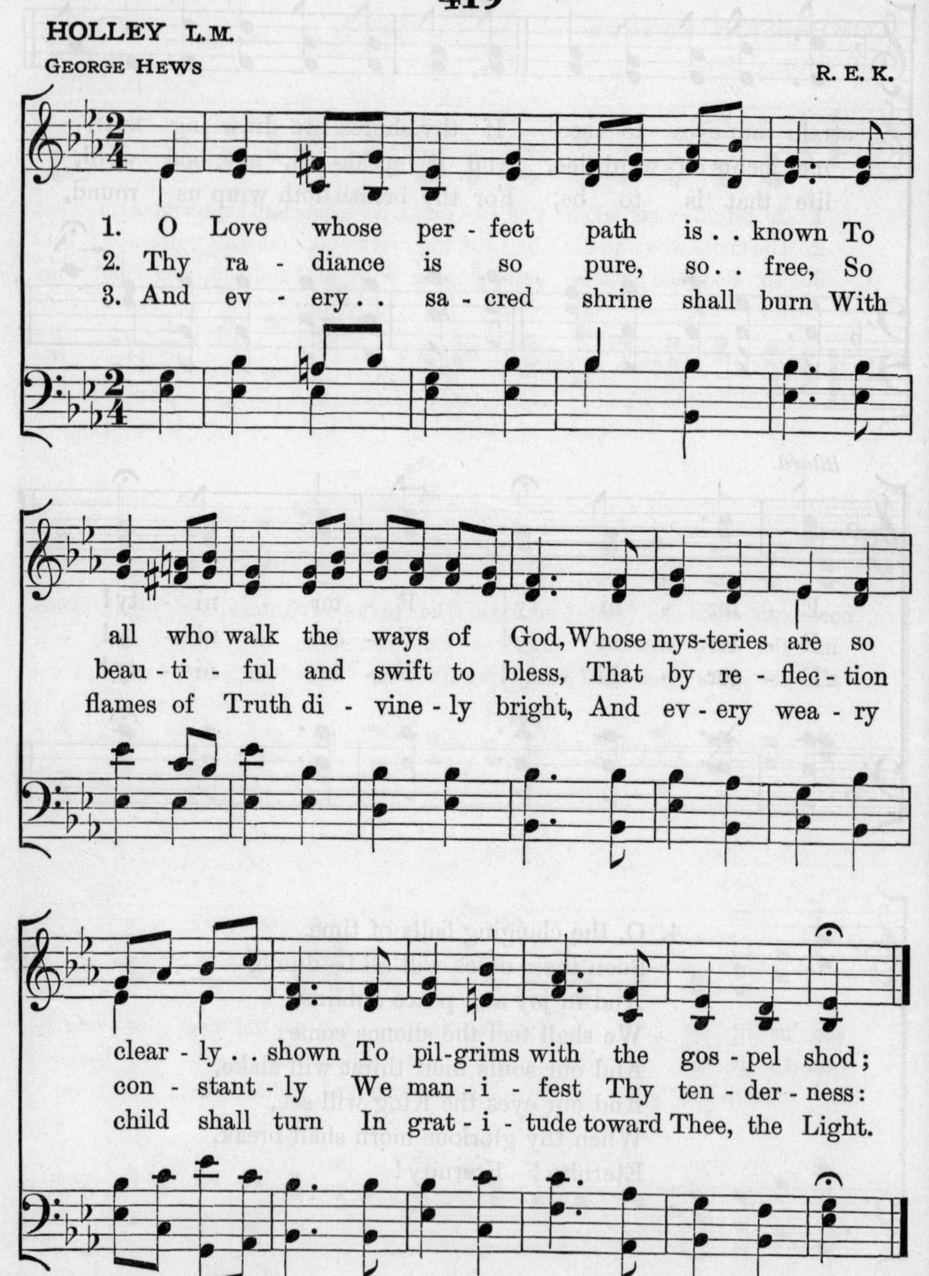
1. O Love whose per - fect path is . . known To all who walk the ways of God, Whose mys-teries are so clear - ly . . shown To pil-grims with the gos - pel shod;
2. Thy ra - diance is so pure, so . . free, So beau - ti - ful and swift to bless, That by re - flec - tion con - stant - ly We man - i - fest Thy ten - der - ness:
3. And ev - ery . . sa - cred shrine shall burn With flames of Truth di - vine - ly bright, And ev - ery wea - ry child shall turn In grat - i - tude toward Thee, the Light.

# 420

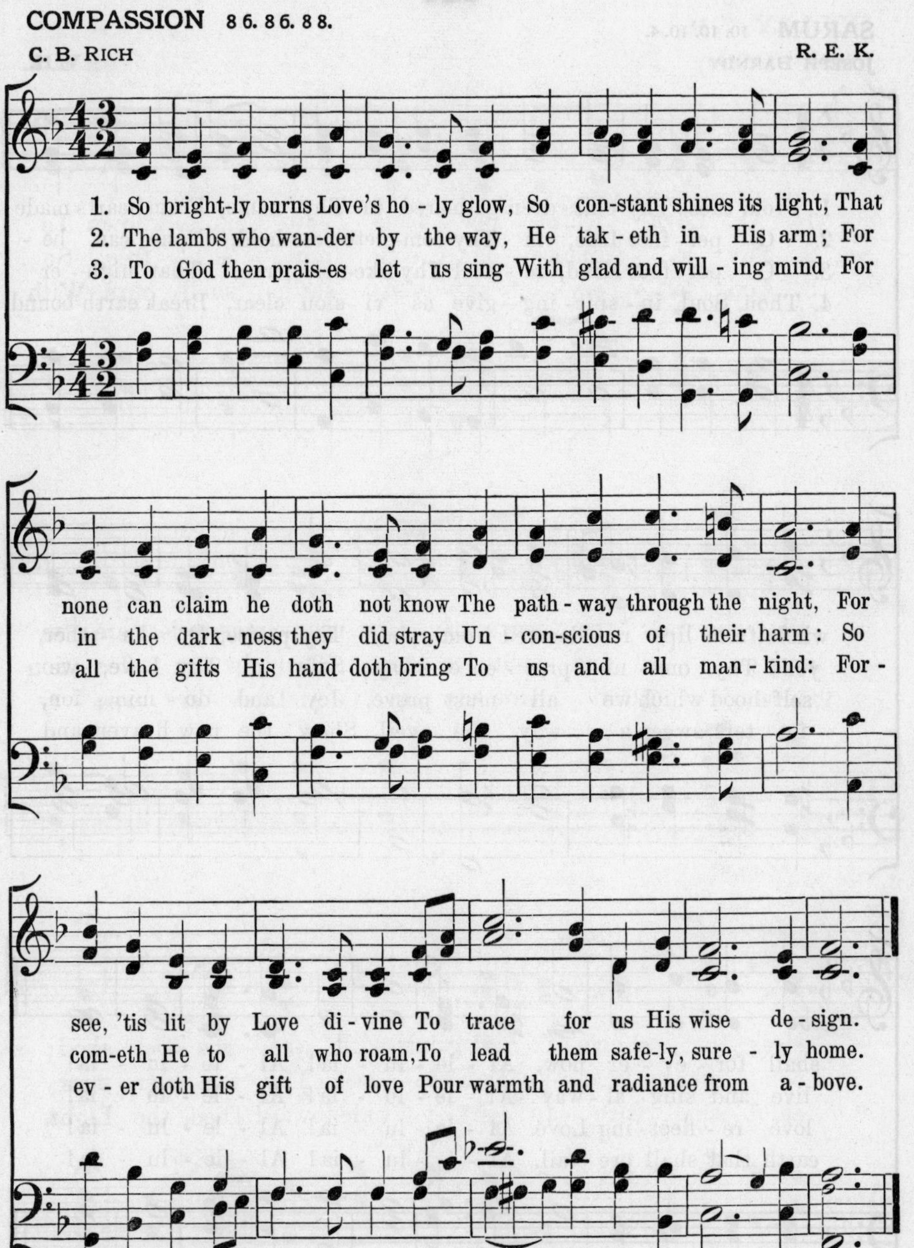
COMPASSION 86. 86. 88.
C. B. RICH
R. E. K.
1. So bright-ly burns Love's ho - ly glow, So con-stant shines its light, That none can claim he doth not know The path - way through the night, For see, 'tis lit by Love di - vine To trace for us His wise de - sign.
2. The lambs who wan-der by the way, He tak - eth in His arm; For in the dark - ness they did stray Un - con-scious of their harm: So com-eth He to all who roam, To lead them safe-ly, sure - ly home.
3. To God then prais-es let us sing With glad and will - ing mind For all the gifts His hand doth bring To us and all man - kind: For - ev - er doth His gift of love Pour warmth and radiance from a - bove.

# 421

SARUM 10. 10. 10. 4.

JOSEPH BARNBY

V. H.

1. From these Thy chil-dren gath-ered in Thy name, From hearts made whole, from lips re-deemed from woe, Thy praise, O Fa-ther, shall for-ev-er flow. Al-le-lu-ia! Al-le-lu-ia!
2. O per-fect Life, in Thy com-plete-ness held, None can be-yond Thy om-ni-pres-ence stray; Safe in Thy Love, we live and sing al-way Al-le-lu-ia! Al-le-lu-ia!
3. O per-fect Mind, re-veal Thy like-ness true, That high-er self-hood which we all must prove, Joy and do-min-ion, love re-flect-ing Love. Al-le-lu-ia! Al-le-lu-ia!
4. Thou, Soul, in-spir-ing—give us vi-sion clear, Break earth-bound fet-ters, sweep a-way the veil, Show the new heaven and earth that shall pre-vail. Al-le-lu-ia! Al-le-lu-ia!

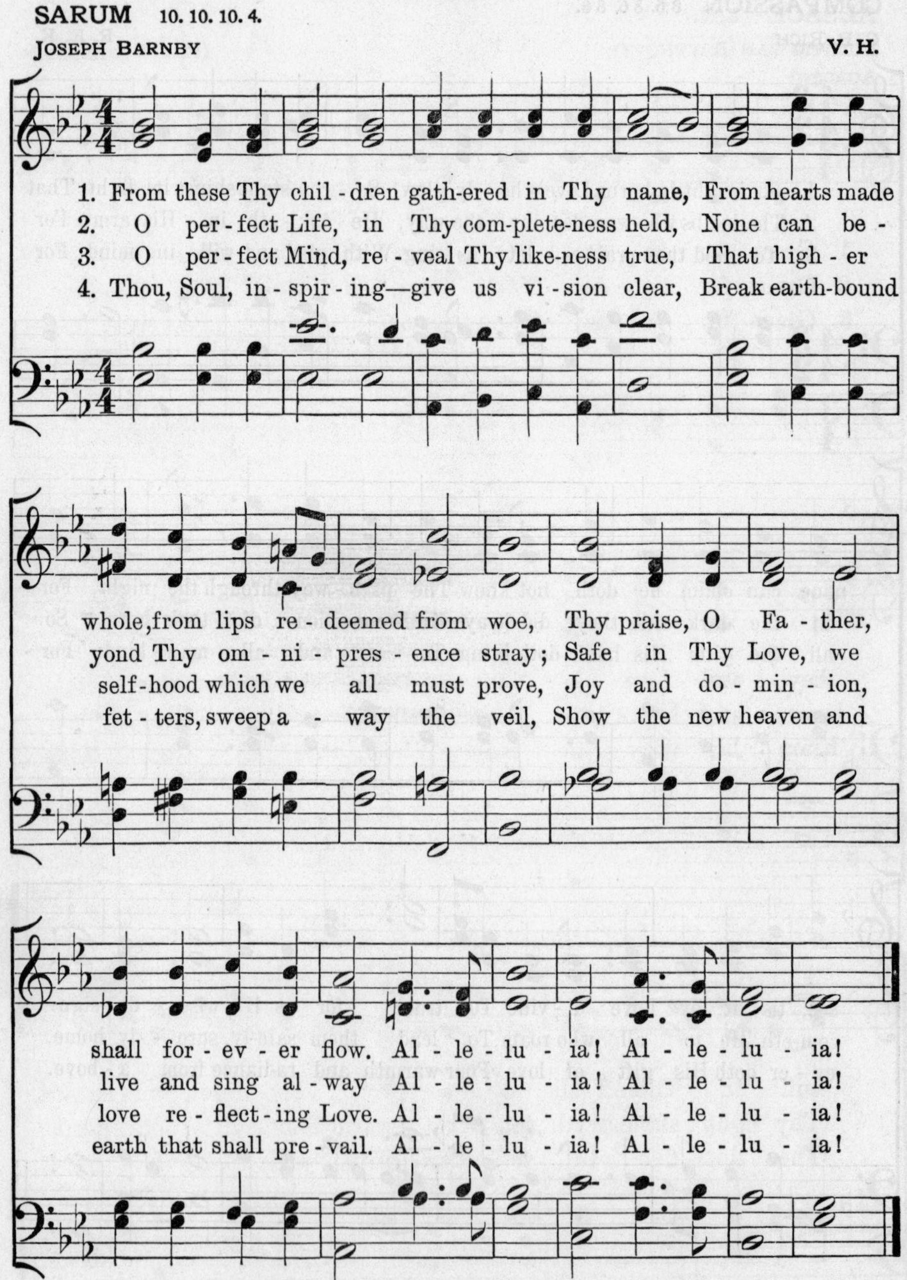

# 422

**ALSACE** L. M.

LUDWIG VAN BEETHOVEN
Arranged

NEMI ROBERTSON

1. Grace for to - day, O Love di - vine, Thee to o -
2. Grace for to - day, Thou Love di - vine, Fam - ish - ing
3. Grace for to - day, Thou Love di - vine, Pa - tient of

bey and love a - lone; Los - ing the mor - tal
hearts and hopes to feed; Blot out all fear, let
heart his way to trace Whose pure af - fec - tions

will in Thine, Find we a joy be - fore un - known.
Thy light shine With ten - der warmth on all our need.
Thee de - fine In ten - der love and per - fect grace.

## 423

**PENITENTIA** 10. 10. 10. 10.

EDWARD DEARLE JAMES J. ROME

1. Give me, O Lord, an un-derstanding heart, That I may learn to know my-self in Thee,.. To spurn the wrong and choose the bet-ter part And thus from sin-ful bondage be set free.
2. Give me, O Lord, a meek and con-trite heart, That I may learn to quell all self-ish pride, Bow-ing be-fore Thee, see Thee as Thou art And 'neath Thy sheltering presence safe-ly hide.
3. Give me, O Lord, a gen-tle, lov-ing heart, That I may learn to be more ten-der, kind,.. And with Thy heal-ing touch, each wound and smart With Christly bands of Love and Truth to bind.

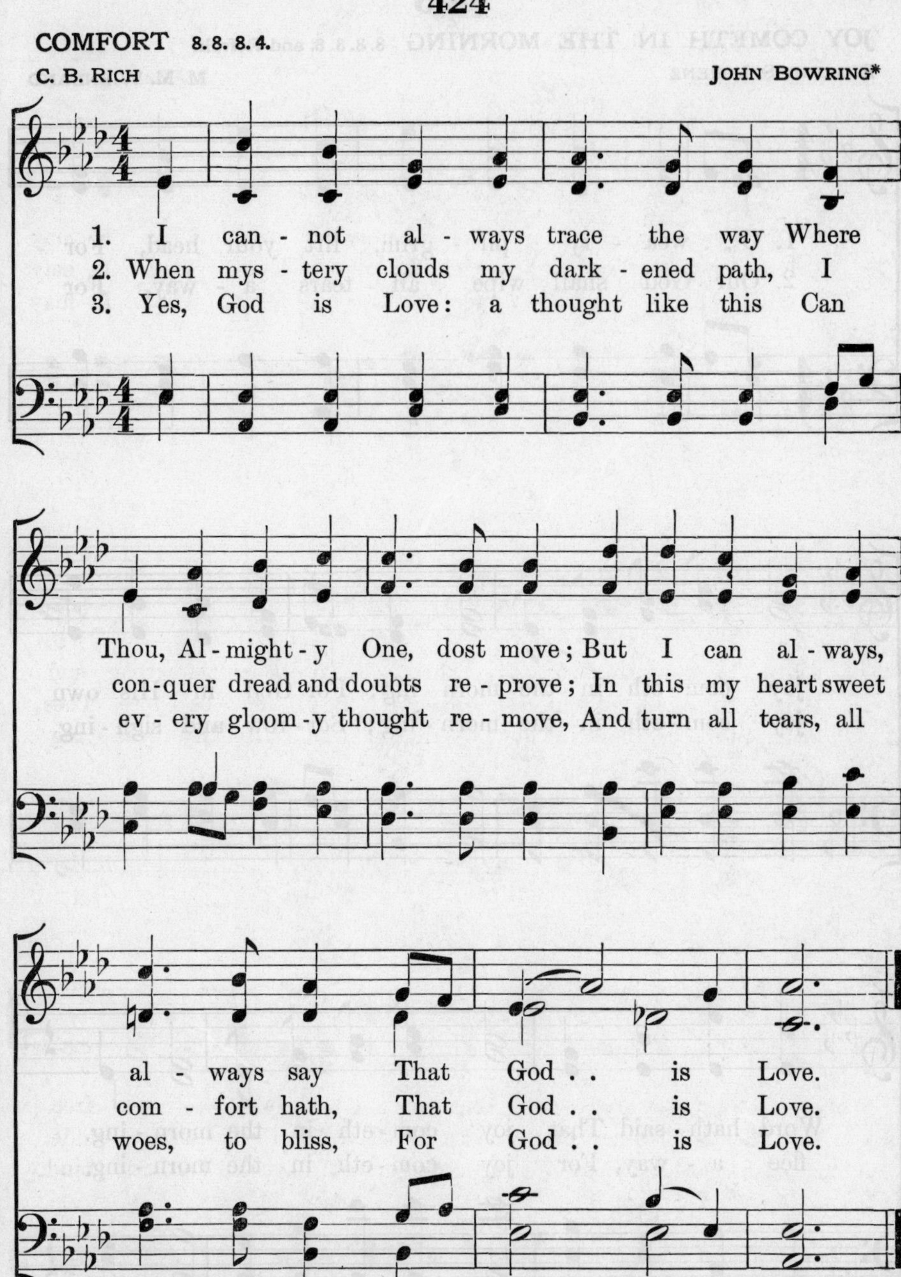
424
COMFORT 8. 8. 8. 4.
C. B. RICH
JOHN BOWRING*
1. I can - not al - ways trace the way Where
2. When mys - tery clouds my dark - ened path, I
3. Yes, God is Love: a thought like this Can
Thou, Al - might - y One, dost move; But I can al - ways,
con - quer dread and doubts re - prove; In this my heart sweet
ev - ery gloom - y thought re - move, And turn all tears, all
al - ways say That God . . is Love.
com - fort hath, That God . . is Love.
woes, to bliss, For God . . is Love.

## JOY COMETH IN THE MORNING 8. 8. 8. 8. and Refrain

EDMUND S. LORENZ — M. M. WIENLAND

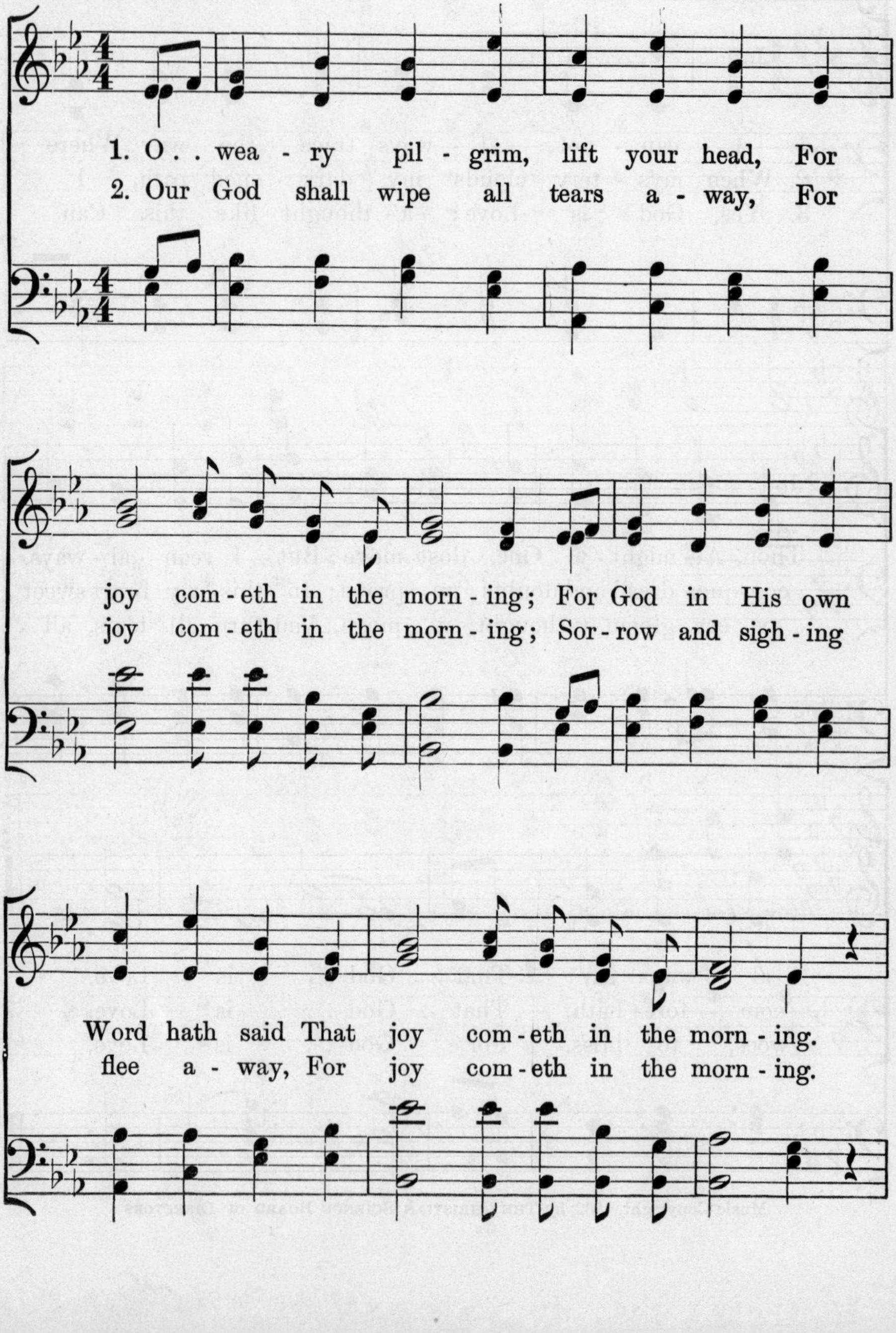

1. O . . wea - ry pil - grim, lift your head, For
2. Our God shall wipe all tears a - way, For

joy com - eth in the morn - ing; For God in His own
joy com - eth in the morn - ing; Sor - row and sigh - ing

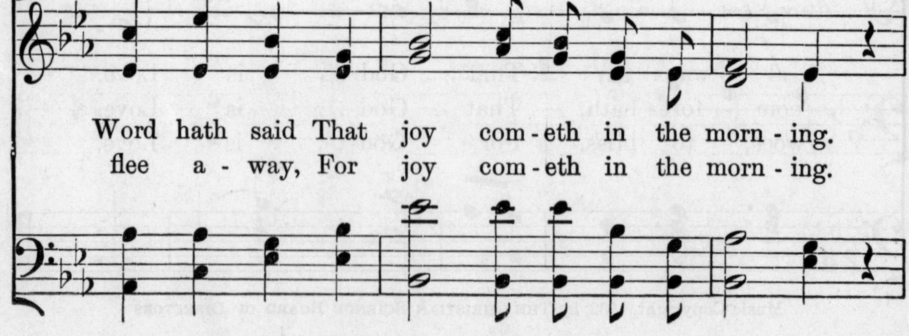
Word hath said That joy com - eth in the morn - ing.
flee a - way, For joy com - eth in the morn - ing.

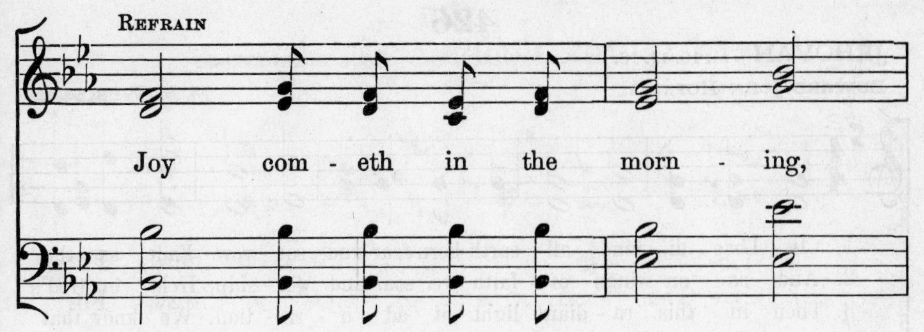
REFRAIN
Joy com - eth in the morn - ing,

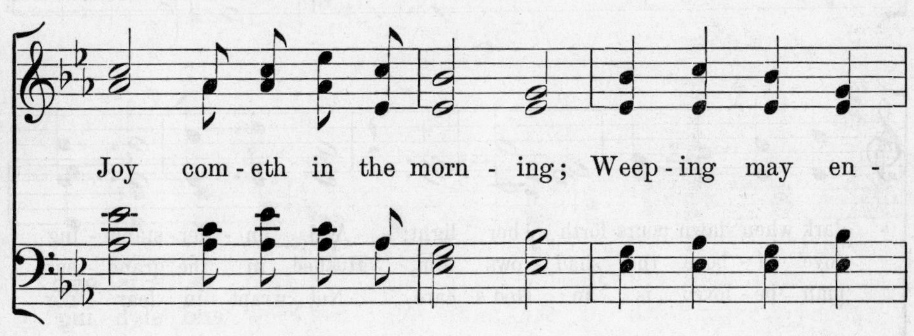
Joy com - eth in the morn - ing; Weep - ing may en -

dure for a night, But joy com - eth in the morn - ing.

# 426

**JEHOVAH** 11. 10. 11. 10.

EDWARD JOHN HOPKINS — S. F. C.

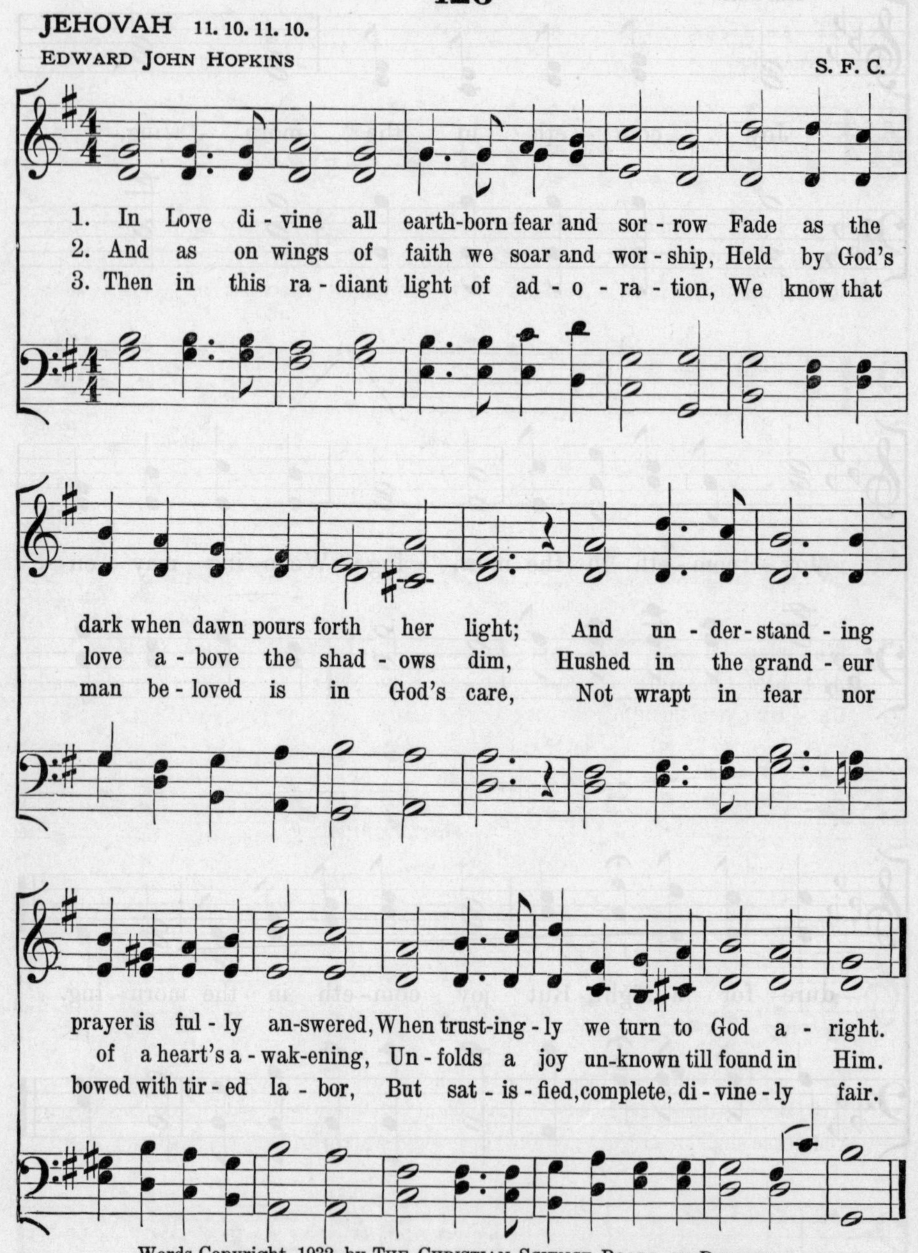

1. In Love di - vine all earth-born fear and sor - row Fade as the
2. And as on wings of faith we soar and wor - ship, Held by God's
3. Then in this ra - diant light of ad - o - ra - tion, We know that
dark when dawn pours forth her light; And un - der - stand - ing
love a - bove the shad - ows dim, Hushed in the grand - eur
man be - loved is in God's care, Not wrapt in fear nor
prayer is ful - ly an-swered, When trust-ing - ly we turn to God a - right.
of a heart's a - wak-ening, Un - folds a joy un-known till found in Him.
bowed with tir - ed la - bor, But sat - is - fied, complete, di - vine - ly fair.

REST 88. 88. 88.

JOHN STAINER — MINNY M. H. AYERS

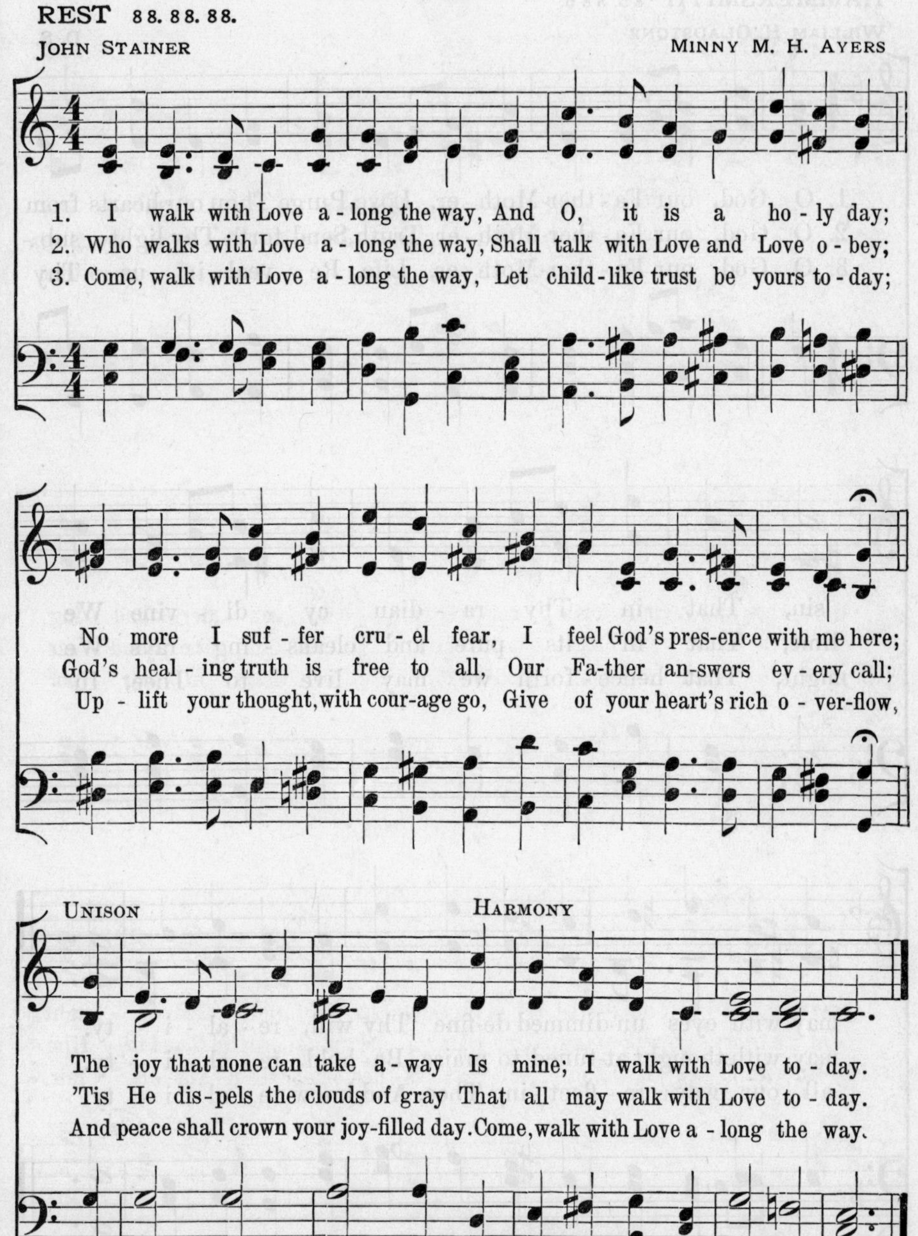
1. I walk with Love a - long the way, And O, it is a ho - ly day;
2. Who walks with Love a - long the way, Shall talk with Love and Love o - bey;
3. Come, walk with Love a - long the way, Let child - like trust be yours to - day;
No more I suf - fer cru - el fear, I feel God's pres-ence with me here;
God's heal - ing truth is free to all, Our Fa-ther an-swers ev - ery call;
Up - lift your thought, with cour-age go, Give of your heart's rich o - ver-flow,
UNISON
HARMONY
The joy that none can take a - way Is mine; I walk with Love to - day.
'Tis He dis-pels the clouds of gray That all may walk with Love to - day.
And peace shall crown your joy-filled day. Come, walk with Love a - long the way.

Music by permission of NOVELLO & Co. Ltd.

# 428

## HAMMERSMITH 86. 886.

WILLIAM H. GLADSTONE

D. S.

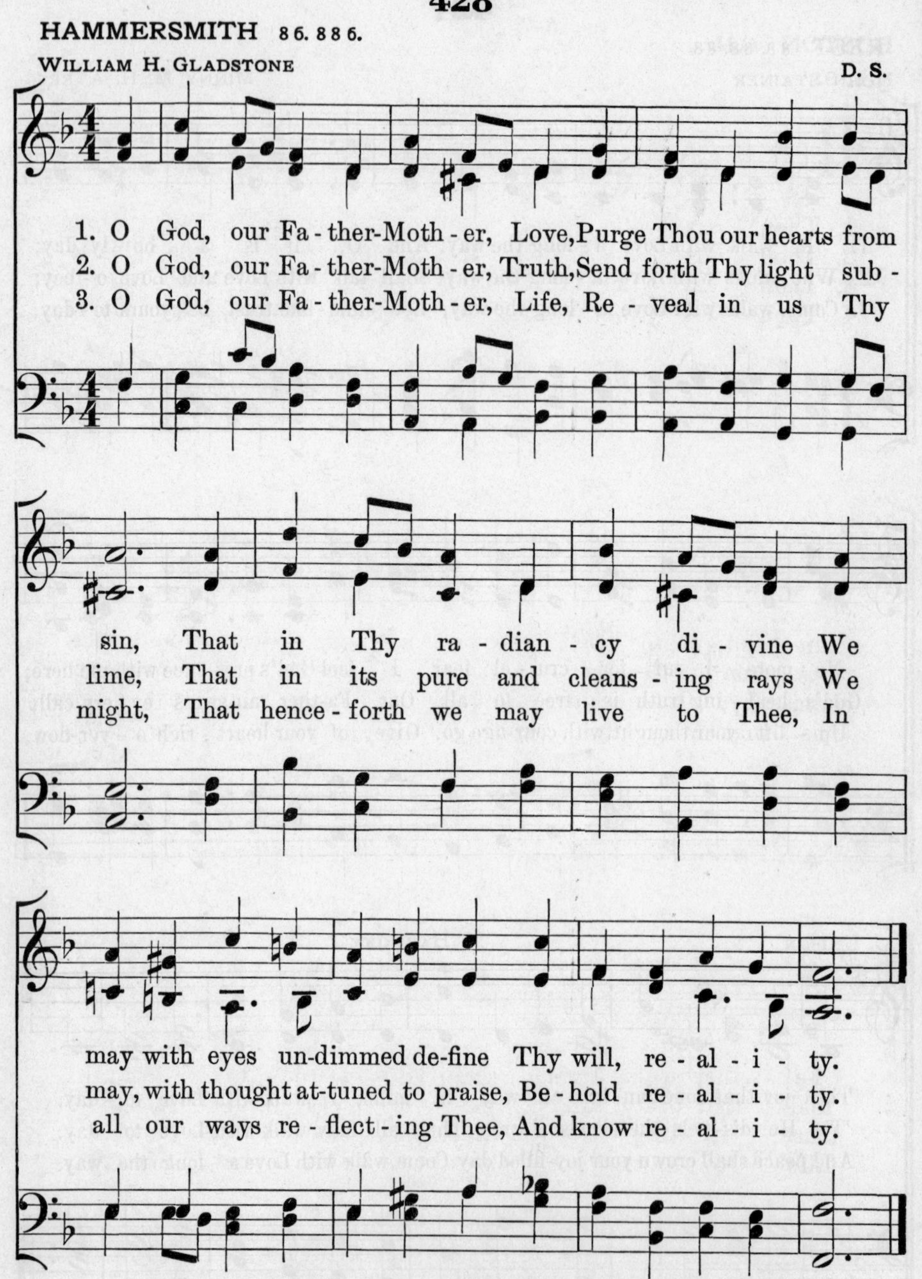
1. O God, our Fa - ther-Moth - er, Love, Purge Thou our hearts from sin, That in Thy ra - dian - cy di - vine We may with eyes un-dimmed de-fine Thy will, re - al - i - ty.
2. O God, our Fa - ther-Moth - er, Truth, Send forth Thy light sub - lime, That in its pure and cleans - ing rays We may, with thought at-tuned to praise, Be - hold re - al - i - ty.
3. O God, our Fa - ther-Moth - er, Life, Re - veal in us Thy might, That hence - forth we may live to Thee, In all our ways re - flect - ing Thee, And know re - al - i - ty.

BOSTON C. M.

E. E. S.

1. Thou art the Way: to thee a - lone From
2. Thou art the Truth: thy word a - lone True
3. Thou art the Life: the rend - ing tomb Pro -
4. Thou art the Way, the Truth, the Life: Grant
sin and death we flee; And he who would the
wis - dom doth im - part; Thou on - ly canst un -
claims thy con-quering arm; And those who put their
us that Way to know, That Truth to trust, that
Fa - ther seek, Must seek Him, Lord, by thee.
fold that Truth, And pu - ri - fy the heart.
trust in thee Nor death nor hell shall harm.
Life to learn, Whose joys e - ter - nal flow.

# INDEXES

# TUNES, ALPHABETICAL

| NAME OF TUNE | NO. | METER | COMPOSER OR SOURCE |
|---|---|---|---|
| Abendlied | 43 | 7.6.7.6.D. | Franz Schubert |
| Abends | 133 | L.M. | Herbert S. Oakeley |
| Abridge | 333 | C.M. | Isaac Smith |
| Ach Gott und Herr | 393 | 8.7.8.7. | Melody by C. Peter |
| Adeste fideles | 123 | 11.11.11.11. | *Composer Unknown* |
| Affection | 219 | L.M. | *Greenwood's Psalmody*, 1838 |
| Alford | 65 | 76.76.76.86. | John B. Dykes |
| All Saints New | 374 | 7.6.7.6.D. | Henry S. Cutler |
| All Souls | 195 | 10.10.10.10. | John Yoakley |
| Alleluia | 171 | 8.7.8.7.D. | Samuel S. Wesley |
| Alma | 154 | 9.8.9.8. | Lyman Brackett |
| Almsgiving | 190 | 8.8.8.4. | John B. Dykes |
| Alsace | 422 | L.M. | Ludwig van Beethoven |
| Altid frejdig naar du gaar | 141 | 7.7.7.7. | Christoph E. F. Weyse |
| Amsterdam | 296 | 7.6.7.6. REF. | James Nares |
| Ancient of Days | 202 | 11.10.11.10. | Horatio W. Parker |
| Angels' Song | 342 | C.M.D. | Mendelssohn. Arr. by Hopkins |
| Angelus | 214 | L.M. | *Cantica Spiritualia*, 1847 |
| Antioch | 417 | C.M. | Händel. Arr. by L. Mason |
| Ar Hyd y Nos | 350 | 84.84.88.84. | *Welsh Melody* |
| Arlington | 372 | C.M. | Thomas A. Arne |
| Armenian Hymn | 113 | 77.745 | *Armenian Liturgy* |
| Atkey | 157 | 87.87.11. | George Dyson |
| Auch jetzt macht Gott | 74 | 86.86.88. | *Koch's Choralbuch*, 1816 |
| Aughton | 95 | L.M. REF. | William B. Bradbury |
| Aurelia | 75 | 7.6.7.6.D. | Samuel S. Wesley |
| Austria | 71 | 8.7.8.7.D. | Franz Joseph Haydn |
| Avon | 266 | C.M. | Hugh Wilson |
| Aynhoe | 16 | S.M. | James Nares |
| Azmon | 320 | C.M. | Carl G. Gläser. Arranged |
| Azmon New | 409 | C.M. | Carl G. Gläser. Adapted |
| | | | |
| Babylon's Streams | 353 | L.M. | Thomas Campion |
| Bairn | 318 | 98.88 4. | *Danish Folk Melody* |
| Ballerma | 126 | C.M. | *Spanish Melody* |
| Bal(l)erma | 403 | C.M. | *Spanish Melody* |
| Bangor | 348 | C.M. | William Tans'ur |
| Beatitudo | 284 | C.M. | John B. Dykes |
| Beecher | 276 | 8.7.8.7.D. | John Zundel |
| Belhaven | 356 | 11.10.11.10. | Thomas C. L. Pritchard |
| Belmont | 205 | C.M. | *Gardiner's Sacred Melodies*, 1812<br>Reharmonized by G. Thalben-Ball |
| | | | |
| Benediction | 208 | 10.10.10.10. | Edward J. Hopkins |
| Benevento | 72 | 7.7.7.7.D. | Samuel Webbe |
| Benevento (Revised) | 405 | 7.7.7.7.D. | Samuel Webbe |
| Benevolence | 309 | 7.5.7.5.D. | E. Norman Greenwood |
| Bentley | 251 | 7.6.7.6.D. | John P. Hullah |
| Bera | 99 | 88.8.88.8. | J. E. Gould. Arr. by W. E. Young |

| NAME OF TUNE | NO. | METER | COMPOSER OR SOURCE |
|---|---|---|---|
| Berno | **249** | 7.6.7.6.D. | Arthur H. Mann |
| Bethany | **192** | 64.64.66.64. | Lowell Mason |
| Bethany | **277** | 8.7.8.7.D. | Henry Smart |
| Bethlehem | **310** | 7.7.7.7.D. REF. | Mendelssohn. Arr. by Cummings |
| Beulah | **131** | C.M. | George M. Garrett |
| Birling | **91** | L.M. | *From an early 19th century MS.* |
| Bishopthorpe | **142** | C.M. | Jeremiah Clark |
| Bohemian Hymn | **189** | 7.6.7.6.D. | *Bohemian Brethren* |
| Boston | **429** | C.M. | E. Elizabeth Siedhoff |
| Bowen | **185** | 9.8.8.8. | Arr. from Franz Joseph Haydn |
| Bristol | **347** | C.M. | Edward Hodges |
| Brockham | **235** | L.M. | Jeremiah Clark |
| Bromley | **388** | L.M. | Jeremiah Clark |
| Bromsgrove | **106** | C.M. | Harmonized by M. M. Bridges *Psalmodia Evangelica*, 1789 |
| Burford | **321** | C.M. | *Chetham's Psalmody*, 1718 |
| Caithness | **215** | C.M. | *Scottish Psalter*, 1635 |
| Camberwell | **124** | S.M. | *European Psalmist*, 1872 |
| Campfields | **104** | 86.886. | Mark J. Monk |
| Canonbury | **322** | L.M. | Robert Schumann. Arranged |
| Capel | **242** | C.M. | *English Traditional Carol Melody* |
| Capetown | **67** | 7.7.7.3. | Friedrich Filitz |
| Carlisle | **396** | S.M. | Charles Lockhart |
| Carne | **366** | 7.7.7.7. | From Michael Praetorius |
| Carol | **9** | 86.86.6. | Arr. from David G. Corner by H. Walford Davies |
| Carol Melody | **237** | 8.7.8.7. | *14th Century Carol* |
| Charity | **180** | 556.866. | C. F. Jæhnigen |
| Charterhouse | **345** | 11.10.11.10. | David Evans |
| Cheerfulness | **141** | 7.7.7.7. | Christoph E. F. Weyse |
| Cheshire | **286** | C.M. | *Este's Psalter*, 1592. Arr. by Wood |
| Chesterfield | **38** | C.M. | T. Haweis. Arr. by S. Webbe, Jr. |
| Christmas | **362** | C.M. | Georg Friedrich Händel |
| Christmas Carol | **223** | 86.86.76.86. | H. Walford Davies |
| Christmas Morn | **24** | 8.4.8.4. | Albert F. Conant |
| Church | **176** | 88.88.888. | Ludvig M. Lindeman |
| Church Triumphant | **290** | L.M. | James W. Elliott |
| Clearway | **400** | C.M. | Henry W. Baker. Arranged |
| Colchester | **182** | C.M. | Henry Purcell |
| Comfort | **424** | 8.8.8.4. | C. B. Rich |
| Communion | **298** | 10 7.77 9. | Lyman Brackett |
| Compassion | **420** | 86.86.88. | C. B. Rich |
| Concord | **306** | 7.5.7.5.D. | William Lyman Johnson |
| Congregation | **130** | 87.87.888. | Harnack O. C. Zinck (?) |
| Consolation | **174** | 12.10.11.10. | F. Mendelssohn-Bartholdy. Arr. |
| Consolation | **194** | C.M. | Arr. from Ludwig van Beethoven |
| Consolator | **40** | 11.10.11.10. | Samuel Webbe |
| Constancy | **229** | L.M.D. | F. Mendelssohn-Bartholdy. Arr. |
| Contemplation | **194** | C.M. | Arr. from Ludwig van Beethoven |
| Corinth | **90** | 87.87.87. | *Samuel Webbe's Motetts or Antiphons*, 1792 |
| Coronation | **86** | C.M. | Oliver Holden |
| Courage | **380** | 8.7.8.7. | *University of Wales.* Arr. by Davies |
| Coventry | **327** | C.M. | *English Melody.* Arr. by Root |
| Creation | **170** | L.M.D. | Franz Joseph Haydn |
| Crispinian | **56** | L.M. | John W. Ivimey |
| Cross of Jesus | **102** | 8.7.8.7. | John Stainer |
| Crusader's Hymn | **275** | 668.668. | *Silesian Melody.* Arr. by Willis |

| NAME OF TUNE | NO. | METER | COMPOSER OR SOURCE |
|---|---|---|---|
| Dalehurst | **410** | C.M. | Arthur Cottman |
| Dalkeith | **297** | 10.10.10.10. | Thomas Hewlett |
| Das walt' Gott | **233** | L.M. | Daniel Vetter<br>Harmony from J. S. Bach |
| David's Harp | **100** | 88.88.88. | Robert King in "*The Divine Companion*," 1772 |
| Day of Rest | **196** | 7.6.7.6.D. | James W. Elliott |
| Dedham | **105** | C.M. | William Gardiner |
| Deerhurst | **370** | 8.7.8.7.D. | James Langran |
| Den store, hvite flokk | **19** | 8.8.8.6.D. | *Norwegian Folk Melody* |
| Den store Mester kommer | **15** | 7.6.8.6. | C. Christian Hoffman |
| Dennis | **22** | 6.4.6.4.(10.10.) | G. Thalben-Ball |
| Dennis | **402** | S.M. | Hans Georg Naegeli |
| Diademata | **312** | S.M.D. | George J. Elvey |
| Dix | **35** | 77.77.77. | Conrad Kocher. Arranged |
| Dominica | **92** | S.M. | Herbert S. Oakeley |
| Dominus regit me | **330** | 8.7.8.7. | John B. Dykes |
| Dransfield | **26** | 8.4.8.4. | G. Thalben-Ball |
| Duke Street | **325** | L.M. | John Hatton |
| Easter | **413** | 8.7.8.7.D. | *Arr. from Lyra Davidica,* 1708 |
| Eeuwig dank en eere | **73** | 10 7.10 7.10 10.77. | *Canzuns Spirituelas, Celerina,* 1765 |
| Egerton | **308** | 7.5.7.5.D. | G. Thalben-Ball |
| Ein' feste Burg. (Key of C) | **10** | 87.87.66.667. | Martin Luther |
| Ein' feste Burg. (Key of D) | **411** | 87.87.66.667. | Martin Luther |
| Eisenach | **80** | L.M. | Melody by Johann H. Schein<br>Harmony from J. S. Bach |
| Elgin | **64** | 11.10.11.10. | George Dyson |
| Elijah | **118** | 7.7.7.7. | Arr. from Mendelssohn |
| Ellacombe | **226** | C.M.D. | *Mainz Gesangbuch,* 1833 |
| Ellers | **208** | 10.10.10.10. | Edward J. Hopkins |
| Ellesdie | **109** | 8.7.8.7.D. | W. A. Mozart. Arr. by H. P. Main |
| Ely | **387** | L.M. | Thomas Turton |
| Epsom | **3** | C.M. | *Arnold's Complete Psalter,* 1756 |
| Erin | **339** | C.M. | *Old Irish Hymn Melody* |
| Ermuntre dich | **13** | 88.88.88. | Johann Schop |
| Es ist ein' Ros' entsprungen | **152** | 76.76.676. | *German Melody,* 1599. Arranged |
| Es ist kein Tag | **191** | 8.8.8.4. | Johann D. Meyer |
| Eschol | **111** | L.M. | George M. Garrett |
| Eternity | **418** | 77.77.77.744. | Philip Paul Bliss |
| Etherington | **132** | C.M. | H. Walford Davies |
| Eucharistica | **172** | 10.10.10.10. | Robert P. Stewart |
| Evan | **357** | C.M. | William H. Havergal |
| Evan New | **407** | C.M. | Arr. from W. H. Havergal |
| Evensong | **156** | 9.8.9.8. | Arthur C. Heberden |
| Eventide | **7** | 10.10.10.10. | William H. Monk |
| Eventide | **8** | 10.10.10.10. | William H. Monk |
| Everton | **29** | 8.7.8.7.D. | Henry Smart |
| Ewing | **148** | 7.6.7.6.D. | Alexander Ewing |
| Expectation | **209** | 10.10.10.10. | Andreas P. Berggreen |
| Faith | **301** | 10 7.77 9. | G. O'Connor-Morris |
| Falmouth | **36** | C.M. | Walter E. Young |
| Federal Street | **352** | L.M. | Henry K. Oliver |
| Feniton Court | **177** | 87.87.87. | Edward J. Hopkins |
| Festus | **138** | L.M. | *From a German Chorale* |
| Fingal | **260** | C.M. | James S. Anderson |
| Firmament | **203** | L.M.D. | H. Walford Davies |
| Forest Green | **5** | C.M.D. | *English Traditional Melody* |
| Fortitude | **161** | 8.4.8.4. | Walter E. Young |

| NAME OF TUNE | NO. | METER | COMPOSER OR SOURCE |
|---|---|---|---|
| Fragment | 316 | C.M. | *From The Sarum Gradual*, 1527<br>Arr. by H. Walford Davies |
| Frainsby | 39 | L.M. | George Dyson |
| Franconia | 44 | S.M. | *König's Choralbuch*<br>Arr. by W. H. Havergal |
| Freedom | 302 | 10 7.77 9. | E. Norman Greenwood |
| Fulda | 238 | L.M. | *Gardiner's Sacred Melodies*, 1812 |
| Fulfillment | 15 | 7.6.8.6. | C. Christian Hoffman |
| Galilee | 259 | L.M. | Philip Armes |
| Galliard | 53 | 7.7.7.7. | Melody by John Dowland |
| Germany | 238 | L.M. | *Gardiner's Sacred Melodies*, 1812 |
| Gerontius | 408 | C.M. | John B. Dykes |
| Gladness (Glädje utan Gud ej finnes) | 263 | 8.7.8.7.D. | Gustaf Düben |
| Gloaming | 160 | 8.4.8.4.D. | John Stainer |
| Glück zu Kreuz | 103 | 8.7.8.7. | *Darmstadt Gesangbuch*, 1698 |
| Golden Sheaves | 392 | 8.7.8.7.D. | Arthur S. Sullivan |
| Gonfalon Royal | 271 | L.M. | Percy C. Buck |
| Gosterwood | 377 | 7.6.7.6.D. | *English Traditional Melody* |
| Gott des Himmels | 166 | 8.7.8.7. | Heinrich Albert |
| Gott des Himmels | 167 | 8.7.8.7. | Albert. Harmonized by Bach |
| Gott will's machen | 55 | 8.7.8.7. | J. Ludwig Steiner |
| Gottlob | 32 | 86.86.88. | Johann Sebastian Bach |
| Grace | 76 | 8.7.8.7.D. | Per U. Stenhammar |
| Grandpont | 21 | 6.4.6.4.(10.10.) | John Stainer |
| Gratitude | 73 | 10 7.10 7.10 10.77. | *Canzuns Spirituelas, Celerina*, 1765 |
| Greenland | 120 | 7.6.7.6.D. | J. Michael Haydn |
| Guidance | 304 | 7.5.7.5.D. | Lyman Brackett |
| Halle | 88 | 77.77.77. | *Schicht's Choralbuch*, 1819 |
| Hamburg | 386 | L.M. | *From a Gregorian Chant* |
| Hammersmith | 428 | 86.886. | William H. Gladstone |
| Hampstead | 232 | 88.886. | H. Walford Davies |
| Hanover | 236 | 10.10.11.11. | William Croft |
| Haydn | 269 | C.M.D. | Franz Joseph Haydn |
| Heath | 183 | S.M. | *Mason and Webb's Collection*, 1850 |
| Heavenward | 136 | C.M.D. | *Irish Melody*. Arr. by Davies |
| Hendon | 186 | 7.7.7.7. | César H. A. Malan |
| Herongate | 45 | L.M. | *English Traditional Melody* |
| Herre, jeg har handlet ille | 84 | 87.87.88. | Ludvig M. Lindeman |
| Herren sig i nåd förklarar | 76 | 8.7.8.7.D. | Per U. Stenhammar |
| Herzlich thut mich verlangen | 252 | 7.6.7.6.D. | Hassler. Harmonized by Bach |
| Hesperus | 244 | L.M. | Henry Baker |
| Holley | 419 | L.M. | George Hews |
| Holy Trinity | 147 | C.M. | Joseph Barnby |
| Home | 34 | L.M. | Arr. from W. A. Mozart |
| Homeland | 245 | 7.6.7.6.D. | Arthur S. Sullivan |
| Horbury | 193 | 64.64.664. | John B. Dykes |
| Horsley | 383 | C.M. | William Horsley |
| Houghton | 294 | 77.77.77. | Samuel S. Wesley |
| Huddersfield | 173 | 7.7.7.5. | Walter Parratt |
| Hursley | 227 | L.M. | *Schicht's Choralbuch*, 1819 |
| Hussite Hymn | 378 | 66.66.3. | *Traditional* |
| Hyfrydol | 175 | 8.7.8.7.D. | Rowland H. Prichard |
| I Love to Tell the Story | 414 | 7.6.7.6.D. REF. | William G. Fischer |
| Illsley | 129 | L.M. | John Bishop |
| Ilsley | 97 | 8.7.8.7.D. | Frank G. Ilsley |

| NAME OF TUNE | NO. | METER | COMPOSER OR SOURCE |
|---|---|---|---|
| In Babilone | **98** | 8.7.8.7.D. | *Dutch Traditional Melody* |
| Infinitas | **27** | 8.4.8.4. | Percy Whitlock |
| Innocents | **83** | 7.7.7.7. | *Old French Melody.* Arr. by Smith |
| Innsbruck | **361** | 776.778. | H. Isaac. Harmonized by Bach |
| Integer vitae | **179** | 11.12.6.7.6. | Friedrich F. Flemming |
| Irish | **145** | C.M. | *Irish Melody*, 1749 |
| Italian Hymn (Moscow) | **346** | 664.66.64. | Arr. from Felice de Giardini |
| Italian Hymn | **401** | 664.66.64. | Arr. from Felice de Giardini |
| | | | |
| Jehovah | **426** | 11.10.11.10 | Edward John Hopkins |
| Jesu, Jesu, du mein Hirt | **89** | 77.77.77. | Melody by Paul Heinlein<br>Harmonized by G. H. Palmer |
| Joy | **58** | 8.7.8.7.D. | Arr. from Ludwig van Beethoven |
| Joy Cometh | **425** | 8.8.8.8. REF. | Edmund S. Lorenz |
| | | | |
| Kærlighed fra Gud | **180** | 556.866. | C. F. Jæhnigen |
| Kingly Vale | **81** | 87.87.47. | Hugh P. Allen |
| King's Lynn | **78** | 7.6.7.6.D. | *English Traditional Melody* |
| Kingsfold | **270** | C.M.D. | *English Traditional Melody* |
| Kington | **25** | 8.4.8.4. | F. Llewellyn Edwards |
| Kirken den er et gammelt hus | **176** | 88.88.888. | Ludvig M. Lindeman |
| Kjærlighet er lysets kilde | **178** | 87.87.88.77. | Ludvig M. Lindeman |
| | | | |
| Langran | **390** | 10.10.10.10. | James Langran |
| Lansdowne | **220** | L.M. | E. Norman Greenwood |
| Lauda anima | **280** | 87.87.87. | John Goss<br>Reharmonized by G. Thalben-Ball |
| Laundon | **300** | 10 7.77 9. | G. Thalben-Ball |
| Leoni | **371** | 6.6.8.4.D. | *Hebrew Melody* |
| Liebster Jesu | **85** | 78.78.88. | Johann R. Ahle. Arr. by Bach |
| Light | **178** | 87.87.88.77. | Ludvig M. Lindeman |
| Lille Guds Barn | **318** | 98.884. | *Danish Folk Melody* |
| Lime Street | **279** | 11.10.11.10. | Geoffrey Shaw |
| Limpsfield | **210** | 10.10.10.10. | Andrew Freeman |
| Linwood | **416** | L.M. | Gioacchino A. Rossini. Arranged |
| Liverpool | **127** | C.M. | Robert Wainwright<br>Harmonized by S. S. Wesley |
| Llanfair | **307** | 7.5.7.5.D. | Arr. from Robert Williams |
| Llansannan | **116** | 8.7.8.7.D. | *Welsh Hymn Melody* |
| Lobe den Herren | **283** | 14.14.47.8. | *Stralsund Gesangbuch*, 1665 |
| Lobt Gott | **101** | 86.86.6. | Nicolas Herman |
| Londonderry | **412** | 11.10.11.10.D. | *Traditional Irish Melody* |
| Love | **30** | 86.86.88. | Walter E. Young |
| Lux benigna | **169** | 10 4.10 4.10.10. | John B. Dykes |
| Lux Eoi | **115** | 8.7.8.7.D. | Arthur S. Sullivan |
| Lyons | **18** | 11.11.11.11. | J. Michael Haydn |
| | | | |
| Manna | **46** | 7.7.7.7. | Arr. from Louis M. Gottschalk |
| Manoah | **121** | C.M. | Arr. from Gioacchino A. Rossini |
| Marching | **364** | 8.7.8.7. | Martin Shaw |
| Martyrdom | **266** | C.M. | Hugh Wilson |
| Maryton | **234** | L.M. | H. Percy Smith |
| Meirionydd | **313** | 7.6.7.6.D. | *Welsh Hymn Melody* |
| Melcombe | **6** | L.M. | Samuel Webbe |
| Melita | **12** | 88.88.88. | John B. Dykes |
| Mendip | **87** | C.M. | *English Traditional Melody* |
| Mendon | **228** | L.M. | *Old German Melody.* Arr. by Dyer |
| Merton | **79** | 8.7.8.7. | William H. Monk |
| Metzler | **367** | C.M. | Richard Redhead |

| NAME OF TUNE | NO. | METER | COMPOSER OR SOURCE |
|---|---|---|---|
| Missionary Chant | 218 | L.M. | Heinrich C. Zeuner |
| Missionary Hymn | 2 | 7.6.7.6.D. | Lowell Mason |
| Mooz Zur | 281 | 77.77.67.67. | *Old Hebrew Melody* |
| Morecambe | 207 | 10.10.10.10. | Frederick C. Atkinson |
| | | | Arr. by Albert F. Conant |
| Morning Hymn | 384 | L.M. | François H. Barthélémon |
| Morning Light | 335 | 7.6.7.6.D. | George J. Webb |
| Mornington | 70 | S.M. | Garret Wellesley |
| Moscow | 346 | 664.66.64. | Arr. from Felice de Giardini |
| Moseley | 267 | 6.6.6.6. | Henry Smart |
| Mount Calvary | 144 | C.M. | Robert P. Stewart |
| Munich | 77 | 7.6.7.6.D. | *Meiningen Gesangbuch*, 1693 |
| | | | Harmonized by Mendelssohn |
| Nativity | 164 | C.M. | Henry Lahee |
| Need | 137 | 6.4.6.4. REF. | Robert Lowry |
| Nestling | 332 | 8 6.8 6.8 8 8. | August H. Winding |
| Neumark | 216 | 98.98.88. | G. Neumark. Harmonized by Bach |
| Newbury | 146 | C.M. | *English Traditional Melody* |
| Newcastle | 206 | 86.886. | Henry L. Morley |
| Nicaea | 117 | 11.12.12.10. | John B. Dykes. |
| Nicht so traurig | 295 | 77.77.77. | Attributed to J. S. Bach |
| Noel | 373 | C.M.D. | *Traditional.* Arr. by Sullivan |
| Norton | 254 | 8.4.8.4. | Lyman Brackett |
| Nottingham | 47 | 7.7.7.7. | Attr. to W. A. Mozart. Arranged |
| Nox praecessit | 261 | C.M. | John B. Calkin |
| Nun danket | 199 | 67.67.66.66. | Johann Crüger. Harmonized by Mendelssohn |
| Nun danket all | 287 | C.M. | Johann Crüger |
| Nun ruhen alle Wälder | 361 | 776.778. | H. Isaac. Harmonized by Bach |
| O christliche Herzen | 389 | 12.11.12.11. | *Portnersches Gesangbuch*, 1831 |
| O Jesu | 311 | 86.86.88. | *Hirschberg Gesangbuch*, 1741 |
| Oblation | 257 | 8.4.8.4. | Percy Whitlock |
| Old Hundredth | 1,62 | L.M. | *Genevan Psalter*, 1551. Arranged |
| Old Hundredth (Original) | 63 | L.M. | *Genevan Psalter*, 1551 |
| Old 124th | 108 | 10.10.10.10. | *Genevan Psalter*, 1551. Arranged |
| Oldown | 256 | 8.4.8.4.D. | Basil Harwood |
| Olmutz | 404 | S.M. | Arr. by Lowell Mason |
| Ombersley | 243 | L.M. | William H. Gladstone |
| Orientis partibus | 114 | 7.7.7.7. | *Old French Melody* |
| Palms of Glory | 395 | 7.7.7.7. | William D. Maclagan |
| Park Street | 59 | L.M. | Frederick M. A. Venua |
| Paschal (Påskemorgen slukker sorgen) | 291 | 77.77.77. | Ludvig M. Lindeman |
| Pater Noster | 4 | C.M. | Percy C. Buck |
| Peace | 93 | L.M. | Arr. from W. A. Mozart |
| Peacefield | 341 | 7.7.7.7. | *Ancient Irish Melody* |
| | | | Harmonized by D. F. R. Wilson |
| Penitentia | 423 | 10.10.10.10. | Edward Dearle |
| Pentatone | 159 | C.M.D. | H. Walford Davies |
| Pentecost | 60 | L.M. | William Boyd |
| Philippine | 363 | L.M. | R. E. Roberts |
| Pilgrim | 415 | 9.11.10.10. REF. | *Italian Melody* |
| Pixham | 20 | L.M. | Horatio W. Parker |
| Pleasant Street | 253 | 8.4.8.4.D. | William Lyman Johnson |
| Plenitude | 165 | C.M. | H. Walford Davies |
| Pleyel's Hymn | 394 | 7.7.7.7. | Ignace J. Pleyel |

| NAME OF TUNE | NO. | METER | COMPOSER OR SOURCE |
|---|---|---|---|
| Potsdam | **14** | S.M. | Arr. from Johann Sebastian Bach |
| Praise | **283** | 14.14.4 7.8. | *Stralsund Gesangbuch*, 1665 |
| Prayer | **285** | C.M. | E. Norman Greenwood |
| Presence | **211** | 10.10.10.10. | Percy Whitlock |
| Protection | **292** | 12.11.13.11. | *Dutch Folk Song* |
| Puer nobis nascitur | **323** | L.M. | Michael Praetorius |
| Purity | **19** | 8.8.8.6.D. | *Norwegian Folk Melody* |
| Purpose | **82** | C.M.D. (Irregular) | H. Walford Davies |
| | | | |
| Quam dilecta | **268** | 6.6.6.6. | Henry L. Jenner |
| Qui laborat orat | **41** | 4.10 10.10 4. | Hugh P. Allen |
| | | | |
| Radlett | **231** | C.M. | E. Norman Greenwood |
| Rathbun | **379** | 8.7.8.7. | Ithamar Conkey |
| Refuge | **255** | 8.4.8.4. | Percy C. Buck |
| Regent Square | **42** | 87.87.87. | Henry Smart |
| Reliance | **376** | 7.6.7.6.D. | Arr. from Mendelssohn |
| Remembrance | **349** | L.M. | Samuel S. Wesley. Reharmonized |
| Repentance | **84** | 87.87.88. | Ludvig M. Lindeman |
| Repton | **50** | 86.886. | C. Hubert H. Parry |
| Rest | **49** | 86.886. | Frederick C. Maker |
| Rest | **427** | 88.88.88. | John Stainer |
| Richmond | **38** | C.M. | T. Haweis. Arr. by S. Webbe, Jr. |
| Rivaulx | **319** | L.M. | John B. Dykes |
| Rockingham | **188** | L.M. | Edward Miller |
| Rustington | **360** | 8.7.8.7.D. | C. Hubert H. Parry |
| Rutherford | **151** | 76.76.676. | Chrétien Urhan |
| | | | |
| Saffron Walden | **48** | 8.8.8.6. | Arthur H. Brown |
| St. Agnes | **37** | C.M. | John B. Dykes |
| St. André | **344** | C.M. | H. Walford Davies |
| St. Anne | **213** | C.M. | William Croft |
| St. Anselm | **329** | 7.6.7.6.D. | Joseph Barnby |
| St. Asaph | **351** | 8.7.8.7.D. | William S. Bambridge |
| St. Asaph | **158** | C.M.D. | Attributed to Giornovichi |
| St. Barnabas | **149** | 11.10.11.10. | Percy C. Buck |
| St. Bees | **273** | 7.7.7.7. | John B. Dykes |
| St. Bernard | **358** | C.M. | From *Tochter Sion*, 1741 |
| St. Cecilia | **382** | 6.6.6.6. | Leighton G. Hayne |
| St. Clement | **381** | 9.8.9.8. | Clement C. Scholefield |
| St. Columba | **339** | C.M. | *Old Irish Hymn Melody* |
| St. Denio | **150** | 11.11.11.11. | *Welsh Hymn Melody* |
| St. Edmund | **241** | S.M. | Edmund Gilding |
| St. Ethelwald | **398** | S.M. | William H. Monk |
| St. George | **201** | S.M. | Henry J. Gauntlett |
| St. George's Windsor | **369** | 7.7.7.7.D. | George J. Elvey |
| St. Gertrude | **264** | 6.5.6.5.D. REF. | Arthur S. Sullivan |
| St. Gregory | **239** | L.M. | *Harmonischer Liederschatz*, 1755<br>Harmonized by W. H. Monk |
| St. Hilda | **221** | 7.6.7.6.D. | Justin H. Knecht |
| St. Hugh | **303** | C.M. | Edward J. Hopkins |
| St. Hugh | **248** | C.M. | *English Traditional Melody* |
| St. Leonard | **224** | C.M.D. | Henry Hiles |
| St. Leonard | **247** | C.M. | Henry Smart |
| St. Louis | **222** | 86.86.76.86. | Lewis H. Redner |
| St. Mabyn | **337** | 8.7.8.7. | Arthur H. Brown |
| St. Magnus | **328** | C.M. | Jeremiah Clark |
| St. Margaret | **406** | 88.886. | Albert L. Peace |

| NAME OF TUNE | NO. | METER | COMPOSER OR SOURCE |
|---|---|---|---|
| St. Matthew | **52** | C.M.D. | William Croft |
| St. Olave | **140** | L.M. | Robert Hudson<br>Harmonized by S. S. Wesley |
| St. Oswald | **33** | 8.7.8.7. | John B. Dykes |
| St. Peter | **125** | C.M. | Alexander R. Reinagle |
| St. Sepulchre | **331** | L.M. | George Cooper |
| St. Stephen | **334** | C.M. | William Jones |
| St. Theodulph | **153** | 76.76.86.76.76. | Melchior Teschner. Arr. by Bach |
| St. Thomas | **354** | S.M. | *Williams' Psalmody*, 1770 |
| St. Vincent | **155** | 9.8.9.8. | S. Neukomm. Arr. by J. Uglow |
| Salzburg | **11** | 7.7.7.7.D. | Jakob Hintze<br>Harmonized by J. S. Bach |
| Sandys | **184** | S.M. | *English Traditional Carol*<br>*Sandys' Collection*, 1833 |
| Sardis | **181** | 8.7.8.7. | Arr. from Ludwig van Beethoven |
| Sarum | **421** | 10.10.10.4. | Joseph Barnby |
| Satis | **162** | 8.4.8.4. | Percy Whitlock |
| Saviour | **299** | 10 7.77 9. | Walter E. Young |
| Sawley | **315** | C.M. | James Walch. Arranged |
| Schönheit | **366** | 7.7.7.7. | Michael Praetorius |
| Science | **197** | 8.7.8.7. | Lyman Brackett |
| Seccomb | **217** | 11.10.11.10. | Charles H. Morse |
| Security | **112** | 8.8.8.8. | Ivar Widéen |
| Selma | **314** | S.M. | *Traditional Melody, Isle of Arran*<br>Arr. by R. A. Smith |
| Selworthy | **28** | 8.4.8.4.D. | E. Norman Greenwood |
| Serenity | **23** | 8.4.8.4. | Arr. from William V. Wallace |
| Serug | **355** | 664.6664. | *S. S. Wesley's European Psalmist* |
| Seymour | **365** | 7.7.7.7. | Arr. from Carl Maria von Weber |
| Shepherd | **305** | 7.5.7.5.D. | Albert F. Conant |
| Sicily | **119** | 8.7.8.7. | *Sicilian Melody* |
| Simpson | **230** | C.M. | Louis Spohr. Arranged |
| Sine nomine | **66** | 10.10.10.4. | R. Vaughan Williams |
| Slingsby | **340** | 8.7.8.7. | Edmund S. Carter |
| Soll's sein | **96** | C.M.D. | From "*Drei schöne neue geistliche Lieder,*" 1637 |
| Solothurn | **385** | L.M. | *Swiss Traditional Melody* |
| Som Hønen klukker mindelig | **332** | 86.86.888. | August H. Winding |
| Song 20 | **397** | S.M. | Orlando Gibbons |
| Song 22 | **212** | 10.10.10.10. | Orlando Gibbons |
| Song 24 | **69** | 10.10.10.10. | Orlando Gibbons |
| Song 67 | **262** | C.M. | Orlando Gibbons |
| Southwell | **399** | C.M. | Herbert S. Irons |
| Spohr | **51** | C.M.D. | Louis Spohr |
| Stracathro | **343** | C.M. | *Scottish Hymn Melody* |
| Strength and Stay | **317** | 11.10.11.10. | John B. Dykes |
| Stuttgart | **265** | 8.7.8.7. | *Arr. from a melody in Psalmodia Sacra, Gotha,* 1715 |
| Surrey | **139** | 88.88.88. | Henry Carey |
| Sursum voces | **282** | 8.7.8.7.D. | H. Elliot Button |
| Sussex | **338** | 8.7.8.7. | *English Traditional Melody.* Arr. |
| Swanage | **200** | 12.11.12.11. | E. Norman Greenwood |
| Tænk, naar engang | **209** | 10.10.10.10. | Andreas P. Berggreen |
| Tallis' Canon | **272** | L.M. | Thomas Tallis |
| Thatcher | **240** | S.M. | Arr. from Georg Friedrich Händel |
| Theodora | **324** | 77.77.77. | Arr. from Georg Friedrich Händel |
| Thornbury | **375** | 7.6.7.6.D. | Basil Harwood |

| NAME OF TUNE | NO. | METER | COMPOSER OR SOURCE |
|---|---|---|---|
| Thy Kingdom Come (Tillkomme ditt rike)....... | 204 | 11 9.11 9.99. | Gunnar Wennerberg |
| Ton-y-Botel............ | 258 | 8.7.8.7.D. | *Welsh Hymn Melody* |
| Toplady................ | 293 | 77.77.77. | Thomas Hastings |
| Toulon................. | 108 | 10.10.10.10. | *Arr. from the Genevan Psalter*, 1551 |
| Treuer Heiland .......... | 35 | 77.77.77. | Conrad Kocher. Arranged |
| Truro.................. | 326 | L.M. | *Psalmodia Evangelica*, 1790 |
| Tryggare kan ingen vara .. | 112 | 8.8.8.8. | Ivar Widéen |
| Tunbridge.............. | 187 | 7.7.7.7. | Jeremiah Clark |
| Uffingham............... | 94 | L.M. | Jeremiah Clark |
| Valerius................ | 246 | 10.10.11.11. REF. | *Old Dutch Hymn* |
| Valete.................. | 288 | 88.88.88. | Arthur S. Sullivan |
| Valour.................. | 61 | L.M. | Hugh P. Allen |
| Vi samles for dit Aasyn her. | 130 | 87.87.888. | Harnack O. C. Zinck (?) |
| Vienna.................. | 274 | 7.7.7.7. | Justin H. Knecht |
| Vigilate................ | 68 | 7.7.7.3. | William H. Monk. Slightly revised |
| Vita.................... | 31 | 86.86.88. | Eaton Faning |
| Vom Himmel hoch....... | 168 | L.M. | *Geistliche Lieder, Leipzig*, 1539<br>Harmony from J. S. Bach |
| Wallog.................. | 278 | 11.10.11.10. | H. Walford Davies |
| Walsall................. | 17 | C.M. | Attributed to Henry Purcell |
| Ward................... | 128 | L.M. | *Scotch Melody.* Arr. by L. Mason |
| Wareham................ | 391 | L.M. | William Knapp |
| Warrington.............. | 163 | L.M. | Ralph Harrison |
| Watchman.............. | 368 | 7.7.7.7.D. | Lowell Mason |
| Welwyn................. | 57 | 11.10.11.10. | Alfred Scott-Gatty |
| Wessex................. | 134 | 86.86.88. | Edward J. Hopkins |
| Westminster............ | 54 | C.M. | James Turle |
| Willingham............. | 359 | 11.10.11.10. | Franz Abt |
| Winchester New.......... | 336 | L.M. | *Musikalisches Handbuch*, 1690 |
| Winchester Old.......... | 122 | C.M. | *Este's Psalter*, 1592 |
| Windermere............. | 143 | S.M. | Arthur Somervell |
| Windsor................ | 107 | C.M. | *Melody from Damon's Psalter*, 1591 |
| Wisdom................. | 198 | 8.7.8.7. | G. Thalben-Ball |
| Wolvercote............. | 250 | 7.6.7.6.D. | W. Harold Ferguson |
| Wordsworth............. | 135 | 7.6.7.6.D. | William H. Monk. Revised |
| Yattendon 12............ | 289 | 88.88.88. | *Old English Melody*<br>Harmonized by H. E. Wooldridge |
| Yattendon 15............ | 225 | C.M.D. | Christopher Tye<br>Arr. by H. E. Wooldridge |
| Zum Frieden............ | 110 | 8.7.8.7.D. | Johann Sebastian Bach |

# TUNES, METRICAL

### S. M. (6.6.8.6.)

SHORT METER

Aynhoe . . . . . . . . . . . . 16
Camberwell . . . . . . . . . . 124
Carlisle . . . . . . . . . . . 396
Dennis (*Nægeli*) . . . . . . . 402
Dominica . . . . . . . . . . . 92
Franconia . . . . . . . . . . . 44
Heath . . . . . . . . . . . . 183
Mornington . . . . . . . . . . 70
Olmutz . . . . . . . . . . . . 404
Potsdam . . . . . . . . . . . 14
St. Edmund . . . . . . . . . . 241
St. Ethelwald . . . . . . . . . 398
St. George . . . . . . . . . . 201
St. Thomas . . . . . . . . . . 354
Sandys . . . . . . . . . . . . 184
Selma . . . . . . . . . . . . 314
Song 20 . . . . . . . . . . . 397
Thatcher . . . . . . . . . . . 240
Windermere . . . . . . . . . . 143

### S. M. D. (6.6.8.6.D.)

SHORT METER DOUBLE

Diademata . . . . . . . . . . 312

### C. M. (8.6.8.6.)

COMMON METER

Abridge . . . . . . . . . . . 333
Antioch . . . . . . . . . . . 417
Arlington . . . . . . . . . . 372
Avon . . . . . . . . . . . . 266
Azmon . . . . . . . . . . . . 320
Azmon New . . . . . . . . . . 409
Ballerma . . . . . . . . . . . 126
Bal(l)erma . . . . . . . . . . 403
Bangor . . . . . . . . . . . . 348
Beatitudo . . . . . . . . . . 284
Belmont . . . . . . . . . . . 205
Beulah . . . . . . . . . . . . 131
Bishopthorpe . . . . . . . . . 142
Boston . . . . . . . . . . . . 429
Bristol . . . . . . . . . . . . 347
Bromsgrove . . . . . . . . . . 106
Burford . . . . . . . . . . . . 321
Caithness . . . . . . . . . . . 215
Capel . . . . . . . . . . . . 242
Cheshire . . . . . . . . . . . 286
Chesterfield . . . . . . . . . . 38
Christmas . . . . . . . . . . . 362
Clearway . . . . . . . . . . . 400
Colchester . . . . . . . . . . 182
Consolation (*Beethoven*) . . . 194
Contemplation . . . . . . . . . 194
Coronation . . . . . . . . . . 86
Coventry . . . . . . . . . . . 327
Dalehurst . . . . . . . . . . . 410
Dedham . . . . . . . . . . . . 105
Epsom . . . . . . . . . . . . 3
Erin . . . . . . . . . . . . . 339
Etherington . . . . . . . . . . 132
Evan . . . . . . . . . . . . . 357
Evan New . . . . . . . . . . . 407
Falmouth . . . . . . . . . . . 36
Fingal . . . . . . . . . . . . 260
Fragment . . . . . . . . . . . 316
Gerontius . . . . . . . . . . . 408
Holy Trinity . . . . . . . . . . 147
Horsley . . . . . . . . . . . . 383
Irish . . . . . . . . . . . . . 145
Liverpool . . . . . . . . . . . 127
Manoah . . . . . . . . . . . . 121
Martyrdom . . . . . . . . . . . 266
Mendip . . . . . . . . . . . . 87
Metzler . . . . . . . . . . . . 367
Mount Calvary . . . . . . . . . 144
Nativity . . . . . . . . . . . . 164
Newbury . . . . . . . . . . . . 146
Nox praecessit . . . . . . . . . 261
Nun danket all . . . . . . . . . 287
Pater Noster . . . . . . . . . . 4
Plenitude . . . . . . . . . . . 165
Prayer . . . . . . . . . . . . 285
Radlett . . . . . . . . . . . . 231
Richmond . . . . . . . . . . . 38
St. Agnes . . . . . . . . . . . 37
St. André . . . . . . . . . . . 344
St. Anne . . . . . . . . . . . 213
St. Bernard . . . . . . . . . . 358
St. Columba . . . . . . . . . . 339
St. Hugh . . . . . . . . . . . 248
St. Hugh (*Hopkins*) . . . . . . 303
St. Leonard (*Smart*) . . . . . . 247
St. Magnus . . . . . . . . . . 328
St. Peter . . . . . . . . . . . 125
St. Stephen . . . . . . . . . . 334
Sawley . . . . . . . . . . . . 315
Simpson . . . . . . . . . . . . 230
Song 67 . . . . . . . . . . . . 262
Southwell . . . . . . . . . . . 399
Stracathro . . . . . . . . . . . 343
Walsall . . . . . . . . . . . . 17
Westminster . . . . . . . . . . 54
Winchester Old . . . . . . . . . 122
Windsor . . . . . . . . . . . . 107

### C. M. D. (8.6.8.6.D.)

COMMON METER DOUBLE

Angels' Song . . . . . . . . . . 342
Ellacombe . . . . . . . . . . . 226
Forest Green . . . . . . . . . . 5
Haydn . . . . . . . . . . . . 269
Heavenward . . . . . . . . . . 136
Kingsfold . . . . . . . . . . . 270
Noel . . . . . . . . . . . . . 373
Pentatone . . . . . . . . . . . 159
Purpose (IRREG.) . . . . . . . . 82
St. Asaph (*Giornovichi*) . . . . 158
St. Leonard (*Hiles*) . . . . . . 224
St. Matthew . . . . . . . . . . 52
Soll's sein . . . . . . . . . . 96
Spohr . . . . . . . . . . . . 51
Yattendon 15 . . . . . . . . . 225

### L. M. (8.8.8.8.)

LONG METER

Abends . . . . . . . . . . . . 133
Affection . . . . . . . . . . . 219
Alsace . . . . . . . . . . . . 422
Angelus . . . . . . . . . . . . 214
Aughton (REF.) . . . . . . . . . 95
Babylon's Streams . . . . . . . 353
Birling . . . . . . . . . . . . 91
Brockham . . . . . . . . . . . 235
Bromley . . . . . . . . . . . . 388
Canonbury . . . . . . . . . . . 322
Church Triumphant . . . . . . . 290
Crispinian . . . . . . . . . . . 56
Das walt' Gott . . . . . . . . . 233
Duke Street . . . . . . . . . . 325
Eisenach . . . . . . . . . . . 80
Ely . . . . . . . . . . . . . 387
Eschol . . . . . . . . . . . . 111
Federal Street . . . . . . . . . 352
Festus . . . . . . . . . . . . 138
Frainsby . . . . . . . . . . . 39
Fulda . . . . . . . . . . . . . 238
Galilee . . . . . . . . . . . . 259

Germany............ 238
Gonfalon Royal........ 271
Hamburg.......... 386
Herongate.......... 45
Hesperus.......... 244
Holley.......... 419
Home.......... 34
Hursley.......... 227
Illsley.......... 129
Lansdowne.......... 220
Linwood.......... 416
Maryton.......... 234
Melcombe.......... 6
Mendon.......... 228
Missionary Chant..... 218
Morning Hymn....... 384
Old Hundreth..... 1, 62, 63
Ombersley.......... 243
Park Street.......... 59
Peace.......... 93
Pentecost.......... 60
Philippine.......... 363
Pixham.......... 20
Puer nobis nascitur..... 323
Remembrance....... 349
Rivaulx.......... 319
Rockingham........ 188
St. Gregory.......... 239
St. Olave.......... 140
St. Sepulchre......... 331
Solothurn.......... 385
Tallis' Canon......... 272
Truro.......... 326
Uffingham.......... 94
Valour.......... 61
Vom Himmel hoch...... 168
Ward.......... 128
Wareham.......... 391
Warrington.......... 163
Winchester New...... 336

L. M. D. (8.8.8.8.D.)

LONG METER DOUBLE

Constancy.......... 229
Creation.......... 170
Firmament.......... 203

4.10 10.10 4.

Qui laborat orat....... 41

5 5 6.8 6 6.

Charity (Kærlighed fra Gud).......... 180

6.4.6.4. (See 10.10.)

Dennis (*Thalben-Ball*) .. 22
Grandpont.......... 21
Need (REF.).......... 137

6 4.6 4.6 6 4.

Horbury.......... 193

6 4.6 4.6 6.6 4.

Bethany.......... 192

6.5.6.5.D. and Refrain

St. Gertrude....... 264

6 6 4.6 6 6 4.

Italian Hymn......... 401
Moscow.......... 346
Serug.......... 355

6.6.6.6.

Moseley.......... 267
Quam dilecta.......... 268
St. Cecilia.......... 382

6 6.6 6.3.

Hussite Hymn........ 378

6.6.8.4.D.

Leoni.......... 371

6 6 8.6 6 8.

Crusader's Hymn...... 275

6 7.6 7.6 6 6 6.

Nun danket.......... 199

7.5.7.5.D.

Benevolence.......... 309
Concord.......... 306
Egerton.......... 308
Guidance.......... 304
Llanfair.......... 307
Shepherd.......... 305

7 6.7 6.6 7 6.

Es ist ein' Ros'....... 152
Rutherford.......... 151

7.6.7.6. and Refrain

Amsterdam.......... 296

7.6.7.6.D.

Abendlied.......... 43
All Saints New........ 374
Aurelia.......... 75
Bentley.......... 251
Berno.......... 249
Bohemian Hymn...... 189
Day of Rest.......... 196
Ewing.......... 148
Gosterwood.......... 377
Greenland.......... 120
Herzlich thut mich verlangen.......... 252
Homeland.......... 245
I Love to Tell (REF.) ...... 414
King's Lynn.......... 78
Meirìonydd.......... 313
Missionary Hymn....... 2
Morning Light........ 335
Munich.......... 77

Reliance.......... 376
St. Anselm.......... 329
St. Hilda.......... 221
Thornbury.......... 375
Wolvercote.......... 250
Wordsworth.......... 135

7 6.7 6.7 6.8 6.

Alford.......... 65

7 6.7 6.8 6.7 6.7 6.

St. Theodulph........ 153

7.6.8.6.

Fulfillment (Den store Mester kommer)...... 15

7 7 6.7 7 8.

Innsbruck (Nun ruhen alle Wälder)........ 361

7.7.7.3.

Capetown.......... 67
Vigilate.......... 68

7 7.7 4 5.

Armenian Hymn....... 113

7.7.7.5.

Huddersfield.......... 173

7.7.7.7.

Carne (Schönheit)...... 366
Cheerfulness (Altid frejdig, naar du gaar).... 141
Elijah.......... 118
Galliard.......... 53
Hendon.......... 186
Innocents.......... 83
Manna.......... 46
Nottingham.......... 47
Orientis partibus...... 114
Palms of Glory....... 395
Peacefield.......... 341
Pleyel's Hymn........ 394
St. Bees.......... 273
Seymour.......... 365
Tunbridge.......... 187
Vienna.......... 274

77.77.67.67.

Mooz Zur.......... 281

77.77.77.

Dix.......... 35
Halle.......... 88
Houghton.......... 294
Jesu, Jesu, du mein Hirt. 89
Nicht so traurig....... 295
Paschal (Påskemorgen slukker sorgen)....... 291
Theodora.......... 324
Toplady.......... 293

7.7.7.7.D.
Benevento.............. 72
Benevento (revised)..... 405
Bethlehem (REF.)....... 310
St. George's Windsor.... 369
Salzburg.............. 11
Watchman.............. 368

77.77.77.744.
Eternity.............. 418

78.78.88.
Liebster Jesu......... 85

8.4.8.4.
Christmas Morn........ 24
Dransfield............ 26
Fortitude............. 161
Infinitas............. 27
Kington............... 25
Norton................ 254
Oblation.............. 257
Refuge................ 255
Satis................. 162
Serenity.............. 23

8.4.8.4.D.
Gloaming.............. 160
Oldown................ 256
Pleasant Street....... 253
Selworthy............. 28

8 4.8 4.8 8.8 4.
Ar Hyd y Nos.......... 350

8 6.8 6.6.
Carol................. 9
Lobt Gott............. 101

8 6.8 6.7 6.8 6.
Christmas Carol....... 223
St. Louis............. 222

8 6.8 6.8 8.
Auch jetzt macht Gott.. 74
Compassion............ 420
Gottlob............... 32
Love.................. 30
O Jesu................ 311
Vita.................. 31
Wessex................ 134

8 6.8 6.8 8 8.
Nestling (Som Honen klukker mindelig)..... 332

8 6.8 8 6.
Campfields............ 104
Hammersmith........... 428
Newcastle............. 206
Repton................ 50
Rest.................. 49

8.7.8.7.
Carol Melody.......... 237
Courage............... 380
Cross of Jesus........ 102
Glück zu Kreuz........ 103
Gott des Himmels.. 166, 167
Gott will's machen.... 55
Marching.............. 364
Merton................ 79
Rathbun............... 379
St. Mabyn............. 337
St. Oswald............ 33
Sardis................ 181
Sicily................ 119
Slingsby.............. 340
Stuttgart............. 265
Sussex................ 338

8.7 8.7 (Iambic)
Ach Gott und Herr..... 393
Dominus regit me...... 330
Science............... 197
Wisdom................ 198

8 7.8 7.4 7.
Kingly Vale........... 81

87.87.66.667.
Ein' feste Burg (C)... 10
Ein' feste Burg (D)... 411

8 7.8 7.8 7.
Corinth............... 90
Feniton Court......... 177
Lauda anima........... 280
Regent Square......... 42

8.7.8.7.D.
Alleluia.............. 171
Austria............... 71
Beecher............... 276
Bethany (*Smart*)...... 277
Deerhurst............. 370
Easter................ 413
Ellesdie.............. 109
Everton............... 29
Gladness (Glädje utan Gud ej finnes)...... 263
Grace (Herren sig i nåd förklarar)........ 76
Hyfrydol.............. 175
Ilsley................ 97
In Babilone........... 98
Joy................... 58
Llansannan............ 116
Lux Eoi............... 115
Rustington............ 360
St. Asaph (*Bambridge*).. 351
Sursum voces.......... 282
Ton-y-Botel........... 258
Zum Frieden........... 110

8.7.8.7.D. (Iambic)
Golden Sheaves........ 392

8 7.8 7.8 8.
Repentance (Herre, jeg har handlet ille)...... 84

8 7.8 7.8 8.7 7.
Light (Kjærlighet er lysets kilde)........... 178

8 7.8 7.8 8 8.
Congregation (Vi samles for dit Aasyn her).... 130

87.87.11.
Atkey................. 157

8.8.8.4.
Almsgiving............ 190
Comfort............... 424
Es ist kein Tag....... 191

8.8.8.6.
Saffron Walden........ 48

8.8.8.6.D.
Purity (Den store, hvite flokk)............ 19

8.8.8.8.
Joy Cometh (REF.)..... 425
Security (Tryggare kan ingen vara)........... 112

8 8.8 8 6.
Hampstead............. 232
St. Margaret.......... 406

8 8.8 8.8 8.
David's Harp.......... 100
Ermuntre dich......... 13
Melita................ 12
Rest.................. 427
Surrey................ 139
Valete................ 288
Yattendon 12.......... 289

8 8.8.8 8.8.
Bera.................. 99

8 8.8.8.8 8 8.
Church (Kirken den er et gammelt hus)....... 176

9.8.8.8.
Bowen................. 185

9 8.8 8 4.
Bairn (Lille Guds Barn) 318

9.8.9.8.
Alma . . . . . . . . . . . . . . . 154
Evensong . . . . . . . . . . . . 156
St. Clement . . . . . . . . . . 381
St. Vincent . . . . . . . . . . . 155

9 8.9 8.8 8.
Neumark . . . . . . . . . . . . 216

9.11.10.10. and Refrain
Pilgrim . . . . . . . . . . . . . . 415

10 4.10 4.10 10.
Lux benigna . . . . . . . . . 169

10 7.7 7 9.
Communion . . . . . . . . . . 298
Faith . . . . . . . . . . . . . . . 301
Freedom . . . . . . . . . . . . 302
Laundon . . . . . . . . . . . . 300
Saviour . . . . . . . . . . . . . 299

10 7.10 7.10 10.7 7.
Gratitude (Eeuwig dank en eere) . . . . . . . . . 73

10.10. (see 6.4.6.4.)
Dennis (*Thalben-Ball*) . . 22
Grandpont . . . . . . . . . . 21

10.10.10.4.
Sarum . . . . . . . . . . . . . . 421
Sine nomine . . . . . . . . . 66

10.10.10.10.
All Souls . . . . . . . . . . . . 195
Benediction . . . . . . . . . . 208
Dalkeith . . . . . . . . . . . . 297
Ellers . . . . . . . . . . . . . . 208
Eucharistica . . . . . . . . . 172
Eventide . . . . . . . . . . . . 7, 8
Expectation (Tænk, naar engang) . . . . . . . . . . 209
Langran . . . . . . . . . . . . 390
Limpsfield . . . . . . . . . . . 210
Morecambe . . . . . . . . . . 207
Old 124th . . . . . . . . . . . 108
Penitentia . . . . . . . . . . . 423
Presence . . . . . . . . . . . . 211
Song 22 . . . . . . . . . . . . . 212
Song 24 . . . . . . . . . . . . . 69
Toulon . . . . . . . . . . . . . 108

10.10.11.11.
Hanover . . . . . . . . . . . . 236
Valerius (REF.) . . . . . . . . 246

11 9.11 9.9 9.
Thy Kingdom Come (Tillkomme ditt rike) . 204

11.10.11.10.
Ancient of Days . . . . . . . 202
Belhaven . . . . . . . . . . . . 356
Charterhouse . . . . . . . . . 345
Consolation (*Mendelss'n*) 174
Elgin . . . . . . . . . . . . . . . 64
Jehovah . . . . . . . . . . . . 426
Lime Street . . . . . . . . . . 279
St. Barnabas . . . . . . . . . 149
Seccomb . . . . . . . . . . . . 217
Strength and Stay . . . . . . 317
Wallog . . . . . . . . . . . . . 278
Welwyn . . . . . . . . . . . . . 57
Willingham . . . . . . . . . . 359

11.10.11.10. (Dactylic)
Consolator . . . . . . . . . . 40

11.10.11.10.D.
Londonderry . . . . . . . . . 412

11.11.11.11.
Adeste fideles . . . . . . . . 123
Lyons . . . . . . . . . . . . . . 18
St. Denio . . . . . . . . . . . . 150

11.12.6.7.6.
Integer vitae . . . . . . . . . 179

11.12.12.10.
Nicæa . . . . . . . . . . . . . . 117

12.10.11.10.
(see 11.10.11.10.)
Consolation (*Mendelss'n*) 174

12.11.12.11.
O christliche Herzen . . . . 389
Protection . . . . . . . . . . . 292
Swanage . . . . . . . . . . . . 200

12.11.13.11.
(see 12.11.12.11.)
Protection . . . . . . . . . . . 292

14.14.4 7.8.
Praise (Lobe den Herren) 283

# COMPOSERS AND SOURCES

*For Christian Scientists and for contemporary composers, no dates are given*
*Arrangements, revisions, and adaptations are marked by asterisks*

ABT, FRANZ
1819–1885
Willingham .......... **359**

AHLE, JOHANN R.
1625–1673
Liebster Jesu .......... **85**

ALBERT, HEINRICH
1604–1651
Gott des Himmels **166, 167**

ALLEN, HUGH P.
Kingly Vale .......... **81**
Qui laborat orat .......... **41**
Valour .......... **61**

ANDERSON, JAMES S.
Fingal .......... **260**

*Armenian Liturgy*
Armenian Hymn .......... **113**

ARMES, PHILIP
1836–1908
Galilee .......... **259**

ARNE, THOMAS A.
1710–1778
Arlington .......... **372**

*Arnold's Psalter*, 1756
Epsom .......... **3**

ATKINSON, FREDERICK C.
1841–1897
Morecambe .......... **207**

BACH, JOHANN SEBASTIAN
1685–1750
*Ach Gott und Herr .......... **393**
*Das walt' Gott .......... **233**
*Eisenach .......... **80**
*Gott des Himmels .......... **167**
Gottlob .......... **32**
*Herzlich thut mich verlangen .......... **252**
*Innsbruck (Nun ruhen alle Wälder) .......... **361**
*Liebster Jesu .......... **85**
*Lobt Gott .......... **101**
*Neumark .......... **216**
Nicht so traurig .......... **295**

(BACH, JOHANN SEBASTIAN)
Potsdam .......... **14**
*St. Theodulph .......... **153**
*Salzburg .......... **11**
*Vom Himmel hoch .......... **168**
Zum Frieden .......... **110**

BAKER, HENRY
1835–1910
Hesperus .......... **244**

BAKER, HENRY W.
1821–1877
Clearway .......... **400**

BAMBRIDGE, WILLIAM S.
1864–1911
St. Asaph .......... **351**

BARNBY, JOSEPH
1838–1896
Holy Trinity .......... **147**
St. Anselm .......... **329**
Sarum .......... **421**

BARTHÉLÉMON, FRANÇOIS H.
1741–1808
Morning Hymn .......... **384**

BEETHOVEN, LUDWIG VAN
1770–1827
Alsace .......... **422**
Contemplation .......... **194**
Germany (Fulda) .......... **238**
Joy .......... **58**
Sardis .......... **181**

BERGGREEN, ANDREAS P.
1801–1880
Expectation (Tænk, naar engang) .......... **209**

BISHOP, JOHN
1665–1737
Illsley .......... **129**

BLISS, PHILIP PAUL
1838–1876
Eternity .......... **418**

*Bohemian Brethren*
Bohemian Hymn .......... **189**

BOYD, WILLIAM
1840–1927
Pentecost .......... **60**

BRACKETT, LYMAN
Alma .......... **154**
Communion .......... **298**
Guidance .......... **304**
Norton .......... **254**
Science .......... **197**

BRADBURY, WILLIAM B.
1816–1868
Aughton .......... **95**

BRIDGES, MATTHEW M.
1800–1894
*Bromley .......... **388**

BROWN, ARTHUR H.
1830–1926
Saffron Walden .......... **48**
St. Mabyn .......... **337**

BUCK, PERCY C.
Gonfalon Royal .......... **271**
Pater Noster .......... **4**
Refuge .......... **255**
St. Barnabas .......... **149**

BUTTON, H. ELLIOT
1861–1925
Sursum voces .......... **282**

CALKIN, JOHN B.
1827–1905
Nox praecessit .......... **261**

CAMPION, THOMAS
1575(?)–1619
Babylon's Streams .......... **353**

*Cantica Spiritualia*, 1847
Angelus .......... **214**

*Canzuns Spirituelas*
1765
Gratitude (Eeuwig dank en eere) .......... **73**

CAREY, HENRY
1692(?)–1743
Surrey .......... **139**

CARTER, EDMUND S.
1845–1923
Slingsby.......... **340**
*Chetham's Psalmody*, 1718
Burford.......... **321**
CLARK, JEREMIAH
1670–1707
Bishopthorpe.......... **142**
Brockham.......... **235**
Bromley.......... **388**
St. Magnus.......... **328**
Tunbridge.......... **187**
Uffingham.......... **94**
*Cologne Gesangbuch*, 1599
Es ist ein' Ros' entsprungen.......... **152**
*Composer Unknown*
Adeste fideles.......... **123**
Thatcher.......... **240**
CONANT, ALBERT F.
Christmas Morn.......... **24**
*Morecambe.......... **207**
Shepherd.......... **305**
CONKEY, ITHAMAR
1815–1867
Rathbun.......... **379**
COOPER, GEORGE
1820–1876
St. Sepulchre.......... **331**
CORBEIL, PIERRE DE(?)
?–1222
Orientis partibus.......... **114**
CORNER, DAVID G.
1587–1648
Carol.......... **9**
COTTMAN, ARTHUR
1842–1874
Dalehurst.......... **410**
CROFT, WILLIAM
1678–1727
Hanover.......... **236**
St. Anne.......... **213**
St. Matthew.......... **52**
CRÜGER, JOHANN
1598–1662
Nun danket.......... **199**
Nun danket all.......... **287**
CUMMINGS, WILLIAM H.
1831–1915
*Bethlehem.......... **310**
CUTLER, HENRY S.
1824–1902
All Saints New.......... **374**
*Damon's Psalter*
1591
Windsor.......... **107**

*Danish Folk Melody*
Bairn (Lille Guds Barn) **318**
*Darmstadt Gesangbuch*
1698
Glück zu Kreuz.......... **103**
DAVIES, H. WALFORD
*Carol.......... **9**
Christmas Carol.......... **223**
*Courage.......... **380**
Etherington.......... **132**
Firmament.......... **203**
*Fragment.......... **316**
Hampstead.......... **232**
*Heavenward.......... **136**
Pentatone.......... **159**
Plenitude.......... **165**
Purpose.......... **82**
St. André.......... **344**
Wallog.......... **278**
DEARLE, EDWARD
1806–1891
Penitentia.......... **423**
*Divine Companion*
1772
David's Harp.......... **100**
DOWLAND, JOHN
1563–1626
Galliard.......... **53**
*Drei geistliche Lieder*
1637
Soll's sein.......... **96**
DÜBEN, GUSTAF
1624–1690
Gladness (Glädje utan Gud ej finnes).......... **263**
*Dutch Hymn*
1626
Valerius.......... **246**
*Dutch Traditional Melodies*
In Babilone.......... **98**
Protection.......... **292**
DYER, SAMUEL
1785–1835
*Mendon.......... **228**
DYKES, JOHN B.
1823–1876
Alford.......... **65**
Almsgiving.......... **190**
Beatitudo.......... **284**
Dominus regit me.......... **330**
Gerontius.......... **408**
Horbury.......... **193**
Lux benigna.......... **169**
Melita.......... **12**
Nicaea.......... **117**

(DYKES, JOHN B.)
Rivaulx.......... **319**
St. Agnes.......... **37**
St. Bees.......... **273**
St. Oswald.......... **33**
Strength and Stay.......... **317**
DYSON, GEORGE
Atkey.......... **157**
Elgin.......... **64**
Frainsby.......... **39**
EDWARDS, F. LLEWELLYN
Kington.......... **25**
ELLIOTT, JAMES W.
1833–1915
Church Triumphant.......... **290**
Day of Rest.......... **196**
ELVEY, GEORGE J.
1816–1893
Diademata.......... **312**
St. George's Windsor. **369**
*English Traditional Melodies*
Capel.......... **242**
Coventry.......... **327**
Forest Green.......... **5**
Gosterwood.......... **377**
Herongate.......... **45**
King's Lynn.......... **78**
Kingsfold.......... **270**
Mendip.......... **87**
Newbury.......... **146**
Noel.......... **373**
St. Hugh.......... **248**
Sandys.......... **184**
Sussex.......... **338**
Yattendon 12.......... **289**
*Este's Psalter*, 1592
Cheshire.......... **286**
Winchester Old.......... **122**
*European Psalmist*, 1872
Camberwell.......... **124**
EVANS, DAVID
Charterhouse.......... **345**
EWING, ALEXANDER
1830–1895
Ewing.......... **148**
FANING, EATON
1850–1927
Vita.......... **31**
FERGUSON, W. HAROLD
Wolvercote.......... **250**
FILITZ, FRIEDRICH
1804–1876
Capetown.......... **67**

FISCHER, WILLIAM G. 1835–1912
I Love to Tell the Story . . . . . 414
FLEMMING, FRIEDRICH F. 1778–1813
Integer vitae . . . . . 179
*Fourteenth Century Carol*
Carol Melody . . . . . 237
FREEMAN, ANDREW
Limpsfield . . . . . 210
*French Melodies*
Innocents . . . . . 83
Orientis partibus . . . . . 114

GARDINER, WILLIAM 1770–1853
*Belmont . . . . . 205
Dedham . . . . . 105
*Germany (Fulda) . . . . . 238
GARRETT, GEORGE M. 1834–1897
Beulah . . . . . 131
Eschol . . . . . 111
GAUNTLETT, HENRY J. 1805–1876
St. George . . . . . 201
*Geistliche Lieder*, 1539
Vom Himmel hoch . . . . . 168
*Genevan Psalter* 1551
Old Hundredth . . . . . 1, 62
Old Hundredth (1551) 63
Toulon (Old 124th) . . . . . 108
*German Chorale*
Festus . . . . . 138
*German Traditional Melodies*
Es ist ein' Ros' entsprungen . . . . . 152
Mendon . . . . . 228
GIARDINI, FELICE DE 1716–1796
Italian Hymn . . . . . 401
Moscow (Italian Hymn) . . . . . 346
GIBBONS, ORLANDO 1583–1625
Song 20 . . . . . 397
Song 22 . . . . . 212
Song 24 . . . . . 69
Song 67 . . . . . 262
GILDING, EDMUND ?–1782
St. Edmund . . . . . 241
GIORNOVICHI, GIOVANNI M. 1745–1804
St. Asaph . . . . . 158

GLADSTONE, WILLIAM H. 1840–1891
Hammersmith . . . . . 428
Ombersley . . . . . 243
GLÄSER, CARL G. 1784–1829
Azmon . . . . . 320
Azmon New . . . . . 409
GOSS, JOHN 1800–1880
Lauda anima . . . . . 280
GOTTSCHALK, LOUIS M. 1829–1869
Manna . . . . . 46
GOULD, JOHN E. 1822–1875
Bera . . . . . 99
GREENWOOD, E. NORMAN
Benevolence . . . . . 309
Freedom . . . . . 302
Lansdowne . . . . . 220
Prayer . . . . . 285
Radlett . . . . . 231
Selworthy . . . . . 28
Swanage . . . . . 200
*Theodora . . . . . 324
*Greenwood's Psalmody Halifax*, 1838
Affection . . . . . 219
*Gregorian Chant*
Hamburg (Arranged by L. Mason) . . . . . 386
HÄNDEL, GEORG FRIEDRICH 1685–1759
*Antioch . . . . . 417
Christmas . . . . . 362
*Theodora . . . . . 324
*Thatcher . . . . . 240
*Harmonischer Liederschatz* 1755
St. Gregory . . . . . 239
HARRISON, RALPH 1748–1810
Warrington . . . . . 163
HARWOOD, BASIL
Oldown . . . . . 256
Thornbury . . . . . 375
HASSLER, HANS L. 1564–1612
Herzlich thut mich verlangen . . . . . 252
HASTINGS, THOMAS 1787–1872
Toplady . . . . . 293
HATTON, JOHN ?–1793
Duke Street . . . . . 325

HAVERGAL, WILLIAM H. 1793–1870
Evan . . . . . 357
Evan New . . . . . 407
*Franconia . . . . . 44
HAWEIS, THOMAS 1734–1820
Richmond (Chesterf'ld) 38
HAYDN, FRANZ JOSEPH 1732–1809
Austria . . . . . 71
Bowen . . . . . 185
Creation . . . . . 170
Haydn . . . . . 269
HAYDN, J. MICHAEL 1737–1806
Greenland . . . . . 120
Lyons . . . . . 18
HAYNE, LEIGHTON G. 1836–1883
St. Cecilia . . . . . 382
HEBERDEN, ARTHUR C.
Evensong . . . . . 156
*Hebrew Melodies*
Leoni . . . . . 371
Mooz Zur . . . . . 281
HEINLEIN, PAUL 1626–1686
Jesu, du mein Hirt . . . . . 89
HERMAN, NICOLAS 1485(?)–1561
Lobt Gott . . . . . 101
HEWLETT, THOMAS 1845–1874
Dalkeith . . . . . 297
HEWS, GEORGE 1806–1873
Holley . . . . . 419
HILES, HENRY 1826–1904
St. Leonard . . . . . 224
HINTZE, JAKOB 1622–1702
Salzburg . . . . . 11
*Hirschberg Gesangbuch*, 1741
O Jesu . . . . . 311
HODGES, EDWARD 1796–1867
Bristol . . . . . 347
HOFFMAN, C. CHRISTIAN 1839–1893
Fulfillment (Den store Mester kommer) . . . . . 15
HOLDEN, OLIVER 1765–1844
Coronation . . . . . 86

HOPKINS, EDWARD J.
1818–1901
*Angels' Song........ 342
Benediction (Ellers) .. 208
Feniton Court....... 177
Jehovah........... 426
St. Hugh........... 303
Wessex........... 134

HORSLEY, WILLIAM
1774–1858
Horsley........... 383

HUDSON, ROBERT
1732–1815
St. Olave.......... 140

HULLAH, JOHN P.
1812–1884
Bentley........... 251

*Hussite Hymn*
Hussite Hymn....... 378

ILSLEY, FRANK G.
1831–1887
Ilsley.......... 97

*Irish Melodies*
Heavenward......... 136
Irish............ 145
Londonderry........ 412
Peacefield........ 341
St. Columba (Erin)... 339

IRONS, HERBERT S.
1834–1905
Southwell.......... 399

ISAAC, HEINRICH
1450–1517
Innsbruck (Nun ruhen alle Wälder)....... 361

*Isle of Arran Melody*
Selma........... 314

*Italian Melody*
Pilgrim........... 415

IVIMEY, JOHN W.
Crispinian.......... 56

JÆHNIGEN, C. F.
1813–1887
Charity (Kærlighed fra Gud)........ 180

JENNER, HENRY L.
1820–1898
Quam dilecta ....... 268

JOHNSON, WILLIAM LYMAN
Concord.......... 306
Pleasant Street...... 253

JONES, WILLIAM
1726–1800
St. Stephen........ 334

JOSEPH, GEORG
1657
Angelus............ 214

KING, ROBERT
1684–1711 (?)
David's Harp........ 100

KNAPP, WILLIAM
1698–1768
Wareham.......... 391

KNECHT, JUSTIN H.
1752–1817
St. Hilda.......... 221
Vienna........... 274

*Koch's Choralbuch*
1816
Auch jetzt macht Gott 74

KOCHER, CONRAD
1786–1872
Dix............ 35

*König's Choralbuch*
1738
Franconia.......... 44

LAHEE, HENRY
1826–1912
Nativity.......... 164

LANGRAN, JAMES
1835–1909
Deerhurst.......... 370
Langran........... 390

LINDEMAN, LUDVIG M.
1812–1887
Church (Kirken den er et gammelt hus)... 176
Light (Kjærlighet er lysets kilde)...... 178
Paschal (Påskemorgen slukker sorgen)..... 291
Repentance (Herre, jeg har handlet ille)..... 84

LLOYD, WILLIAM
1786–1852
Meirionydd......... 313

LOCKHART, CHARLES
1745–1815
Carlisle........... 396

LORENZ, EDMUND S.
Joy Cometh in the Morning ......... 425

LOWRY, ROBERT
1826–1899
Need............ 137

LUTHER, MARTIN
1483–1546
Ein' feste Burg (C)... 10
Ein' feste Burg (D)... 411

*Lyra Davidica*, 1708
Easter........... 413

MACLAGAN, WILLIAM D.
1826–1910
Palms of Glory....... 395

MAIN, H.P.
1839–1928
*Ellesdie.......... 109

*Mainz Gesangbuch*, 1833
Ellacombe.......... 226

MAKER, FREDERICK C.
1844–1927
Rest............ 49

MALAN, CÉSAR H. A.
1787–1864
Hendon........... 186

MANN, ARTHUR H.
1850–1929
Berno............ 249

MASON, LOWELL
1792–1872
*Antioch.......... 417
*Azmon New........ 409
Bethany.......... 192
*Hamburg......... 386
*Heath........... 183
Missionary Hymn.... 2
Olmutz........... 404
*Ward........... 128
Watchman......... 368

*Meiningen Gesangbuch*
1693
Munich.......... 77

MENDELSSOHN-BARTHOLDY, FELIX, 1809–1847
Angels' Song........ 342
Bethlehem......... 310
Consolation........ 174
Constancy ......... 229
Elijah............ 118
*Munich.......... 77
*Nun danket........ 199
Reliance.......... 376

MEYER, JOHANN D.
1692
Es ist kein Tag...... 191

MILLER, EDWARD
1731–1807
Rockingham......... 188

MONK, MARK J.
Campfields......... 104

MONK, WILLIAM H.
1823–1889
Eventide......... 7
Eventide......... 8
Merton.......... 79
St. Ethelwald....... 398

(MONK, WILLIAM H.)
*St. Gregory.......... 239
Vigilate.............. 68
Wordsworth........ 135
MORLEY, HENRY L.
Newcastle.......... 206
MORSE, CHARLES H.
1853–1927
Seccomb........... 217
MOZART, WOLFGANG AMADEUS, 1756–1791
Ellesdie............ 109
Home.............. 34
Nottingham.......... 47
Peace.............. 93
*Musikalisches H'dbuch*, 1690
Winchester New..... 336
NAEGELI, HANS GEORG
1773–1836
Dennis............ 402
NARES, JAMES
1715–1783
Amsterdam......... 296
Aynhoe............ 16
NEUKOMM, SIGISMUND
1778–1858
St. Vincent.......... 155
NEUMARK, GEORG
1621–1681
Neumark (Wer nun den lieben Gott lässt walten)........... 216
*Early Nineteenth Century MS.*
Birling............ 91
*Norwegian Folk Melody*
Purity (Den store, hvite flokk)......... 19
OAKELEY, HERBERT S.
1830–1903
Abends............ 133
Dominica........... 92
O'CONNOR-MORRIS, G.
Faith............. 301
OLIVER, HENRY K.
1800–1885
Federal Street....... 352
PALMER, G. H.
*Jesu, Jesu du mein Hirt 89
PARKER, HORATIO W.
1863–1919
Ancient of Days..... 202
Pixham............. 20
PARRATT, WALTER
1841–1924
Huddersfield........ 173
PARRY, C. HUBERT H.
1848–1918
Repton............. 50
Rustington.......... 360
PEACE, A. L.
1844–1912
St. Margaret........ 406
PETER, C.
1655
Ach Gott und Herr.. 393
PLEYEL, IGNACE J.
1757–1831
Pleyel's Hymn....... 394
*Portnersches Gesangbuch*
1831
O christliche Herzen.. 389
PRAETORIUS, MICHAEL
1571–1621
Carne (Schönheit)....366
Puer nobis nascitur... 323
PRICHARD, ROWLAND H.
1811–1887
Hyfrydol............ 175
PRITCHARD, THOMAS C. L.
Belhaven........... 356
*Psalmodia Evangelica*
1789
Bromsgrove......... 106
Truro.............. 326
*Psalmodia Sacra*, 1715
Stuttgart........... 265
PURCELL, HENRY
1658–1695
Colchester.......... 182
Walsall............ 17
REDHEAD, RICHARD
1820–1901
Metzler............ 367
REDNER, LEWIS H.
1831–1908
St. Louis.......... 222
REINAGLE, ALEXANDER R.
1799–1877
St. Peter.......... 125
RICH, C. B.
Comfort........... 424
Compassion......... 420
ROBERTS, R. E.
Philippine.......... 363
ROOT, FREDERIC W.
*Coventry.......... 327
ROSSINI, GIOACCHINO A.
1792–1868
Linwood........... 416
Manoah............ 121
*Sandys' Collection*, 1833
Sandys............ 184
*Sarum Gradual*, 1527
Fragment.......... 316
SCHEIN, JOHANN H.
1586–1630
Eisenach........... 80
*Schicht's Choralbuch*, 1819
Halle.............. 88
Hursley........... 227
SCHOLEFIELD, CLEMENT C.
1839–1904
St. Clement........ 381
SCHOP, JOHANN
?–1664
Ermuntre dich....... 13
SCHUBERT, FRANZ
1797–1828
Abendlied (Sanft glänzt) 43
SCHUMANN, ROBERT
1810–1856
Canonbury.......... 322
SCOTT-GATTY, ALFRED
1847–1918
Welwyn............ 57
*Scottish Hymn Melodies*
Stracathro.......... 343
Ward.............. 128
*Scottish Psalter*, 1635
Caithness.......... 215
SHAW, GEOFFREY
Lime Street......... 279
SHAW, MARTIN
Marching........... 364
*Sicilian Melody*
Sicily............. 119
SIEDHOFF, E. ELIZABETH
Boston............ 429
*Silesian Melody*
Crusader's Hymn.... 275
SMART, HENRY
1813–1879
Bethany........... 277
Everton............ 29
Moseley........... 267
Regent Square....... 42
St. Leonard......... 247
SMITH, H. PERCY
1825–1898
Maryton........... 234
SMITH, ISAAC
1725–1800
Abridge........... 333

SMITH, JOSEPH
1800–1873
*Innocents.......... **83**

SMITH, R. A.
1780–1829
*Selma.............. **314**

SOMERVELL, ARTHUR
Windermere.......... **143**

*Spanish Melody*
Bal(l)erma ...... **126, 403**

SPOHR, LOUIS
1784–1859
Simpson............. **230**
Spohr............... **51**

STAINER, JOHN
1840–1901
Cross of Jesus........ **102**
Gloaming............ **160**
Grandpont........... **21**
Rest................ **427**

STEINER, J. LUDWIG
1688–1761
Gott will's machen.... **55**

STENHAMMAR, PER U.
1829–1875
Grace (Herren sig i nåd förklarar)..... **76**

STEWART, ROBERT P.
1825–1894
Eucharistica.......... **172**
Mount Calvary....... **144**

*Stralsund Gesangbuch*
1665
Praise (Lobe den Herren)............. **283**

SULLIVAN, ARTHUR S.
1842–1900
Golden Sheaves...... **392**
Homeland........... **245**
Lux Eoi............. **115**
*Noel.............. **373**
St. Gertrude......... **264**
Valete.............. **288**

*Swiss Traditional Melody*
Solothurn........... **385**

TALLIS, THOMAS
1510–1585
Tallis' Canon ....... **272**

TANS'UR, WILLIAM
1706–1783
Bangor.............. **348**

TESCHNER, MELCHIOR
1615
St. Theodulph....... **153**

THALBEN-BALL, G.
*Belmont........... **205**
Dennis.............. **22**
Dransfield........... **26**
Egerton............. **308**
*Lauda anima ....... **280**
Laundon............ **300**
Wisdom............. **198**

*Tochter Sion*, 1741
St. Bernard.......... **358**

TURLE, JAMES
1802–1882
Westminster......... **54**

TURTON, THOMAS
1780–1864
Ely................. **387**

TYE, CHRISTOPHER
1497–1572
Yattendon 15........ **225**

UGLOW, JAMES
1814–1884
*St. Vincent......... **155**

*University of Wales*
Courage............. **380**
Plenitude........... **165**

URHAN, CHRÉTIEN
1790–1845
Rutherford.......... **151**

VENUA, FREDERICK M. A.
1788–1872
Park Street.......... **59**

VETTER, DANIEL, 1713
Das walt' Gott....... **233**

WAINWRIGHT, ROBERT
1748–1782
Liverpool........... **127**

WALCH, JAMES
1837–1901
Sawley............. **315**

WALLACE, WILLIAM V.
1814–1865
Serenity............ **23**

WEBB, GEORGE J.
1803–1887
Morning Light....... **335**

WEBBE, SAMUEL
1740–1816
Benevento........ **72, 405**
Consolator.......... **40**
Melcombe.......... **6**

*Webbe's (Samuel) Motetts or Antiphons*, 1792
Corinth............. **90**

WEBBE, SAMUEL Jr.
1770–1843
*Richmond (Chesterfield)........ **38**

WEBER, CARL MARIA VON
1786–1826
Seymour........... **365**

WELLESLEY, GARRET
1735–1781
Mornington......... **70**

*Welsh Melodies*
Ar Hyd y Nos........ **350**
Llanfair............. **307**
Llansannan.......... **116**
Meirionydd.......... **313**
St. Denio........... **150**
Ton-y-Botel......... **258**

WENNERBERG, GUNNAR
1817–1901
Thy Kingdom Come (Tillkomme ditt rike) **204**

WESLEY, SAMUEL S.
1810–1876
Alleluia............ **171**
Aurelia............. **75**
Houghton........... **294**
*Liverpool.......... **127**
Remembrance....... **349**
*St. Olave.......... **140**
*Serug............. **355**

WEYSE, CHRISTOPH E. F.
1774–1842
Cheerfulness (Altid frejdig, naar du gaar).. **141**

WHITLOCK, PERCY
Infinitas............ **27**
Oblation............ **257**
Presence............ **211**
Satis............... **162**

WIDÉEN, IVAR
Security (Tryggare kan ingen vara).... **112**

*Williams' Psalmody*
1770
St. Thomas.......... **354**

WILLIAMS, ROBERT
1781–1821
Llanfair............ **307**

WILLIAMS, R. VAUGHAN
Sine nomine ........ **66**

WILLIS, RICHARD S.
1819–1900
*Crusader's Hymn.... **275**

WILSON, DAVID F. R.
*Peacefield .......... 341

WILSON, HUGH
1766–1824
Martyrdom (Avon) ... 266

WINDING, AUGUST H.
1835–1899
Nestling (Som Hønen klukker mindelig) .. 332

WOOD, CHARLES
1866–1926
*Cheshire .......... 286
*Glück zu Kreuz ..... 103

WOOLDRIDGE, H. E.
1845–1917
*Yattendon 12 ....... 289
*Yattendon 15 ....... 225

YOAKLEY, JOHN
All Souls ............ 195

YOUNG, WALTER E.
*Bera ............... 99
Falmouth ........... 36
Fortitude ........... 161
Love ................ 30
Saviour ............ 299

ZEUNER, HEINRICH C.
1795–1857
Missionary Chant .... 218

ZINCK, HARNACK O. C.
1746–1832
Congregation (Vi samles for dit Aasyn her) 130

ZUNDEL, JOHN
1815–1882
Beecher ............ 276

# TEMPO INDICATIONS

## INTRODUCTORY

For various reasons, there is never a fixed speed (tempo) for any piece of music, not even that indicated by the composer. Eminent editors and conductors show, in their markings and interpretations of standard compositions, decided tempo variations. The size of the congregation, the nature and shape of the auditorium, the kind of accompanying instrument—any or all of these things may influence the speed of a hymn; while various stanzas may call for noticeable variations in tempo.

And yet, within the rather wide range of taste and practical conditions, experience can furnish serviceable approximations; and, in consultation with those able to give advice based on experience and extensive observation, a metronome mark is given for each tune. Some may prefer a slower tempo for tunes of the chorale type.

The abbreviations H, Q, E mean Half Note (Minim), Quarter Note (Crotchet) and Eighth Note (Quaver). Each indication covers three markings of the standard metronome. Thus, the interpretation of the first item of the Index is: sixty-three to sixty-nine half notes to the minute; of the second, one hundred to one hundred and eight quarter notes to the minute; of the fifty-first, one hundred and twenty to one hundred and thirty-two eighth notes to the minute.

The metronome mark between the two given is regarded as the best standard single marking. Thus, for No. 1, a single marking would be: H 66; for No. 2, Q 104; for No. 51, E 126. If a metronome of the Maelzel model is not available, a pendulum metronome of the tape-measure type may be found at a music store or at an educational supply house. As these pocket metronomes lack some of the lower markings, it is necessary to set them, for instance, at 80 to give the speed of 40, counting two swings as one.

A note with Hold (Pause, Fermata) is sustained for two, three, or occasionally four beats, depending on basic rhythm, breath requirements, and intelligent phrasing. The effect of the Hold—whether placed over note, rest, or bar—may also be described as delaying the following beat by sustaining or resting for the duration of one, two, or three interpolated beats. All authorities agree that it is impossible to make a concise and precise statement as to the meaning of the Fermata; but all concur that the difficulty is chiefly that of statement, since musical judgment and experience solve the problem acceptably. In many hymnals and in many older editions of the Classics, the Fermata merely marks the endings of lines or sections, and has no effect on tempo.

Mechanical adherence to a metronome mark can greatly interfere with music's helpfulness. Indeed, the organist or pianist should, at every moment, be mindful of a natural phrasing based on the text of the poem and on breath requirements, thus rendering the words while rendering the music; should maintain a fundamentally steady tempo, always remembering that abrupt or capricious modifications cannot be made by a congregation. In a word, the organist should guide and support the congregational singing, but never dominate it.

**1**. . . . . . . . H 63–69
**2**. . . . . . . . Q 100–108
**3**. . . . . . . . Q 112–120
**4**. . . . . . . . H 80–88
**5**. . . . . . . . Q 84–92
**6**. . . . . . . . Q 80–88
**7**. . . . . . . . Q 92–100
**8**. . . . . . . . Q 92–100
**9**. . . . . . . . Q 100–108
**10**. . . . . . . . Q 72–80

**11**. . . . . . . . H 69–76
**12**. . . . . . . . Q 80–88
**13**. . . . . . . . H 72–80
**14**. . . . . . . . H 76–84
**15**. . . . . . . . Q 88–96
**16**. . . . . . . . Q 92–100
**17**. . . . . . . . H 56–60
**18**. . . . . . . . Q 92–100
**19**. . . . . . . . Q 100–108
**20**. . . . . . . . Q 96–104

**21**. . . . . . . . Q 92–100
**22**. . . . . . . . Q 84–92
**23**. . . . . . . . Q 84–92
**24**. . . . . . . . Q 88–96
**25**. . . . . . . . H 72–80
**26**. . . . . . . . H 84–92
**27**. . . . . . . . H 52–56
**28**. . . . . . . . Q 76–84
**29**. . . . . . . . Q 92–100
**30**. . . . . . . . Q 84–92

**31**. . . . . . . . Q 84–92
**32**. . . . . . . . H 88–96
**33**. . . . . . . . H 92–100
**34**. . . . . . . . Q 88–96
**35**. . . . . . . . Q 88–96
**36**. . . . . . . . Q 76–84
**37**. . . . . . . . Q 96–104
**38**. . . . . . . . Q 96–104
**39**. . . . . . . . Q 76–84
**40**. . . . . . . . Q 88–96

**41**. . . . . . . . H 60–66
**42**. . . . . . . . Q 96–104
**43**. . . . . . . . Q 80–88
**44**. . . . . . . . Q 88–96
**45**. . . . . . . . Q 100–108
**46**. . . . . . . . Q 92–100
**47**. . . . . . . . Q 96–104
**48**. . . . . . . . Q 92–100
**49**. . . . . . . . Q 88–96
**50**. . . . . . . . Q 80–88

**51**. . . . . . . . E 120–132
**52**. . . . . . . . Q 100–108
**53**. . . . . . . . E 112–120
**54**. . . . . . . . Q 84–92
**55**. . . . . . . . Q 76–84
**56**. . . . . . . . Q 92–100
**57**. . . . . . . . Q 92–100
**58**. . . . . . . . H 92–100
**59**. . . . . . . . Q 96–104
**60**. . . . . . . . Q 100–108

**61**. . . . . . . . H 56–60
**62**. . . . . . . . H 80–88
**63**. . . . . . . . H 63–69
**64**. . . . . . . . H 52–56
**65**. . . . . . . . Q 104–112
**66**. . . . . . . . Q 88–96
**67**. . . . . . . . Q 88–96
**68**. . . . . . . . Q 88–96
**69**. . . . . . . . H 76–84
**70**. . . . . . . . Q 100–108

**71**. . . . . . . . Q 80–88
**72**. . . . . . . . Q 92–100
**73**. . . . . . . . Q 88–96
**74**. . . . . . . . H 80–88
**75**. . . . . . . . Q 100–108
**76**. . . . . . . . Q 80–88
**77**. . . . . . . . Q 96–104
**78**. . . . . . . . Q 88–96
**79**. . . . . . . . Q 84–92
**80**. . . . . . . . H 69–76

**81**. . . . . . . . H 76–84
**82**. . . . . . . . H 80–88
**83**. . . . . . . . Q 88–96
**84**. . . . . . . . Q 80–88
**85**. . . . . . . . H 72–80
**86**. . . . . . . . Q 96–104
**87**. . . . . . . . Q 84–92
**88**. . . . . . . . Q 108–116
**89**. . . . . . . . H 72–80
**90**. . . . . . . . Q 80–88

**91**. . . . . . . . Q 88–96
**92**. . . . . . . . Q 100–108
**93**. . . . . . . . Q 84–92
**94**. . . . . . . . H 88–96
**95**. . . . . . . . Q 88–96
**96**. . . . . . . . Q 96–104
**97**. . . . . . . . Q 76–84
**98**. . . . . . . . H 80–88
**99**. . . . . . . . H 58–63
**100**. . . . . . . . H 76–84

**101**. . . . . . . . H 80–88
**102**. . . . . . . . Q 80–88
**103**. . . . . . . . Q 96–104
**104**. . . . . . . . Q 88–96
**105**. . . . . . . . H 72–80
**106**. . . . . . . . Q 104–112
**107**. . . . . . . . Q 84–92
**108**. . . . . . . . Q 92–100
**109**. . . . . . . . Q 88–96
**110**. . . . . . . . H 80–88

**111**. . . . . . . . Q 84–92
**112**. . . . . . . . H 72–80
**113**. . . . . . . . Q 80–88
**114**. . . . . . . . Q 100–108
**115**. . . . . . . . Q 88–96
**116**. . . . . . . . H 80–88
**117**. . . . . . . . Q 88–96
**118**. . . . . . . . H 66–72
**119**. . . . . . . . H 60–66
**120**. . . . . . . . Q 96–104

**121**. . . . . . . . Q 104–112
**122**. . . . . . . . Q 88–96
**123**. . . . . . . . Q 100–108
**124**. . . . . . . . Q 88–96
**125**. . . . . . . . Q 92–100
**126**. . . . . . . . Q 108–116
**127**. . . . . . . . Q 88–96
**128**. . . . . . . . Q 104–112
**129**. . . . . . . . Q 80–88
**130**. . . . . . . . Q 72–80

**131**. . . . . . . . Q 84–92
**132**. . . . . . . . H 84–92
**133**. . . . . . . . Q 88–96
**134**. . . . . . . . Q 76–84
**135**. . . . . . . . H 92–100
**136**. . . . . . . . H 84–92
**137**. . . . . . . . H 84–92
**138**. . . . . . . . H 88–96
**139**. . . . . . . . Q 92–100
**140**. . . . . . . . Q 84–92

**141**. . . . . . . . Q 80–88
**142**. . . . . . . . Q 92–100
**143**. . . . . . . . Q 80–88
**144**. . . . . . . . Q 80–88
**145**. . . . . . . . H 88–96
**146**. . . . . . . . Q 88–96
**147**. . . . . . . . Q 92–100
**148**. . . . . . . . Q 96–104
**149**. . . . . . . . H 52–56
**150**. . . . . . . . Q 92–100

**151**. . . . . . . . Q 92–100
**152**. . . . . . . . Q 80–88
**153**. . . . . . . . H 88–96
**154**. . . . . . . . Q 92–100
**155**. . . . . . . . Q 84–92
**156**. . . . . . . . H 52–56
**157**. . . . . . . . H 50–54
**158**. . . . . . . . Q 96–104
**159**. . . . . . . . Q 92–100
**160**. . . . . . . . H 88–96

**161**. . . . . . . . Q 84–92
**162**. . . . . . . . H 63–69
**163**. . . . . . . . Q 88–96
**164**. . . . . . . . Q 100–108
**165**. . . . . . . . H 63–69
**166**. . . . . . . . H 60–66
**167**. . . . . . . . H 52–56
**168**. . . . . . . . H 60–66
**169**. . . . . . . . H 63–69
**170**. . . . . . . . Q 104–112

| No. | Note | Tempo |
|---|---|---|
| **171** | Q | 80– 88 |
| **172** | H | 52– 56 |
| **173** | Q | 76– 84 |
| **174** | H | 52– 56 |
| **175** | H | 92–100 |
| **176** | Q | 92–100 |
| **177** | Q | 84– 92 |
| **178** | Q | 92–100 |
| **179** | Q | 96–104 |
| **180** | Q | 88– 96 |
| **181** | Q | 76– 84 |
| **182** | Q | 92–100 |
| **183** | Q | 88– 96 |
| **184** | Q | 84– 92 |
| **185** | Q | 88– 96 |
| **186** | H | 80– 88 |
| **187** | H | 72– 80 |
| **188** | Q | 88– 96 |
| **189** | H | 80– 88 |
| **190** | Q | 88– 96 |
| **191** | H | 66– 72 |
| **192** | Q | 88– 96 |
| **193** | Q | 69– 76 |
| **194** | Q | 84– 92 |
| **195** | Q | 96–104 |
| **196** | H | 96–104 |
| **197** | Q | 80– 88 |
| **198** | Q | 76– 84 |
| **199** | H | 69– 76 |
| **200** | Q | 96–104 |
| **201** | Q | 92–100 |
| **202** | Q | 88– 96 |
| **203** | H | 76– 84 |
| **204** | Q | 92–100 |
| **205** | Q | 96–104 |
| **206** | H | 84– 92 |
| **207** | Q | 84– 92 |
| **208** | Q | 92–100 |
| **209** | Q | 92–100 |
| **210** | Q | 92–100 |
| **211** | Q | 88– 96 |
| **212** | Q | 88– 96 |
| **213** | Q | 80– 88 |
| **214** | Q | 88– 96 |
| **215** | Q | 84– 92 |
| **216** | H | 76– 84 |
| **217** | H | 56– 60 |
| **218** | H | 60– 66 |
| **219** | Q | 72– 80 |
| **220** | Q | 80– 88 |
| **221** | Q | 88– 96 |
| **222** | Q | 92–100 |
| **223** | Q | 88– 96 |
| **224** | Q | 88– 96 |
| **225** | Q | 84– 92 |
| **226** | Q | 96–104 |
| **227** | Q | 92–100 |
| **228** | Q | 88– 96 |
| **229** | Q | 100–108 |
| **230** | Q | 92–100 |
| **231** | Q | 80– 88 |
| **232** | H | 76– 84 |
| **233** | H | 63– 69 |
| **234** | Q | 92–100 |
| **235** | Q | 84– 92 |
| **236** | Q | 96–104 |
| **237** | Q | 88– 96 |
| **238** | Q | 92–100 |
| **239** | Q | 84– 92 |
| **240** | Q | 88– 96 |
| **241** | Q | 96–104 |
| **242** | Q | 84– 92 |
| **243** | Q | 96–104 |
| **244** | Q | 88– 96 |
| **245** | Q | 96–104 |
| **246** | Q<br>E | 88– 96<br>116–126 |
| **247** | H | 80– 88 |
| **248** | Q | 80– 88 |
| **249** | Q | 80– 88 |
| **250** | Q | 92–100 |
| **251** | Q | 92–100 |
| **252** | H | 60– 66 |
| **253** | Q | 63– 69 |
| **254** | Q | 84– 92 |
| **255** | H | 44– 48 |
| **256** | H | 80– 88 |
| **257** | Q | 84– 92 |
| **258** | H | 58– 63 |
| **259** | Q | 88– 96 |
| **260** | Q | 80– 88 |
| **261** | Q | 92–100 |
| **262** | Q | 80– 88 |
| **263** | H | 84– 92 |
| **264** | Q | 100–108 |
| **265** | Q | 88– 96 |
| **266** | Q | 92–100 |
| **267** | Q | 88– 96 |
| **268** | Q | 88– 96 |
| **269** | Q | 84– 92 |
| **270** | Q | 80– 88 |
| **271** | H | 76– 84 |
| **272** | Q | 76– 84 |
| **273** | Q | 84– 92 |
| **274** | Q | 88– 96 |
| **275** | Q | 92–100 |
| **276** | Q | 88– 96 |
| **277** | Q | 84– 92 |
| **278** | Q | 92–100 |
| **279** | H | 56– 60 |
| **280** | Q | 76– 84 |
| **281** | H | 72– 80 |
| **282** | Q | 88– 96 |
| **283** | Q | 84– 92 |
| **284** | Q | 96–104 |
| **285** | Q | 72– 80 |
| **286** | H | 88– 96 |
| **287** | Q | 96–104 |
| **288** | Q | 80– 88 |
| **289** | H | 76– 84 |
| **290** | Q | 88– 96 |
| **291** | Q | 69– 76 |
| **292** | Q | 84– 92 |
| **293** | H | 69– 76 |
| **294** | Q | 84– 92 |
| **295** | H | 60– 66 |
| **296** | Q | 104–112 |
| **297** | Q | 92–100 |
| **298** | Q | 96–104 |
| **299** | Q | 92–100 |
| **300** | Q | 92–100 |
| **301** | H | 69– 76 |
| **302** | H | 52– 56 |
| **303** | Q | 76– 84 |
| **304** | Q | 88– 96 |
| **305** | Q | 80– 88 |
| **306** | Q | 80– 88 |
| **307** | Q | 80– 88 |
| **308** | Q | 84– 92 |
| **309** | Q | 80– 88 |
| **310** | Q | 96–104 |
| **311** | Q | 76– 84 |
| **312** | Q | 92–100 |
| **313** | Q | 96–104 |
| **314** | Q | 92–100 |
| **315** | Q | 92–100 |
| **316** | H | 40– 48 |
| **317** | Q | 92–100 |
| **318** | Q | 96–104 |
| **319** | Q | 92–100 |
| **320** | Q | 88– 96 |
| **321** | H | 100–108 |
| **322** | Q | 76– 84 |
| **323** | Q | 92–100 |
| **324** | Q | 76– 84 |
| **325** | Q | 108–116 |
| **326** | Q | 80– 88 |
| **327** | Q | 96–104 |
| **328** | H | 76– 84 |
| **329** | Q | 88– 96 |
| **330** | Q | 84– 92 |
| **331** | Q | 84– 92 |
| **332** | Q | 88– 96 |
| **333** | H | 84– 92 |
| **334** | Q | 76– 84 |
| **335** | Q | 96–104 |
| **336** | Q | 76– 84 |
| **337** | Q | 88– 96 |
| **338** | Q | 80– 88 |
| **339** | Q | 92–100 |
| **340** | Q | 84– 92 |

| No. | | Tempo | No. | | Tempo | No. | | Tempo |
|---|---|---|---|---|---|---|---|---|
| **341** | Q | 96–104 | **371** | Q | 88– 96 | **401** | Q | 92–100 |
| **342** | Q | 80– 88 | **372** | H | 80– 88 | **402** | Q | 92–100 |
| **343** | Q | 92–100 | **373** | Q | 92–100 | **403** | Q | 96–104 |
| **344** | H | 84– 92 | **374** | Q | 92–100 | **404** | H | 63– 69 |
| **345** | Q | 96–104 | **375** | Q | 84– 92 | **405** | Q | 92–100 |
| **346** | Q | 96–104 | **376** | Q | 92–100 | **406** | Q | 69– 76 |
| **347** | Q | 84– 92 | **377** | Q | 92–100 | **407** | H | 58– 63 |
| **348** | H | 76– 84 | **378** | H | 48– 52 | **408** | Q | 84– 92 |
| **349** | Q | 72– 80 | **379** | Q | 100–108 | **409** | H | 63– 69 |
| **350** | Q | 88– 96 | **380** | H | 76– 84 | **410** | Q | 84– 92 |
| **351** | Q | 96–104 | **381** | Q | 84– 92 | **411** | Q | 69– 76 |
| **352** | Q | 104–112 | **382** | Q | 88– 96 | **412** | Q | 52– 56 |
| **353** | H | 84– 92 | **383** | Q | 88– 96 | **413** | Q | 84– 92 |
| **354** | H | 84– 92 | **384** | Q | 84– 92 | **414** | Q | 92–100 |
| **355** | Q | 88– 96 | **385** | Q | 100–108 | **415** | Q | 72– 80 |
| **356** | Q | 92–100 | **386** | H | 58– 63 | **416** | Q | 92–100 |
| **357** | H | 63– 69 | **387** | H | 84– 92 | **417** | Q | 80– 88 |
| **358** | Q | 84– 92 | **388** | Q | 92–100 | **418** | Q | 76– 84 |
| **359** | Q | 88– 96 | **389** | Q | 84– 92 | **419** | Q | 56– 60 |
| **360** | Q | 84– 92 | **390** | H | 52– 56 | **420** | Q | 92–100 |
| **361** | H | 66– 72 | **391** | Q | 92–100 | **421** | Q | 92–100 |
| **362** | H | 88– 96 | **392** | Q | 88– 96 | **422** | Q | 92–100 |
| **363** | Q | 88– 96 | **393** | H | 60– 66 | **423** | Q | 92–100 |
| **364** | Q | 80– 88 | **394** | Q | 84– 92 | **424** | Q | 88– 96 |
| **365** | Q | 80– 88 | **395** | Q | 80– 88 | **425** | Q | 88– 96 |
| **366** | Q | 88– 96 | **396** | Q | 80– 88 | **426** | Q | 92–100 |
| **367** | Q | 92–100 | **397** | H | 80– 88 | **427** | Q | 80– 88 |
| **368** | E | 144–160 | **398** | Q | 84– 92 | **428** | Q | 76– 84 |
| **369** | Q | 100–108 | **399** | Q | 84– 92 | **429** | Q | 76– 84 |
| **370** | Q | 84– 92 | **400** | Q | 84– 92 | | | |

# AUTHORS AND SOURCES

*For Christian Scientists and for contemporary authors, no dates are given*

ADAMS, ELIZABETH C.
Father, we Thy loving children...... **58**
God giveth light to all.............. **70**
No eye hath seen, nor tongue declared **188**

ADAMS, SARAH FLOWER, 1805–1848
Nearer, my God, to Thee....... **192, 193**

AINGER, ARTHUR C., 1841–1919
God is working His purpose out...... **82**

*Anonymous*
Be firm and be faithful.............. **18**
Scorn not the slightest word or deed.. **303**
Well for him who, all things losing **379, 380**

*Armenian Liturgy*
Holiness becomes Thy house......... **113**

AUBER, HARRIET, 1773–1862
Praise our great and gracious Lord.... **281**
Vainly, through night's weary hours.. **364**

*Author Unknown*
A glorious day is dawning............ **2**
O daughter of Zion, awake from thy sadness.......................... **200**
The God who made both heaven and earth........................ **327, 328**
To Thee, our loving Father, God..... **357, 358, 407**

AVERY, STANLEY J.
Truth comes alike to all............ **355**

AYERS, MINNY M. H.
I walk with Love along the way . **139, 427**

BAHNMAIER, JONATHAN F., 1774–1841
Word of Life, most pure, most strong. **394, 395**

BAKER, HENRY WILLIAMS, 1821–1877
The King of Love my Shepherd is.... **330**

BALLOU, HOSEA, 1771–1852
When God is seen with men to dwell . **384**

BARING-GOULD, SABINE, 1834–1924
Onward, Christian soldiers.......... **264**
Through the night of doubt and sorrow **351**

BARLOW, CHARLES H.
Why search the future and the past... **391**

BARTON, BERNARD, 1784–1849
Walk in the light, so thou shalt know. **367**

BATES, DAVID, 1810–1870
Speak gently, it is better far..... **315, 316**

BATHURST, WILLIAM H., 1796–1877
O for a faith that will not shrink..... **205**

BAUM, MARIA LOUISE
Here, O God, Thy healing presence.. **109, 110**
High to heaven let song be soaring... **112**
If the Lord build not the house...... **141**
In Thee, my God and Saviour........ **153**
Like as a mother, God comforteth His children......................... **174**
Put on the whole armor of pure consecration.......................... **292**
Rouse ye, soldiers of the cross....... **296**

BEDDOME, BENJAMIN, 1717–1795
O Spirit, source of light......... **240, 241**
'Tis God the Spirit leads............ **354**

BELL, M. BETTIE
Press on, dear traveler, press thou on. **288, 289**

BERG, LINA SANDELL, 1832–1903
O Father, Thy Kingdom is come upon earth.......................... **204**

BOËTHIUS, JAKOB, 1647–1718
God is known in loving-kindness..... **76**

BONAR, HORATIUS, 1808–1889
Beloved, let us love.............. **21, 22**
Church of the ever-living God....... **36**
Here, O my Lord, I'd see Thee face to face.......................... **108**
Make haste, O man, to do....... **183, 184**
Not what I am, O Lord, but what Thou art......................... **195**

BORTHWICK, JANE, 1813–1897
Come, labor on.................. **41**
Now is the time approaching....... **196**

BOWRING, JOHN, 1792–1872
God is Love: His mercy brightens ... **79**
How sweetly flowed the gospel sound. **128, 129**
I cannot always trace the way... **133, 424**
Upon the Gospel's sacred page....... **363**
Watchman, tell us of the night.. **368, 369**

BRADY, NICHOLAS, 1659–1726
Be Thou, O God, exalted high....... 1
He that hath God his guardian made. 99, 100

BREWER, EDITH GADDIS
God of Truth, eternal good.......... 85
Prayer with our waking thought ascends.................... 287, 408

BROOKS, PHILLIPS, 1835–1893
O little town of Bethlehem...... 222, 223

BRORSON, HANS A., 1694–1764
Behold, they stand in robes of white.. 19

BROWNE, SIMON, 1680–1732
Come, gracious Spirit, heavenly Love. 39

BRUCE, MICHAEL, 1746–1767
O happy is the man who hears....... 215

BULFINCH, STEPHEN G., 1809–1870
Hath not thy heart within thee burned 94

BURLEIGH, WILLIAM H., 1812–1871
Abide not in the realm of dreams.... 6

BURNETT, VIVIAN
O, when we see God's mercy .... 249, 250

BURTON, JOHN, 1803–1877
Holy Bible, book divine............. 114

CAMERON, WILLIAM, 1751–1811
Supreme in wisdom as in power..... 320, 321, 409

CAMPBELL, MARION SUSAN
Angels at the Saviour's birth......... 11
Christ comes again with holy power.. 34

CAMPBELL, SUSAN F.
In Love divine all earth-born fear and sorrow.................. 149, 426

CASTELLAIN, LEWIE PRITTIE
O Father, may we bear each hour .... 203

CASWELL, MISS L. T., Dates unknown
I am the way, the truth, the life.. 131, 132

CHARLES, ELIZABETH, 1828–1896
True, the heart grows rich in giving... 360

COLBY, KATE L.
Be true and list the voice within.... 20, 416

CONDER, JOSIAH, 1789–1855
Day by day the manna fell......... 46, 47

COTTERILL, THOMAS, 1779–1823
Our God is Love, and all His sons.... 266

COWPER, WILLIAM, 1731–1800
O Lord, where'er Thy people meet ... 227
Sometimes a light surprises.......... 313
The spirit breathes upon the Word... 334
Ye timid saints, fresh courage take 399, 400

COXE, ARTHUR C., 1818–1896
Thy works, how beauteous, how divine...................... 352, 353

DANA, M. S. B. (See Shindler)

DAYTON, MARY ALICE
Eternal Mind the Potter is........ 51, 52

DENNIS, ETHEL WASGATT
A grateful heart a garden is......... 3

DIX, WILLIAM CHATTERTON, 1837–1898
Come unto me, ye weary............ 43

DOANE, GEORGE W., 1799–1842
Thou art the Way: to thee alone.....343, 344, 429

DODDRIDGE, PHILIP, 1702–1751
How gentle God's commands.... 124, 402
Ye servants of the Lord.............. 398

DRUMMOND, WILLIAM H., 1772–1856
One cup of healing oil and wine...... 259

DUNN, JOHN RANDALL
Sing, ye joyous children, sing......... 310
We thank Thee and we bless Thee 374, 375

EDDY, MARY BAKER
Blest Christmas morn, though murky clouds............ 23, 24, 25, 26, 27, 28
Brood o'er us with Thy shelt'ring wing 30, 31, 32
It matters not what be thy lot 160, 161, 162
O gentle presence, peace and joy and power...... 207, 208, 209, 210, 211, 212
O'er waiting harpstrings of the mind . 253, 254, 255, 256, 257
Saw ye my Saviour? Heard ye the glad sound...... 298, 299, 300, 301, 302
Shepherd, show me how to go.......304, 305, 306, 307, 308, 309

ELLIOTT, CHARLOTTE, 1789–1871
Gird thy heavenly armor on....... 67, 68

EVANS, JONATHAN, 1748 (1749?)–1809
Come, Thou all-transforming Spirit... 42

EVEREST, CHARLES W., 1814–1877
Take up thy cross, the Saviour said... 325

FABER, FREDERICK W., 1814–1863
God's glory is a wondrous thing..... 86, 87
There's a wideness in God's mercy ... 340

*Fitzgerald's Collection*, 1830
O daughter of Zion, awake from thy sadness.......................... 200

*Foundling Collection*
Praise the Lord, ye heavens, adore Him 282

FOX, FRANCES A.
In Thee, O Spirit true and tender.... 154, 155, 156

FROTHINGHAM, NATHANIEL L., 1793–1870
O God, whose presence glows in all... 214

GASKELL, WILLIAM, 1805–1884
Mighty God, the First, the Last... 186, 187
Press on, press on, ye sons of light... 290

GATES, ELLEN M. H., Dates unknown
O, the clanging bells of time........ **418**
GERHARDT, PAUL, 1607–1676
Holy Spirit, source of gladness....... **119**
Trust all to God, the Father........ **361**
GILL, THOMAS H., 1819–1906
O walk with God along the road **247, 248**
GILMAN, CAROLINE, 1794–1888
Sweet hour of holy, thoughtful prayer **322, 323**
GILMORE, JOSEPH H., 1834–1918
He leadeth me, O blessed thought.... **95**
GLADDEN, WASHINGTON, 1836–1918
O Lord of life, to Thee we lift........ **226**
O Master, let me walk with thee.. **234, 235**
GLOVER, ELLEN J.
In speechless prayer and reverence... **151, 152**
GOODE, WILLIAM, 1762–1816
How blest are they whose hearts are pure.................. **121, 122**
GOODENOUGH, LUCY M.
Thou living light of pentecostal glory. **345**
GOUGH, BENJAMIN, 1805–1877
How beauteous on the mountains.... **120**
GOULD, SABINE BARING. (See Baring-Gould, Sabine)
GRANT, ROBERT, 1785–1838
The starry firmament on high....... **336**
GREENWOOD, SAMUEL
No mortal sense can still or stay.. **194, 410**
GRUNDTVIG, NIKOLAJ F. S., 1783–1872
Long hast thou stood, O church of God **176**
Love is life's true crown and glory.... **178**
Suffer the children to come to me.... **318**
The Lord is in His holy place......... **332**

"H"
In atmosphere of Love divine.... **144, 145**
Thy will, almighty Father, Thine.... **349**
HACKETT, ROSEMARY B.
Loving Father, we Thy children..... **181**
HALE, MARY W., 1810–1862
Whatever dims thy sense of truth... **383**
HANKEY, KATHERINE, 1834–1911
I love to tell the story.............. **414**
HASTINGS, THOMAS, 1784–1872
Come, ye disconsolate, where'er ye languish.......................... **40**
He that goeth forth with weeping... **97, 98**
HAVERGAL, FRANCES RIDLEY, 1836–1879
From glory unto glory.............. **65**
Take my life, and let it be.......... **324**
HAWKS, ANNIE S., 1835–1918
I need Thee every hour............ **137**

HAY, VIOLET
All glory be to God most high....... **9**
Arise ye people, take your stand... **12, 13**
From sense to Soul my pathway lies before me........................ **64**
From these Thy children gathered in Thy name................... **66, 421**
I love Thy way of freedom, Lord..... **136**
Jesus' prayer for all his brethren...... **157**
Lo, He sent His Word and healed them **175**
HEBER, REGINALD, 1783–1826
Holy, Holy, Holy, Lord God Almighty **117**
HEERMANN, JOHANN, 1585–1647
God is known in loving-kindness..... **76**
HEMANS, FELICIA D., 1793–1835
Come to the land of peace........... **44**
HEYWOOD, FLORENCE L.
Breaking through the clouds of darkness............................ **29**
Hear our prayer, O gracious Father **102, 103**
HILL, FRANCES THOMPSON
Let us sing of Easter gladness .... **171, 413**
We turn to Thee, O Lord........... **378**
HOLDEN, OLIVER, 1765–1844
They who seek the throne of grace... **341**
HOLMES, OLIVER WENDELL, 1809–1894
Sun of our life, thy quickening ray.... **319**
HOSMER, FREDERICK L., 1840–1919
Father, to Thee we turn away from sorrow......................... **57**
One thought I have, my ample creed.. **260**
HOW, WILLIAM WALSHAM, 1823–1897
O Word of God, most holy...... **251, 252**

INGEMANN, BERNHARD S., 1789–1862
As gold by fire is tested............. **15**
Through the night of doubt and sorrow **351**
*Isaiah 40*
O Thou who spreadest the heaven like a tent........................ **246**

JACOBI, JOHN CHRISTIAN, 1670–1750
Holy Spirit, source of gladness ....... **119**
JOHNSON, SAMUEL, 1822–1882
City of God, how broad and far..... **37, 38**
I praise Thee, Lord, for blessings sent **138**
Onward, Christian, though the region **265**

*"K" in Rippon's Selection*, 1787
How firm a foundation............ **123**
KEBLE, JOHN, 1792–1866
If on our daily course, our mind..... **140**
KELLY, REV. THOMAS, 1769–1855
Look, ye saints, the day is breaking.. **177**
KER SEYMER, VIOLET
As sings the mountain stream....... **16**
In God I find a precious gift..... **146, 147**

Key, Robert Ellis
O Love whose perfect path is known . . 233, 419
So brightly burns Love's holy glow 311, 420

Lias, Una R.
Though mountains may depart from thee . . . 347, 348
Linn, Fay
O may we be still and seek Him . . . 237
Livermore, Abiel Abbot, 1811–1892
A holy air is breathing round . . . 4
Livermore, Mary A., 1820–1905
Jesus, what precept is like thine . . . 163
Lloyd, William F., 1791–1853
Wait, my soul, upon the Lord . . . 365, 366
*London Inquirer*
Scorn not the slightest word or deed . . 303
Longfellow, Samuel, 1819–1892
Holy Spirit, Light divine . . . 118
I look to Thee in every need . . . 134
O Life that maketh all things new . . . 218, 219, 220
O, still in accents sweet and strong . . 242
One holy church of God appears . . 261, 262
The loving friend to all who bowed . . . 333
Lowell, James Russell, 1819–1891
Oft to every man and nation . . . 258
Lynch, Roberta B.
Science, the angel with the flaming sword . . . 297
Lynch, Thomas Toke, 1818–1871
Gracious Spirit, dwell with me . . . 88, 89
Lyte, Henry Francis, 1793–1847
Abide with me; fast falls the eventide. 8
Know, O child, thy full salvation. 166, 167
Praise, my soul, the King of heaven . . . 280
Praise the Lord, ye heavens, adore Him 282

Macduff, John R., 1818–1895
Everlasting arms of Love . . . 53
Mace, Nellie B.
To Thee, O God, we bring our adoration 356
We are hid with Christ forever . . . 370
Mann, Frederic. Dates unknown
My God, my Father, make me strong 190, 191
Mant, Richard, 1776–1848
Let all the earth with songs rejoice . . . 168
Marriott, John, 1780–1825
Thou whose almighty Word . . . 346, 401
Martineau, Harriet, 1802–1876
Faith grasps the blessing she desires . . 54
Massie, Richard, 1800–1887
I know no life divided . . . 135
Matters, Margaret Glenn
O Jesus, our dear Master . . . 221
O Love, our Mother, ever near . . . 232, 406

McKenzie, William P.
Happy the man whose heart can rest. 93
In mercy, in goodness, how great is our King . . . 150
O Love divine, that dwells serene . . . 228
Praise now creative Mind . . . 275
There are none friendless, none afraid. 339
Trust the Eternal when the shadows gather . . . 359
What brightness dawned in resurrection . . . 381
Mesechre, Mary I.
Arise, arise and shine . . . 14
Milton, John, 1608–1674
How lovely are Thy dwellings, Lord . . 125
Monsell, John S. B., 1811–1875
Fight the good fight with all thy might. 59, 60, 61
Montgomery, James, 1771–1854
Call the Lord thy sure salvation . . . 33
God comes, with succor speedy . . . 75
God is my strong salvation . . . 77, 78
God is our refuge and defense . . . 80
God made all His creatures free . . . 83
Prayer is the heart's sincere desire . . . 284, 285, 286
Sow in the morn thy seed . . . 314
The Christian warrior, see him stand . . 326
When like a stranger on our sphere . . . 388
Moore, Thomas, 1779–1852
Come, ye disconsolate, where'er ye languish . . . 40
Morison, John, 1749–1798
To us a Child of Hope is born . . . 362
Morrison, Margaret
Love one another, — word of revelation . . . 179
We lift our hearts in praise . . . 371

Neale, John M., 1818–1866
Holy Father, Thou hast taught us 115, 116
Neander, Joachim, 1650–1680
Praise we the Lord . . . 283
Neumark, Georg, 1621–1681
O he who trusts in God's protection . . . 216
Newman, John Henry, 1801–1890
Lead, kindly Light . . . 169
Newton, John, 1725–1807
Glorious things of thee are spoken . . . 71
Quiet, Lord, my froward heart . . . 291
Newton, Maude de Verse
He sent His Word, His holy Word . . . 101
Nourse, Laura C.
Now sweeping down the years untold. 197, 198

With love and peace and joy supreme 392, 393

OLDENBURG, THEODOR V., 1805–1842
God's eternal Word is spoken........ 84

P. M.
Pilgrim on earth, home and heaven are within thee.................. 278, 279

PALMER, RAY, 1808–1887
Father, Thou joy of loving hearts.... 56

PARSONS, CHARLES
O do not bar your mind........ 201, 404

PETERS, MARY, 1813–1856
Through the love of God our Saviour. 350

PRAY, BENJAMIN S.
Master and Lord, 'tis good to be here. 185

*Psalm 36*
How wondrous is Thy mercy, Lord... 130

*Psalm 121*
Mine eyes look toward the mountains. 189

RANDALL, LAURA LEE
This is the day the Lord hath made.. 342

REED, ANDREW, 1787–1862
Holy Spirit, Light divine............ 118

RINKART, MARTIN, 1586–1649
Now thank we all our God.......... 199

ROBERTSON, NEMI
Grace for to-day, O Love divine .. 91, 422

ROME, JAMES J.
Give me, O Lord, an understanding heart...................... 69, 423

ROOT, FREDERIC W.
All power is given unto our Lord (C).. 10
All power is given unto our Lord (D). 411
O tender, loving Shepherd........... 245
Our God is Love, unchanging Love 269, 270
Rock of Ages, Truth divine . 293, 294, 295
The heavens declare the glory....... 329

RUTGERS, ABRAHAM, 1751–1809
Glory, honor, praise and pure oblations 73

RYLAND, JOHN, 1753–1825
O Lord, I would delight in Thee.. 224, 225

SANDELL, LINA BERG (See Berg, Lina Sandell)

SARGANT, EDMUND BEALE
Be firm, ye sentinels of Truth........ 17
Dear Father-Mother, Thou dost grant 48
Go forth and stand upon the mount.. 74

SCHJØRRING, JENS NIKOLAJ LUDWIG, 1825–1900
Love the Lord thy God............. 180

SCOTT, THOMAS, 1705–1775
Imposture shrinks from light........ 143
The lifted eye and bended knee...... 331

SCOTT, WALTER, 1771–1832
When Israel, of the Lord beloved..... 385

SEAL, EMILY F.
Our God is All-in-all............ 267, 268
What is thy birthright, man......... 382

SEARS, EDMUND H., 1810–1876
It came upon the midnight clear 158, 159

SEYMER, VIOLET KER (See Ker Seymer, Violet)

SHERWIN, WILLIAM F., 1826–1888
Why is thy faith in God's great love so small.............................. 390

SHINDLER, MARY S. B. DANA
Dates unknown
I'm a pilgrim, and I'm a stranger.... 415

SINCLAIR, DUNCAN
Help us, O Lord, to bear the cross.... 104
O God, our Father-Mother, Love.... 206, 428

SMITH, SAMUEL F., 1808–1895
The morning light is breaking....... 335

SNELLING, JAMES PALMER
Dear God, how glorious is Thy name. 45

SPITTA, CARL J. P., 1801–1859
I know no life divided.............. 135

STENERSEN, STENER J., 1789–1835
Trust all to God, the Father......... 361

STONE, ELLA A.
O sweet and tender as the dawn.. 243, 244

STOWE, HARRIET BEECHER, 1811–1896
Still, still with Thee when purple morning breaketh.......................... 317

SWAIN, JOSEPH, 1761–1796
How sweet, how heavenly is the sight. 126, 127, 403

TATE, NAHUM, 1652–1715
Be Thou, O God, exalted high....... 1
He that hath God his guardian made. 99, 100

TAYLOR, JOHN, 1750–1826
Glory be to God on high........ 72, 405

THAXTER, CELIA, 1836–1894
Lift up thy light, O man, arise and shine 172

TOMLINSON, IRVING C.
A voice from heaven we have heard... 5
O peace of the world, O hope in each breast.......................... 236

TOURIAN, LEON. Dates unknown
Holiness becomes Thy house......... 113

TRENCH, RICHARD C., 1807–1886
Make channels for the streams of Love 182

TURNER, ROSA M.
O dreamer, leave thy dreams.... 202, 412

*Unknown* (See Author Unknown)
UPHAM, THOMAS COGSWELL, 1799–1872
Happy the man who knows .......... **92**

VOKES, MRS. Dates unknown
Ye messengers of Christ ........ **396, 397**

WALLIN, JOHAN OLOF, 1779–1839
God is known in loving-kindness ..... **76**
Only God can bring us gladness ..... **263**
WARING, ANNA L., 1820–1910
In heavenly Love abiding ........... **148**
WATERSTON, ROBERT C., 1812–1893
Theories, which thousands cherish **337, 338**
WATTS, ISAAC, 1674–1748
From all that dwell below the skies **62, 63**
High in the heavens, eternal God .... **111**
Joy to the world, the Lord is come ... **164, 165, 417**
O God, our help in ages past ........ **213**
Our God shall reign where'er the sun .. **271, 272**
Supreme in wisdom as in power ..... **320, 321, 409**
When Jesus our great Master came **386, 387**
WESLEY, CHARLES, 1707–1788
Christ, whose glory fills the skies ..... **35**
Glory be to God on high ......... **72, 405**
Help us to help each other, Lord ..... **105, 106, 107**
Partners of a glorious hope ....... **273, 274**
Peace be to this congregation .... **276, 277**
Soldiers of Christ, arise ............ **312**
WHITNEY, M. FANNIE
We thank Thee, heavenly Father **376, 377**

WHITTIER, JOHN GREENLEAF, 1807–1892
Dear Lord and Father of us all .... **49, 50**
He stood of old, the holy Christ ..... **96**
Immortal Love, forever full ......... **142**
Let every creature hail the morn ..... **170**
O, he whom Jesus loved has truly spoken ........................ **217**
O Love divine, whose constant beam .. **229**
O Love, O Life, our faith and sight **230, 231**
O, sometimes gleams upon our sight .. **238, 239**
We may not climb the heavenly steeps **372, 373**
WIENLAND, M. M. Dates unknown
O weary pilgrim, lift your head ...... **425**
WILLIAMS, THEODORE C., 1855–1915
God is with me, gently o'er me ...... **81**
WILLIAMS, WILLIAM, 1717–1792
Guide me, O Thou great Jehovah .... **90**
WILLIS, LOVE MARIA, 1824–1908
Father, hear the prayer we offer ...... **55**
WINKWORTH, CATHERINE, 1829–1878
Now thank we all our God ......... **199**
Well for him who, all things losing **379, 380**
Word of Life, most pure, most strong . **394, 395**
WOODS, BERTHA H.
Abide with me; fast breaks the morning light ........................ **7**
WORDSWORTH, CHRISTOPHER, 1807–1885
Love is kind and suffers long ........ **173**

YOUNG, WILLIAM. Dates unknown
While Thou, O my God, art my help and defender ....................... **389**

# FIRST LINES

***First lines of hymns by Mary Baker Eddy are printed in italics***

| FIRST LINE | NO. |
|---|---|
| [Communion Doxology] | 1 |
| A glorious day is dawning | 2 |
| A grateful heart a garden is | 3 |
| A holy air is breathing round | 4 |
| A voice from heaven we have heard | 5 |
| Abide not in the realm of dreams | 6 |
| Abide with me; fast breaks the morning light | 7 |
| Abide with me; fast falls the eventide | 8 |
| All glory be to God most high | 9 |
| All power is given unto our Lord | 10, 411 |
| Angels at the Saviour's birth | 11 |
| Arise, arise and shine | 14 |
| Arise ye people, take your stand | 12–13 |
| As gold by fire is tested | 15 |
| As sings the mountain stream | 16 |
| Be firm and be faithful | 18 |
| Be firm, ye sentinels of Truth | 17 |
| Be Thou, O God, exalted high | 1 |
| Be true and list the voice within | 20, 416 |
| Behold, they stand in robes of white | 19 |
| Beloved, let us love | 21–22 |
| *Blest Christmas morn* | 23–28 |
| Breaking through the clouds of darkness | 29 |
| *Brood o'er us with Thy shelt'ring wing* | 30–32 |
| Call the Lord thy sure salvation | 33 |
| Christ comes again with holy power | 34 |
| Christ, whose glory fills the skies | 35 |
| Church of the ever-living God | 36 |
| City of God, how broad and far | 37–38 |
| Come, gracious Spirit, heavenly Love | 39 |
| Come, labor on | 41 |
| Come, Thou all-transforming Spirit | 42 |
| Come to the land of peace | 44 |
| Come unto me, ye weary | 43 |
| Come, ye disconsolate | 40 |
| Day by day the manna fell | 46–47 |
| Dear Father-Mother, Thou dost grant | 48 |
| Dear God, how glorious is Thy name | 45 |
| Dear Lord and Father of us all | 49–50 |
| Eternal Mind the Potter is | 51–52 |
| Everlasting arms of Love | 53 |
| Faith grasps the blessing she desires | 54 |
| Father, hear the prayer we offer | 55 |
| Father, Thou joy of loving hearts | 56 |
| Father, to Thee we turn away from sorrow | 57 |
| Father, we Thy loving children | 58 |
| Fight the good fight with all thy might | 59–61 |
| From all that dwell below the skies | 62–63 |
| From glory unto glory | 65 |
| From sense to Soul my pathway lies | 64 |
| From these Thy children gathered in Thy name | 66, 421 |
| Gird thy heavenly armor on | 67–68 |
| Give me, O Lord, an understanding heart | 69, 423 |
| Glorious things of thee are spoken | 71 |
| Glory be to God on high | 72, 405 |
| Glory, honor, praise and pure oblations | 73 |
| Go forth and stand upon the mount | 74 |
| God comes, with succor speedy | 75 |
| God giveth light to all | 70 |
| God is known in loving-kindness | 76 |
| God is Love; His mercy brightens | 79 |
| God is my strong salvation | 77–78 |
| God is our refuge and defense | 80 |
| God is with me, gently o'er me | 81 |
| God is working His purpose out | 82 |
| God made all His creatures free | 83 |
| God of Truth, eternal good | 85 |
| God's eternal Word is spoken | 84 |
| God's glory is a wondrous thing | 86–87 |
| Grace for today, O Love divine | 91, 422 |
| Gracious Spirit, dwell with me | 88–89 |
| Guide me, O Thou great Jehovah | 90 |
| Happy the man who knows | 92 |
| Happy the man whose heart can rest | 93 |
| Hath not thy heart within thee burned | 94 |
| He leadeth me; O blessed thought | 95 |
| He sent His Word, His holy Word | 101 |
| He stood of old, the holy Christ | 96 |
| He that goeth forth with weeping | 97–98 |
| He that hath God his guardian made, I | 99 |
| He that hath God his guardian made, II | 100 |
| Hear our prayer, O gracious Father | 102–103 |
| Help us, O Lord, to bear the cross | 104 |
| Help us to help each other, Lord | 105–107 |
| Here, O God, Thy healing presence | 109–110 |
| Here, O my Lord, I'd see Thee face to face | 108 |
| High in the heavens, eternal God | 111 |

| FIRST LINE | NO. |
|---|---|
| High to heaven let song be soaring | 112 |
| Holiness becomes Thy house | 113 |
| Holy Bible, book divine | 114 |
| Holy Father, Thou hast taught us | 115–116 |
| Holy, Holy, Holy, Lord God Almighty | 117 |
| Holy Spirit, Light divine | 118 |
| Holy Spirit, source of gladness | 119 |
| How beauteous on the mountains | 120 |
| How blest are they whose hearts | 121–122 |
| How firm a foundation | 123 |
| How gentle God's commands | 124, 402 |
| How lovely are Thy dwellings, Lord | 125 |
| How sweet, how heavenly is the sight | 126–127, 403 |
| How sweetly flowed the gospel sound | 128–129 |
| How wondrous is Thy mercy, Lord | 130 |
| I am the way, the truth, the life | 131–132 |
| I cannot always trace the way | 133, 424 |
| I know no life divided | 135 |
| I look to Thee in every need | 134 |
| I love Thy way of freedom, Lord | 136 |
| I love to tell the story | 414 |
| I need Thee every hour | 137 |
| I praise Thee, Lord, for blessings sent | 138 |
| I walk with Love along the way | 139, 427 |
| If on our daily course, our mind | 140 |
| If the Lord build not the house | 141 |
| I'm a pilgrim, and I'm a stranger | 415 |
| Immortal Love, forever full | 142 |
| Imposture shrinks from light | 143 |
| In atmosphere of Love divine | 144–145 |
| In God I find a precious gift | 146–147 |
| In heavenly Love abiding | 148 |
| In Love divine all earth-born fear and sorrow | 149, 426 |
| In mercy, in goodness, how great is our King | 150 |
| In speechless prayer and reverence | 151–152 |
| In Thee, my God and Saviour | 153 |
| In Thee, O Spirit true and tender | 154–156 |
| It came upon the midnight clear | 158–159 |
| *It matters not what be thy lot* | 160–162 |
| Jesus' prayer for all his brethren | 157 |
| Jesus, what precept is like thine | 163 |
| Joy to the world, the Lord is come | 164–165, 417 |
| Know, O child, thy full salvation | 166–167 |
| Lead, kindly Light | 169 |
| Let all the earth with songs rejoice | 168 |
| Let every creature hail the morn | 170 |
| Let us sing of Easter gladness | 171, 413 |
| Lift up thy light, O man, arise and shine | 172 |
| Like as a mother, God comforteth His children | 174 |
| Lo, He sent His word and healed them | 175 |
| Long hast thou stood, O church of God | 176 |
| Look, ye saints, the day is breaking | 177 |
| Love is kind and suffers long | 173 |
| Love is life's true crown and glory | 178 |
| Love one another, — word of revelation | 179 |
| Love the Lord thy God | 180 |
| Loving Father, we Thy children | 181 |
| Make channels for the streams of Love | 182 |
| Make haste, O man, to do | 183–184 |
| Master and Lord, 'tis good to be here | 185 |
| Mighty God, the First, the Last | 186–187 |
| Mine eyes look toward the mountains | 189 |
| My God, my Father, make me strong | 190–191 |
| Nearer, my God, to Thee | 192–193 |
| No eye hath seen, nor tongue declared | 188 |
| No mortal sense can still or stay | 194, 410 |
| Not what I am, O Lord, but what Thou art | 195 |
| Now is the time approaching | 196 |
| Now sweeping down the years untold | 197–198 |
| Now thank we all our God | 199 |
| O daughter of Zion, awake from thy sadness | 200 |
| O do not bar your mind | 201, 404 |
| O dreamer, leave thy dreams | 202, 412 |
| O Father, may we bear each hour | 203 |
| O Father, Thy kingdom is come upon earth | 204 |
| O for a faith that will not shrink | 205 |
| *O gentle presence* | 207–212 |
| O God, our Father-Mother, Love | 206, 428 |
| O God, our help in ages past | 213 |
| O God, whose presence glows in all | 214 |
| O happy is the man who hears | 215 |
| O he who trusts in God's protection | 216 |
| O, he whom Jesus loved has truly spoken | 217 |
| O Jesus, our dear Master | 221 |
| O Life that maketh all things new | 218–220 |
| O little town of Bethlehem | 222–223 |
| O Lord, I would delight in Thee | 224–225 |
| O Lord of life, to Thee we lift | 226 |
| O Lord, where'er Thy people meet | 227 |
| O Love divine, that dwells serene | 228 |
| O Love divine, whose constant beam | 229 |
| O Love, O Life, our faith and sight | 230–231 |
| O Love, our Mother, ever near | 232, 406 |
| O Love whose perfect path is known | 233, 419 |
| O Master, let me walk with thee | 234–235 |
| O may we be still and seek Him | 237 |
| O peace of the world, O hope in each breast | 236 |
| O, sometimes gleams upon our sight | 238–239 |
| O Spirit, source of light | 240–241 |
| O, still in accents sweet and strong | 242 |
| O sweet and tender as the dawn | 243–244 |
| O tender, loving Shepherd | 245 |
| O, the clanging bells of time | 418 |
| O Thou who spreadest the heaven like a tent | 246 |
| O walk with God along the road | 247–248 |
| O weary pilgrim, lift your head | 425 |

| FIRST LINE | NO. |
|---|---|
| O, when we see God's mercy | 249–250 |
| O Word of God, most holy | 251–252 |
| *O'er waiting harpstrings of the mind* | 253–257 |
| Oft to every man and nation | 258 |
| One cup of healing oil and wine | 259 |
| One holy church of God appears | 261–262 |
| One thought I have, my ample creed | 260 |
| Only God can bring us gladness | 263 |
| Onward, Christian soldiers | 264 |
| Onward, Christian, though the region | 265 |
| Our God is All-in-all | 267–268 |
| Our God is Love, and all His sons | 266 |
| Our God is Love, unchanging Love | 269–270 |
| Our God shall reign where'er the sun | 271–272 |
| Partners of a glorious hope | 273–274 |
| Peace be to this congregation | 276–277 |
| Pilgrim on earth, home and heaven are within thee | 278–279 |
| Praise, my soul, the King of heaven | 280 |
| Praise now creative Mind | 275 |
| Praise our great and gracious Lord | 281 |
| Praise the Lord, ye heavens, adore Him | 282 |
| Praise we the Lord, for His mercy | 283 |
| Prayer is the heart's sincere desire | 284–286 |
| Prayer with our waking thought | 287, 408 |
| Press on, dear traveler, press thou on | 288–289 |
| Press on, press on, ye sons of light | 290 |
| Put on the whole armor of pure consecration | 292 |
| Quiet, Lord, my froward heart | 291 |
| Rock of Ages, Truth divine | 293–295 |
| Rouse ye, soldiers of the cross | 296 |
| *Saw ye my Saviour?* | 298–302 |
| Science, the angel with the flaming sword | 297 |
| Scorn not the slightest word or deed | 303 |
| *Shepherd, show me how to go* | 304–309 |
| Sing, ye joyous children, sing | 310 |
| So brightly burns Love's holy glow | 311, 420 |
| Soldiers of Christ, arise | 312 |
| Sometimes a light surprises | 313 |
| Sow in the morn thy seed | 314 |
| Speak gently, it is better far | 315–316 |
| Still, still with Thee when purple morning breaketh | 317 |
| Suffer the children to come to me | 318 |
| Sun of our life, thy quickening ray | 319 |
| Supreme in wisdom as in power | 320–321, 409 |
| Sweet hour of holy, thoughtful prayer | 322–323 |
| Take my life, and let it be | 324 |
| Take up thy cross, the Saviour said | 325 |
| The Christian warrior, see him stand | 326 |
| The God who made both heaven and earth | 327–328 |
| The heavens declare the glory | 329 |
| The King of Love my Shepherd is | 330 |

| FIRST LINE | NO. |
|---|---|
| The lifted eye and bended knee | 331 |
| The Lord is in His holy place | 332 |
| The loving friend to all who bowed | 333 |
| The morning light is breaking | 335 |
| The spirit breathes upon the Word | 334 |
| The starry firmament on high | 336 |
| Theories, which thousands cherish | 337–338 |
| There are none friendless, none afraid | 339 |
| There's a wideness in God's mercy | 340 |
| They who seek the throne of grace | 341 |
| This is the day the Lord hath made | 342 |
| Thou art the Way: to thee alone | 343–344, 429 |
| Thou living light of pentecostal glory | 345 |
| Thou whose almighty Word | 346, 401 |
| Though mountains may depart | 347–348 |
| Through the love of God our Saviour | 350 |
| Through the night of doubt and sorrow | 351 |
| Thy will, almighty Father, Thine | 349 |
| Thy works, how beauteous, how divine | 352–353 |
| 'Tis God the Spirit leads | 354 |
| To Thee, O God, we bring our adoration | 356 |
| To Thee, our loving Father, God | 357–358, 407 |
| To us a Child of Hope is born | 362 |
| True, the heart grows rich in giving | 360 |
| Trust all to God, the Father | 361 |
| Trust the Eternal when the shadows gather | 359 |
| Truth comes alike to all | 355 |
| Upon the Gospel's sacred page | 363 |
| Vainly, through night's weary hours | 364 |
| Wait, my soul, upon the Lord | 365–366 |
| Walk in the light, so thou shalt know | 367 |
| Watchman, tell us of the night | 368–369 |
| We are hid with Christ forever | 370 |
| We lift our hearts in praise | 371 |
| We may not climb the heavenly | 372–373 |
| We thank Thee and we bless Thee | 374–375 |
| We thank Thee, heavenly Father | 376–377 |
| We turn to Thee, O Lord | 378 |
| Well for him who, all things losing | 379–380 |
| What brightness dawned in resurrection | 381 |
| What is thy birthright, man | 382 |
| Whatever dims thy sense of truth | 383 |
| When God is seen with men to dwell | 384 |
| When Israel, of the Lord beloved | 385 |
| When Jesus our great Master came | 386–387 |
| When like a stranger on our sphere | 388 |
| While Thou, O my God, art my help | 389 |
| Why is thy faith in God's great love so small | 390 |
| Why search the future and the past | 391 |
| With love and peace and joy supreme | 392–393 |
| Word of Life, most pure, most strong | 394–395 |
| Ye messengers of Christ | 396–397 |
| Ye servants of the Lord | 398 |
| Ye timid saints, fresh courage take | 399–400 |

[1252–50M]